Flora of County Dublin

by

THE DUBLIN NATURALISTS' FIELD CLUB

Compiled and edited by

**Declan Doogue, David Nash, John Parnell,
Sylvia Reynolds and Peter Wyse Jackson.**

With contributions by

**Catriona Brady, Con Breen, Rosaleen Fitzgerald, Philip Grant, Pauline Hodson,
Daniel Kelly, Eimear Nic Lughadha, Margaret Norton, Paddy Reilly,
Julian Reynolds, Gerry Sharkey, Micheline Sheehy Skeffington,
Michael Wyse Jackson and Patrick Wyse Jackson.**

THE DUBLIN NATURALISTS' FIELD CLUB, DUBLIN

THE DUBLIN NATURALISTS' FIELD CLUB
DUBLIN

First published in 1998
by The Dublin Naturalists' Field Club
Dublin.

Design and typesetting by Juliette Moreau
Photography for plates 2-17 by Michael O'Gorman
Colour separations by Lithographic Plate Plan Ltd., Dublin
Printing by Betaprint, Dublin

ISBN 0 9530037 0 1 Hardback

ISBN 0 9530037 1 X Special Limited Edition

This *Flora* is dedicated to the memory of two

distinguished members of The Dublin Naturalists' Field Club,

who participated in the field work for this *Flora*:

Helen O'Reilly (1922-1987)

and

Howard Joseph Hudson (1909-1996).

CONTENTS

Part I

Part II

LIST OF FIGURES

LIST OF TABLES

LIST OF COLOUR PLATES

LIST OF BLACK AND WHITE PLATES

Plates 1 and 18 are from herbarium sheets in the Botany Department, Trinity College, Dublin, believed to have formed part of an early 18th century Hortus Siccus belonging to Caleb Threlkeld. Plates 19 to 24 are from pen and Chinese ink drawings by Wendy Walsh.

PREFACE

The varied flora of Co. Dublin has long engaged the attention of botanists, resulting in published records and herbarium specimens dating back for several centuries. About one hundred years ago, Nathaniel Colgan (1851-1919) saw the need to produce a complete Flora of the metropolitan county of Ireland which would also incorporate earlier records. He spent nine years in a "systematic personal exploration of the county" carrying out a comprehensive survey which resulted in his *Flora of the County Dublin*, published in 1904. Colgan was a clerk in the Dublin Metropolitan Police Courts and a member of the Dublin Naturalists' Field Club (DNFC). His obituary, written by Robert Lloyd Praeger, is reproduced in Appendix 3. Colgan's *Flora* is widely regarded as an excellent and detailed work and one of the finest County Floras ever produced in Ireland. The book has remained a very valuable reference work on the flora of Co. Dublin despite the many changes that have subsequently occurred.

From 1935 onwards, members of the DNFC carried out intensive field work to provide an up-to-date picture of the flora. Their records were drawn together by J.P. Brunker, H.J. Hudson, A.L.K. King, H.M. Parkes and M.J.P. Scannell, on behalf of the DNFC, in *A Supplement to Colgan's Flora of the County Dublin* (Anon. 1961). The *Supplement* gives brief details of the distribution of each species and includes many post-1904 records not previously published.

A more recent project of the DNFC has been a study of the flora of that part of Dublin City between the Grand and Royal Canals, published as *The Flora of Inner Dublin* (Wyse Jackson and Sheehy Skeffington 1984). This modestly-scaled survey produced very interesting information, both on the residual native flora and also on the presence of alien species, many of which are now frequent and well established. The project presented an opportunity for the DNFC to build an enthusiastic team of field botanists, both amateur and professional, which quickly gained the experience to undertake the challenge of re-surveying the flora of the whole county.

To mark the DNFC's centenary in 1986, Declan Doogue and Peter Wyse Jackson initially proposed an up-dating of H.C. Hart's *The Flora of Howth* (1887). However, it was decided that a much more ambitious enterprise was required and the idea of surveying the flora of the entire county of Dublin was born. John Parnell was invited to join Doogue and Wyse Jackson on the editorial team. A Plant Group was set up, and some members of this group (District Recorders) were given responsibility for the co-ordination of field work in the eight Districts originally defined by Colgan.

Plant recording began in earnest in 1983 and continued into the early 1990s. The field work was led by Declan Doogue who marshalled the recorders, organised field meetings, held workshops, checked identifications and monitored progress. Each of the approximately one thousand 1 km x 1 km squares was visited, many of them several times, and the plants present were recorded on pre-printed cards which listed some 450 species. Information on additional species, usually the less common ones, was entered on individual record cards, giving details of location and population size. Data were also collected by other members of the DNFC. Altogether more than 1300 taxa were recorded for the *Flora*.

Various members of the DNFC assisted in tasks such as the abstraction of herbarium records, the survey of the literature for published records and the assembly of the data for the production of draft distribution maps from mastercards on which data had been aggregated for 2 km x 2 km squares. Peter Wyse Jackson produced a first draft of the Systematic Lists. Then, using this as a base, Declan Doogue and John Parnell developed and analysed the data, and produced a series of revised drafts, distribution maps and draft introductory chapters. These drafts were passed back to Peter Wyse Jackson for further refinement, the selection and addition of historical records, and the initial design of the publication. David Nash and Sylvia Reynolds undertook the remaining stages of the editorial work which included the completion of the text and final revisions and corrections.

In the process of carrying out the field work and in the writing of the *Flora*, much information has been gleaned about the habitats and flora of Co. Dublin, and it has been a source of satisfaction to be able to confirm many historical records reported by Colgan and earlier workers, and to make interesting new discoveries. However, Co. Dublin has undergone many changes since the turn of the century. Urbanisation has changed the face of the county, especially from the 1960s onwards, most notably through the construction of houses, roads and industrial estates. Agricultural practices and patterns have also altered and afforestation has transformed much of the uplands. In addition, there is concern that climatic change due to human activities will have an impact. While the flora has retained its diversity in terms of the number of species surviving, the populations of many species have been very dramatically reduced and a large number of populations totally destroyed. It is also feared that the remaining populations of some native species are no longer viable and will become extinct. We believe that we have established a baseline against which any consequential changes in the local flora may be measured. It is to be hoped that elected representatives, planners, developers and the other citizens of Co. Dublin will become increasingly sensitive to the value of the existing native flora and habitats. We must all ensure that our remaining natural and diverse plant heritage is effectively conserved so that it may continue to be there for future generations.

The Editors
Dublin, August 1998

ACKNOWLEDGEMENTS

We acknowledge with gratitude the contributions of the very many members of the Dublin Naturalists' Field Club who have collaborated in the collection of data and others who generously made information available to us. The following were the principal field workers: Catriona Brady, Declan Doogue, Rosaleen Fitzgerald, Philip Grant, Pauline Hodson, the late Howard Hudson, Eimear Nic Lughadha, David Nash, Margaret Norton, the late Helen O'Reilly, John Parnell, Paddy Reilly, Sylvia Reynolds, Jonathan Shackleton, Gerry Sharkey, Michael Wyse Jackson and Peter Wyse Jackson.

Many of the sites visited and referred to in the text are in private grounds and we would like to express our gratitude to the owners and occupiers for their co-operation in allowing access to Field Club members, especially during the field work for this *Flora*.

Special acknowledgement is made to the following for their individual contributions to the *Flora*:

John Akeroyd for helping to stimulate and initiate the project.

Christine Allen who typed the extracts from Colgan's *Flora* included in the text.

David Allen of Winchester who visited Dublin and helped with the study and identification of the Brambles (*Rubus fruticosus* agg.).

The many members of the Botanical Society of the British Isles (BSBI) who gave generously of their time and expertise in the identification of critical specimens.

Con Breen, Maura Scannell and Micheline Sheehy Skeffington for their incisive and constructive comments on drafts of the text.

Marcella Campbell for her cheerful support and assistance.

Deirdre Hardiman for her meticulous drafting of the District and Topographical maps, and for proof reading.

Pauline Hodson for her indispensable support and guidance in bringing the *Flora* to publication, and for the co-ordination of the photography.

Jimmy King for his work on the Stoneworts (Charophytes) and for his comments on the final draft.

Tony McNally for data on reservoir and canal water quality.

R.D. Meikle for visiting Dublin during field work and for the determination of Willow (*Salix*) specimens.

Margaret Norton for extraction of herbarium records from the Herbarium at the National Botanic Gardens (**DBN**).

M.L. Otte for access to his unpublished report on Cord-grass (*Spartina*) at North Bull Island.

Grace Pasley for permission to use the Dandelion photograph on the dust jacket.

C.D. Preston of the Institute of Terrestrial Ecology, Monks Wood, for his determination of Pondweed (*Potamogeton*) specimens.

Julian Reynolds for critical reading of the text and for many constructive suggestions.

A.J. Richards of Newcastle-upon-Tyne and the late C.C. Haworth of Whitehaven for their extensive work on the identification of Dandelions (*Taraxacum officinale* agg.).

A.J. Silverside of Paisley for Eyebright (*Euphrasia officinalis* agg.) identification.

Wendy Walsh for reproduction rights to her pen and Chinese ink drawings which were specially commissioned by Declan Doogue.

Patrick Wyse Jackson who assisted in many aspects of the production of the *Flora* including the digitisation of distribution maps and the formatting of them for printing.

We would also like to thank the following:

The late Aidan Brady, former Director of the National Botanic Gardens, Glasnevin, M.J.P. Scannell (Maura) (retired) Head of the Herbarium and one time Assistant Keeper, Natural History Division, National Museum of Ireland, and Donal Synnott, Director of the National Botanic Gardens, for access to herbarium specimens and for use of the library. Grace Pasley and Berni Shine for their assistance in the Herbarium.

D.H.S. Richardson and M.B. Jones, Heads of the Department of Botany, Trinity College, Dublin, for the use of laboratory, computer, herbarium and library facilities, and the Curator for permission to include Plates 1 and 18.

The Department of Geology, Trinity College, Dublin, for the use of its map-scanner.

The Board and Trustees of Botanic Gardens Conservation International for the use of their computer and copying facilities.

The National Parks and Wildlife Service for access to a plant list from Rockabill; and Tom Curtis for information on the status of Cord-grass (*Spartina*) in Co. Dublin.

The Ordnance Survey Office for permission to reproduce and print maps (Permit No. 6493).

The many members of the Dublin Naturalists' Field Club and their friends who contributed through fund-raising activities. Particular recognition is owed to Catriona Brady, Pauline Hodson, Daniel Kelly, Niamh Lennon, Margaret Norton, Gerry Sharkey, Mary Ward and Patrick Wyse Jackson of the Fund Raising Committee, and Petra Coffey, Jonathan and Daphne Shackleton.

The Helen O'Reilly Fund for sponsoring the drawings and colour plates.

Henry Ford & Son for a Ford Irish Conservation Award.

The Office for the Protection of the Environment, Department of the Environment, for an Environment Awareness Award.

The Heritage Council, Kilkenny, for support under its Publications Grant Scheme.

The BSBI Bequest for a loan towards the cost of publication.

Dublin Corporation for its financial support.

M.J.P. Scannell, Sean O Criadain, Geraldine Roche, the late Dr. Arthur Brooks and other individual donors.

PART I

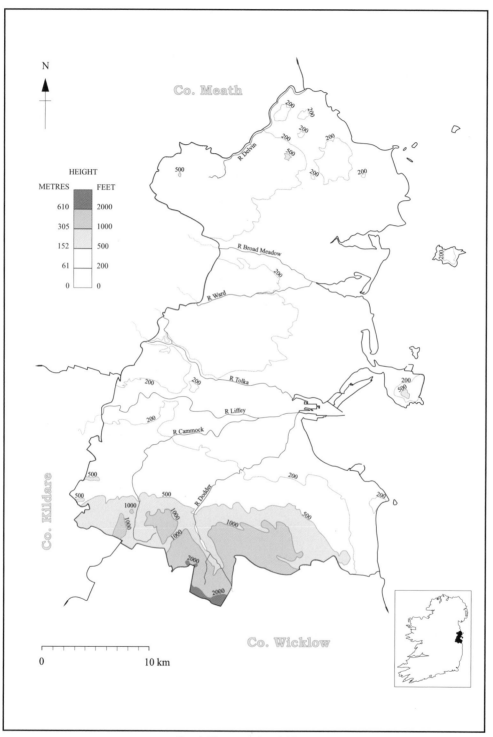

N

HEIGHT

METRES | FEET
610 | 2000
305 | 1000
152 | 500
61 | 200
0 | 0

Co. Meath

R Delvin

200
200
200
200
200
500

200
200
200

500

R Broad Meadow

200

R Ward

R Tolka
200
200

200
500

R Liffey

200

R Cammock

Co. Kildare

500

500

500
500

1000

1000

1000

R Dodder

1000

1000

200

500

200

2000

2000

Co. Wicklow

0 _____ 10 km

Fig. 1 Topographical Map

GENERAL TOPOGRAPHY

J. Parnell and C. Breen

Co. Dublin is situated on the east coast of Ireland between latitudes 53.10° N and 53.38° N and longitudes 5.59° W and 6.33° W. It is the smallest Irish county, apart from Carlow and Louth, covering an area of about 92 square kilometres. Its length is 51.2 km and its breadth, at its maximum, is 29 km. Despite its relatively small size, its altitudinal range of 757 metres is significant. Dublin ranks seventh in altitudinal range among the Irish counties with maritime coastline. This factor, coupled with its indented coastline in the driest part of Ireland, has endowed the county with a wide range of habitats and a correspondingly varied flora.

Approximately two-thirds of Co. Dublin lies north of the River Liffey, as may be seen from Fig. 1. In contrast, most of metropolitan Dublin lies in the southern half of the county. Nearly all of the higher ground in the county also lies south of the River Liffey. Here, most of the land is over 60 metres, rising ultimately to the highest point of the county on Kippure (757 m). Other high mountains in the same region are Seahan (648 m), Glendoo (586 m), Prince William's Seat (556 m) and Fairy Castle (536 m) (Fig. 5). In all, about one fifth of the county is above the 300 metre contour. North of the River Liffey a few areas of high ground occur in the Naul area (179 m) and on Howth Head (171 m). Otherwise the north of the county is generally low-lying with a gentle slope eastwards towards the coast. The drainage pattern of the county likewise runs west to east and all the major rivers, the Dodder, Liffey, Tolka, Ward, Broad Meadow and Delvin, follow this pattern. The Royal and Grand Canals also cross the county from west to east to their confluences with the Liffey in the dockland area of Dublin.

The largest and most important river in the county is the Liffey. Although its headwaters are in the mountains of Co. Wicklow and its main drainage and catchment area is in Co. Kildare, over 19 km of its relatively gentle course lie in Co. Dublin before it enters the Irish Sea at Dublin Bay. In contrast, the River Dodder rises in the southern uplands of Dublin and all of its short and rapid course lies within the county. The Tolka, Ward, Broad Meadow and Delvin Rivers drain the part of the county north of the Liffey catchment area. Some of these rivers have significant estuaries which are characterised by extensive coastal features such as sand-dune systems, spits, saltmarshes and mud-flats.

Co. Dublin does not have extensive areas of open water in the form of lakes or pools. It is estimated that about 0.4% of the surface area of the county is covered in freshwater, a figure which has changed little over the years. Nowadays, the only large open water bodies in the county are the reservoirs, principally in the south, and the two canals.

The coast is about 113 km long, its dominant feature being Dublin Bay. Most of the north coast is low-lying with sand, shingle and mud shorelines and large sand-dune systems at Rush, Portrane, Donabate (Malahide Island), Portmarnock, The Cosh (Sutton) and North Bull Island. By contrast, the coast south of the River Liffey has no well-developed dune systems and few saltmarshes of note apart from a small one at Booterstown. Extensive saltmarshes occur in the north at Baldoyle, Donabate, Rogerstown and North Bull Island. Coastal cliffs of significance occur only on the mainland at Howth Head and Killiney and off-shore on Lambay Island and Ireland's Eye. Rocky shores and low cliffs occur at Killiney in the south and at Portrane and Loughshinny in the north. Glacial boulder clay cliffs occur between Bray and Killiney in the south and near Balbriggan, Skerries and Loughshinny in the north.

Most of the islands in Co. Dublin occur in the northern half of the county. The Skerries, a group of five small rocky islands comprising St Patrick's Island, Red Island, Rockabill, Colt Island and Shenick's Island occur off-shore from Skerries village. A little further south is Lambay Island, Dublin's largest island, which is some 240 ha in extent. Still further south is Ireland's Eye (about 12 ha). The North Bull Island, composed of deposited sediments, is 300 ha in extent. The only significant island south of Dublin Bay is Dalkey Island (about 9 ha).

The most notable feature of the county is its built-up area which has expanded and developed enormously this century mainly because of major increases in the population following the industrial and commercial development of the city and other areas of the county. In the 90 years between 1901 (about the time that field work for Colgan's *Flora* was being completed) and 1991, the population of the county more than doubled from 448,206 to 1,025,304. This is a dramatic increase when compared with the population changes in the State as a whole which increased by 9.5% over the same period. The concentration of population in Co. Dublin has also increased relative to the population of the surrounding region comprising the counties of Meath, Kildare and Wicklow. In 1901 Co. Dublin accounted for 70% of the population of this region as compared with 75.9% in 1991.

These very sizeable population increases have also been accompanied by similar changes in the distribution of the overall population of the Dublin area, with losses at the centre and gains on the fringe. It is estimated that approximately 88% of the population resided within 7 km of the city centre in the first decade of the 20th century. By 1991 this percentage had fallen to 56%. In the period up to the late 1960s the growth in the population was mainly suburban. From the late 1960s onwards population growth has occurred on a much more widespread basis, so that while the population within 15 km of the city centre rose by almost 20%, the population in the 16-31 km zone increased by 148% (Horner 1985, 1994).

These population changes have been reflected in the expansion of the built-up area in Dublin City and County. It is estimated that the extent of the built-up area within 31 km of the city centre which had increased by only 53% between the first decade of the 20th century and the late 1930s, increased by 164% between this latter period and 1973 and by a further 40% in the following period up to 1988. The extent of the built-up area within 31 km of the city centre increased by only 75 ha a year in the period between the first decade of the 20th century and 1936 as compared with 286 ha per annum in the period between 1936 and 1973, and 457 ha per annum in the period 1973 to 1988 (Horner 1985, 1994). The increase in the built-up area has had a profound effect on the topography of the county with the conversion of many former wild habitats to buildings, roads, parks, and gardens with the consequent loss of green fields, woodlands, hedgerows, wetlands and many other features of the rural landscape.

CLIMATE

C. Breen

Co. Dublin has a mild maritime climate in keeping with the general character of the Irish climate. The frontal systems and depressions associated with the western atmospheric circulation of middle latitudes bring fairly frequent changes in meteorological conditions. Extremes of climate are rare and generally fall within a relatively narrow range. Air temperature seldom exceeds 30° C, seldom drops below freezing point and rarely remains below 0° C for more than 24 hours (Anon. 1983).

The principal meteorological elements which comprise the climate of Co. Dublin are described in the following paragraphs. Except where explicitly stated, the data presented relate to the Phoenix Park (Ordnance Survey Office) where weather observations have been made on a regular basis since 1837.

Air and Soil Temperature and Relative Humidity

Mean air temperature for the period 1961 to 1990 was 9.3° C with the following pattern of seasonal variation: spring 8.1° C; summer 14.4° C; autumn 9.8° C; winter 4.8° C. July is the warmest month of the year with an average mean air temperature of 15.1° C, while January is the coldest month with an average mean air temperature of 4.5° C. The greatest mean daily range is 6.5° C in June while the least mean daily range of 1.5° C occurs in January. In the higher parts of the county average mean temperatures will generally be lower by 1° C for every 150 m increase in height. In keeping with the absence of extremes of climate, temperature fluctuations are relatively moderate. The greatest difference between mean daily maximum and minimum temperatures, which occurs in June and July, is 9.1° C, while the smallest difference of 5.5° C occurs in December and January. The range of diurnal temperature variation is also moderate with the greatest mean daily range of 6.5° C occurring in June and the lowest mean daily range of 1.5° C occurring in December (data for Casement Aerodrome, Baldonnel, 1961-1990). Long term trends in air temperatures suggest a tendency for an increase in average mean spring and autumn temperatures since 1930 by comparison with the period before 1930. Annual mean air temperatures, which rose until the end of the decade 1941-1950, declined slightly in the period 1951-1970 and since then have risen slightly but have still remained less than the levels reached in the period 1930-1950. Analysis of temperature data at Dublin Airport for the period 1951 to 1980 suggests that winter minimum temperatures have been increasing faster than winter maximum temperatures and that summer maximum temperatures have been increasing faster than summer minimum temperatures (Daultrey 1995). This indicates a reduction in winter temperature range and an increase in summer temperature range. In fact the closing years of the 1980s, 1989 and 1990, were both very warm years, the former being the third warmest year of the century, at that time. Extremes of low air temperature in the 20th century have been very rare, the most notable example being the period 11th to 28th January 1963 when continuous air temperatures below 0° C were experienced. While air temperatures below 0° C have been recorded at stations near sea level in all months except July and August, such frosts seldom occur before late October / early November and seldom after mid-April / mid-May. The incidence of air frost, based on data for the period 1971-1980, is also relatively low with an annual average of 45 days per year, ranging from an average monthly occurrence of 6.8 days in November to a maximum of 9.9 days in January followed by a slight decline to 6.7 days in February, a rise to 7.9 days in March, declining subsequently to 4.2 days and 1.1 days respectively in April and May.

Ground frost and soil temperature patterns closely parallel the annual seasonal pattern exhibited by air temperature. The highest incidence of ground frost, measured as grass minimum temperature, occurs in the period November to April. Ground frost occurs on average on 10 days in each month during this period. The highest number of days on which ground frost was recorded was 18 in each of the months of January and March. Mean soil temperature, taken at a depth of 10 cm at Dublin Airport over the period 1981-1990, show soil temperatures at their maximum in July (17.9° C) falling to their lowest in January (4.1° C). On the basis of the normally accepted criterion for plant growth, i.e. soil temperatures above 6° C, the number of days available for plant growth, based on data at Dublin Airport, is 258 days with some variation in individual years. Low soil water levels in some areas of the county between June and September, deduced from evapo-transpiration measurements, may restrict plant growth in this period.

A feature of the climate resulting from large conurbations, is the occurrence of an urban "heat island" with higher air temperature than in the surrounding outer suburban and rural locations, particularly at night (Sweeney 1987, Graham 1993). Thus, mean annual air temperature at Trinity College was 10.7° C as compared with 9.8° C for the outer suburbs (Glasnevin Botanic Gardens and Rathfarnham Castle) declining to 9.5° C for Kinsealy and 9.3° C for Casement Aerodrome. The urban/rural contrast is most marked during winter nights with light winds and clear skies when differences of over 6.5° C may be anticipated. As a result of the effect created by the "heat island", air temperatures are higher in city centre areas and the daily range of air temperature is less in the city centre than in the outer suburbs and rural locations. The general character of the Dublin heat island is similar to that of other large cities in the mid-latitudes.

Rainfall

Co. Dublin is the driest part of Ireland containing the only sizeable area of the country with a mean annual precipitation, principally rainfall, of less than 750 mm. This compares with a mean annual average in excess of 1400 mm for many locations in western and south-western areas of Ireland. The relatively moderate rainfall pattern experienced in Co. Dublin is also illustrated by the fact that the mean annual number of days with 1 mm or more is only 130, with the number of days being evenly distributed throughout the year. This contrasts with the west and south-west of Ireland where the values approach or exceed 200 days per year. However, there are noteworthy variations in annual rainfall within the county which appear to have some influence on the distribution of the native flora. Based on the period 1961 to 1990, low values in the range 685 mm to 720 mm annual average rainfall occurred in city centre and northern coastal areas, rising to values in the range 800 mm to 1000 mm for locations in the foothills of the Dublin mountains. Values in excess of 1000 mm a year are recorded in the more mountainous areas, for example, Brittas, Ballyedmonduff and Glenasmole, and it is likely that values are in the range 1500 mm to 2000 mm a year in the higher parts of the Dublin mountains. The distribution of rainfall in Co. Dublin, based on selected locations, is shown as follows:-

Table 1. Annual Averages of Rainfall for Co. Dublin
(Fitzgerald and Forrestal 1996)

STATION	RAINFALL/mm	HEIGHT ABOVE MEAN SEA LEVEL/m
Clontarf	691	5
Merrion Square	695	13
Balbriggan	719	40
Phoenix Park	761	49
Saggart	810	107
Dundrum	814	61
Rathfarnham (St Columba's College)	961	134
Brittas	1048	244
Ballyedmonduff	1131	277
Glenasmole (Castlekelly)	1272	183

The average seasonal distribution of rainfall in Co. Dublin is as follows: spring 167 mm; summer 180 mm; autumn 206 mm; winter 208 mm. December is the wettest month with average rainfall of 82 mm while July with 50 mm is the driest month. April is the second driest month with 53 mm rainfall.

Snow and Sleet
In keeping with its very mild climate, the mean number of days with falls of snow or sleet is relatively low, ranging from 21 at Dublin Airport to less than 12 in the centre of the city. Any snow that occurs is generally short-lived. Snow lying on the ground in the morning has been recorded on average for only 9.5 days at Casement Aerodrome, falling to only 3.3 days in the city centre. In the Dublin mountains it is estimated that snow can lie for periods in excess of 30 days. Because of the relatively low incidence of frost and snow, the use of de-icing salts to treat affected roads is relatively limited so that, unlike major roads in Britain, there is no record of any spread of salt-tolerant plant species.

Sunshine and Cloud Cover
The annual mean daily duration of bright sunshine averages 3.9 hours at Dublin Airport (Table 2). However, in locations closer to the city centre, this value can be up to 0.3 hours lower because of urban effects which increase contaminants and cloud cover. Studies have shown that sunshine values for higher ground in the south of Co. Dublin can, on average, be lower still. In line with Ireland's situation off the western seaboard of Europe close to the path of the Atlantic low pressure systems, Co. Dublin has relatively high and constant average cloudiness. Mean cloud cover at Dublin Airport was 5.6 okta, being somewhat less than that in western locations, which may reach 5.9 okta, but higher than the value of 5.4 okta in the south-east at Rosslare. The period December to February, shows the greatest level of cloudiness (5.8 okta) while the lowest annual value of 5.3 okta occurs in April.
(**Note**: 1 okta represents cloud cover of one eighth of the sky).

Table 2. Sunshine Levels at Dublin Airport for 1981 to 1990 (1)

MONTH	J	F	M	A	M	J	J	A	S	O	N	D	ANNUAL AVERAGE
Mean daily bright sunshine/hr	2.0	2.5	3.4	5.1	6.1	5.5	5.8	4.7	4.3	3.2	2.2	1.6	3.9
Max. daily sunshine/hr	8.0	8.9	11.9	13.3	15.4	15.9	15.4	14.0	12.4	9.9	8.5	6.6	11.7
Mean no. days without bright sunshine/day	8	7	4	2	2	1	1	1	2	5	7	11	5

(1) Data from Meteorological Service

An important feature of long-term climatological trends in the Dublin area is the decline in annual mean sunshine from over 4 hours in the earlier part of the century to less than 3.7 hours in each of the decades 1971/1980 and 1981/1990. This may be a combination of the increased occurrence of haze due to greater air pollution and the general increase in cloudiness in the Northern Hemisphere revealed in international climatological studies (Daultrey 1995).

Surface Wind

Mean annual wind speed at Dublin Airport over the period 1962 to 1984 was 5.2 metres per second, a relatively modest level, as compared with corresponding values for other locations of 5.6 for Valentia, Co. Kerry, 5.9 for Rosslare, Co. Wexford and 6.7 for Belmullet, Co. Mayo, but higher than values of 4.4 or less at inland locations. The location of the Dublin mountains shelters the county from southern winds and deflects them to a south-easterly or south-westerly direction. As a result the Dublin area has a marked deficiency of southerly winds when compared with other locations and an excess of winds from a westerly direction. 45% of winds are from a westerly or south-westerly direction, 12% from an easterly direction but only 8% from a southerly direction. Generally, January is the windiest month with a wind speed of 6.2 metres per second at Dublin Airport. August is the calmest month with a wind speed of only 1.5 metres per second being recorded (Rohan 1986). Gales are relatively infrequent, occurring on average on 7 days per year.

Fog, Mist, Air Pollution and Haze

The incidence of fog, mist and haze in Co. Dublin is the product of its maritime location, topography and predominantly urban character. While the incidence of fog and mist is minor given its location, the occurrence of haze is relatively high, reflecting the marked concentration of urban pollutants. In addition, during periods when continental anti-cyclones bringing air from industrial areas of England and the Continent occur, the eastern part of Ireland, including Co. Dublin, is affected by haze to a considerably greater extent than other parts of Ireland.

Because of its large built-up area, significantly higher levels of air pollution occur in Co. Dublin than in other areas of Ireland. The two principal pollutants, sulphur dioxide and smoke, arise from the burning of fossil or other fuels and emission of chemicals produced as by-products of industrial processes. Normally such pollutants are dispersed by wind and rain, and hence values for particular years can be affected by the prevailing weather conditions. This is especially true in years when calm conditions occur particularly at evening or at night in the period November to January, often under the influence of anti-cyclones centred over or near Ireland, or when localised temperature inversions occur.

Records of the mean levels of concentration of sulphur dioxide and smoke are available on a continuous basis since the 1970s. Levels of both pollutants declined generally until the early 1980s (Table 3). The concentration levels of sulphur dioxide, which at one stage exceeded smoke concentration levels, continued to decline generally throughout the 1980s having been accelerated by the change to natural gas in electricity generating stations, and actually fell below smoke concentration levels. Smoke concentration levels on the other hand rose substantially, reflecting increased dependence on solid fuel heating systems by domestic consumers with particularly high concentrations being experienced in the winters of 1981/1982, 1984/85 and 1986/87. Smoke concentration levels continued to exceed sulphur dioxide concentration levels until the early 1990s. By this time, a "clean air" policy involving a complete ban on sales of bituminous coal in the greater Dublin area resulted in smoke concentration levels declining dramatically in the 1990s to less than 25% of previous maximum levels, aided also by a succession of mild and windy winters. Sulphur dioxide levels also continued to decline in the 1990s reflecting the combined effects of the change from fuel oil to natural gas in Dublin power stations, a decrease in the sulphur content of gas oil and a decrease in fuel oil combustion in industry. These trends are illustrated by Table 3.

Table 3. Mean Annual Smoke and Sulphur Dioxide Levels in micrograms per cubic metre, in Dublin City (1)

Year	1972/73	1981/82	1982/83	1984/85	1986/87	1988/89	1990/91	1992/93
Smoke	51	55	34	53	60	49	27	13
Sulphur dioxide	89	68	46	42	48	29	26	20

(1) Data from Dublin Corporation Network

Similar trends are also evident for monitoring stations in the county area although the levels of smoke and sulphur dioxide recorded were lower than in the city area.

No clear evidence is available on whether the increase in air pollution has affected the distribution of native higher plants although some garden plants, in particular evergreen plants, as well as many native bryophytes and lichens, have suffered as a consequence of increased atmospheric pollution. With the advent of the new clean air regime this adverse trend may, in time, be reversed even with increased urbanisation in Co. Dublin.

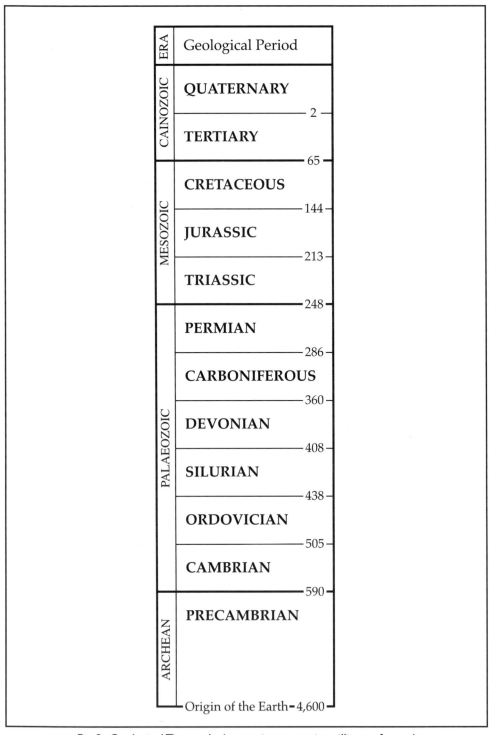

Fig. 2 Geological Timescale (approximate age in millions of years)

GEOLOGY

Patrick Wyse Jackson

The rocks that occur in Co. Dublin are all, with the exception of the latest Pleistocene glacial tills, of Palaeozoic age, having formed between 590 and 350 million years ago during the Cambrian to Carboniferous periods (see Fig. 2). The physical landscape that we are familiar with owes its origins to the interaction between the underlying solid geology, the processes of weathering and erosion, and the effects of ice and rivers which have played an important role in moulding present day Co. Dublin. A quick examination of a map of the county shows rounded mountains to the south, away from which stretches a long plain which reaches out towards the Boyne valley to the north and the Bog of Allen to the west. The coast undulates in a series of bays and headlands which are controlled by the resistivity of certain rock types to erosion. The mountains are granitic as is the headland at Killiney while Howth is similarly composed of resistant rocks, which include quartzites and greywackes. Softer, less resistant sedimentary rocks occur south of Killiney, and limestones and older silty sedimentary rocks underlie Dublin City and the plain to the north (Fig. 3) (Holland 1981a, McConnell and Philcox 1995, McConnell et al. 1995, Wyse Jackson et al. 1993).

The geological history of an area even as small as Co. Dublin is often quite complex. Periods of sedimentation may be followed by large scale earth movements, intrusion of large masses of molten igneous rocks, prolonged volcanic activity and regional metamorphism. These events may give way to quieter episodes of sedimentation and reef-building in shallow warm tropical seas containing a rich and diverse marine community. Colder icy millennia may result in the development of mountain glaciers and large ice sheets which mould the landscape and veil it with a thin veneer of till as they recede. Periods of uplift may cause rocks deposited in deep oceans to occur on land and be subjected to prolonged weathering and erosion so that they are removed altogether and are unseen by present-day geologists.

Piecing together the geological past is time consuming and it may take many years of study by many geologists to arrive at a reasonable explanation of the geology of an area. Geologists have been seriously studying the Dublin area since about 1800 when the (Royal) Dublin Society commissioned a survey of the mineralogy of the county. Research is continuing today. By examining the succession of rocks found, determining their relationships one to another, and gathering information related to the environments in which the rocks were formed the geological history may be determined. These data vary depending on the rock types under study. Igneous rocks may display a variety of mineralogy and textures which can be related to their genesis and cooling history respectively. Metamorphic rocks may also show textures which indicate whether they were formed by the effects of pressure or heat, and new minerals which formed as the rock re-equilibrated with the new constraints give a thermobarometer. The environments in which sedimentary rocks formed may be deduced by examination of features such as the nature and coarseness of sediment, the thickness of bedding, the occurrence of ripples and mud cracks or other sedimentary structures and the fossil content. Fossils may also indicate the date of rock deposition.

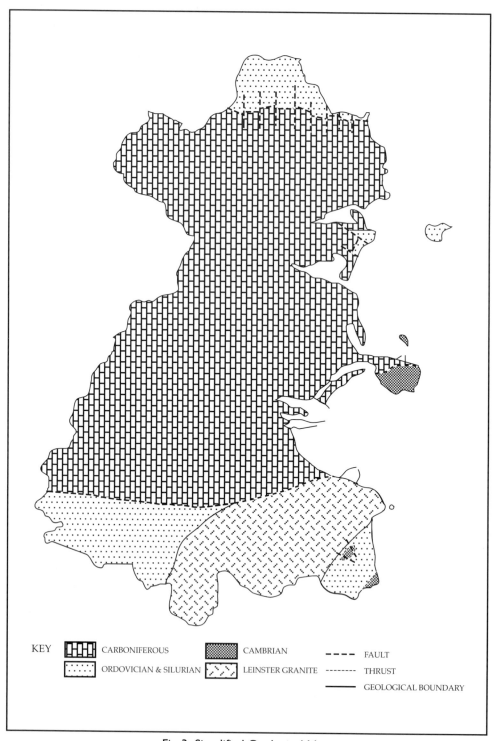

KEY   CARBONIFEROUS   CAMBRIAN   ---- FAULT

ORDOVICIAN & SILURIAN   LEINSTER GRANITE   ------ THRUST

——— GEOLOGICAL BOUNDARY

Fig. 3 Simplified Geological Map

Lower Palaeozoic. Cambrian – Silurian: 590–400 million years ago

The oldest rocks that appear on the surface, or crop out, in Co. Dublin are the Cambrian greywackes and quartzites that form the resistant headland of Howth (Holland 1981b), the island of Ireland's Eye and the rounded hill of Carrickgollogan near Ballycorus. Greywackes are moderately fine-grained blue-green-grey coloured rocks composed of fine sediment which was deposited at the margin of the continental shelf and then cascaded off the continental slope and finally came to rest at its bottom in a jumble. Structures such as slumps and folds may be seen at various points around the coastal cliffs on Howth. These rocks also contain trace fossils (preserved marks in rocks which indicate activity by an organism) such as burrows and feeding traces, and include *Oldhamia*, first described from rocks collected from Bray Head in Co. Wicklow (Brück and Reeves 1976), which is characteristic of Middle Cambrian rocks of Europe and North America. The quartzites which occur as large isolated 'rafts' within the greywackes are pale recrystallised coarse grained sandstones, which are very resistant to weathering and stand out as ridges on Howth Summit. They were exploited for road making in the last century.

During the Cambrian, Ordovician and Silurian periods, the area which was later to become the present-day British Isles, was affected by the slow closure of a major ocean by means of the collision of two continents. This resulted in shallowing of the ocean, increased volcanic activity during the Ordovician, intrusion of granite masses such as those in Leinster and final closure of the ocean during the Silurian, the elevation of north-east to south-west trending mountains, and large scale regional metamorphism.

Exposed on the south-eastern side of the Dublin mountains is a belt of Lower Ordovician slates, mudstones and quartzites with occasional thin volcanic horizons which form areas of low relief. The north-western flank of the granite gives way to a similar Ordovician succession of shales and slates nearly 700 metres in thickness (Brück et al. 1974). These are overlain by later Silurian sediments. These areas have subsequently been covered by a generous thickness of glacial till, and now support good agricultural land.

North of Howth, a small inlier (an area of older rocks surrounded by younger rocks) of Upper Ordovician rocks crop out along the coast at Portrane. The succession consists of volcanic andesitic lavas overlain by blue-grey cherty limestones, which have yielded a brachiopod-coral-bryozoan assemblage, against which Silurian siltstones and greywackes have been thrust faulted from the south. The island of Lambay is partially composed of similar lavas that were extruded from an active volcano into a shallow warm water sea. In the area around Balbriggan in the north of the county, a folded and faulted succession of Ordovician and Silurian mudstones and sandstones is poorly exposed beneath glacial deposits.

The granite that comprises the Dublin and Wicklow mountains is termed the Leinster Granite, and was intruded in five plutons, igneous bodies that are usually cylindrical in shape, which together formed a larger igneous mass or batholith some 1500 square kilometres in size, in or around 400 million years ago during an event known to geologists as the Caledonian orogeny. Melting of adjacent rocks at depth resulted in the formation of plumes of molten magma which moved slowly through and assimilated the overlying rocks. Crystallisation of the granite due to cooling occurred during a 20 million year period after implacement. The granite is composed of quartz, feldspar and mica, and accessory minerals such as beryl and tourmaline are found. The Leinster Granite has been used for building in Dublin City between Georgian times and the present (Wyse Jackson 1993). Surrounding the Leinster Granite is a thin aureole or band of metamorphic rocks, which is the product of contact metamorphism between the granite and the material into which it intruded. The relationship between the two rock types is probably best exposed at Killiney where mica schists, which contain large tabular crystals of andalusite, are exposed beside the pale crystalline granite. At Killiney, as well as at Ballycorus, evidence of 18th century mining activity can be found, when mineral veins or lodes were exploited for galena - a dense grey-coloured lead ore.

Upper Palaeozoic. Devonian – Carboniferous: 400–300 million years ago

The intense activity of the Lower Palaeozoic was followed in Ireland by the Devonian period when much of the land surface was exposed, and in which dry arid conditions prevailed. A marine basin was present in what is now the southern part of Munster. This was the period during which sandstones and conglomerates (Old Red Sandstone), best exposed in the counties of Cork and Kerry, were deposited. Smaller areas of similar rock types are found in the north-east of Ireland and at Portrane, Co. Dublin, where they form thin beds of a quartz-jasper conglomerate. However, the latter have been dated as being early Carboniferous and not Devonian in age.

The Lower Carboniferous was a time when a shallow sea migrated northwards over the Devonian continent at a rate of 3 cm per year. Within the Dublin region a deep fault-controlled basin, known as the Dublin Basin, developed and infilled with various sediments (Nolan 1989). At first, coarse conglomerates were laid down, followed by muddy carbonate sediments over which developed carbonate mudmounds that formed topographic highs on the sea bed. The muddy limestones are generally well bedded and are locally known as calp, and are extensively developed around Lucan, where they were quarried from medieval times. The carbonate Waulsortian mudmounds which developed in shallow early Lower Carboniferous seas, with their typical fauna of bryozoans, brachiopods, cephalopods and crinoids, are best seen exposed at Feltrim (Hudson et al. 1966). Overlying the mudmounds are deepwater shales and flat-bedded limestones. On the shelf north of the Dublin Basin the first sediments deposited were the coarse red sediments over which are found purer limestones such as those exposed at the foreshore at Malahide. Later still, small carbonate mounds, younger than the Waulsortian variety just to the south, propagated on the shallow sea bed.

Across the British Isles, shallowing of the seas at the end of the Lower Carboniferous produced swampy environments in which the coal measures were deposited. Subsequently an arid terrestrial environment during the Permian and the Triassic prevailed. It is possible that rocks younger than the Lower Carboniferous were deposited in the Dublin region. However, evidence for them onshore is not seen, and if they occurred at all they have been removed due to the uplift and erosion and the later scouring of the area by ice during the Pleistocene. Extensive movement of the Earth's crust took place during the Hercynian orogeny, or mountain building event, that caused the Lower Carboniferous limestones at Loughshinny to be folded into spectacular erect chevron folds.

Post–Palaeozoic Offshore Geology

Within the Irish Sea, just offshore of Dublin, is the Kish Bank Basin. This is a fault-bound structure or trough in which a succession of rocks ranging in age from Carboniferous to Jurassic (150 million years ago) are found beneath younger Pleistocene sediments. The younger rocks in the Kish Bank Basin may have some hydrocarbon (oil and gas) potential, and have been drilled to depths of over 2 km.

Fossils of Jurassic age have been found near Stillorgan, Co. Dublin, in boulder clay deposited there by the Irish Sea Glacier. This glacier, which moved southwards from Scotland, plucked the fossils from the Jurassic rocks of the Kish Bank Basin over which it passed.

Pleistocene - Holocene: 2,000,000 years ago to the present day

In the last 2 million years, towards the end of the Tertiary and into the Quaternary period, fluctuations of temperature resulted in an ice age (Mitchell and Ryan 1997). At least eight episodes of ice expansion, known as glacials, occurred during this time and these were separated by warmer periods known as interglacials. In Ireland evidence for several, but not all, of these glacials and interglacials may be seen. The Dublin region has been most strongly affected by two glacials: the Munsterian (300,000 - 132,000 years ago) and the Midlandian (120,000 - 10,000 years ago) with the effects of the latter being most strongly imprinted on the landscape (Coxon 1992).

During the Midlandian, ice from three sources was present in the region. A glacier moved from the north down the Irish Sea from Scotland; ice sheets covered most of the Irish midlands and moved across Dublin from the north-east, and a mountain ice cap was perched on the Dublin and Wicklow Mountains. In the mountains, initial ice accumulation was in corries - deepened chair-like depressions - such as at Lough Nahanagan and Lough Bray. Glaciers developed from these and moved downslope through valleys such as Glendalough, Glendasan, Glenmalure and Glencree. These valleys were all deepened and now show a typical U-shaped profile indicative of glacial erosion. The valley glaciers coalesced with the ice-sheets of the lower ground.

The ice sheets from the Midlands blanketed much of Dublin under a layer of limestone-rich till (or boulder clay). Till is a poorly sorted mixture of rock types which range in size from pulverised rockflour to large boulders. The Irish Sea Glacier also produced till which contains a characteristic blue granite from Ailsa Craig in the Clyde Estuary. The presence of this material in tills along the east coast demonstrates the direction of the flow of the Irish Sea Glacier from north to south (Hoare 1975).

As the ice melted, water was impounded in a number of glacial lakes between the mountains and the ice to the north and east. Subsequently, with increased volumes of water, some was lost towards the north through what are known as spillways. No extensive glacial lakes occurred in Co. Dublin (in contrast to Co. Wicklow at Blessington and Enniskerry) but a number of small spillways are found, such as at Kilmashogue (Hoare 1976). In the north of the county meltwater deposits produced sinuous elongated deltas called eskers which are dominated by gravel-grade sediment. In Dublin many of these features have been removed through quarrying for gravels but remnants survive at Greenhills and Lucan, and support typical calcicole or lime-loving vegetation.

The extinct Giant Irish Deer *Megaloceros giganteus* roamed Ireland about 12,500 - 11,000 years ago. Although this animal lived in mainland Europe as well as in the British Isles, its fossilised remains have been found in large numbers in Ireland, particularly at Ballybetagh and at Howth, preserved beneath peat. A cold spell which occurred about 11,000 years ago caused its demise. Soon afterwards a warmer period, the Holocene, began which continues to the present day. Many plants and animals returned to Ireland, it is thought from the south via France and Britain, and with the development of soils the familiar Dublin flora began to emerge.

Note: Literature relating to the geology of Co. Dublin is dispersed throughout several books which are contained in the references and in serial publications including the *Irish Journal of Earth Sciences, Bulletin of the Geological Survey of Ireland, Proceedings of the Royal Irish Academy, Scientific Proceedings of the Royal Dublin Society* and the *Journal of the Royal Geological Society of Ireland* and its predecessor the *Journal of the Geological Society of Dublin*. Additional valuable information may be obtained from the maps of the Geological Survey of Ireland, particularly from McConnell and Philcox (1995) which includes the southern half of the county. The northern half will be included in the forthcoming 1:100,000 map Sheet 13 Meath - Louth.

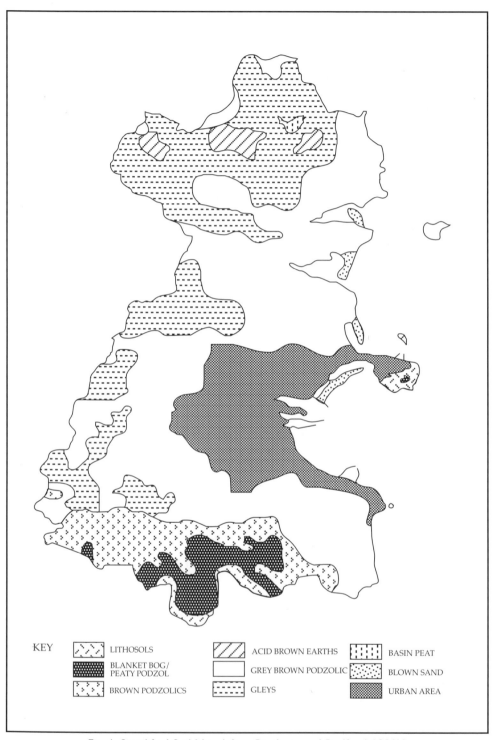

KEY

⬙ LITHOSOLS		⬙ ACID BROWN EARTHS		⬙ BASIN PEAT	
⬙ BLANKET BOG/ PEATY PODZOL		⬙ GREY BROWN PODZOLIC		⬙ BLOWN SAND	
⬙ BROWN PODZOLICS		⬙ GLEYS		⬙ URBAN AREA	

Fig. 4 Simplified Soil Map (after Gardiner and Radford 1980b)

SOILS

Patrick Wyse Jackson

The soils that now cover Dublin have developed in the last 11,000 years on top of parent material which, as we have seen earlier, may be granite, quartzite, shale and sandstone, limestone, or alkaline boulder clay. Parent material is one of several important factors in soil formation; others include climate, topography, time, and human influence. Modification of soils to enhance agricultural yield is widespread, and the constant expansion of urban areas is diminishing the open areas in Co. Dublin. It is estimated that some 20% of the county is now covered by urban development.

A cursory comparison of the geological and soil maps of Co. Dublin shows that there is some correlation between geology and the overlying soil type (Fig. 3 and Fig. 4). An important factor too is the derivation and constituents of glacial tills which can mask the influence of the underlying geology. The distribution of plant types is not always clearly defined in terms of underlying geological influence. On the Howth Peninsula, on its north-eastern side, calcicole plants thrive on limestone-rich boulder clay that sits directly on top of acidic quartzites and greywackes. At Killiney such calcicole plants can be found growing close by calcifuge species, with each community supported by soils derived from limestone boulder clay and granite parent materials respectively.

Major soil types

(Fig. 4): these are more fully described in Gardiner and Radford (1980a). The number in parentheses refers to their classification of soil associations and the figure in square brackets refers to the percentage area of the soil type in the county excluding the built-up area.

Lithosols and bedrock (4): these are very immature, thin, stony soils, that directly overlie bedrock. In the Dublin and north Co. Wicklow area such soils are developed on the Cambrian quartzites of the Sugar Loaf and on the granite peaks of the Dublin Mountains where the blanket bog has eroded away. Such soils generally support heath communities, upland grassland, or are barren of vegetation. [2%].

Blanket Bog - Peaty Podzols (1): Blanket Bog occurs sparingly on the Howth Peninsula and, more extensively, on more level areas and gentle slopes of the Dublin mountains. The area around the upper Dodder is covered by a thin layer of Blanket Bog which grades into Peaty Podzols in other areas above 150 metres. Peaty Podzols are acidic soils that have been subjected to heavy leaching by rainwater and whose uppermost 0.5 metres contains a high percentage of organic matter (10-30%). Most suited to sheep grazing. [5%].

Brown Podzolics (8 and 9): soils usually < 1 metre thick; moderately depleted in nutrients due to leaching, which results in an acidic soil. Modification by fertilisation can create good agricultural land. This soil type, which has developed on granite and mica schists, is found on the lower slopes of the Dublin mountains between 150 and 200 metres, and supports heath, bracken communities or grassland and, more recently, coniferous plantations. [8% (8); 5% (9)].

Acid Brown Earths (16 and 19): a mature soil which is not divided into distinct horizons. Well drained, friable mineral soils which are often extensively cultivated. Developed on Upper Carboniferous shales, on higher ground around Naul and Garristown in the north of the county. This soil also underlies the peninsula of Malahide Island where it is covered by blown sand and has no influence on the vegetation cover. [5% (16); 2% (19)].

Grey Brown Podzolics (30 and 38): in a crescent surrounding Dublin City, extending from Skerries in the north to Maynooth and Clondalkin in the west and to Bray in the south, Grey Brown Podzolic soils are found developed on glacial tills of Irish Sea origin on land below 60 metres. They are moderately well drained loamy textured soil types, and support good pasture land, suitable for vegetable growing in the north of the county. Due to extensive agriculture, plant communities are poorly defined. [0.5% (30); 46% (38)].

Gleys (40): these soils occur in association with the preceding type, but on land over 60 metres. They are best developed in the northernmost areas of the county on Silurian shales and sandstones overlain by Midlandian glacial tills, but also occur in the east of the county. They are generally poorly draining soils due to high concentrations of clay minerals or the presence of a high water table, and have a poor agricultural potential unless drained. As with the Grey Brown Podzolic soils, plant communities are not well defined. [24%].

Raised bog/basin peat (44): occurs at the Bog of the Ring, near Balrothery, north Co. Dublin, which in recent years has shown major signs of degradation following drainage. [1%].

Blown sand: In a number of areas along the coast of Dublin blown sand has accumulated into extensive dune areas. Such dunes are best seen at Malahide Island, Portmarnock, Portrane, and North Bull Island. The sand is rich in calcareous shelly material and supports a rich calcicole flora. [1.5%].

HISTORY OF THE STUDY
OF THE FLORA OF CO. DUBLIN

D. Doogue

If we draw a veil over early literary allusions to the occurrence of plants such as Ramsons *Allium ursinum* at Howth, which is chronicled in the heroic sagas of Diarmuid and Grainne, the first formal botanical record for Co. Dublin was contributed by Richard Heaton (1601-1666), Rector of Birr. Heaton, originally from Yorkshire, lived for some time in Ireland acquiring land at Ballyskenagh in Co. Offaly, now the site of Mount Saint Joseph Abbey (Walsh 1978). He was a Cambridge graduate and was known to John Ray, the major botanist in Britain at the time. He contributed a number of original Irish botanical records to one of the first printed works on British botany - *Phytologia Britannica* - mainly from the midlands and west of Ireland (How 1650). Included in his communications is a reference to *Hyacinthus stellarius vernus pumilus, The small spring starred Hyacinth,* the plant better known nowadays as *Scilla verna* or Spring Squill which he had discovered "At the Ring's-End neere Dublin". Colgan (1904) was later to lament the disappearance of this species from the Ringsend area, even then attributing its decline to the expansion of the city.

Concentrated botanical studies of the Dublin flora commenced, however, with the work of Caleb Threlkeld (1676-1728), another north of England churchman, and later medical doctor, who came from Cumberland to Ireland in 1713 and who produced the first book on the indigenous plants of Ireland - *Synopsis Stirpium Hibernicarum* (Threlkeld 1726). His *Synopsis* is now a very rare work but has recently been made available in facsimile with a detailed introduction and glossary of equivalent modern plant names (Nelson 1988).

In common with many similar botanical works of the time, Threlkeld's text was intended primarily as a herbal, listing the medicinal properties of various species of Irish plants. However, by his incorporation into the text of numerous biblical and classical allusions, including several references to botanical issues raised as a consequence of Bishop Bedel's translation of the Bible into the Irish language in 1685, it becomes clear that this was no straightforward herbal. In many cases Threlkeld used the text as a platform from which to launch attacks on a cocktail of necromancers, sorcerers, astrologers and many other forms of unbelievers who incurred his displeasure. He also, unfortunately, criticised some of the more important botanists of the time, especially Dillenius, who had recently completed the revision of the third edition of Ray's *Synopsis Methodica Stirpium Britannicarum* (Ray 1724). The venom of some of these attacks, often with very slight justification, may have had more to do with the national and international politics of the time than with purely botanical issues.

Recent research has tended to question the originality of Threlkeld's work. It has been demonstrated that different elements in the individual species accounts, particularly the sections relating to the medicinal properties of plants, had been appropriated directly from previously published sources. Records from Ray's *Synopsis* are included but are not acknowledged as such (Mitchell 1974). Similarly, several of the most interesting plant records had been recycled from other published sources - particularly those of Richard Heaton and William Sherard. Threlkeld's text also incorporated Irish names for many of the plants featured. These are believed to have been abstracted from a manuscript list, compiled long before his arrival in Ireland, and have sometimes been attributed to Richard Heaton who was certainly in a position to develop such a list.

However, in addition to its herbal lore, much of which was in the public domain by the end of the 17th century, numerous original topographical references are included in Threlkeld's accounts of species. The bulk of the records, and particularly those from the Dublin district are unquestionably authentic, though whether they result from Threlkeld's own work or were contributed by some unknown associates is not always clear. He makes several references to plants having been sent to him by others. In relation to Soapwort *Saponaria officinalis* he states "It has been brought to me, but I omitted setting down the Place it grows in". More convincingly, references are often included to the habitats of some of these plants, which suggests a direct familiarity with the species in the wild. For example, Brookweed *Samolus valerandi*, a native plant, is recorded as growing in moist holes among the stones near the sea between Dun Laoghaire and Dalkey. This is precisely the habitat in which this species still occurs in several locations along the north Dublin coast, although it has not been seen in recent years at Threlkeld's original locality. Similarly, Sea-milkwort *Glaux maritima* is recorded as being "plentifully near the Sea just above Ballybaugh [Ballybough] Bridge near the Rivulet's [River Tolka] side". Opportunist species, such as Weld or Yellow Weed *Reseda luteola*, were correctly recognised as growing spontaneously upon rubbish and fallow fields, and near the old windmill at Dolphin's Barn. Ecologically accurate remarks such as these suggest a degree of original observation on Threlkeld's part as well as the capacity to extract relevant new knowledge from mere background information. The format of his *Synopsis* resembles Ray's *Catalogus Plantarum circa Cantabrigiam Nascentium* which appeared in 1660 and in this sense it conforms to and amplifies the developing *genre* of the Local Flora in which not only the plants, but also their geographical distributions and habitats, were considered to be of intrinsic intellectual interest rather than as materials intended solely for the relief of human discomfort. Threlkeld had cut his botanical teeth in the north of England and was familiar with the standard reference works of the time, including the earlier editions of Ray. The title of his work, *Synopsis Stirpium Hibernicarum* (as well as the peripheral content of many of the individual species accounts) is structured closely on that of Ray's *Synopsis Methodica Stirpium Brittanicarum*. Threlkeld had used an earlier version of this work (which had been first published in 1690) in Britain when learning his plants in the company of other botanists and was clearly, by inclination, an intuitive field botanist. He began to form a *Hortus Siccus* or collection of dried plants, following his arrival in Ireland. The recent discovery of a number of dried plant specimens, apparently from this herbarium, tends to confirm his status as a competent botanist (Doogue and Parnell 1992). Indeed many of these species can still be found in inner city localities from which they were originally recorded (Doogue 1984). The same applies to records from further afield. Common Gromwell *Lithospermum officinale* was found "at the foot of Inisacore-hill [Inchicore] and under the Brow above Palmerstown Mills". It is still present nearby on hilly slopes in the Furry Glen in the Phoenix Park. One of the most characteristic species of the Dublin district, Yellow Archangel *Lamiastrum galeobdolon*, was recorded (under the pre-Linnean polynomial LAMIUM LUTEUM FOLIO OBLONGO LUTEUM) among bushes beyond Roper's-rest. Though widespread in old deciduous woodland along the Liffey Valley, it has only been reliably recorded from three other Irish counties - Wicklow, Carlow and Wexford. Another present-day rarity, Blue Fleabane *Erigeron acer* (as CONYZA CAERULEA ACRIS), was found upon a dry hilly pasture near Blackrock. Similarly, Wild Clary *Salvia verbenaca* was recorded (as HORMINUM SYLVESTRE LAVENDULAE FLORAE) upon the brow below the Hospital of Kilmainham near the road, and in such sandy places about the city. Wild Clary persisted for many years nearby and was recorded by several authors from the Phoenix Park area long after Threlkeld's time. He also found Sea-kale *Crambe maritima*, or Sea Colewort (as BRASSICA SYLVESTRIS) as it was known in those days, on the seashore near Dun Laoghaire. Individual colonies of Sea-kale have a reputation for disappearing for many years and then reappearing, depending perhaps on the activity of winter storms which bring dormant seed to a position where it can germinate. R.Ll. Praeger found it on Ireland's Eye in 1894 where it re-appeared on the shingle beach in 1974 and again in 1981.

But how can a botanist of Threlkeld's ability, operating out of Mark's Alley, nowadays a short laneway off Francis Street, Dublin, have survived in isolation from other botanists? He qualified as a medical doctor in the University of Edinburgh in January 1713 and slightly more than two months later arrived in Dublin to begin a new life. Botanical studies were a standard feature of medical courses at that time. The overwhelming herbal character of the *Synopsis* indicates its true market as well as the altering circumstances of Threlkeld's own employment. The list of subscribers to the work, in which Galwegians are disproportionately well-represented, lacks the name of any well-known Irish botanist among the usual smattering of churchmen, titled personages, druggists and apothecaries, with the outstanding exception of Thomas Molyneux (1661-1733), brother of the better-known William (Simms 1982).

The plant names in Threlkeld's work are laid out in alphabetical generic order (which, by 1726, was an archaic arrangement in view of the availability of Ray's more natural classification) using the cumbersome Latin polynomials that comprised the contemporary system of plant nomenclature which was to persist until Linnaeus took matters in hand a generation later (Linnaeus 1753). Herbalists would have been more concerned with quickly finding an account of a species rather than grappling with the complexities of taxonomic relationships. Similarly, no descriptions of the plants are included, perhaps because these were already available, albeit in Latin, in Ray's *Synopsis*. In these respects Threlkeld's essay harks back to How's *Phytologica Britannica* rather than to the contemporary Dillenian edition of Ray. Strangely, a similar alphabetical format had been previously adopted by another Cumbrian botanist, William Nicolson, who studied the flora of Cumberland and Westmorland from 1690 and who was later to become Bishop of Derry, taking with him his botanical notebooks to Ireland following his appointment in 1719 (Whittaker 1981). Whether Nicolson's manuscript served as a template for Threlkeld's book or whether they ever had personal contact is unknown.

An Appendix to the main work is based on a plant list supplied by Thomas Molyneux. Molyneux had been well-connected with the embryonic local scientific circle that had flourished as the Dublin Philosophical Society (1683-1708) and which functioned as a local counterpart of the Royal Society of London and included in its membership distinguished public figures such as William Petty and George Berkeley (Hoppen 1970). Threlkeld had arrived in Dublin between the demise of the Dublin Philosophical Society (1708) and the formation of the Dublin Society (1731) and thus had little opportunity to take part in the scientific community of the time. Molyneux, who had originally compiled his list around 1700, added a number of species to Threlkeld's list, most notably Adder's-tongue *Ophioglossum vulgatum* from Stockhole, between Cloghran and St Doolagh's, and Marsh Hawk's-beard *Crepis paludosa* from Three Rock Mountain.

A near neighbour of Threlkeld's, Isaac Butler (1689-1755), lived at the corner of Bull Alley and Patrick Street in Dublin. He is best known as a compiler of Almanacks, and was employed by the Physico-Historical Society to assist in the preparation of material for a description of the district of Dublin. Butler's brief was to search for fossils, rare plants and other natural curiosities. He reported his discoveries to Dr. John Rutty (1697-1775), an English Physician who ultimately produced the well-known *Natural History of the County of Dublin* (Rutty 1772). In this work Rutty retained the complex polynomials of Ray and others despite the then availability of *Flora Anglica* which had established a concordance between the earlier polynomials and the much neater Linnean binomials (Linnaeus 1754, 1759). Unfortunately, although there is a comprehensive list of the plants of Dublin, both wild and cultivated, included in this work, very few records are localised.

This position was not to be rectified for Irish botanists until the appearance of Walter Wade's *Catalogus Systematicus Plantarum Indigenarum in Comitatu Dublinensi Inventarum* (Wade 1794). This work was based on his personal observations in the county. Some years earlier (c. 1787), Wade had attempted to produce and market a much more lavish *Flora Dublinensis*, structured on the *Flora Londinensis* of Curtis. This work was to include hand-coloured engravings and a proposal for subscribers had been issued (Nelson 1980). The prospectus included a beautifully-executed engraving of Henbane *Hyoscyamus niger*, possibly from Kilmainham where he himself had recorded it, and which still flourishes, sometimes in great profusion, on the shingle shore of Ireland's Eye. Most of the urban habitats from which it was found in the past have been destroyed by building operations. Unfortunately Wade's scheme did not prove financially viable and the subsequent appearance of the very much scaled-down *Catalogus* is a tribute to his persistence and energy. This work bears the stamp of authority and good exploratory field work. He recorded plants from many parts of the county, not just a sampling from the better sites, and discovered many uncommon plants with very restricted distributions in Ireland. A number of them still survive where he first found them more than two centuries ago. His records for species now legally protected in the Irish Republic such as Hairy Violet *Viola hirta* (in hilly and bushy pastures near the shore near Raheny) and Red Hemp-nettle *Galeopsis angustifolia* (by the roadside and in hedgebanks between Chapelizod and Luttrellstown) are from sites long since destroyed, but other plants recorded by him persist despite urban development. One of the most impressive survivors is so-called Wild Parsnip *Pastinaca sativa*, which is occasionally recorded as a fairly obvious short-term escape, in circumstances where it is unlikely to perpetuate itself. Wade first found it plentifully about the quarry at Finglas Bridge sometime before 1794, precisely where Colgan was to rediscover it in abundance a century later. For almost another hundred years it persisted and was still a conspicuous feature on grassy slopes near Finglas Bridge until about 1985 when the colony was almost wiped out by building and amenity landscaping. Wade had been appointed Professor of Botany with care of the herbarium of the Dublin Society in 1797 and became curator of its Botanic Gardens at Glasnevin, which later became the National Botanic Gardens. It is likely that he discovered *Pastinaca* at Finglas Bridge, not a celebrated botanical venue, while on some excursion from the nearby Botanic Gardens.

Walter Wade (c.1740-1825) continued with his botanical field work long after the publication of his *Catalogus* and, in 1804, produced a supplementary work on behalf of the Dublin Society under the title *Plantae rariores in Hibernia inventae* which included many Dublin references. He found Oysterplant *Mertensia maritima* in a number of locations on the shore between Balbriggan and Loughshinny. By Colgan's time this species was considered to be extinct in Co. Dublin and repeated searches since then have failed to reveal any further colonies. Wade's later work included lectures for the general public, including a series of lectures on meadow and pasture grasses as part of his duties for the dynamic Dublin Society. He communicated to J.T. Mackay a record for Yellow Bird's-nest *Monotropa hypopitys* from under beech trees at St Catherine's in the Liffey Valley. Unfortunately no-one has rediscovered it at this site since, although the habitat is still suitable for the species.

John Templeton (1776-1825), from Belfast, who worked extensively on both the flora and fauna of Ireland, came to Dublin on a number of occasions from the end of the 18th century onwards. He visited the three principal botanical areas of the county - Howth, the Liffey Valley and Bohernabreena (Glenasmole Valley) - where in company with Mackay he discovered another species now legally protected in this country - Bog Orchid *Hammarbya paludosa* - where it continues to survive in wet boggy ground to this day. He also discovered, sometime before 1820, Small-white Orchid *Pseudorchis albida* (as *Habenaria albida*) in pastures on the side of Kelly's Glen where it persisted into recent times, though it has not been found since 1970. Templeton was in contact with the leading naturalists of the day, including Hooker, Sowerby and Dawson Turner.

The appointment of J.T. Mackay (c.1775-1862) as assistant Botanist in Trinity College and later curator of the Trinity Botanic Garden, then in Ballsbridge, led to a flood of new botanical discoveries, the first tranche of which was published in the Transactions of the Dublin Society (Mackay 1806). This work included Dublin localities for two species in particular, now both nationally rare: Rough Poppy *Papaver hybridum* and Bird's-foot *Ornithopus perpusillus*, the former from near the old church at Kilbarrack on the road to Howth and the latter from bare sandy pasture fields on the south side of the Howth peninsula. Bird's-foot still occurs in a few small colonies in shallow, unimproved heathy grassland on Howth. Few living botanists have seen Rough Poppy in Ireland, although it made a fleeting re-appearance recently in another of its old sites in the Portrane area where it had first been found by Colgan in 1893. In 1825 Mackay published his larger catalogue of the flowering plants and ferns, *A catalogue of the indigenous plants found in Ireland* (Mackay 1825). His introduction reveals this to be in several respects a transitional work. The first two volumes of Smith's monumental *English Flora* had recently appeared. Mackay had realised the appropriateness of the Linnean system of classification and in the interim had adopted the nomenclature of Smith's summary overview *Compendium Florae Britannicae* (Smith 1818). It also reveals some insights into his views on the future direction of his botanical researches. He was already considering the preparation of a major descriptive work of the Irish flora, which appeared in 1836 under the title *Flora Hibernica*. He also announced his intention to prepare a Botanist's Guide to the counties of Dublin and Wicklow which never materialised. While he was preparing his 1825 account, the *History of the City of Dublin* was published (Warburton et al. 1818). This work included an Appendix featuring the plants of the Dublin coast from Malahide to Killiney. This work is usually attributed to Robert Walsh but is believed to have been revised by Mackay. Additional species recorded for Dublin include Spring Vetch *Vicia lathyroides,* Meadow Saxifrage *Saxifraga granulata* and Meadow Barley *Hordeum secalinum*, all of which are nowadays considered to be national rarities and are listed in the Red Data Book (Curtis and McGough 1988). Walsh's Appendix does not give detailed localities for most species. However, Mackay (1825) includes localities for the first two without credit to Walsh: Spring Vetch (sandy fields near Kilbarrack Church) and Meadow Saxifrage (on dry sandy ditch banks between Baldoyle and Portmarnock). So it may be that Mackay discovered these himself and had graciously allowed them to be included in Walsh's Appendix. The Meadow Barley record may have been included *fide* J. White, who found it (as *H. maritimum*) on sandy and gravelly banks along the shore between Swords and Rush.

A further tantalising glimpse of Mackay's vision appears in a brief potted summary of the Botany of Ireland which was included as a supplement to James Fraser's *Guide through Ireland* - a fairly conventional contemporary traveller's guide (Fraser 1838). Mackay clearly subscribed to the view that botany was a subject to be appreciated by the general travelling public. This model, listing the more interesting plants on an area-by-area basis and directing the interested traveller to their general locations, was to become a feature of many local guide books of the time such as the *History of the County of Dublin* (D'Alton 1838) and was later taken up and greatly expanded by Praeger (1909, 1934).

Mackay's *Catalogue* added a number of plants that are now considered rare or endangered, notably the fairly conspicuous Hairy St John's-wort *Hypericum hirsutum* in woods at Salmon-leap (= Leixlip), where he considered it abundant, and the less obvious Dune Fescue *Vulpia fasciculata* (as *Festuca uniglumis*). The Liffey Valley is now known to be the Irish headquarters of Hairy St John's-wort, a Protected Species, where it occurs in large colonies by tracks and on open ground in broad-leaved woodland on dry sandy soils. The detection of the far less conspicuous Dune Fescue on Portmarnock sands at its first known Irish locality, where it still survives, is more indicative of his skill as a field botanist.

Mackay's *Catalogue* and his *Flora Hibernica* are remarkable both in respect of the contacts he had with the leading British botanists of the day and in the manner in which he integrated

Irish plant records into the system of nomenclature espoused in the massive pioneering work of Smith (1824). Smith had acquired the herbarium of Linnaeus, established the Linnean Society of London and had set about popularising the Linnean system of classification in Britain. In retrospect, Mackay's work is innovative in that it produces clear statements describing the habitats (as distinct from the geographical locations) of the individual species, accounts which demonstrate a first-hand familiarity with the plants in the field. Mackay included and credited in both works many of the Dublin records of his fellow-Scot James Drummond (d. 1835), sometime curator of the Cork Botanic Garden, John Templeton from Belfast and Robert Scott (1757-1808) from Co. Fermanagh, the Professor of Botany at Trinity College. However despite the assistance of these workers, Mackay could not cover all the ground. As a result, his distributional information is not as comprehensive as are his taxonomic and ecological insights. The great value of both his major works lies in their cross-references both to Smith's *English Flora* and the *Compendium*, and to the series of illustrations by Sowerby that appeared at intervals, with the text by Smith, under the title of *English Botany* (Sowerby and Smith 1790).

Mackay also included some records from John White (1757-1808) of the Glasnevin Botanic Gardens who had earlier produced a book on the grasses of Ireland (White 1808). This was essentially a work for those concerned with the economic aspects of grasses, and contains few topographical records. Many of White's records for other species were subsequently incorporated into Katherine Baily's (later Lady Kane) *Irish Flora* (Anon. 1833), which includes the first reliable record of Green-winged Orchid *Orchis morio* from lands about Loughlinstown. Most of the Dublin locations for this species have been destroyed as a result of the conversion of their thin grassland habitat to high-yielding Rye-grass swards in which few native species can survive. This work also mentions Heath Cudweed *Gnaphalium sylvaticum* on high ground on Howth. It has never been seen there since and may have been confused with Common Cudweed *Filago vulgaris* (*F. germanica*) which was found in a number of Howth sites, though not in recent times. Colgan himself was later to find *Gnaphalium sylvaticum* on Slieve Thoul, Saggart, in 1895. It is now one of the rarest Irish species and one of a suite of plants of sandy acid soils that have declined spectacularly in recent years as a result of the virtual disappearance of tillage (and the subsequent fallow land) from upland areas.

Mackay maintained his enthusiasm for field botany and continued to make interesting discoveries. As late as 1840 he was still out botanising with friends in one of his favourite haunts, Portmarnock, where Basil Thyme *Clinopodium acinos* (as *Calamintha acinos*) was found in a sandy field, and was still publishing to within a few years of his death (Mackay 1859, 1860). Basil Thyme, a legally Protected Species not been seen in Dublin for many years, is now known mostly from sandy and gravelly areas in the Irish midlands.

One of Mackay's pupils and his assistant at the Trinity Botanic Garden, David Moore (1807-1879) from Dundee in Scotland, was employed by the Ordnance Survey to examine the flora of Co. Londonderry. This work was part of a much grander scheme to survey the entire island of Ireland for every branch of natural history, but the scheme foundered shortly afterwards.

Moore later became Director of the Botanic Gardens at Glasnevin. Although most of his field botany took place elsewhere, he discovered a number of rare species in the Dublin district. He was responsible for finding Opposite-leaved Pondweed *Groenlandia densa* (as *Potamogeton densus*) in the Grand Canal at Portobello (where it still persists), conveyed by the movement of turf-boats from the Bog of Allen. He also recorded Divided Sedge *Carex divisa* and Borrer's Saltmarsh-grass *Puccinellia fasciculata*, both new to Co. Dublin. The *Carex divisa* record was made along the side of a ditch in the marshes of the North Strand which have long since been filled in. The site of this record was known to A.G. More who later found it in a damp meadow close to the glass works on the north bank of the Liffey where it was rediscovered by Colgan in 1894. The Dublin colonies seem to have been obliterated by 1903, as a result of the continued development of Dublin Port. However, Moore's second discovery *Puccinellia fasciculata*, a plant with rather similar habitat preferences, still survives in the Dublin district. Moore found it in saltmarshes and waste ground close to the sea in the North Lotts, near the mouth of the Liffey and also at Sandymount and along Dublin Bay. He also suspected the presence of hybrids but, at that stage the extent of variation within *P. fasciculata* was not fully understood. The two variants known in Dublin are *P. fasciculata* var. *fasciculata*, with unilateral panicles and obliquely erect branches, and var. *pseudodistans*, with symmetrical panicles and spreading branches. Their relationship, which has perplexed taxonomists to this day, requires further study (Jones and Newton 1970, Sell and Murrell 1996). Moore's horticultural background would have given him deeper insights into the potential of hybridisation in the Irish flora, a feature which was explored by Praeger (1951) in some detail many years later. Earlier botanists had sometimes recorded, as species, plants that subsequently were recognised as hybrids. Mackay, for instance, following the classification of Smith's *Compendium*, had recorded Hybrid Woundwort *Stachys ambigua*, the taxon now known to be the hybrid between Marsh Woundwort *S. palustris* and Hedge Woundwort *S. sylvatica*.

A. G. More (1830-1895), another British naturalist, was appointed to a position in the Natural History Museum in Dublin in 1867 and became Keeper of the Natural History Division in 1881. Some years previously H.C. Watson had produced a summary of the distribution of species in the British flora (Watson 1847). In 1859 Professor C.C. Babington, in a paper read before the Dublin University Zoological and Botanical Association, outlined a similar scheme for Ireland, suggesting that the island be divided into 12 botanical districts (Babington 1859). Some years after, More responded to Babington's outline and proposed a similar project to David Moore. *Cybele Hibernica*, the synthesis of their collaboration, appeared within three years (Moore and More 1866). This work concerned itself with distribution and habitat but did not provide descriptions of species. However, topical issues such as the altitudinal ranges of plants were current at the time and they suggested this as a line for future investigation by others, urging that measurements be made with barometers. These ideas were clearly coming from Moore, who had been in a position to collect similar data relating to the elevation of plants in Co. Londonderry. The compilers of *Cybele Hibernica* were better supplied with correspondents and were equally prepared to discard any species they considered recorded in error from Ireland. In the preparation of the work they enjoyed the support of Babington and of Watson himself. The list of subscribers to the volume, which includes Charles Darwin,

J.D. Hooker and J.T. Boswell Syme, is equally illustrative of the degree to which the project was widely supported in Britain. By mid-century, natural history was becoming increasingly popular as a leisure-time activity in Ireland. In 1850, the Natural History Museum in Dublin was visited by over 40,000 members of the public, despite being open for only two days per week for nine months of the year (O'Riordan 1983). Thirty six years later the Dublin Naturalists' Field Club came into existence.

The *Cybele* differed from *Flora Hibernica* in that the authors listed not only the localities and habitats as Mackay had done but also attempted to estimate the range and frequency of each species. They also attempted to envisage the distribution of certain key species in the greater European context, modelling their constructs on the distributional types identified initially by Watson and placed in a broader context by Forbes (1846) and subsequently refined by Watson (1847). In this later scheme, distinct floristic elements were assigned to their main centres of distribution. British, English, Scottish, Highland, Germanic, Atlantic and Local elements had been recognised in the British flora. The Watsonian system of geographical classification has been criticised for its lack of a broader geographical overview (e.g. Matthews 1937). More and Moore certainly also tried to cast their view of the Irish flora in a broader European context, a topic later summarised by Webb (1983). More, having been installed in Glasnevin by Moore (Webb 1986), bore the brunt of the work of actually writing the *Cybele* and in particular the references to earlier records and the preface. More's principal contributions to the Dublin flora are not of rare species previously overlooked, but are of more critical species awaiting his keen eye and perspicacity. He subsequently prepared a Supplement to *Cybele Hibernica* (More 1872), in which he incorporated some notable additions to the Dublin flora, in particular a record by David Orr of one of the rarest Irish species, Lesser Centaury *Centaurium pulchellum*, from North Bull Island where it still occurs in wildly fluctuating numbers on bare sandy ground and on the margins of damp hollows occasionally inundated by the sea.

More continued his interest in Irish botany, but entrusted Nathaniel Colgan (1851-1919) and his friend Reginald Scully (1858-1935), author of the *Flora of County Kerry* (Scully 1916) with the revision of the first edition of *Cybele Hibernica*. The Royal Irish Academy had made some funds available for the groundwork for the next edition. More had encouraged many naturalists during his tenure at the Natural History Museum including R.M. Barrington, H.C. Hart, H.C. Levinge, T.H. Corry, S.A. Stewart as well as Colgan and Scully, all of whom were subsequently to make significant contributions to Irish botany either as compilers of County Floras or as substantial contributors to the second edition of *Cybele Hibernica*. Scully, a person of independent means, resided in Dublin and had the free time to pursue his botanical interests. Colgan similarly worked away quietly on his chosen projects in his time free from his duties as an official in the Dublin Metropolitan Police Court.

The preparation of the second edition of *Cybele Hibernica* (Colgan and Scully 1898) did not add much to the flora of Co. Dublin, principally because Colgan's most significant discoveries were appearing regularly in print in the pages of *The Irish Naturalist*. This monthly publication, edited by R.Ll. Praeger and G.H. Carpenter, was founded in 1892 with the support of all the

Irish natural history societies. It provided a rapid means of disseminating information and provided an ideal format for short botanical and zoological notes as well as more erudite articles, and it ran for thirty-three years to be succeeded by *The Irish Naturalists' Journal* in 1925. In its immediacy and vigour, it developed a momentum of its own, providing both a vehicle and a framework for the presentation of information, as well as a rapid means of scientific communication in a world where the telephone did not exist and the different social classes had little scientific contact. In that period Colgan made two very significant additions to the Dublin flora - Small Cudweed *Filago minima* on bare stony and sandy ground in quarry workings on Three Rock Mountain (Colgan 1894), where it still survives, and Green Figwort *Scrophularia umbrosa* by the Liffey in Lucan demesne (Colgan 1896). The Liffey valley has subsequently been shown to be the national headquarters of *S. umbrosa* and its geographical distribution was the subject of a special survey by Praeger (1932). The work on *Cybele* was greatly aided by the assistance of a number of English-based botanists, several of whom had visited Ireland, named critical specimens or extracted records from sources not available to Irish-based naturalists. Arthur Bennet was particularly helpful, as was James Britten of the British Museum, E.S. Marshall, W. Moyle Rogers (Brambles) and H. and J. Groves (aquatic plants). These contacts were directly or indirectly to prove invaluable at a later stage when Colgan was preparing his *Flora of the County Dublin*.

In the meantime, the Watsonian system of representation of geographical distribution was gaining acceptance over the more unwieldly districts of the British and Irish *Cybeles* (Watson 1873). This system was based on finer units, usually the administrative county or subdivisions thereof. Praeger (1865-1953) had already been acknowledged by Colgan and Scully in their preface to *Cybele* as the person upon whom the task of preparing an Irish equivalent of Watson's *Topographical Botany* was to descend. Praeger persuaded many of the field botanists still active in Ireland to submit lists of the flora of their favoured areas. Colgan was no exception and supplied Praeger with full lists of the plants of Co. Dublin, prior to the publication of *Irish Topographical Botany* in 1901. In that work, Praeger confirmed the Dublin species total at 750. Colgan's summaries conform to a format adopted by Praeger, where one or two localities are attributed to a county, followed by a generalised comment describing the distribution of the species in question in the county - such as rare, local etc. As a result of Colgan's work, there was little for Praeger to do in Dublin and he was thus freed to pursue field work elsewhere. Praeger was interested in the broad picture, Colgan was more concerned with working out the finer details of distribution at a local level. This may have been more to do with resources and personality than anything else. Industrious Praeger, driven and driver, was well prepared to move around the country searching for new county records. Colgan, the scholarly intellectual, was much more self-effacing. In the period between 1885 and the appearance of *Irish Topographical Botany* in 1901, he had produced only 25 notes and papers in his own name. In a shorter period, the industrious Praeger had produced 120 notes and papers. Despite his retiring temperament, Colgan had botanised as far afield as Morocco, had initiated the exchange of herbarium specimens with foreign botanists and had written many travel articles. Colgan often botanised in Ireland and Europe with his friend Rev. C.F. D'Arcy who added Beech Fern *Phegopteris connectilis*, from Seahan mountain, to the Dublin flora. A great insight into Colgan's life and character can be gleaned from his writing (D'Arcy 1934).

Henry Chichester Hart (1847-1908), one of A.G. More's recruits, started work on the *Flora of the County Donegal* (Hart 1898) around 1864 but spent a good deal of his life in Dublin. Family connections led him to Howth and in time he produced a local flora of the Howth area (Hart 1887) and an earlier flora of Lambay Island (Hart 1883). He was famous for his transmontane marches in search of plants, and as a result of his mountaineering skills was able to access areas of the Howth cliffs that most naturalists still fear to approach. It is only recently that the value of such close-range studies of this kind has been appreciated, in planning and local biogeography.

Colgan made no secret of his high regard for the inspirational qualities of More, who died in 1895 three years before the publication of the second edition of *Cybele Hibernica*. Colgan had been quietly accumulating material for a contemplated Flora of Dublin for some years before More's death. His apprenticeship to More had broadened his botanical perspectives while his work on the *Cybele* had greatly honed his critical and editorial skills. Freed from this duty he was now free to pursue his own botanical interests, and resumed his botanical researches in the Spring of 1899, culminating in the publication of the *Flora of the County Dublin* in 1904. Colgan's *Flora*, which served as a model for many others (Scully 1916, Brunker 1950, Booth 1979, Webb and Scannell 1983) is a testimony to the manner in which the dedicated amateur naturalist can produce a work of the highest standard with very limited resources.

Colgan, in his Preface and in the layout of the systematic part of his work, employed the nomenclature of the *Cybele*. He was concerned about the possibility of name changes and set down a conservative marker, clearly seeing the plants and their distributions as being the prime subjects of his interest. His text, species concept and nomenclature conform closely to that of the *Manual of British Botany* by Babington (1881), but in his Dublin *Flora* he was prepared to depart where necessary from received wisdom. He commented on the morphology of plants when he considered that his field observations were at variance with the descriptions of the equivalent species in British Floras. He realised, for instance, that many of the plants resembling *Viola reichenbachiana* in their narrower and non-overlapping petals differed from that species in having calycine appendages that were too prominent - a feature that continues to perplex field botanists in many parts of Ireland. Colgan had several objectives in mind when he embarked seriously on the Dublin project. He wished to confirm the presence of every species that had previously been recorded from the county, their vertical ranges, flowering seasons, soil affinities and he also wished to collect the vernacular names of the plants then in use in the county. He included statements showing the relative affinity of certain species for soil with a high or low preference for lime. Plants whose occurrence was strongly favoured by the presence of lime were classified as Calcicole A species; those relatively less dependent as Calcicole B and C species. Species that shunned lime-rich soils were termed Calcifuge C, B and A in progressive order of avoidance. Those with no distinct affiliation were not classified. This system had been adopted previously in *Cybele Hibernica* and had been adapted from the continental researches of Contejean (1881).

In addition to the helpers of *Cybele Hibernica*, Colgan also enlisted the aid of F.J. Hanbury, W.R. Linton (*Hieracium*), and H.W. Pugsley (*Fumaria*). He had access to the developing herbarium in the Dublin Science and Art Museum and David Moore's herbarium at Glasnevin. Scully helped with the identification of critical species, with the design of the book and with the revision of proofs. His work, envisaged as a tribute to his mentor A.G. More and propelled by a *fin-de-siecle* spirit, looks forward to the rising generation of Dublin botanists. What became of this generation of botanists is unclear. Colgan, his botanical work largely completed, turned his attentions to marine invertebrates and later published a number of papers on the Mollusca of Co. Dublin. He retained his interest in botanical matters but more in the context of the increasing interest in vegetation studies which were to become a feature of Irish university courses. Unfortunately neither Colgan nor Praeger had a university posting from which to influence future generations. Praeger, under the *aegis* of the Irish Field Club Union and the Royal Irish Academy, organised teams of local and visiting naturalists to explore many interesting and underworked parts of Ireland. His greatest achievement was the famous Clare Island Survey, which to some extent arose from a smaller study conducted on Lambay Island off the coast of Co. Dublin, the significance of which is dealt with elsewhere (Collins 1985, White 1982). This study also appears to have confirmed Praeger's interest in vegetation studies to the extent that with G.H. Pethybridge, he conducted a major study of the vegetation (as distinct from the flora) of an area in the Dublin mountains (Pethybridge and Praeger 1905) which was subsequently re-appraised by J.J. Moore (1960). Pethybridge also conducted a vegetation survey of the north Co. Dublin coast from Bull Island to north of Balbriggan (White 1982). Colgan maintained an interest in these new lines of investigation and prepared several short papers on the flora of burnt ground on Killiney Hill (Colgan 1912, 1913) though these were essentially follow-on studies provoked by the pioneering work of Pethybridge (1908), Adams (1908a, 1908b) and Praeger (1908). Colgan died in 1919. Despite his heavy duties, Praeger continued to be generous to the Dublin Naturalists' Field Club and honoured the Club by holding the positions of President, Vice President and Hon. Secretary at different times. Vegetation studies were to engage the interest of another past-President of the DNFC, Helen O'Reilly, who surveyed the saltmarsh vegetation of the north Dublin coast (O'Reilly and Pantin 1957).

Scully followed in Colgan's path, producing his own *Flora of County Kerry* twelve years later, which is closely modelled on the template that they had jointly developed (Scully 1916). Three years later Scully met up with J.P. Brunker who was later to become a leading member of the Dublin Naturalists' Field Club. He took Brunker's botanical education in hand and for some years explored the Wicklow area, until ill-health obliged him to give up strenuous field work. From 1923, Brunker's botanical education was continued by the all-round naturalist A.W. Stelfox, who three years previously had obtained an appointment in the National Museum of Ireland where he served for twenty-eight years. In time, Brunker gathered about him a group of friends who were concerned mainly with exploring the botany of Co. Wicklow. He retired early from work to put the finishing touches to his own county Flora (Brunker 1950) which is modelled closely on those of Colgan and Scully, particularly in its use of the baronial boundaries as units of territorial subdivision and in the use of Calcicole/Calcifuge terminology. Many of those who were recruited to help with the Wicklow flora were drawn from the ranks of the Dublin Naturalists' Field Club (The Dublin Naturalists' Field Club 1986). Chief among these was H.J. Hudson (1909-1996), a founder member of An Taisce, who did so much work on behalf of the DNFC for over 60 years. Brunker also worked with A.A. Lisney who, though best known as a lepidopterist of international repute, was the discoverer of the very rare Mackay's Horsetail *Equisetum x trachyodon* in Bride's Glen, near Shankhill where he was born. J.P. Brunker, H.J. Hudson, A.W. Stelfox, J.S. Thompson and others had been accumulating records in the course of DNFC outings or *ad-hoc* private excursions. The appointment of M.J.P. Scannell to the Botany Department of the Natural History Museum, then housed in Kildare Street, provided a focus for the preparation of *A Supplement to Colgan's Flora* (Anon. 1961). This work conformed closely to Colgan's work, and employed an essentially similar nomenclature and species-concept. Again it was a transitional work, compiled and written between the appearance of the first and second editions of the *Flora of the British Isles* (Clapham *el al*. 1952, 1962) and arriving with the advent of 10 km dot-mapping, a cartographic tool that was to dominate broad-brush distribution studies in the flora of Britain and Ireland to the end of the twentieth century (Perring and Walters 1962). The first volume of *Flora Europaea* which was to become the taxonomic and nomenclatural base-line for a generation, had yet to appear (Tutin *et al*. 1964).

The momentum generated by these projects encouraged other local studies by the Plant Group of the DNFC in the Duleek area of Co. Meath and some years later in Dublin's Inner City (Wyse Jackson and Sheehy Skeffington 1984). These projects provided a magnificent informal forum for the botanical education of many of the present generation of field botanists (Wyse Jackson *et al*. 1988). Their success was greatly enhanced in the manner by which various professional botanists made themselves available on weekends and Wednesday evenings as tutors. The formation of a separate committee of the Botanical Society of the British Isles (BSBI) in 1963 to deal with Irish botanical matters greatly increased the opportunities for prospective botanists to improve their fieldcraft and plant recognition skills, and many of the crop of field botanists have become County Recorders for the BSBI in Ireland. Increased leisure time, greater mobility and an enhanced supply of affordable modern reference books have greatly increased the volume of botanical records. Modern botanists do not have to struggle with identification of straightforward species in the same way as Wade or Mackay may have done, though obligate taxonomists still find satisfaction in the intricacies of *Taraxacum, Hieracium* and *Rubus*. Colgan's research work, conducted at the end of the 19th century, created a detailed factual basis for future researches into the flora of Co. Dublin. The quality of his field work, and its focus and precision, enable clear comparisons to be made between the state of the flora of his time and the present day. Finer recording units, (10 km, 2 km, or even 1 km squares), the continued loss of key habitats, the curtailed access to many parts of the countryside and the disappearance of traditional Natural History from the educational syllabi, combined with the political demands of wildlife conservation, have all increased the amateur naturalist's burden, although the accessibility of computers has enhanced the capacity of individuals to store and sort their data. Whether greater knowledge on the part of a few will lead to a greater collective environmental wisdom remains to be seen.

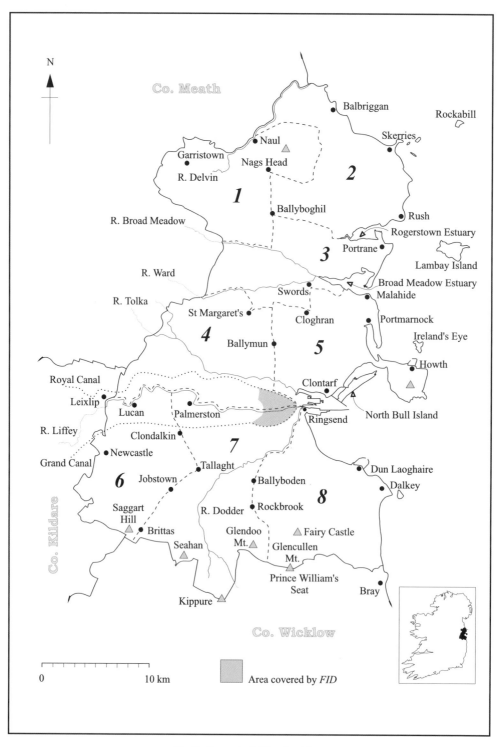

Fig. 5 Botanical District Map

BOTANICAL DISTRICT ACCOUNTS

During the Field Club's survey of the county, plants were recorded in each one of approximately one thousand I km x I km squares based on the Irish National Grid. The resulting plant records were then attributed to the appropriate Botanical Districts which were first devised and used by Nathaniel Colgan in his *Flora of the County Dublin* (1904). The eight Districts (Fig. 5) and their names correspond, in the main, to the old baronial divisions. The reason for retaining Colgan's Districts was to permit a valid comparison and quantification of the floral changes that have taken place in Co. Dublin in the twentieth century.

The urban area surveyed for *The Flora of Inner Dublin* (FID) (Wyse Jackson and Sheehy Skeffington 1984) forms part of Districts 4 and 7. Only the more notable FID records are included in the Systematic and Supplementary Lists, and the reader is referred to the original work for further details. Any post-FID records for the inner city have been assigned to their respective Districts.

Below are listed the District Recorders who co-ordinated the field work, undertook a lead role in the recording in each District, and received and compiled records:

District I - Balrothery West   Gerry Sharkey
District 2 - Balrothery East   Declan Doogue and Rosaleen Fitzgerald
District 3 - Nethercross   Paddy Reilly
District 4 - Castleknock   Margaret Norton and Jonathan Shackleton
District 5 - Coolock   Howard Hudson, Eimear Nic Lughadha and David Nash
District 6 - Newcastle   John Parnell
District 7 - Uppercross   Peter Wyse Jackson and Michael Wyse Jackson
District 8 - Rathdown   Helen O'Reilly and Sylvia Reynolds.

Catriona Brady and Philip Grant carried out extensive recording in a number of Districts.

In the following accounts, which have been prepared by District Recorders, the boundaries are described and information is given for some of the more significant sites of botanical interest within each District. Species listed for particular sites complement the examples given for the same sites in the Habitat Accounts.

District 1 – Balrothery West   G. Sharkey
Approximate area: 109 square kilometres.
Boundary: Starting at Naul, the District I boundary follows the county boundary west through Beshellstown and south past Garristown and Curragha to the Broad Meadow River (= Broad Meadow Water) just west of Fieldstown House. It runs east along the Broad Meadow River to Roganstown Bridge. From there it turns north and follows the roads through Ballyboghil to Nags Head, east to The Five Roads, north by Balrothery Lough and finally west by Matt Bridge and through Dallyhaysy back to Naul.

The north-west of the county was described by Colgan as largely "a featureless stretch of pasture land", "barren of interesting species" and "botanically the poorest of all eight districts", and because the area was both somewhat remote and the least worked botanically, he hoped that further study might yield interesting results. Sadly his hope proves to be as forlorn as his account is accurate.

Three of the interesting botanical sites mentioned by Colgan, Curragha and Garristown Bogs and a small remnant of peat at Streamstown, have now completely disappeared, and along with them most of the small number of typical calcifuge plants extant in his time. In addition, Golden Dock *Rumex maritimus* has not been seen recently, though its ability to survive as seed for prolonged periods may yet allow for a spectacular return.

Practically the entire area is given over to sheep and cattle grazing of an intensive nature, and from the highest points near Garristown (157 m) and in the Naul Hills (179 m) to the lowest lands near the Broad Meadow River in the south, the soil is a type of clay derived from glacial drift, with extremely low habitat diversity. A long history of intensive agriculture has culminated in Rye-grass-Clover *Lolium-Trifolium* grassland which is botanically barren.

The almost total absence of limestone, sand and gravel means that typical calcicole plants are missing. Similarly calcifuges are in scarce supply. The perimeter of the active quarry at Nags Head supports both Heath Bedstraw *Galium saxatile* and Sheep's-bit *Jasione montana*, this being the closest that District 1 gets to having an upland community.

The only real wetland in the District is the Bog of the Ring, also known as Ring Commons, just west of Balrothery. This was a favourite haunt of the Dublin Naturalists' Field Club until the mid-1960s. Since then, a combination of drainage, nutrient run-off from intensively farmed surrounding land and dumping of agricultural waste has reduced it to an unpleasant and foul-smelling series of stagnant pools surrounded by extensive stands of Soft-rush *Juncus effusus*. Drainage channels around the Bog still, however, contain some genuine wetland species such as Common Marsh-bedstraw *Galium palustre*, Marsh Willowherb *Epilobium palustre* and the increasingly rare Celery-leaved Buttercup *Ranunculus sceleratus*. Paradoxically, the Bog of the Ring has yielded one of the few re-discoveries for District 1. Wild Teasel *Dipsacus fullonum* has established itself on the banks of the deep drain on the southern extremity of the Bog.

Reclaimed land to the south-east of the Bog of the Ring has been used as cricket grounds, this part of District 1 sharing with neighbouring parts of District 2 the distinction of being home to the Republic of Ireland's only genuine village cricket league, complete with make-shift club-houses and carefully attended squares. Cricket is not the only reminder of a colonial past in District 1. Most townlands, while having no real woodland, contained a 'big house' which often had trees planted for either shelter or ornamentation, and the remnants of these plantations, sometimes reduced to the outline of an avenue, frequently still remain. The floor of these relict plantations is often identifiable by a sward of Ramsons *Allium ursinum* or by scattered occurrences of Rose-of-Sharon *Hypericum calycinum* in the hedgerows. Former and older habitations may also be indicated by stands of Alexanders *Smyrnium olusatrum* and White Dead-nettle *Lamium album*.

Echoes of a more ancient woodland or scrubland can be found through the presence in most hedgerows of Primrose *Primula vulgaris* accompanied, especially just north of Oldtown, by Early Dog-violet *Viola reichenbachiana*, Goldilocks Buttercup *Ranunculus auricomus* and, more rarely, Bluebells *Hyacinthoides* spp., although the latter are often varieties which have escaped from gardens.

To the north of the higher ground surrounding Garristown lies a flat plain with a regular geometric array of streams and ditches. This is all that is now left of Garristown Bog. A single small neglected field on the north-facing slope to the west of the Garristown-Ardcath road contains several springs, and features an extensive stand of Common Fleabane *Pulicaria dysenterica* with Common Twayblade *Listera ovata* which also grows on the roadside bank outside the field. This is probably the site mentioned in *A Supplement to Colgan's Flora* (Anon. 1961) as 'between Commons Upper and Cockle's Bridge'.

In Colgan's time the banks and upper reaches of the Broad Meadow River, which forms the boundary between Districts 1 and 3, supported a rich wetland flora, including Water Dock *Rumex hydrolapathum*. However the river has had its influence drastically reduced by the combination of chemicals in agricultural run-off and the permanent damage to its course caused by canalisation through mechanical dredging during the 1960s.

Unusually for a rural area so close to the capital city, the north-west corner is little known to Dubliners other than those who live there. There has been some building around the villages in recent years, but there is no area that could be described as urban and, accordingly, no real urban flora. Even garden weeds are scarce. This is an area that was associated with fruit-growing earlier in the century. In response to increasing consumer demand for organically grown produce there has been a growth in 'pick-your-own' and 'farm-shop' enterprises which has resulted in the return of some of the market-gardening type of horticulture. This, coupled with economic and other pressures to use less fertiliser in agriculture, may result in the re-emergence from seed banks (seed lying dormant in the soil) of a whole group of agricultural weeds currently thought to be extinct.

While there is little tillage in District 1, Corn Spurrey *Spergula arvensis*, Field Pansy *Viola arvensis* and Swine-cress *Coronopus squamatus* are found in the few areas under cultivation. In Ballyboghil, an agricultural machinery company (Pentony's) used to maintain a sizeable demonstration plot which was ploughed twice yearly. This regular turnover of the soil allowed a population of annuals, notably Field Pansy, to persist. The Field Pansy population showed a large variation in flower size, the largest of which were in the size range of Wild Pansy *Viola tricolor*.

Botanically, the Naul Hills remain the most interesting area. The hills contain several steep-sided valleys of which one, at Hynestown, was dammed in the 1930s forming the Hynestown Reservoir. The bed of the upper reaches of the reservoir becomes exposed in dry spells. It then supports a community which completely covers the mud, containing Amphibious Bistort *Persicaria amphibia*, Redshank *P. maculosa* and Water-pepper *P. hydropiper*. Trifid Bur-marigold

Bidens tripartita and the form of Common Water-crowfoot *Ranunculus aquatilis* with finely-divided leaves are also present in large numbers. The banks around the perimeter of the reservoir contain Corn Mint *Mentha arvensis*. Upstream from the reservoir is a luxuriant stand of Great Horsetail *Equisetum telmateia*, a feature of most of the spring-fed streamlets in the hills. Lady-fern *Athyrium filix-femina*, Navelwort *Umbilicus rupestris* and Smith's Pepperwort *Lepidium heterophyllum* are frequent, and the north-facing slopes of the hills support a variety of microspecies of Bramble *Rubus fructicosus* agg.

District 1, mainly because of its inland nature and its lack of habitat diversity, has by far the poorest flora of the eight botanical Districts of Co. Dublin. The current phase of major roadway construction will almost inevitably lead to this hitherto exclusively rural area being opened up to urban and industrial development. From a botanical point of view this will add to the list of weed species, and the disruption and soil disturbance caused by major construction works may produce some interesting, although short-term, results.

District 2 – Balrothery East   D. Doogue
Approximate area: 113 square kilometres.
Boundary: Starting at Naul, the District 2 boundary follows the county boundary north and east along the Delvin River to the sea east of Gormanstown. Then it follows the coast south by Balbriggan, Skerries and Rush, and through Rogerstown Estuary to Daws Bridge at the head of Rogerstown Creek. From there it runs along the main road north nearly to Corduff Bridge, turning west inland through Richardstown to Ballyboghil. It then follows the roads north to Nags Head, east to The Five Roads and north past Balrothery Lough before turning west by Matt Bridge, through Dallyhaysy to Naul. District 2 includes the islands off Skerries - St Patrick's, Red Island, Colt and Shenick's, as well as Rockabill some 7 km from the coast.

Settlement patterns, dating back to Neolithic times, indicate a long history of human occupation in north Co. Dublin. More tellingly, the sustained and highly successful Anglo-Norman occupation of the area, centred on Lusk, Swords and Balrothery, coupled with the survival of extensive ecclesiastical landholding systems well into the Middle Ages, have resulted in the retention of elements of classical medieval field patterns and testify to a long history of mixed agriculture. The chief botanical casualty of this extended regime has been the woodland flora. Many widespread shade-tolerant species that are common elsewhere in Dublin are extremely rare in District 2. Familiar species such as Lords-and-Ladies *Arum maculatum* and Hazel *Corylus avellana* are exceedingly rare in the north-eastern part of the county.

The nature and disposition of the tilled areas constitutes an early recognition of the fertility of the soils, particularly near the coast - an appreciation that finds modern expression in the largely co-extensive greenhouse and market-gardening areas of north Dublin. This distinct agricultural tradition accounts for the survival of the most characteristic feature of the flora of District 2 - the occurrence of a number of plant species that were formerly associated with sandy fallow land.

These fallow areas comprised individual parcels of agriculturally-marginal land, which when exhausted were rested and fertilised with natural manures such as seaweed. These areas, which are most conveniently examined from the network of lanes and trackways linking Rush and Rogerstown, now constitute the national headquarters of a number of very rare species.

Landholdings were traditionally organised into dense networks of tiny fields, whose meerings, composed of simple earthen banks, are still discernible, now forming boundary lines between recently-built suburban bungalows or holiday homes. For much of the time the unusual botanical diversity of these areas is suppressed by the excessive zeal of gardeners, who have mown, sprayed, chopped and weeded this very unusual flora almost into oblivion. Occasionally however, when gardens are tilled, roads widened or drains dug, this interesting group of mostly annual species springs up from dormant seeds buried in the nutrient-enriched warm sandy ground.

The most widespread and regularly-occurring components of this loosely-defined botanical assemblage are White Campion *Silene latifolia*, Bugloss *Anchusa arvensis* and Small Nettle *Urtica urens*, all of which are still widespread at various points along the east coast although recent drastic changes in land use and management have resulted in their almost complete disappearance from many inland areas. Some of the rarer species also occur occasionally on thinly-vegetated roadside verges and neglected fields. These include Prickly Poppy *Papaver argemone*, Flixweed *Descurainia sophia*, Small-flowered Crane's-bill *Geranium pusillum*, White Ramping-fumitory *Fumaria capreolata*, Common Fiddleneck *Amsinckia micrantha*, Henbit Dead-nettle *Lamium amplexicaule* and Great Brome *Anisantha diandra*. The most enigmatic species of this assemblage is, without doubt, Purple Ramping-fumitory *Fumaria purpurea*, a species which is reputedly endemic to Britain and Ireland. It is an extremely rare plant in Ireland but survives in a few pockets along the north Dublin coast.

The regularly-tilled grounds of the Rogerstown area also have a number of unusual weeds. Cut-leaved Dead-nettle *Lamium hybridum* is often commoner than the widespread Red Dead-nettle *Lamium purpureum* and the much larger Northern Dead-nettle *L. confertum* - a nationally rare species - re-appears, year after year, in a few cabbage fields. Away from the coast, on the rising ground nearer Baldongan Castle, the base-poor character of the soils becomes more apparent, as indicated by the increasing incidence of Field Woundwort *Stachys arvensis*, Common Hemp-nettle *Galeopsis tetrahit*, Corn Marigold *Chrysanthemum segetum* and Corn Spurrey *Spergula arvensis*.

Many of these species are not considered to be truly indigenous to Ireland, but are believed to have followed the northward migrations of Neolithic *Homo sapiens* as the ice-fronts of the last glaciation retreated. Nowadays they are confined almost entirely to land that is occasionally disturbed. Whatever their mode of origin on this island, most were clearly well-established in Balrothery East in Colgan's time. Two obvious exceptions are Common Fiddleneck *Amsinckia micrantha* and Great Brome *Anisantha diandra*. The latter species has its national headquarters in the area but was only mentioned by Colgan in the Appendix to his *Flora*. Both may be relatively recent arrivals, brought in accidentally with imported seeds. Thus, their collective arrival in Balrothery East becomes a matter of considerable botanical, historical, geographical and cultural interest to students of Fingallian Dublin.

The rocky seashores from Loughshinny northwards are relatively undamaged botanically, mainly because of their very limited agricultural potential. Here and there, in areas of stable shingle, small clumps of Yellow Horned-poppy *Glaucium flavum* still grow. The shore at Skerries still has a few large plants of Ray's Knotgrass *Polygonum oxyspermum* subsp. *raii*, a species that has greatly declined in Ireland in recent times for reasons that are not yet clear. Colgan recorded the presence of a number of fen and marsh species on the Balrothery coast. His accounts suggest a group of species growing on damp clay banks above the sea. On occasions these banks may have slumped outwards to form accumulations of lime-rich well-watered earth on the foreshore. These habitats have almost entirely disappeared since then. The exact reason for their loss is not certain. Coastal erosion, particularly south of Balbriggan, may have accounted for some of the losses. A second reason may entail the gradual rationalisation of the land drainage system of the area. Instead of gradually percolating downwards towards the sea and dripping down the face of low earthen cliffs, groundwater now issues at fewer points - not necessarily where nature would have intended. The virtual exclusion of light grazing has further reduced the interest of this narrow coastal strip, resulting in an overgrowth of tall herbs such as Hemp-agrimony *Eupatorium cannabinum*, Great Horsetail *Equisetum telmateia* and low shrubs - principally Blackthorn *Prunus spinosa*. Some elements of the original flora persist. Occasionally, Brookweed *Samolus valerandi* can be found on dripping sea cliffs, even in the spray zone, along with the Yellow-sedge *Carex viridula* subsp. *brachyrrhyncha*, Lesser Clubmoss *Selaginella selaginoides*, Black Bog-rush *Schoenus nigricans* and Slender Club-rush *Isolepis cernua*.

Where the rocks run down to the sea, communities of plants associated with saltmarshes in the Dublin area, consisting mainly of Thrift *Armeria maritima*, Saltmarsh Rush *Juncus gerardii*, Sea Rush *Juncus maritimus*, Sea Arrowgrass *Triglochin maritimum* and Sea Plantain *Plantago maritima*, form a recurrent species-grouping on small sheltered areas. In a few places just south of Balbriggan, where saltwater is not free to flow quickly back to the sea, Saltmarsh Flat-sedge *Blysmus rufus* and Parsley Water-dropwort *Oenanthe lachenalii* survive in small quantity. Higher up on the shore, but still in the spray zone, Strawberry Clover *Trifolium fragiferum* may be found. Sea Wormwood *Seriphidium maritimum* may also have been an element of these communities, but now survives only as a few plants on the shore at Red Island, Skerries, where the coastal vegetation is being eroded. A few clumps of Sea Wormwood also grow in the saltmarsh on the north shore of the Rogerstown Estuary. On slightly higher ground, a little in from the sea, these saltmarshes give way to lightly grazed grassland. Although protected in some areas by levees, saltwater occasionally backs up along the open land drains and enables species tolerant of brackish conditions to survive some distance from the sea. Sea Club-rush *Bolboschoenus maritimus* is the most conspicuous brackish-drain species. However, in the Balleally area one or two of the adjoining pastures contain large stands of Meadow Barley *Hordeum secalinum* - a Protected Species that has been destroyed in many of its former inland sites. The shore near the dump contains an eclectic mixture of species. Some of these are associated naturally with nutrient-rich areas on sea cliffs - Bristly Oxtongue *Picris echioides* and Tree-mallow *Lavatera arborea*, and there are unusually large forms of what appears to be Borrer's Saltmarsh-grass *Puccinellia fasciculata*.

The sand-dune elements of the flora have been very much reduced by the construction of holiday homes and by the disastrous invasion of Sea-buckthorn *Hippophae rhamnoides*, a shrub that was planted to stabilise naturally mobile dunes and which now dominates them to the exclusion of the native flora. The construction of golf-links, on the other hand, may be responsible for the survival of Green-winged Orchid *Orchis morio* and other uncommon dune species that survive in the light rough. These include Heath Dog-violet *Viola canina*, unusual forms of Wild Pansy *Viola tricolor* subsp. *curtisii,* Hound's-tongue *Cynoglossum officinale* and Dune Fescue *Vulpia fasciculata*.

District 3 – Nethercross   P. Reilly
Approximate area: 83 square kilometres.
Boundary: Starting from Daws Bridge at the head of Rogerstown Creek, the District 3 boundary follows the main road north nearly to Corduff Bridge before turning west through Richardstown to Ballyboghil. Then it turns south along the road to Roganstown Bridge and west along the Broad Meadow River until it reaches the county boundary. It follows the county boundary south to where it is intersected by the Ward River. From there it runs east along the Ward River as far as Chapelmidway Bridge, south along the road by the old church at St Margaret's, east by Forrest Great and Forrest Little to Cloghran, then north to Swords. It goes east along the road towards Malahide until it reaches the small stream at Yellow Walls, and passes down this stream to the Malahide Estuary (= Broad Meadow Estuary). Then it follows the coast around Malahide Island, north past Portrane and through Rogerstown Estuary back to Daws Bridge. The District includes Lambay Island which lies 5 km off the coast at Portrane.

District 3 is divided into two parts by the Dublin-Belfast Road between Daws Bridge and Malahide Estuary. East of this line lies the arrow-shaped Portrane peninsula, bordered on the north by Rogerstown Estuary and on the south by Malahide Estuary. To the west of the road, the agricultural hinterland extends inland for 14 km. The District's largest town is Swords which has expanded considerably in recent years, as a residential area for workers at Dublin Airport and as a result of the new high-technological industries around the town.

The soil is mainly calcareous, although a more acidic type occurs in association with outcrops of old red sandstone and porphyry in several places, near the coast between Donabate and Portrane, in the grounds of Newbridge House and on Lambay Island. The District is drained by the Broad Meadow and Ward Rivers and their numerous feeder streams. The land is flat and used principally for grazing livestock and for recreational purposes. Crops are grown near Newbridge House and along Malahide Estuary.

There are several golf-courses in the District. Two of them are links at Corballis and three others, built inland on agricultural land at Donabate, Ballisk and Forrest Little, have retained many of the old hedgerows and drainage ditches on their boundaries. Three large areas of open ground, which were formerly demesnes, remain intact. Newbridge House has been developed as a public park with two small lakes and a wild unmanaged section. St Ita's Hospital, Portrane, has woodland, marsh and some agricultural land. The grounds of Turvey House, near Donabate, are mainly in pasture, but also contain some woodland and a cultivated area used for tillage and garden allotments.

Until recently, apart from the expansion of the town of Swords, the construction of new golf-courses and the building of some holiday chalets at Donabate and Portrane, the character of the District and its flora is much as it was in Colgan's time. Most of the important plants given in Colgan's *Flora* can still be found at their original stations. However, there is recent evidence of further building development in the northern part of the Portrane Peninsula.

The inland portion of the District, west of the Belfast Road, has a number of interesting and accessible sites. Two disused reservoirs, at Lubbers Wood and Knocksedan, provide suitable habitats for a range of plants, especially aquatics. Spiked Water-milfoil *Myriophyllum spicatum*, Curled Pondweed *Potamogeton crispus* and Bog Stitchwort *Stellaria uliginosa* grow at Knocksedan; Goldilocks Buttercup *Ranunculus auricomus* and Pink Water-speedwell *Veronica catenata* at Lubbers Wood. Spear Mint *Mentha spicata*, Giant Fescue *Festuca gigantea*, Mare's-tail *Hippuris vulgaris* and Marjoram *Origanum vulgare* are established in sandpits by the Ward River east of Knocksedan Bridge. New stations were discovered for two plants quite rare in Co. Dublin: Dwarf Elder *Sambucus ebulus* on waste ground at Forrest Little and Ragged-Robin *Lychnis flos-cuculi* in a marsh in River Valley Park, at Swords. By the Malahide Estuary, Rough Chervil *Chaerophyllum temulum* grows in a hedgerow and Ivy Broomrape *Orobanche hederae* on ivy along a bank and on a wall. In the farmed part of this inland section, access to the land is often difficult and botanical explorations have been mainly confined to the hedgerows and roadside drainage ditches.

The southern part of the Portrane Peninsula extends southwards from Corballis to the Malahide Estuary and is commonly referred to as 'The [Malahide] Island'. It contains some of the highest sand-dunes in Ireland, rising to a height of 20 metres, and extensive dune-slacks and saltmarsh. Most of the middle section is occupied by two golf-links. The peripheral dunes and dune-slacks and the saltmarshes are undisturbed. The dunes have a rich flora characteristic of sandy calcareous ground including Hairy Violet *Viola hirta*, a Protected Species, Bee Orchid *Ophrys apifera*, Marsh Helleborine *Epipactis palustris*, Adder's-tongue *Ophioglossum vulgatum*, Creeping Willow *Salix repens*, Burnet Rose *Rosa pimpinellifolia* and Carline Thistle *Carlina vulgaris*. Characteristic grasses are Red Fescue *Festuca rubra*, Crested Hair-grass *Koeleria macrantha* and Squirreltail Fescue *Vulpia bromoides*. The areas of saltmarsh on the southern part of the Island have never been directly modified by human interference. The vegetation includes Rock Sea-lavender *Limonium binervosum*, the Glassworts *Salicornia europaea* and *S. dolichostachya*, Sea-purslane *Atriplex portulacoides* and Sea-milkwort *Glaux maritima*. There is a shingle strand on the western side of the Island where Sea-holly *Eryngium maritimum* and Yellow Horned-poppy *Glaucium flavum* were recorded. Yellow-wort *Blackstonia perfoliata* and Common Centaury *Centaurium erythraea* grow in the backing dunes. Further north and inland near the road at Corballis, the rare Milk Thistle *Silybum marianum* and Prickly Poppy *Papaver argemone* are found together with the more common Hound's-tongue *Cynoglossum officinale*,

Red Campion *Silene dioica*, Goat's-beard *Tragopogon pratensis*, Bloody Crane's-bill *Geranium sanguineum* and Bugloss *Anchusa arvensis*. The Greater Pond-sedge *Carex riparia* grows in a drainage ditch near the caravan park.

At Donabate, the central section of the peninsula, Corn Marigold *Chrysanthemum segetum* is established in fallow fields and Guelder-rose *Viburnum opulus* in a hedge. Fat Duckweed *Lemna gibba* has been found in a pond at Ballisk. On the cliff path, *en route* to Portrane, a large patch of Hoary Cress *Lepidium draba* grows by the wall of St Ita's Hospital. Further along the path Spring Squill *Scilla verna*, Thrift *Armeria maritima*, Rock Samphire *Crithmum maritimum*, Tree-mallow *Lavatera arborea*, Sea Fern-grass *Catapodium marinum* and Sea Wormwood *Seriphidium maritimum* may be seen. Wood Anemone *Anemone nemorosa* and Three-cornered Garlic *Allium triquetrum* grow in the hospital grounds.

The northern arm of the Portrane Peninsula extends from Portrane Green to Rogerstown Estuary. Its sand-hills and dune-slacks are much smaller than those at Corballis, nevertheless the area is botanically diverse. A small number of holiday chalets has been built on the higher ground near the road, but the dunes and dune-slacks are undisturbed. Crops are planted occasionally in the fields west of the dunes but most of the land is fallow. A number of rare plants are found here, for example, Green-winged Orchid *Orchis morio* and Rough Poppy *Papaver hybridum*, both of which are Protected Species, Flixweed *Descurainia sophia* and Small-flowered Crane's-bill *Geranium pusillum* together with Pale Flax *Linum bienne* and Tall Rocket *Sisymbrium altissimum*. Hard-grass *Parapholis strigosa* grows on the edges of the saltmarsh.

Lambay Island is in private ownership and access is by permission only. The western section, where the land is sheltered and gently sloping, is grazed by sheep and cattle. There is a small herd of fallow deer. The "swarms of rabbits", observed by Praeger (1907), were wiped out by myxomatosis in the 1950s and the grazing area has been extended. The high ground consists of exposed rock with some shallow soil. The remainder of the island is comprised of sea cliffs, up to 60 m in height, and their rocky approaches. In contrast to the mainland, the island's soil is usually non-calcareous and peaty. The island's flora was surveyed by H.C. Hart in 1881-1882 (Hart 1883) and by Robert Lloyd Praeger who published an amended list (Praeger 1907). Records for the present work were collected in 1988 by D.M. Synnott (1990), who also investigated the bryophyte flora, and by the DNFC in 1992. Praeger observed the presence of Blunt-flowered Rush *Juncus subnodulosus* and the Stonewort *Chara vulgaris* in marshy places, indicating the presence of some lime-rich water, the limestone presumably being provided by glacial calcareous drift. Praeger recorded plants mostly associated with heath and acid soils, notably Heather *Calluna vulgaris*, Bell Heather *Erica cinerea*, Bracken *Pteridium aquilinum*, Heath Bedstraw *Galium saxatile* and Wood Sage *Teucrium scorodonia*. Of these, Heather and Bell Heather are now very rare, but Bracken, Bramble *Rubus fruticosus* agg. and wind-stunted Elder *Sambucus nigra* still survive. In addition, the following were noted in 1988 and 1992: Southern Polypody *Polypodium cambricum*, Field Mouse-ear *Cerastium arvense*, Sea Pearlwort *Sagina maritima*, Knotted Clover *Trifolium striatum*, Hemlock *Conium maculatum*, Spring Squill *Scilla verna*, Wall Speedwell *Veronica arvensis*, Blinks *Montia fontana*, English Stonecrop *Sedum anglicum*, Biting Stonecrop

S. acre and Frosted Orache *Atriplex laciniata*. Henbane *Hyoscyamus niger* and Good-King-Henry *Chenopodium bonus-henricus* have since been found, but Blunt-flowered Rush *Juncus subnodulosus* and Stinking Iris *Iris foetidissima*, reported by Praeger (1907), were not refound. The latter two species may still be seen nearby on the mainland.

District 4 – Castleknock   M. Norton
Approximate area: 131 square kilometres.
Boundary: Starting where the Royal Canal enters the River Liffey at North Wall Quay, the District 4 boundary runs west along the Liffey to the county boundary just east of Leixlip. From there it follows the county boundary north to where it is intersected by the Ward River. It runs east along the Ward River as far as Chapelmidway Bridge, then turns south along the road to the old church at St Margaret's and east to where it meets the District 5 boundary just south of Forrest Great. It shares that boundary south (crossing Dublin Airport runways) through Ballymun to Cross Guns Bridge at Phibsborough, and south-east along the Royal Canal back to North Wall Quay.

The District has changed much during the past century. Undoubtedly the major modification has been the degree of urbanisation. It can be difficult to grasp just how much urban expansion there has been, but some idea can be gained by remembering that Finglas and Blanchardstown were both small isolated villages at the beginning of the 20th century. Nevertheless, even today, substantial areas of green space remain in the built-up area, most notably the Phoenix Park and the National Botanic Gardens, Glasnevin. Much of the Phoenix Park is improved grassland, but areas of interest remain such as the calcareous slopes on the south side of the park containing Salad Burnet *Sanguisorba minor*, Hairy Violet *Viola hirta* and Common Gromwell *Lithospermum officinale*. Records accumulated in the Phoenix Park during work for this *Flora* have been incorporated into *Wild Plants of the Phoenix Park* (Reilly 1993), where localities for species are given. The National Botanic Gardens are important as they contain many introduced species, not only in cultivation, but also as weeds that have become established there, such as Sharp-leaved Fluellen *Kickxia elatine*. The Gardens are also a potential source for future introductions to the flora of Co. Dublin.

The soils of the District are almost entirely calcareous and calcifuge species are virtually absent. Despite the lack of soil diversity and the intensity of urbanisation, the flora is relatively rich. This is mainly due to the presence of the river valleys of the Liffey and Tolka, together with the Royal Canal corridor.

The River Liffey valley is remarkable not only for its aquatic flora but also for its associated woodlands and sand-quarries. The riverine flora is now strongly influenced by eutrophication which is exemplified by the dominance of Fennel Pondweed *Potamogeton pectinatus* in many places. Nevertheless, the river contains rarities such as Flowering-rush *Butomus umbellatus*, which is common along much of its length. On its banks, Green Figwort *Scrophularia umbrosa*, listed in the *Irish Red Data Book* (Curtis and McGough 1988) as vulnerable, is widespread.

The most important habitat in the Liffey valley is the woodland which persists on the steep slopes at St Catherine's and Luttrellstown. A number of rare Irish species may be found in these woods, most notably Hairy St John's-wort *Hypericum hirsutum*, a Protected Species, and Yellow Archangel *Lamiastrum galeobdolon*. Ivy Broomrape *Orobanche hederae* and Bearded Couch *Elymus caninus* are frequent along the valley and a number of less rare, but nevertheless noteworthy species which include Broad-leaved Helleborine *Epipactis helleborine*, Toothwort *Lathraea squamaria* and Thin-spiked Wood-sedge *Carex strigosa*, also occur.

The sand-quarry system, where glacial sediments are exploited, is a third feature of the Liffey valley. At Astagob there are sand-pits which, while not containing any real Irish rarities, have a rich flora including Wild Teasel *Dipsacus fullonum* and Salad Burnet *Sanguisorba minor*. Equally interesting is the sand-quarry system near Clanaboy House which contains Carline Thistle *Carlina vulgaris*, Hairy St John's-wort *Hypericum hirsutum* and Wood Vetch *Vicia sylvatica* at its only site in the county.

The slopes of the Tolka River Valley are less steep than those of the Liffey and fewer wooded areas remain. Instead, discontinuous areas of marsh with occasional areas of unimproved calcareous grassland adjoin the river. Good examples of both of these habitats are to be found on the northern bank of the river immediately north-west of Blanchardstown. Here the marsh contains species such as Marsh Hawk's-beard *Crepis paludosa*, Bogbean *Menyanthes trifoliata*, Bog Pimpernel *Anagallis tenella* and Slender Tufted-sedge *Carex acuta*. The calcareous grassland at this site includes Common Rest-harrow *Ononis repens*, Salad Burnet *Sanguisorba minor*, Pyramidal Orchid *Anacamptis pyramidalis* and Bee Orchid *Ophrys apifera*. Verge species common along the length of the Tolka River include Branched Bur-reed *Sparganium erectum*, Hemlock Water-dropwort *Oenanthe crocata*, Marsh Yellow-cress *Rorippa palustris* and Pink Water-speedwell *Veronica catenata*. Unfortunately Giant Hogweed *Heracleum mantegazzianum*, a dangerous invasive alien plant, has become established on sections of the river bank towards the east of the District as at Cardiff's Bridge.

The Royal Canal corridor contains not only aquatic habitats, but also unimproved calcareous grassland. The canal itself contains Greater Spearwort *Ranunculus lingua*. This species, rare in Co. Dublin, is common in the midlands and along the River Shannon, from where it most likely spread, via the canal, to Dublin. Whorled Water-milfoil *Myriophyllum verticillatum* is especially common along the western portion of the canal in Dublin, where it appears to have replaced other aquatics previously recorded here. A wide range of Stoneworts have been found (Nash and King 1993, King and Nash 1994). Coincidentally, during the course of work for this *Flora*, the canal was dredged to facilitate navigation, with the consequence that species such as Variegated Horsetail *Equisetum variegatum* and Tubular Water-dropwort *Oenanthe fistulosa* were not refound despite intensive searches at previously known stations. It can only be hoped that a management regime, based on sound conservation principles which will allow re-establishment, will be put in place.

Of equal botanical interest are the adjoining strips of species-rich calcareous grassland and the occasional limestone outcrops which occur along the Royal Canal. The calcicoles Upright

Brome *Bromopsis erecta*, Rough Hawkbit *Leontodon hispidus* and Marjoram *Origanum vulgare* are widespread. A good example of such a habitat may be found between Kennan Bridge and Kirkpatrick Bridge. Nearby a deep gorge, with limestone outcrop, contains Whitlowgrass *Erophila verna*, Parsley-piert *Aphanes arvensis* and Keeled-fruited Cornsalad *Valerianella carinata*, all growing together. At Cross Guns Bridge, the intersection of the railway line and the Royal Canal has preserved a small unimproved area. Here, Common Broomrape *Orobanche minor*, Fragrant Orchid *Gymnadenia conopsea*, Pyramidal Orchid *Anacamptis pyramidalis*, Common Spotted-orchid *Dactylorhiza fuchsii*, Yellow Oat-grass *Trisetum flavescens* and Carline Thistle *Carlina vulgaris* may be found. These species are not very common in the county as a whole and are certainly very rare in the urban parts (Wyse Jackson and Sheehy Skeffington 1984). The canal environs at Cross Guns Bridge also support two aliens, a Hawkweed *Hieracium gougetianum* and Stinking Tutsan *Hypericum hircinum*.

Several other features and areas within the District are worthy of brief mention. A substantial number of rare agricultural weeds were found near St Margaret's where road construction resulted in soil disturbance. Amongst them were Cornflower *Centaurea cyanus*, Musk Stork's-bill *Erodium moschatum* and Smooth Brome *Bromus racemosus*. Dunsoghly, a botanically rich marsh extant in Colgan's time, has been drained, but many species of interest remain there in drainage ditches including Greater Spearwort *Ranunculus lingua* and Greater Pond-sedge *Carex riparia*. The esker remnant at Finglas Bridge retains species such as Carline Thistle *Carlina vulgaris*, Yellow Oat-grass *Trisetum flavescens*, Common Restharrow *Ononis repens* and a few plants of Wild Parsnip *Pastinaca sativa*, despite the threat from ever encroaching development.

District 5 – Coolock   D. Nash
Approximate area: 100 square kilometres.
Boundary: Starting at North Wall Quay where the Royal Canal enters the River Liffey, the District 5 boundary follows that of District 4 along the Royal Canal north-west to Cross Guns Bridge at Phibsborough. From there it turns north through Ballymun (and with the main part of Dublin Airport on its east side) until it meets the southern boundary of District 3 at Forrest Great. It goes east to Cloghran, north to Swords and along the road towards Malahide until it reaches the small stream at Yellow Walls. The boundary follows this stream north to the Broad Meadow Estuary and continues along the coast by Malahide, Portmarnock, the Howth Peninsula, Clontarf and the northern part of Dublin Port to its starting point at North Wall Quay. Also included in the District are Ireland's Eye and North Bull Island.

While prime sites such as Feltrim Hill (a victim of limestone quarrying) and Santry Woods have virtually disappeared, several very interesting coastal areas continue to beckon the botanist. The coastal areas of District 5 have undergone considerable change in the 20th century. Much of Dublin Port was reclaimed from the sea and now provides new wasteground habitats for the many alien plants which arrive as cargo contaminants. Some of these such as Hoary Mustard *Hirschfeldia incana* and Bastard Cabbage *Rapistrum rugosum* look set to stay, while others are more transitory. North Bull Island also owes its existence, more indirectly, to human activity (Jeffrey 1977). Captain William Bligh's survey of 1798 showed the North

Bull as a sandbar with a small dry spot. Deposition of sediment had been increasing rapidly as a result of engineering work in the port which included the building of a "south pier" for Dublin Port. In 1804 it was noted that marine plants had colonised the "stripe" of the island that remained dry at high water. The North Bull Wall itself was completed in 1825. The island is now almost 5 km from north to south. It seems that there have always been threats to the island. In 1868 plans to dump sewage on the island were thwarted. In 1964 the controversial causeway was built. This facilitated access to the island by more motorists and thus contributed to an increase in the number of visitors. The uniqueness of the island and its botanical, zoological and geological features have been recognised by its designation as a UNESCO Biosphere Reserve.

Botanically North Bull Island has many areas of interest. The saltmarshes and mudflats on the landward side contain Sea-purslane *Atriplex portulacoides* and the introduced Common Cord-grass *Spartina anglica*. The initially green carpet of Glasswort *Salicornia* spp. becomes more prominent in its autumnal colours. Early flowering plants include Common Scurvygrass *Cochlearia officinalis* and Thrift *Armeria maritima* which give way later in the year to the purple Sea-lavenders *Limonium* spp. Lesser Centaury *Centaurium pulchellum*, a Protected Species, is found near the high tide zone and elsewhere on the island in salt pans. There are two alder marshes on the Bull. The most developed is in the northern part. In early summer, amongst Willows *Salix* spp. and Alder *Alnus glutinosa* and on the edges of the marsh, a profusion of flowering plants are seen. The Marsh Helleborine *Epipactis palustris* is abundant together with several other species of orchids including the Early Marsh-orchid *Dactylorhiza incarnata*. Other prominent plants include Yellow-wort *Blackstonia perfoliata* and the pink Common Centaury *Centaurium erythraea*. Later in the year the marsh is covered with dark blue Devil's-bit Scabious *Succisa pratensis*; Adder's-tongue *Ophioglossum vulgatum* and Autumn Gentian *Gentianella amarella* are plentiful; and the tiny orchid Autumn Lady's-tresses *Spiranthes spiralis* awaits the sharp-sighted visitor.

The newer sand-dunes are stabilised by Marram *Ammophila arenaria* and Sand Sedge *Carex arenaria*, and the older dunes and slacks have a floral display at almost any time of year. Early spring brings the displays of the tiny white flowers of Common Whitlowgrass *Erophila verna* and Little Mouse-ear *Cerastium semidecandrum*. Wild Pansy *Viola tricolor* subsp. *curtisii* has a long flowering season. Pyramidal Orchids *Anacamptis pyramidalis* are abundant in mid-summer and scattered Bee Orchids *Ophrys apifera* can be located. Wild Clary *Salvia verbenaca* may be found at its only remaining wild station in the county. Many legumes such as Rough Clover *Trifolium scabrum*, Kidney Vetch *Anthyllis vulneraria* and Spring Vetch *Vicia lathyroides* occur; the parasitic Common Broomrape *Orobanche minor* grows in small colonies and the hemi-parasitic Eyebrights *Euphrasia* spp. are very plentiful. Occasional sightings of other plants include Evening-primrose *Oenothera* spp., Sea Bindweed *Calystegia soldanella* and Sea-holly *Eryngium maritimum*.

Hart's *Flora of Howth* (1887) lists 545 plants of which 25 were described as introduced species. There have been a considerable number of losses, due to changes in land usage, and gains where plants have 'jumped' garden walls. By walking from Sutton to Howth Village along the coastal path, a substantial cross-section of the peninsular flora can be seen. Near Redrock, along the cliffs, Thrift *Armeria maritima*, Rock Sea-spurrey *Spergularia rupicola*, Common Restharrow *Ononis repens*, Sea-purslane *Atriplex portulacoides* and Rock Sea-lavender *Limonium binervosum* grow close to the pathway, and higher up some of the rarer legumes may be discovered on rocky knolls. Hairy Violet *Viola hirta* was formerly quite common but is no longer found. In May, the grassy promontories towards Drumleck are covered by blue Spring Squill *Scilla verna*. Near Drumleck the slopes are covered with Heather *Calluna vulgaris*, Bell Heather *Erica cinerea* and Western Gorse *Ulex gallii*. Rock Samphire *Crithmum maritimum* and Sea Wormwood *Seriphidium maritimum* are found in crevices; Heath Groundsel *Senecio sylvaticus* thrives on burnt ground and Sea Spleenwort *Asplenium marinum* is hidden in deep cliff crevices below in the spray zone. Towards the Baily Lighthouse we pass through the 'garden zone' where many exotics and garden escapes, such as the Hottentot-fig *Carpobrotus edulis* and White Bryony *Bryonia dioica*, have colonised new territory. Bloody Crane's-bill *Geranium sanguineum*, believed to be native here, is quite common. An occasional rarity, such as Climbing Corydalis *Ceratocapnos claviculata* and a prostrate form of Broom *Cytisus scoparius* subsp. *maritimus*, may be seen and Wild Madder *Rubia peregrina* climbs the hedgerows. Sea Campion *Silene uniflora* flourishes along the cliffs. Along the walk to Howth village, occasional calcicoles like Carline Thistle *Carlina vulgaris* and Burnet-saxifrage *Pimpinella saxifraga* can be observed and Black Bog-rush *Schoenus nigricans* has been found on one wet slope. Stunted Sycamore *Acer pseudoplatanus*, Hawthorn *Crataegus monogyna*, Blackthorn *Prunus spinosa* and Elder *Sambucus nigra* seek any available shelter. On the higher ground near the Ben of Howth, Bog Asphodel *Narthecium ossifragum*, Round-leaved Sundew *Drosera rotundifolia* and Lesser Clubmoss *Selaginella selaginoides* still persist in small isolated stations. While Early-purple Orchid *Orchis mascula* has not been observed lately anywhere in the District, isolated sites for both Green-winged Orchid *Orchis morio* and Frog Orchid *Coeloglossum viride* have recently been discovered on lower ground.

Ireland's Eye is but a short boat journey from Howth Harbour. Since the abandonment of farming on the island, coarser vegetation, including Bracken, has spread. However, the island still contains a small but significant variety of maritime and non-maritime plants. Stonecrops, *Sedum anglicum* and *S. acre,* grow on rock and Navelwort *Umbilicus rupestris* and Polypody *Polypodium vulgare* are found in rock crevices. Slender Thistle *Carduus tenuiflorus*, Wall Barley *Hordeum murinum*, and Dove's-foot Crane's-bill *Geranium molle* can be found together with more common 'weeds' such as Chickweed *Stellaria media*. Spring Squill *Scilla verna* grows on the grassy slopes and under the cover of Bracken *Pteridium aquilinum*. Thrift *Armeria maritima*, Common Scurvygrass *Cochlearia officinalis*, Rock Spurrey *Spergularia rupicola*, Sea Beet *Beta vulgaris* subsp. *maritima* and Sea Campion *Silene uniflora* are quite plentiful. Sea Rocket *Cakile maritima* and Sea Sandwort *Honckenya peploides* are found on the edge of the sandy beach, sometimes together with the erratically-appearing Henbane *Hyoscyamus niger*. Stinking Iris *Iris foetidissima* has been known here since Hart's time.

Silting in the Baldoyle Estuary, which receives water from the Mayne River, has been accelerated by the spread of Cord-grasses *Spartina* spp. Eelgrasses *Zostera noltii* and *Z. angustifolia* grow in the muddy channels. Upstream, the tidal section of the river overflows its bank during spring tides and three species of Saltmarsh-grass *Puccinellia* spp. are found. Common Saltmarsh-grass

P. maritima is frequently inundated; Borrer's Saltmarsh-grass *P. fasciculata*, a Protected Species, grows on bare mud; and Reflexed Saltmarsh-grass *P. distans* grows on drier ground. Meadow Barley *Hordeum secalinum*, another Protected Species, survives in the saltmarsh meadow. In spring, the pools which have formed during winter contain Brackish Water-crowfoot *Ranunculus baudotii,* which is also found in the marshy Portmarnock Brickfields beside the Sluice River and in the ponds on Portmarnock Golf-course. The Portmarnock sand-hills, which have recently been further enclosed by a second golf-course, contain a large colony of Hairy Violet *Viola hirta*, a Protected Species and the food plant of the Dark-green Fritillary butterfly. Special management measures have been taken to protect the Hairy Violet which is within the golf-course. Other plants of note include Green-flowered Helleborine *Epipactis phyllanthes*, Grass-of-Parnassus *Parnassia palustris*, Lesser Meadow-rue *Thalictrum minus*, Bugloss *Anchusa arvensis* and the prostrate form of Variegated Horsetail *Equisetum variegatum*.

District 6 – Newcastle   J. Parnell
Approximate area: 105 square kilometres.
Boundary: Starting at the River Liffey just east of Leixlip, the District 6 boundary runs south along the county boundary through Hazelhatch, west of Newcastle and crosses the Dublin to Naas road. It continues along the county boundary south-eastwards until it meets the District 7 boundary on the Blessington road just south of Brittas. From there it shares that boundary north-east through Brittas, along the road between Verschoyles Hill and Mount Seskin, through Jobstown to Tallaght. Just east of 'The Square' Shopping Centre in Tallaght, the District 7 boundary turns north following the main road through Clondalkin. The boundary then runs to the east of St Loman's Hospital and meets the River Liffey on the east side of the Hermitage Golf-course. From there it follows the Liffey west past Lucan to just east of Leixlip.

This, the westernmost of the Districts south of the River Liffey, was considered by Colgan to be botanically rather dull. Nowadays the picture is somewhat different. Although the urban area of Dublin has expanded considerably in a westerly direction with many housing developments around Lucan, Clondalkin and especially Tallaght, and the development of a number of major new roads (such as the Naas dual carriageway), District 6 remains largely rural. The rather rugged topography of the south-eastern part of the District has reduced, to some extent, the development of the intensive systems of agriculture that has occurred in Districts 1, 2 and 3. Nevertheless, the District's landscape has changed considerably in the 20th century. Many of the upland areas, for example, have been covered by forestry plantations which have eliminated many choice botanical locations, such as those on Slieve Thoul (in part now known as Saggart Hill). Additionally, agricultural land in many upland areas, such as on the summit of Mount Seskin, has been improved, again with a loss of natural habitats. The soils of this District are very varied ranging from the calcareous soils in the valley of the River Liffey to acid mineral soils on land south-east of Saggart. There are also remnants of an esker ridge near Esker.

The development of two aerodromes in this District has had a significant impact with mixed effects. One is the private Weston Aerodrome and the second is the military Casement

Aerodrome (= Baldonnel Aerodrome). Casement Aerodrome was the main civil airfield in the east of the country before Dublin Airport opened in 1940. Although it has expanded a little in size over the years, it is much smaller than Dublin Airport and the vegetation of the surrounding countryside has had time to mature and recover, having been protected, to some extent, from agricultural development by the aerodrome. District 6 has a large number of golf-courses. Some of these occupy large areas of land, for example, at Lucan, Knockandinny and Clondalkin, which were formerly of botanical importance.

Due to land use changes, a number of species appear to have been lost from this District, for example, Stag's-horn Clubmoss *Lycopodium clavatum* from Slieve Thoul. Nevertheless, some botanically interesting localities survive. Two are particularly worthy of mention. Although considerable clearance has occurred along the Grand Canal, due to dredging, its banks are still very rich in floral diversity. At Gollierstown, there is a species-rich calcareous system of hummocks and hollows (spoil heaps and quarry holes) which supports a number of rare plant populations, such as Autumn Gentian *Gentianella amarella* and Lesser Water-plantain *Baldellia ranunculoides,* as well as an unusual variety of Restharrow *Ononis repens* var. *horrida*. Unfortunately, further to the west, a marsh at Hazelhatch, which was formerly of importance, now appears to be drying out. However, to the east between Gollierstown and Ballymakaily Mill, the canal and its banks are botanically rich. At the mill itself a number of rare plants occur, such as Common Gromwell *Lithospermum officinale,* Blunt-fruited Water-starwort *Callitriche obtusangula* and a hybrid Horsetail *Equisetum* x *litorale*.

The area to the north of Brittas is also botanically interesting. In Crooksling Glen Red Campion *Silene dioica* still occurs, together with the introduced Londonpride *Saxifraga* x *urbium*. Brittas Ponds, one of the few large areas of open water in the county, are situated nearby. Recently the northern pond has been drained, perhaps permanently, and the exposed mud has been densely covered with Shoreweed *Littorella uniflora,* Marsh Yellow-cress *Rorippa palustris* and Red Goosefoot *Chenopodium rubrum.* These two linked reservoirs are surrounded by an extensive wetland and by some calcareous grassland. In the Brittas area a number of very rare species occur, such as Moonwort *Botrychium lunaria* in its only known site in the District and Water-purslane *Lythrum portula* at one of its few stations in the county. This area is also notable for two species of Lady's-mantle, *Alchemilla filicaulis* subsp. *vestita* and *A. glabra*.

District 7 – Uppercross   M. Wyse Jackson
Approximate area: 158 square kilometres.
Boundary: Starting from the mouth of the River Dodder at Ringsend, the District 7 boundary runs west along the River Liffey to the east side of the Hermitage Golf-course which is west of Palmerston. From there it shares the District 6 boundary south past St Loman's Hospital and along the main road through Clondalkin to Tallaght. From just east of 'The Square' Shopping Centre in Tallaght, the boundary goes south-west through Jobstown, along the road between Verschoyles Hill and Mount Seskin and through Brittas to the county boundary. It follows the county boundary east over the mountains, over Seahan, Corrig, Seefingan, Kippure and to the south of Killakee Mountain until it meets the District 8 boundary between Glendoo and Glencullen Mountains. From there, the boundary runs north across the Glencullen Valley and

then north-west between Tibradden and Kilmashogue Mountains to Rockbrook. It follows the Owendoher River north through Ballyboden to where that river joins the River Dodder just west of Rathfarnham, and finally north-east along the River Dodder to its mouth at Ringsend.

This is the largest of the Districts and contains much of the high ground in the county as well as its highest point, Kippure (757 m). The soils of the northern, low-lying part of the District are predominantly calcareous, formed from glacial drift deposits, sand, gravel and clay. These deposits can be clearly seen in profile in the valley of the River Dodder where the river has cut a channel through them. Although hardly evident nowadays, there are still very small remnants of esker ridges at Greenhills. The calcareous drift is not confined to the lowlands, but intrudes, in places quite deeply, into the southern, more elevated areas of the District, as for example, in the Glenasmole Valley. In general, however, the soils in the southern third of the District are acidic in nature, being either peat soils or mineral soils formed from the underlying acidic rocks.

District 7 has been heavily urbanised in the 20th century, particularly at its northern end, resulting in the loss of some sites of botanical interest. In the southern more rural parts of the District, little intensive agriculture has been carried out, as a consequence of the relatively poor soils and the steep slopes, and many sites of interest have survived.

This District is the most densely wooded of all the Districts, due to the large areas of commercial coniferous forest which have been planted on the lower slopes of the Dublin Mountains, as at Mount Seskin, Ballinascorney, Ballymorefinn Hill, Mountpelier (Hell Fire Club), Killakee and Cruagh Mountains. These plantations are generally species-poor and do not hold any scarce plants. Small stands of semi-natural or planted broad-leaved woodland, mixed woodland and scrub also occur in the District, for example, on the east side of the Glenasmole Valley, near Ballymaice, at Killakee (Massey Woods), Bushy Park, in the River Liffey Valley and as a narrow strip fringing the River Dodder (in places only scattered trees). These woodlands provide habitats for a wide range of typical woodland plant species, including several rarities.

Blanket bog, heath and upland grassland are found on the Dublin Mountains. Blanket bog is particularly well developed in the upper River Dodder valley (the area south of Glenasmole, between the peaks of Seahan, Corrig, Seefingan, Kippure and Killakee Mountains), and ascends almost to the summits of Seefingan and Kippure, where it is much eroded. The upper River Dodder valley, with its upland blanket bog, heathland, streams (including the River Dodder, Cot Brook and Slade Brook), flushes and dense Bracken is notable for the occurrence of several species that are not found elsewhere in the county, i.e. Cowberry *Vaccinium vitis-idaea*, Starry Saxifrage *Saxifraga stellaris*, Alpine Clubmoss *Diphasiastrum alpinum*, Wilson's Filmy-fern *Hymenophyllum wilsonii*, Lemon-scented Fern *Oreopteris limbosperma*, Beech Fern *Phegopteris connectilis* and for many other scarce Dublin species, for example, Bog-rosemary *Andromeda polifolia*, Fir Clubmoss *Huperzia selago*, Stag's-horn Clubmoss *Lycopodium clavatum*, Pale Butterwort *Pinguicula lusitanica*, Dioecious Sedge *Carex dioica*, Smooth-stalked Sedge *Carex laevigata* and Wood Horsetail *Equisetum sylvaticum*. Typical mountain plants in District 7 include Crowberry *Empetrum nigrum*, Deergrass *Trichophorum cespitosum* and Hare's-tail Cottongrass *Eriophorum vaginatum*. The nationally rare and legally protected Bog Orchid *Hammarbya paludosa* is found here in its only remaining Dublin site, on wet boggy ground near the Southern Reservoir in the Glenasmole Valley. Mountain Pansy *Viola lutea*, a nationally scarce species, is restricted to two sites in the county, one in heathy grassland just west of Tallaght Hill.

The Glenasmole Valley, located north of Kippure, contains a high diversity of habitats, plant communities and species. The River Dodder flows through on its way northward and has been impounded here to form two reservoirs which together comprise the largest area of open water in the county. Many rare Dublin plants are found in the valley, several of which grow in the reservoirs or in marginal wetlands, for example, Shoreweed *Littorella uniflora*, Perfoliate Pondweed *Potamogeton perfoliatus*, Lesser Bulrush *Typha angustifolia* and Water Sedge *Carex aquatilis*. St Anne's Fields, an area of species-rich, unimproved wet grassland, is found on the east side of the Glenasmole Valley near St Ann's Chapel. Particularly notable is the range of orchids that have been recorded there since Colgan's day, including Frog Orchid *Coeloglossum viride*, Northern Marsh-orchid *Dactylorhiza purpurella*, Marsh Helleborine *Epipactis palustris*, Fragrant Orchid *Gymnadenia conopsea*, Early-purple Orchid *Orchis mascula* and Greater Butterfly-orchid *Platanthera chlorantha*. Pale Sedge *Carex pallescens*, Zigzag Clover *Trifolium medium*, Meadow Thistle *Cirsium dissectum* and its hybrid with Marsh Thistle *C. palustre*, all scarce Dublin plants, are also found at St Anne's Fields. Broad-leaved Cottongrass *Eriophorum latifolium* was formerly found near the Southern Reservoir at Glenasmole (Anon. 1961), but it has not been recorded here or elsewhere in the county in recent years. Other rare Dublin species found in the Glenasmole Valley include Broad-leaved Helleborine *Epipactis helleborine*, Yellow Archangel *Lamiastrum galeobdolon*, Yellow Bird's-nest *Monotropa hypopitys* (McMullen 1967), Fen Bedstraw *Galium uliginosum*, Hawkweed *Hieracium umbellatum*, Tawny Sedge *Carex hostiana*, Hairy Wood-rush *Luzula pilosa*, Narrow-leaved Helleborine *Cephalanthera longifolia* and two Protected Species, Green-winged Orchid *Orchis morio* and Small-white Orchid *Pseudorchis albida* (Piper 1970).

In the valley of the River Dodder below Bohernabreena the presence of calcareous glacial drift has given rise to the development of dry calcareous grassland along the river. In Colgan's day this grassland was quite common in the valley and supported several Dublin rarities. Today, however, much of the grassland has been lost to development and only a few small fragments remain. These support species typical of such grassland, for example, Yellow-wort *Blackstonia perfoliata*, Quaking-grass *Briza media*, Carline Thistle *Carlina vulgaris*, Common Centaury *Centaurium erythraea*, Pale Flax *Linum bienne*, Kidney Vetch *Anthyllis vulneraria*, Rough Hawkbit *Leontodon hispidus*, Downy Oat-grass *Helictotrichon pubescens* and Yellow Oat-grass *Trisetum flavescens*. A few rarities have managed to survive, for example, the Hawkweeds *Hieracium umbellatum* and *H. sabaudum* and Greater Knapweed *Centaurea scabiosa*. An area of damp grassland by the River Dodder at Oldbawn is notable for the presence of Spiked Sedge *Carex spicata*, in its only Co. Dublin station.

Esker ridges with dry calcareous grassland formerly occurred around Greenhills. Although virtually all of these have now been levelled, some of the associated flora remains in the area, for example, Greater Knapweed *Centaurea scabiosa*, Hoary Ragwort *Senecio erucifolius*, and Salad Burnet *Sanguisorba minor*. Other species, such as Hairy Violet *Viola hirta* and Blue Fleabane *Erigeron acer*, which occurred on eskers in the area have apparently not survived.

The Grand Canal enters the District at Clondalkin and is a significant area of standing water that encircles the south side of the inner city of Dublin from Kilmainham to Ringsend. It has allowed the spread into the heart of the city of many wetland plants which would otherwise not occur, or whose distribution in the county would be considerably more restricted. Fringing beds of a variety of emergent species, including Common Reed *Phragmites australis*, Reed Sweet-grass *Glyceria maxima*, Reed Canary-grass *Phalaris arundinacea*, Common Club-rush *Schoenoplectus lacustris*, Yellow Iris *Iris pseudacorus* and Bulrush *Typha latifolia*, occur at intervals along its length. The canal contains a rich and diverse aquatic flora, including an abundance of Rigid Hornwort *Ceratophyllum demersum*, and several rarities, for example, Needle Spike-rush *Eleocharis acicularis*, which occurs at Drimnagh, Opposite-leaved Pondweed *Groenlandia densa*, a nationally rare and legally Protected Species which occurs abundantly in the District 7 section of the canal, and the hybrid Pondweed *Potamogeton* x *lintonii*, recorded near Baggot Street Bridge, in its only Dublin site.

The River Liffey forms the northern boundary of the District. Its valley contains a diversity of habitats, including broad-leaved woodlands, grasslands, the river itself and associated wetland areas, for example, Palmerston Marsh, and is notable for the many rare or scarce plants which are found there (see Doogue and Walsh 1989). Species of note occurring in the District 7 section of the valley include Hairy St John's-wort *Hypericum hirsutum*, a Protected Species, Yellow Archangel *Lamiastrum galeobdolon*, Green Figwort *Scrophularia umbrosa*, Wood Fescue *Festuca altissima*, Rough Horsetail *Equisetum hyemale*, Greater Bladderwort *Utricularia vulgaris*, Flowering-rush *Butomus umbellatus* and Ivy Broomrape *Orobanche hederae*. A nationally rare Hawkweed, *Hieracium diaphanum*, occurs on walls by the river at Kingsbridge and Islandbridge.

Most of the northern third of the District is urbanised and consequently few natural habitats have survived. The floristic interest of this part of the District lies mainly in the presence of many introduced species intermixed with some natives, in a variety of artificial habitats such as wastegrounds, walls, pavements, car parks, derelict buildings, private gardens and parks (Wyse Jackson and Sheehy Skeffington 1984). A number of species, which are mostly naturalised introductions, are characteristic of the city flora and occur commonly in ruderal habitats, for example, Wall Barley *Hordeum murinum*, Annual Mercury *Mercurialis annua*, Eastern Rocket *Sisymbrium orientale* and Butterfly-bush *Buddleja davidii*. Dublin rarities recorded in the District 7 section of the city include London-rocket *Sisymbrium irio*, Small Balsam *Impatiens parviflora* and Maidenhair Fern *Adiantum capillus-veneris*. Sticky Groundsel *Senecio viscosus* (Nash 1995), which was formerly quite rare in Dublin, has recently been spreading and is now to be seen in the District at several sites.

District 8 – Rathdown   S. Reynolds
Approximate area: 126 square kilometres.
Boundary: Starting from the mouth of the River Dodder at Ringsend, the District 8 boundary runs along that river south-west to where it is joined by the Owendoher River just west of Rathfarnham. It follows the Owendoher River south through Ballyboden to Rockbrook, then south-east between Kilmashogue and Tibradden Mountains and south across the Glencullen Valley to the county boundary between Glendoo and Glencullen Mountains. From there it

goes along the county boundary east over Prince William's Seat, by Glencullen Bridge, through the Scalp, along the Ballyman River, to Little Bray and the coast. Thereafter it follows the coast north by Killiney, Dalkey, Dun Laoghaire, Blackrock, Booterstown and Irishtown until it reaches the mouth of the River Dodder at Ringsend. Dalkey Island is in this District.

District 8 lies in the south-east of the county. The built-up area extends south from Dublin City and along the coast, covering about half the District. Although the coastline is long, it lacks the variety of habitats, particularly well-developed saltmarsh and sand-dunes, such as are found along the north Co. Dublin coast. The lowland soils are mostly calcareous and, where not built over, land is used for pasture and rarely tilled. There is little deciduous woodland and only small bodies of open water. The two main rivers are the Dodder and Glencullen Rivers; smaller streams are often modified or even culverted. Semi-natural vegetation survives in or around managed open spaces, for example, University College at Belfield, Leopardstown Race Course, public parks and golf-courses. The extensive uplands in the south-west of the District reach a high point of 556 m on Prince William's Seat. Much of this area is blanket bog and heathland on acid soils with the lower slopes providing rough grazing. Since Colgan's time, large coniferous forests have been planted on Ticknock and on Kilmashogue, Two Rock and Glencullen Mountains.

The most interesting botanical locality in District 8 is centred on Killiney Hill and includes Dalkey Hill, Roches Hill and Dalkey Island. The hills are composed of granite and mica schists and the lower seaward-facing slopes have a thick covering of calcareous drift. Despite the large number of people who use the area for recreation, over 200 native plant species have been recorded in a variety of habitats here. Rock Samphire *Crithmum maritimum* and Golden-samphire *Inula crithmoides* grow on rocks just above the sea and Sea Spleenwort *Asplenium marinum* persists in crevices around the entrance to the old lead mines at Whiterock. Bloody Crane's-bill *Geranium sanguineum*, Burnet Rose *Rosa pimpinellifolia* and Salad Burnet *Sanguisorba minor* grow on the drift above the Vico Bathing Place while Wild Madder *Rubia peregrina*, Bristly Oxtongue *Picris echioides* and Portland Spurge *Euphorbia portlandica* are found on the cliff top. Silver Ragwort *Senecio cineraria*, introduced about 1875, remains conspicuous around Killiney Bay where it also hybridises with Common Ragwort *Senecio jacobaea*.

Much of Killiney Hill is wooded with a mixture of introduced and native trees including two rare Whitebeams, *Sorbus hibernica* and *S. intermedia*, which are also found in Dalkey Quarry. In contrast, Roches Hill, just west-south-west of Killiney Hill, is not wooded and in the spring, Bluebell *Hyacinthoides non-scripta* and Greater Stitchwort *Stellaria holostea* may be seen among Bracken there. Another distinctive plant on Killiney Hill and Roches Hill is Climbing Corydalis *Ceratocapnos claviculata* which is abundant under gorse, especially after burning. In Dalkey Quarry, there are several calcifuge species, for example, Sheep's-bit *Jasione montana,* otherwise only found in the mountainous part of the District. A feature of this whole area is the occurrence of four scarce clovers, restricted to coastal habitats. Knotted Clover *Trifolium striatum* and Bird's-foot Clover *T. ornithopodioides* are found in short turf below the obelisk on Killiney Hill and Bird's-foot Clover is also found on Dalkey Hill and Dalkey Island. Two more species, Western Clover *T. occidentale* and Rough Clover *T. scabrum* only occur on Dalkey Island in this District.

The Glencullen Valley and mountains on either side of it have a largely calcifuge flora. Where there is blanket bog, ericaceous plants, sedges and grasses are dominant. Lesser Twayblade *Listera cordata*, typically hidden under heather, is quite common near Prince William's Seat and on Two Rock Mountain. Marsh St John's-wort *Hypericum elodes*, not found elsewhere in the county, Common Butterwort *Pinguicula vulgaris* and Pale Butterwort *P. lusitanica* occur in wet places on both sides of the valley. A good example of sheep-grazed acid grassland is found above the Glencullen River east of Boranaraltry Bridge. South-west of Glencullen Bridge is the only remaining site in the county for Ivy-leaved Bellflower *Wahlenbergia hederacea*. The Protected Species, Bog Orchid *Hammarbya paludosa*, formerly grew nearby, but its site was drained and planted with conifers in the early 1990s. However, another Protected Species, Small Cudweed *Filago minima*, survives on granitic gravel at a disused quarry on Three Rock Mountain and one patch of the rare Sand Spurrey *Spergularia rubra* was found on a track in the same area. East of Glencullen, Ballybetagh Bog, which is important as the site where many Giant Irish Deer skeletons were found, is dominated by Greater Tussock-sedge *Carex paniculata*. Marsh cinquefoil *Potentilla palustris* and Bogbean *Menyanthes trifoliata* grow between the tussocks, with Trailing St John's-wort *Hypericum humifusum* on the drier margins. Wet meadows to the south of Ballybetagh Bog and on the boundary with Co. Wicklow are noted for the variety of Marsh-orchids *Dactylorhiza* spp. and Sedges *Carex* spp.

While deciduous woodland is not common in the District, among the more interesting is Fitzsimon's Wood near Sandyford where Downy Birch *Betula pubescens* is the dominant tree species. Dense scrub woodland fills the Dingle, a small gorge just north-east of Kiltiernan. This woodland contains Hazel *Corylus avellana* and Spindle *Euonymus europaeus* with three uncommon plants, Climbing Corydalis *Ceratocapnos claviculata*, Hairy Wood-rush *Luzula pilosa* and Wood Melick *Melica uniflora*, in the herb layer. The most mature wood, which includes large trees of Oak *Quercus*, Elm *Ulmus*, Beech *Fagus sylvatica*, Pine *Pinus* and Sycamore *Acer pseudoplatanus*, is in Druid's Glen near Carrickmines. There is much Great Wood-rush *Luzula sylvatica*, and in spring Wood Anemone *Anemone nemorosa*, Sanicle *Sanicula europaea*, Goldilocks Buttercup *Ranunculus auricomus*, Violets *Viola* spp., Wood-sorrel *Oxalis acetosella* and Wood Speedwell *Veronica montana* flower there. Pendulous Sedge *Carex pendula* grows along the stream.

Along the approximately 23 km of coast, plant habitats include cliffs, stony and sandy shores, a saltmarsh, retaining walls and piers. The cliffs around Killiney Bay and on Dalkey Island support common maritime species as well as the less common Spring Squill *Scilla verna* and Sea Stork's-bill *Erodium maritimum*. Marram *Ammophila arenaria*, Lyme-grass *Leymus arenarius* and Sea Sandwort *Honckenya peploides* are found below Killiney Railway Station and near the mouths of the Deansgrange Stream and Shanganagh River, and also on sand near the Pigeon House at Ringsend. Elsewhere the littoral flora is poorly developed. Booterstown Marsh, the only saltmarsh in the District, was formed when this area was cut off around 1834 by construction of the railway. It is a site for Borrer's Saltmarsh-grass *Puccinellia fasciculata*, a Protected Species. The mingling of freshwater inflows and saline water permits a diversity of fresh, brackish and saltwater species to thrive. In one area of the marsh, Sea Arrowgrass *Triglochin maritimum* and Marsh Arrowgrass *T. palustre* grow together - an unusual occurrence.

There are several other small areas of botanical interest. The gravel car park at Leopardstown Race Course (partially built over in 1996) has Rue-leaved Saxifrage *Saxifraga tridactylites*, Long-stalked Crane's-bill *Geranium columbinum*, Small Toadflax *Chaenorhinum minus*, Squirreltail Fescue *Vulpia bromoides* and Rat's-tail Fescue *V. myuros*. These plants were possibly introduced with limestone chippings used to surface the car park. Moschatel *Adoxa moschatellina* and Blue Anemone *Anemone apennina* are naturalized in adjacent woodland. A small marsh beside Ballyman Glen Bridge contains Dioecious Sedge *Carex dioica* and Few-flowered Spike-rush *Eleocharis quinqueflora*, while the only site in the District for Spiked Water-milfoil *Myriophyllum spicatum* and Intermediate Water-starwort *Callitriche hamulata* is the lake at the Ballycorus Roadstone works. Greater Butterfly-orchid *Platanthera chlorantha* grows in a field near the top of the Ticknock Road with Wood Horsetail *Equisetum sylvaticum* which is also on nearby roadside banks. On a steep bank by the main Bray road below Loughlinstown Hospital, Bee Orchid *Ophrys apifera* and Pyramidal Orchid *Anacamptis pyramidalis* grow together. In tilled fields along the railway, just east of Shanganagh cemetery and south-east of Shankill, an assemblage of rare arable weeds which included Field Woundwort *Stachy arvensis*, Dwarf Spurge *Euphorbia exigua* and a few plants of Sharp-leaved Fluellen *Kickxia elatine*, a Protected Species, was found in the mid-1980s.

The reclaimed land at Ringsend Dump is a rich hunting ground for casual and alien species. Some, such as Hoary Mustard *Hirschfeldia incana* and Bastard Cabbage *Rapistrum rugosum*, which persisted in large numbers for many years, were being replaced by Ribbed Melilot *Melilotus officinalis* in the mid-1990s. Casual species such as Dwarf Mallow *Malva neglecta*, Round-leaved Crane's-bill *Geranium rotundifolium* and Toothed Medick *Medicago polymorpha* are found only occasionally.

During the course of the Field Club's survey, a number of good habitats in this District were much altered or even destroyed as a result of further road building, suburban spread, upland drainage and afforestation. A few rare species were not refound, for example, Sea Wormwood *Seriphidium maritimum*, formerly on the cliffs around Killiney Bay and Wood Vetch *Vicia sylvatica* on the east side of Killiney Hill, while the sites for Strawberry Clover *Trifolium fragiferum* by the Shanganagh River and Bog Orchid *Hammarbya paludosa* in the Glencullen Valley have been destroyed. Finally, there has been a noticeable decline or loss of several species generally common elsewhere in Ireland, for example, Early-purple Orchid *Orchis mascula* and Purple-loosestrife *Lythrum salicaria*.

HABITAT ACCOUNTS

The following accounts, which describe some of the more important plant habitat types in the county, are intended to complement the information on plant distribution in the Systematic Section of the *Flora*. The accounts are largely based on field surveys undertaken in 1990 and 1991. No attempt has been made to classify the vegetation using currently recognised floristic associations, and the reader is referred to the Bibliography (in Appendix 1) for published work on the vegetation of Co. Dublin (e.g. White 1982). An attempt has been made, however, to produce an overview of the major habitats in order to make them accessible to the reader who is not a trained botanist, and to link them to some of the sites of particular interest in the different Districts (indicated here by District numbers in brackets, see Fig. 5). Species listed in the Habitat Accounts complement the lists for the same sites in the District Accounts.

MARITIME AND SUB–MARITIME COMMUNITIES

A number of distinct habitats are found along the coast of Co. Dublin - mud flats, saltmarshes, sandy and stony shores, sand-dunes, rocky cliffs and boulder clay banks. The north coast is characterised by a series of estuaries which have extensive mudflats, saltmarshes and sand-dunes supporting some of the best examples of the vegetation of these habitats in Ireland. The mudflats and saltmarshes are also the largest wetland areas in the county and are of international importance due to the numbers of wildfowl and waders which feed there (Sheppard 1993). There are only a few areas with cliffs exceeding 65 m in height, and these are formed mainly of hard siliceous rocks on Howth Head and Ireland's Eye (5) and of granite at Dalkey and Killiney (8). They support a diverse flora as do the lower rocky cliffs, less than 20 m high, which occur, for example, at Loughshinny (2), Portrane (3) and near Killiney. Around Dublin Bay, much of the coast is built-up, but some places still provide considerable botanical interest, for example, Booterstown Marsh (8), Dublin Port (5) and North Bull Island (5).

Mud Flats   M. Sheehy Skeffington

The only truly sub-tidal higher plant in these waters is Eelgrass *Zostera*, an important food for geese. Three species occur in Ireland and Eelgrass *Z. marina* is the most common, though it has not lately been recorded for Co. Dublin. The first record in Ireland for Dwarf Eelgrass *Zostera noltii* (as *Z. nana*) was on mud at Baldoyle (5) (Moore and More 1866) where it still grows. These authors refer also to Narrow-leaved Eelgrass *Z. angustifolia* (as *Z. marina* var. *angustifolia*), noting it to be growing with *Z. noltii* at Baldoyle, and there is a specimen in **DBN** collected in 1867 from Baldoyle by H.G. Carroll. However, Colgan (1904) overlooks this Baldoyle record and lists it - also as var. *angustifolia* - only for Malahide, Portmarnock and Raheny (5). Much later *Z. angustifolia* was given its specific status (as *Z. hornemanniana*) in Ireland (Webb 1953). A detailed survey has recently been carried out on the status of *Zostera* in Co. Dublin (Madden *et al.* 1993). The authors note its disappearance from Rogerstown

Estuary (2 and 3) and its decline at Malahide (3) and Baldoyle Estuaries, but report that it is still present at Merrion (8), where it was recorded only relatively recently in 1954 (Anon. 1961). They refer to a 'wasting disease' which devastated *Z. marina* in western Europe, but are unable to say whether it influenced the decline in Irish populations. The other two species are thought not to have been as susceptible. Reasons for their decline in Co. Dublin are discussed and include landfill which, in the form of a refuse tip, is thought to be the cause of the extinction of *Zostera* at Rogerstown. The expansion of Cord-grass *Spartina* is often also blamed and maps drawn by G.H. Pethybridge in *c.*1900 show *Zostera* to have been very common in areas where *Spartina* is now abundant at Baldoyle, Malahide and Rogerstown (Madden *et al.* 1993). At Malahide and Baldoyle *Zostera* grows amongst *Spartina* plants and the suggestion is that *Spartina* is displacing it. However, Otte (1994) contests this view and points out that *Zostera* is declining in other areas in the absence of *Spartina*. In the northern part of Dublin Bay, eutrophication, which has brought about the growth of dense green algal mats, may be the cause of the decline of *Zostera* (Madden *et al.* 1993).

The perennial Cord-grass *Spartina*, a genus native to North America, was first introduced from southern England to the Lee estuary, Co. Cork, in 1925 in order to stabilise harbour muds. Soon afterwards it was introduced into several other estuaries round the coast (Praeger 1932). The original introduction was called *S. townsendii* (referred to by Praeger as the "fertile hybrid *S. alterniflora* x *S. stricta*"), but is now thought likely to have been both the (non-fertile) hybrid (*S.* x *townsendii*) and its fertile allotetraploid, Common Cord-grass *S. anglica* (Boyle 1977). *Spartina* has spread rapidly and invaded many areas of mud flats in Britain and Ireland and is now considered by some to be a pest. *S. anglica* is the more aggressive, especially as it sets seed in addition to spreading by an extensive rhizome system. *Spartina* was first planted in Co. Dublin at Baldoyle, probably in early 1932 from Poole Harbour in the south of England (Boyle 1972). It was first noted on North Bull Island (5) (as *S. townsendii*) in 1934 by Professor Joseph Doyle. P.J. Boyle (1977) gives an account of its taxonomic problems and spread there. North Bull Island is the only site where she was certain that *S.* x *townsendii* itself was established. Attempts to eradicate all *Spartina* there have been at the expense of this hybrid. By the early 1950s '*S. townsendii*' had spread extensively in the Baldoyle Estuary and was present in one part of the Broad Meadow Estuary (= Malahide Estuary) but not at all in the Rogerstown Estuary (O'Reilly and Pantin 1957). By the mid 1970s it was noted (as *S. anglica*) to be quite extensive in the tidal channels of the Malahide saltmarshes, in the Broad Meadow Estuary (Ní Lamhna 1982) and it is extensive to-day in the Rogerstown estuary. Boyle (1976) also notes an unusual form of *Spartina* in Co. Dublin which she names as *S. maritima* forma *dublinensis*. Though an unusual form of *Spartina* has been located recently on North Bull Island (M. Otte pers. comm.), it is not clear whether it is the same form. So it seems both *S. maritima* forma *dublinensis* and *S.* x *townsendii* have disappeared from North Bull Island in recent decades. It is possible that *S. anglica*, which is currently the dominant species around Ireland (pers. obs. and T. Curtis pers. comm.), is now the only species of Cord-grass in the Co. Dublin saltmarshes.

Glasswort Flats and Saltmarshes   M. Sheehy Skeffington
Species of annual Glasswort *Salicornia* occur extensively in the summer and early autumn on the mud flats. They usually grow on slightly raised areas of mud or sand, but are also to be

found on the lower edges of saltmarshes and in salt pans. The common name refers to the very fleshy and slightly translucent, apparently leafless stems. The fleshiness and reduced growth form are an adaptation to a highly variable saline environment. Unlike completely submerged plants, saltmarsh plants are subjected to changes in salinity which can vary periodically from less than 10% to in excess of 150% of that of seawater. This variation depends on the frequency of submergence by the tides and of exposure to either continuous rain or long spells of sunshine which can concentrate the salts at or below the mud surface. Saltmarsh plants are therefore truly remarkable in their ability to alter their physiological processes according to the prevailing conditions. The most obvious external manifestation of this adaptation is the fleshy leaves, which have a large volume to surface area ratio.

The mud flats and lower edges of saltmarshes are, paradoxically, subjected to less extreme variations of salinity, as they are usually covered daily by the tide. Glasswort can form extensive beds on exposed muds together with green and brown algae, such as *Enteromorpha*, *Ulva* and *Fucus*. This is particularly evident on the landward side of North Bull Island (5) and in parts of the Malahide Estuary (3). Glasswort, an annual, changes colour in the autumn and dies back. The colour first turns bright golden-yellow and often changes to vivid pinks and reds which are very conspicuous from a distance. There are several species of annual Glasswort, but they are quite difficult to distinguish and only one species, *S. herbacea*, was recognised in Dublin in the early 20th century (Praeger 1901, Colgan 1904). In Ireland, the taxonomy of *Salicornia* was not fully addressed until the Ph.D. work of Ferguson (1964) and six species were subsequently listed in Scannell and Synnott (1972). Three species are fairly common especially at Rush (2), Donabate (3), Portrane (3) and North Bull Island (5). These are Purple Glasswort *S. ramosissima*, Long-spiked Glasswort *S. dolichostachya* and Common Glasswort *S. europaea*. This last species is perhaps more frequent on slightly higher ground and is common, for example, on North Bull Island saltmarsh, especially in the salt pans.

Saltmarshes on the east coast of Ireland are extensive, having built up gradually through mud accretion from the adjacent estuaries. They have a gently sloping seaward gradient and are not usually grazed by farm livestock. Consequently they support characteristic vegetation zones which are not so clearly evident on many marshes of the west coast (Sheehy Skeffington and Wymer 1991, Curtis and Sheehy Skeffington 1998). The lower zone, nearest the sea, is flooded about 200 times in the year and is the most unstable, due to reworking of mud by the tides, especially during storms. Annuals such as Glassworts *Salicornia* spp. and Annual Sea-blite *Suaeda maritima* thrive in this zone together with the perennial Common Saltmarsh-grass *Puccinellia maritima* which is tolerant of waterlogging. Other species which are common a little further from the edge and also along the channels or creeks are Lax-flowered Sea-lavender *Limonium humile* and Greater Sea-spurrey *Spergularia media*. In late August, the lower reaches of the marshes, especially at Malahide and Donabate (O'Reilly and Pantin 1957, Ní Lamhna 1982), are hazy purple with flowers of the two Sea-lavenders, *L. humile* and Rock Sea-lavender *L. binervosum*. Gradually the front edge of the marsh grades into an extensive area of almost flat marsh, interspersed by the creeks and salt pans. This area is dominated by plant species with rosettes of slightly succulent leaves and large tap roots (for food storage) which can survive extremes of salinity (see McNamee and Jeffrey 1977). These are species such as

Sea Plantain *Plantago maritima*, Thrift *Armeria maritima*, Sea Arrowgrass *Triglochin maritimum* and Sea Aster *Aster tripolium*. This "middle marsh" area would therefore look like an extensive flat grassland (Common Saltmarsh-grass *Puccinellia maritima* gradually gives way to Red Fescue *Festuca rubra*) were it not for the presence of the only shrubby saltmarsh species in Ireland, Sea-purslane *Atriplex portulacoides*. This gives a very distinctive appearance to the saltmarshes of the eastern and southern Irish coasts. Its presence on these marshes seems to be linked with the notable absence of grazing by farm livestock (Curtis and Sheehy Skeffington in press). However, it has only relatively recently become predominant on North Bull Island (Moore and O'Reilly 1977).

In an evenly-sloping saltmarsh, such as occurs at North Bull Island, the "middle" zone grades into an upper marsh community with increasing height above sea level. Red Fescue *Festuca rubra* becomes increasingly dominant and the small Saltmarsh Rush *Juncus gerardii* forms a distinct zone, before giving way to extensive clumps of the much larger Sea Rush *J. maritimus* which dominates the physiognomy of the upper regions of the saltmarsh. Amongst these clumps, Common Scurvygrass *Cochlearia officinalis* is plentiful. Sea Plantain *Plantago maritima* and Thrift *Armeria maritima* are also present, with a much larger growth habit than in the more saline middle marsh region. The saltmarsh vegetation ends abruptly just above the extreme high water mark and grassland species usually intolerant of tidal submergence predominate, such as Creeping Bent *Agrostis stolonifera*, Ribwort Plantain *Plantago lanceolata* and Common Mouse-ear *Cerastium fontanum*, as well as Red Fescue.

Sand-dunes   P. Grant and P. Reilly

Extensive, well developed sand-dunes are generally restricted to the coastal area north of the River Liffey (see Curtis 1991a, 1991b) and all are associated with river estuaries. From south to north the key sites are North Bull Island (5) (see Jeffrey 1977), the Cosh, Sutton (5), Portmarnock (5), Malahide Island (3) (see Ní Lamhna 1982), Portrane Peninsula (3) and Rush (2).

The sand-dune systems, with the exception of the Cosh which has been extensively altered and disturbed, can be divided into zones, each with distinct vegetation types. Moving from the shore inland these are the developing fore-dunes, the unstable primary dune-ridge and the fixed secondary dune-ridges and dune-slacks.

Fore-dunes: The vegetation of the fore-dunes is similar at all of the sites mentioned above. Annual species such as Sea Rocket *Cakile maritima*, Frosted Orache *Atriplex laciniata*, Spear-leaved Orache *Atriplex prostrata* and Prickly Saltwort *Salsola kali* are the first colonisers. They are joined by the perennial grasses Sea Couch *Elytrigia juncea*, Lyme-grass *Leymus arenarius* and Marram *Ammophila arenaria*. In general, Co. Dublin fore-dunes may be unusual, in that Sea Sandwort *Honckenya peploides* is not a common plant along the foreshore, although it is often referred to in the literature as being important in sand-dune development in Ireland and elsewhere.

Primary Dune-ridges: The vegetation of the primary dune-ridge is similar at all sites in Dublin being dominated by the rhizomatous grass Marram *Ammophila arenaria*. Other common species are Lyme-grass *Leymus arenarius*, which is rather rarer on North Bull Island (first discovered by J.P. Brunker and A.W. Stelfox in 1922 (Moore 1977)) than at the other sites, Sea Spurge *Euphorbia paralias*, Common Ragwort *Senecio jacobaea*, Cat's-ear *Hypochaeris radicata* and Dandelion *Taraxacum officinale* agg. The occurrence of a number of species of the Daisy family (Asteraceae / Compositae) reflects, in part, the high degree of human disturbance and the subsequent degradation of the primary dunes. For example, on North Bull Island, which is very disturbed in places, Oxford Ragwort *Senecio squalidus* has been recorded and Smooth Sow-thistle *Sonchus oleraceus* is frequent.

Fixed Dunes: The vegetation of the fixed dunes changes according to the age of the ridges. This is a result of increasing stability, the gradual accumulation of humus and improved water-holding capacity. Marram *Ammophila arenaria* is dominant on the younger dunes. Red Fescue *Festuca rubra*, Sand Sedge *Carex arenaria*, Wild Pansy *Viola tricolor* subsp. *curtisii*, Sea Mouse-ear *Cerastium diffusum*, Common Whitlowgrass *Erophila verna*, Sand Cat's-tail *Phleum arenarium*, Kidney Vetch *Anthyllis vulneraria*, Hare's-foot Clover *Trifolium arvense*, Lady's Bedstraw *Galium verum*, Cat's-ear *Hypochaeris radicata* and Lesser Hawkbit *Leontodon saxatilis* are also important and are associated with the development of a humus layer on the dune surface involving mosses (often *Tortula* spp.). On older dunes Red Fescue *Festuca rubra* is dominant (Curtis 1991b), with lesser amounts of Marram present. Smooth Meadow-grass *Poa pratensis* and Creeping Bent *Agrostis stolonifera* may also be important, as are Common Bird's-foot-trefoil *Lotus corniculatus*, Lady's Bedstraw *Galium verum*, Kidney Vetch *Anthyllis vulneraria*, Hare's-foot Clover *Trifolium arvense*, Common Restharrow *Ononis repens*, Fairy Flax *Linum catharticum*, Common Centaury *Centaurium erythraea* and Common Dog-violet *Viola riviniana*. Shrubs become established on the older dunes, with Creeping Willow *Salix repens* and Burnet Rose *Rosa pimpinellifolia* being dominant, except on North Bull Island where this community has not developed.

Other important shrub species of the dunes include Gorse *Ulex europaeus* and Sea-buckthorn *Hippophae rhamnoides*, the latter an introduced shrub common at Rush and parts of Portrane. Sea-buckthorn stands are extremely dense and cast very deep shade and, as a result, their associated ground flora is species-poor or even absent. Where the stands are more open, Common Nettle *Urtica dioica* and Cleavers *Galium aparine* are often abundant. Almost certainly the association of Common Nettle (a nitrophilous species) with the Sea-buckthorn stands is due to the nitrogen fixing properties of the latter. The Sea-buckthorn at these sites is clearly spreading and may need to be controlled before it takes over too much of the dune systems.

Other species found in *Salix/Rosa* dune vegetation are Carline Thistle *Carlina vulgaris*, Harebell *Campanula rotundifolia*, Quaking-grass *Briza media*, Common Milkwort *Polygala vulgaris* and Eyebright *Euphrasia* spp.. Pyramidal Orchid *Anacamptis pyramidalis* is quite common and Bee Orchid *Ophrys apifera* is found in small numbers on North Bull Island, Malahide Island and Portmarnock Peninsula. The vegetation types discussed above grade into coastal grassland communities.

Dune-slacks: At North Bull Island, Malahide Island and Portrane the dune-slack vegetation has developed in the damper hollows between the fixed dune-ridges. Here, Creeping Bent *Agrostis stolonifera* is typically dominant with Smooth Meadow-grass *Poa pratensis*, Jointed Rush *Juncus articulatus*, Hard Rush *Juncus inflexus,* Glaucous Sedge *Carex flacca,* Silverweed *Potentilla anserina,* Creeping Buttercup *Ranunculus repens,* Yellow-rattle *Rhinanthus minor,* Selfheal *Prunella vulgaris* and Field Horsetail *Equisetum arvense.* In the wetter areas, such as the Alder Marsh on North Bull Island, Alder *Alnus glutinosa* and Grey Willow *Salix cinerea* subsp. *oleifolia* are common, with Marsh Pennywort *Hydrocotyle vulgaris,* Water Mint *Mentha aquatica,* Devil's-bit Scabious *Succisa pratensis,* Meadowsweet *Filipendula ulmaria,* Autumn Gentian *Gentianella amarella* and Adder's-tongue *Ophioglossum vulgatum* also plentiful. Marsh Helleborine *Epipactis palustris* and Early Marsh-orchid *Dactylorhiza incarnata* subsp. *coccinea* are found at several sites while Northern Marsh-orchid *D. purpurella* is reported only from the Alder Marsh. Green-flowered Helleborine *Epipactis phyllanthes* is occasionally seen at Portmarnock.

Rocky Cliffs

D. Nash, S. Reynolds and M. Sheehy Skeffington

The rocky cliffs of Co. Dublin are mostly hard acid quartzites typified by the rusty yellow rocks of Howth Head (5), or granites such as at Killiney (8). Hard and durable, they erode slowly, but, due to their high quartz mineralogy, they are also poor in nutrients and support a low species diversity. Nonetheless, the influence of sea spray tossed right up the cliffs provides for a rich intermingling of coastal and crag flora.

Many saltmarsh species, including Thrift *Armeria maritima*, Sea Plantain *Plantago maritima* and Sea Aster *Aster tripolium*, thrive on coastal cliffs, as well as species more common on shingle or rocky shores, such as Sea Beet *Beta vulgaris* subsp. *maritima*, Rock Samphire *Crithmum maritimum*, Golden-samphire *Inula crithmoides*, Rock Sea-spurrey *Spergularia rupicola*, Sea Pearlwort *Sagina maritima* and Sea Campion *Silene uniflora*. A fern, Sea Spleenwort *Asplenium marinum*, common in coastal rock crevices elsewhere in Ireland, is surprisingly rare in Co. Dublin and seems to have its headquarters around the east side of Howth Head from the Nose of Howth to Drumleck. English Stonecrop *Sedum anglicum* and Biting Stonecrop *S. acre*, plants characteristic of rocks, wall tops and dry areas, are frequent. Where the gradient allows, a closed turf can form, often on pockets of glacial drift which may be more fertile. Here the sward is dominated by Red Fescue *Festuca rubra* and includes some coastal species along with grassland species such as Common Bird's-foot-trefoil *Lotus corniculatus*, Autumn Hawkbit *Leontodon autumnalis*, Ribwort Plantain *Plantago lanceolata*, Cat's-ear *Hypochaeris radicata* and Clovers *Trifolium* spp. Several nationally rare clovers are found in this habitat: Rough Clover *Trifolium scabrum* is found, for example, at Red Island, Skerries (2) and on Dalkey Island (8); and sites for Western Clover *Trifolium occidentale* include Red Island, Howth Head and Dalkey Island.

Species which are characteristic of acid rocks and soils include Goldenrod *Solidago virgaurea* and Sheep's-bit *Jasione montana*. A peculiar prostrate form of Broom *Cytisus scoparius* subsp. *maritimus*, which is found on some exposed coasts in Ireland, occurs on Howth. Inland, sheltered from direct exposure to sea spray, heathland is often present, especially on Howth Head. This supports species such as Heather *Calluna vulgaris*, Bell Heather *Erica cinerea*, Wood Sage *Teucrium scorodonia* and Western Gorse *Ulex gallii*. When this heath burns, as frequently occurs on Howth, it is colonised by a mixture of heath and coastal species. Sea plantain *Plantago maritima*, Thrift *Armeria maritima*, Rock Sea-spurrey *Spergularia rupicola*, Biting Stonecrop *Sedum acre*, Heath Groundsel *Senecio sylvaticus*, Gorse *Ulex europaeus* and Western Gorse *U. gallii* are among the first colonisers.

The cliffs in the Killiney area and on Howth abound with garden escapes and naturalized aliens from different parts of the world. At Killiney, Silver Ragwort *Senecio cineraria* (from the Mediterranean) and its hybrid with Common Ragwort *S. jacobaea* are conspicuous, while on Howth Head the fleshy-leaved Hottentot-fig *Carpobrotus edulis* (from South Africa), with its magenta-coloured flowers, has spread on the cliffsides. Hedge Veronica *Hebe* x *franciscana* (of horticultural origin and of New Zealand parentage) is self-sown around Sorrento Point and is also abundant on the south side of Howth with other garden escapes which include Three-cornered Garlic *Allium triquetrum*, Snow-in-summer *Cerastium tomentosum*, Red-hot-poker *Kniphofia* sp., Montbretia *Crocosmia* x *crocosmiiflora*, Greater Periwinkle *Vinca major* and Chilean-iris *Libertia formosa*.

Boulder Clay Banks and Deeper Coastal Soils
D. Nash, S. Reynolds and
M. Sheehy Skeffington

Much of the coastline north of Dublin City is dominated by glacial deposits. The clay banks are low and are more susceptible to erosion than those formed of rock. As the deposits are often derived from adjacent limestone, the soils are neutral to alkaline. Where the soils are not over-influenced by fertiliser run-off from adjacent fields, they can be quite species-rich. Many of the saltmarsh and sea cliff species are again present here. Where freshwater from the land mixes with seawater or sea-spray, brackish water species such as Saltmarsh Flat-sedge *Blysmus rufus* and Parsley Water-dropwort *Oenanthe lachenalii*, Brookweed *Samolus valerandi* and, very rarely, Wild Celery *Apium graveolens* may be found. The drains from the land contain brackish water and Sea Club-rush *Bolboschoenus maritimus* is found in them. Typically on the clay banks at the edge of agricultural land there is a more closed grassland sward, dominated usually by Red Fescue *Festuca rubra*. If the sward is not too tall, a delight in May is the relatively rare Spring Squill *Scilla verna*, which carpets areas along the cliff paths at Portrane (3), Howth (5) and on Lambay Island (3), Ireland's Eye (5) and Dalkey Island (8). Another colourful species, more commonly associated with the Burren in Co. Clare, is the Bloody Crane's-bill *Geranium sanguineum*, which seems to have had a more widespread coastal distribution in the county (Colgan 1904) and is now largely confined to cliffs on Howth and at Killiney (8). Slightly poorer grasslands may be colonised by Burnet Rose *Rosa pimpinellifolia*. Bracken *Pteridium aquilinum* frequently invades rough open areas away from direct spray. It flourishes on Ireland's Eye, often reaching well over 1 m in height. This provides a canopy for a woodland-type flora, and Bluebell *Hyacinthoides non-scripta* is prolific there in the spring. On deeper, fairly neutral soils where grazing is light, grasses can be fairly tall and rank, dominated by Creeping Bent *Agrostis stolonifera* and Cock's-foot *Dactylis glomerata*. Tall herbs such as Common Knapweed *Centaurea nigra*, the predominately coastal umbellifer Alexanders *Smyrnium olusatrum*, Creeping Thistle *Cirsium arvense*, Wild Carrot *Daucus carota* and Yarrow *Achillea millefolium* also thrive. Where scrub develops, it is often dominated by Blackthorn *Prunus spinosa* and Bramble *Rubus fruticosus* agg., with Elder *Sambucus nigra* in more sheltered areas. Ivy *Hedera helix* is common on the ground and, along with Honeysuckle *Lonicera periclymenum*, climbs the few stunted trees which may be present. Calcicoles such as Lady's Bedstraw *Galium verum*, Carline Thistle *Carlina vulgaris*, Restharrow *Ononis repens*, Glaucous Sedge *Carex flacca*, and the ferns Hart's-tongue *Phyllitis scolopendrium* and Soft Shield-fern *Polystichum setiferum* occur in these coastal areas, and also on Howth's grassy cliff slopes, confirming the presence locally of limestone-derived glacial drift.

GRASSLANDS

Most of the lowland areas of Co. Dublin have underlying carboniferous rock with overlying grey brown podzolic or gley soils, thus providing agricultural land that is either neutral or calcareous (Fig. 3 and Fig. 4). These soils, with the provision of some drainage where needed, are productive as grassland and for other agricultural and horticultural crops. In upland areas the underlying neutral or acid rock, in combination with higher rainfall and leaching, result in soils which are more acidic and less productive.

In the 20th century there has been substantial loss of agricultural land due to urbanisation and industrialisation and substantial changes in agricultural practice (Table 4). The amount of land in agricultural use has declined by a third since 1926. The area under corn, other tillage crops and upland conifer forestry has increased. There has been a shift from haymaking to silage production. The latter change, especially where the meadow is cut more than once in the season, has resulted in a decline of hay meadow species. Pasture area has declined dramatically and the rough grazing area has also been reduced in the past thirty years. There has been a substantial increase in the use of fertilisers, a re-seeding of many pastures, an extension in drainage and reclamation using modern machinery and equipment, and a widespread use of herbicides for weed control in pasture and tillage. Fertilisation of grassland, often accompanied by liming to raise the pH, generally results in a decline in species diversity because many plants cannot successfully compete with the more vigorous grasses which then dominate. While the total number of cattle has declined by a third there has been an upsurge in the number of sheep with almost a doubling of numbers. Many of these changes have been accelerated by the European Union Common Agricultural Policy which, together with financial incentives for afforestation, have had very significant qualitative and quantitative impacts on the flora of the county.

Table 4. Land Usage in Co. Dublin (units of 1000 hectares) (1)

Year	1926	1960	1975	1980	1995
Agricultural total	76.8*	68.4	62.5	57.9	50.8
Ploughed	9.5	16.2	18.8	22.6	24.0
Hay	15.8	10.9	10.3	9.4	4.3(a), 3.6(b)
Pasture	51.6	41.4	29.3	22.8	16.9
Rough grazing	-	-	4.1	3.1	2.0
Other land	15.3*	23.8*	29.7	34.3	41.4

(1) from (Anon. 1926-95)   * = estimated   (a) = silage   (b) = hay

Today, there are relatively few areas of 'natural' or unimproved lowland grassland in the county. The fragments that do remain are generally in marginal areas such as woodland fringes, banks in steep-sided valleys and coastal areas that for a variety of reasons have escaped improvement. The uplands generally have more acidic soils, although in some areas limestone glacial drift has been deposited. While some upland areas have been improved, there remains a substantial area of acid grassland which often merges into moor and heath. Bracken, which has spread significantly during the 20th century, dominates in some areas.

Unimproved Calcareous Grassland   R. Fitzgerald

Examples of unimproved sites may be found in the Phoenix Park near the Magazine Fort (4), along the Grand Canal at Gollierstown (6), the Royal Canal at Clonsilla (4), on seaside cliffs and banks at Loughshinny (2) and at Killiney (8). The coastal sand-dune systems in the north of the county are described in an earlier section. Some of the above sites have a characteristic calcicole flora, while other areas are more neutral often as a consequence of leaching. Sometimes, in areas which were formerly grazed by cattle or sheep, populations of rabbits have helped to maintain diversity.

In the Phoenix Park, calcareous grassland is found east of Chapelizod Gate, especially on the grassy banks and slopes. Here Salad Burnet *Sanguisorba minor* is common and Pale Flax *Linum bienne* together with Fairy Flax *L. catharticum* are found on the lower banks. Wild Thyme *Thymus polytrichus*, Common Milkwort *Polygala vulgaris*, Burnet-saxifrage *Pimpinella saxifraga*, Mouse-ear Hawkweed *Pilosella officinarum*, Common Bird's-foot-trefoil *Lotus corniculatus*, Common Restharrow *Ononis repens*, Bulbous Buttercup *Ranunculus bulbosus* and Lady's Bedstraw *Galium verum* are also represented here. Grasses typical of calcareous habitats found include Yellow Oat-grass *Trisetum flavescens*, Downy Oat-grass *Helictotrichon pubescens*, Erect Brome *Bromopsis erecta* and Quaking-grass *Briza media*. They are accompanied by Timothy *Phleum pratense,* Hairy Violet *Viola hirta* a Protected Species, and the orchid Autumn Lady's-tresses *Spiranthes spiralis*. Where substantial leaching has occurred the flora changes and a typical grass then found is Heath-grass *Danthonia decumbens*.

Rough ground along the Grand Canal at Gollierstown, modified by quarrying related to canal construction, has escaped the intensive agricultural interventions suffered by the adjacent fields. The wide variety of plants that grow here includes Yellow Oat-grass *Trisetum flavescens*, Eyebrights *Euphrasia* spp., Autumn Hawkbit *Leontodon autumnalis*, Pyramidal Orchid *Anacamptis pyramidalis*, Black Medick *Medicago lupulina*, Common Bird's-foot-trefoil *Lotus corniculatus* and Salad Burnet *Sanguisorba minor*. They are accompanied by widespread species such as Red Clover *Trifolium pratense*, Yarrow *Achillea millefolium*, Ribwort Plantain *Plantago lanceolata*, Glaucous Sedge *Carex flacca*, Silverweed *Potentilla anserina* and Creeping Thistle *Cirsium arvense*. A similar range of species may be found along the Royal Canal at Clonsilla. Gollierstown is also home to the Autumn Gentian *Gentianella amarella* and the Irish Whitebeam *Sorbus hibernica*. The latter tree, rare in the east of Ireland, grows on the edge of one of the quarries.

At Loughshinny, unimproved pasture grazed by cattle slopes gently down to the beach. Bulbous Buttercup *Ranunculus bulbosus*, Red Clover *Trifolium pratense*, Common Bird's-foot-trefoil *Lotus corniculatus*, Fairy Flax *Linum catharticum*, Germander Speedwell *Veronica chamaedrys*, Eyebrights *Euphrasia* spp. and Yarrow *Achillea millefolium* are some of the commonest herbs present. The most frequent grasses are Yorkshire-fog *Holcus lanatus,* Cock's-foot *Dactylis glomerata,* Perennial Rye-grass *Lolium perenne* and Meadow Fescue *Festuca pratensis.* The absence of some of the species found at Gollierstown and the presence of species such as Common Sorrel *Rumex acetosa* indicate the more neutral soils.

At Killiney, the steep seaward facing banks above the Vico Bathing Place are covered with well-drained limestone glacial drift. The grasses include Red Fescue *Festuca rubra,* Upright Brome *Bromopsis erecta,* Cock's-foot *Dactylis glomerata,* False Brome *Brachypodium sylvaticum* and Tall Fescue *Festuca arundinacea.* The variety of plants, frequently associated with calcareous soils, found here include Salad Burnet *Sanguisorba minor,* Wild Carrot *Daucus carota,* Wild Thyme *Thymus polytrichus,* Kidney Vetch *Anthyllis vulneraria,* Bloody Crane's-bill *Geranium sanguineum,* Burnet Rose *Rosa pimpinellifolia* and Lady's Bedstraw *Galium verum.*

Improved Calcareous Grassland   R. Fitzgerald

Most of the grassland in the county may be described as improved or modified. Frequently the changes are substantial where hedgerows have been removed to make larger fields and to facilitate the use of ever larger machinery, pipes have been laid to improve drainage of wetter areas and re-seeding has taken place. Re-seeding frequently results in botanically uninteresting fields, dominated by Perennial Rye-grass and White Clover, suitable for intensive fertilisation, strip-grazing by cattle and silage production. The use of selective herbicides to control Thistles *Cirsium* spp., Common Ragwort *Senecio jacobaea* and Docks *Rumex* spp. has had a devastating effect on grassland flora. However, where the land has not been so intensively managed, modified or fertilised, or where cultivation has been discontinued and land has been allowed to revert to pasture and a less managed regime, the changes in the flora have not been quite so catastrophic and a greater diversity is found. A small number of grasses tend to dominate and occasional weedy species are found. The most common grasses are Perennial Rye-grass *Lolium perenne,* Yorkshire-fog *Holcus lanatus,* Creeping Bent *Agrostis stolonifera* and Cock's-foot *Dactylis glomerata.* Often, Timothy *Phleum pratense* (a vigorous grass which in the past was often sown in hayfields), False Oat-grass *Arrhenatherum elatius* (a species of disturbed soils) and Common Couch *Elytrigia repens* (a scourge in the tilled field and the garden plot) are present. Common Knapweed *Centaurea nigra,* Creeping Thistle *Cirsium arvense,* Creeping Buttercup *Ranunculus repens,* Yarrow *Achillea millefolium* and Dandelion *Taraxacum officinale* agg. may also thrive. The latter two species, with their deep tap roots, flourish following dry summers. Where originally sown or where fertilisation is absent, the nitrogen-fixing White and Red Clovers *Trifolium repens* and *T. pratense* enrich the soils. If grassland is lightly grazed or abandoned for farming, succession commences with the spread of scrub, as the native species, Brambles *Rubus fruticosus* agg., Hawthorn *Crataegus monogyna,* Blackthorn *Prunus spinosa* and Gorse *Ulex europaeus,* attempt to reverse human modification of the vegetation.

Acid Grassland   Peter Wyse Jackson and D. Nash

Acid grasslands often develop in uplands where the underlying rocks are siliceous. These rocks are very hard and consequently weather slowly to form thinnish soils which are quite deficient in minerals such as calcium (lime) and magnesium. The soils are acidic in nature, often with a pH in the range 4 to 5 or lower. In addition, uplands are usually subject to higher rainfall than the adjacent lowlands. Higher rainfall increases soil leaching and further augments mineral scarcity. Acid grasslands occur throughout Europe especially in the Atlantic, sub-Atlantic and sub-continental regions. They have a relatively low diversity of plant species as a consequence of their soil mineral deficiencies. The commonest associated grass species are Mat-grass *Nardus stricta*, the Bent grasses *Agrostis canina* and *A. capillaris*, Sheep's Fescue *Festuca ovina* and Sweet Vernal-grass *Anthoxanthum odoratum*, which may be present in different proportions (Riely and Page 1990).

It is difficult to draw a definitive line between heath and acid grassland vegetation in parts of Co. Dublin without recourse to detailed vegetational analysis and classification. Many heaths contain small or large areas of acid grassland and indeed many former acid grasslands have subsequently reverted to being heaths into which Western Gorse *Ulex gallii* and ericaceous species, such as Heather *Calluna vulgaris*, Bell Heather *Erica cinerea* and Bilberry *Vaccinium myrtillus*, have spread when agricultural management has faltered. Similarly, many acid grasslands have been transformed into Bracken *Pteridium aquilinum*-dominated vegetation. Extensive conifer afforestation has resulted in a further reduction of acid grassland. The major agricultural usage of the remaining acid grasslands has been for rough grazing for sheep (Table 4) which has increased in intensity in recent years. In areas where grazing pressure is high, there has been a consequent expansion of Mat-grass *Nardus stricta,* a tough wiry species generally unpalatable to sheep. The expansion of Mat-grass is also a consequence of changes in sheep stocking policies, encouraged by the European Union Common Agricultural Policy Headage Payment Schemes. Wethers do eat this grass, but they have been replaced for economic reasons by ewes and lambs which avoid it (M.J. Sheehy Skeffington pers. comm.).

In the uplands to the south of the county in Districts 6, and especially in 7 and 8, there is still a significant amount of acid grassland. In much of Districts 7 and 8 the underlying rock is Leinster Granite, and here acid soils have developed, namely brown podzolics on the lower slopes which grade into peaty podzols on higher ground (Fig. 4). The annual average rainfall is 1272 mm, or more, per annum in Glenasmole compared to, for example, 761 mm in the Phoenix Park. Examples of acid grassland may be found in the Glencullen valley (8) and on Tallaght Hill (6 and 7). In the less-elevated District 6, the Mat-grass component is absent. These grasslands have developed on dark peaty soils and fall within what Pethybridge and Praeger (1905) termed the "hill-pasture zone" in their classic paper on the vegetation of the district lying south of Dublin city, a zone that ranges in altitude from 300 m to about 400 m. Small areas of acid grassland also occurred in Colgan's time in the north of the county, most notably on Lambay Island (3) and Howth Head (5). More intensive farming now takes places on Lambay and this vegetation community has disappeared. On Howth Head there has been much human interference - urban and golf-course development, periodic burning - and Bracken has extended to areas no longer grazed. Consequently acid grassland is now effectively confined to the most southerly part of the county.

A site in District 8, on the south side of the Glencullen River south-east of Boranaraltry Bridge, is a typical example of sheep-grazed *Agrostis-Festuca* acid grassland with tufts of Mat-grass. Grasses found there include Common Bent *Agrostis capillaris*, Red Fescue *Festuca rubra*, Sheep's Fescue *F. ovina*, Sweet Vernal-grass *Anthoxanthum odoratum*, Crested Dog's-tail *Cynosurus cristatus*, Smooth

Meadow-grass *Poa pratensis* and Yorkshire-fog *Holcus lanatus*. Heath Bedstraw *Galium saxatile* and Tormentil *Potentilla erecta*, both characteristic acid grassland species, occur together with Soft-rush *Juncus effusus*, Sorrel *Rumex acetosa*, Creeping Buttercup *Ranunculus repens* and Meadow Buttercup *R. acris*. The site also contains some Heath Rush *Juncus squarrosus* and Green-ribbed Sedge *Carex binervis*, and gradually makes the transition into heathland with Heather *Calluna vulgaris*, Bilberry *Vaccinium myrtillus*, Great Wood-rush *Luzula sylvatica* and Western Gorse *Ulex gallii*.

Bracken–dominated Communities   C. Brady

Bracken *Pteridium aquilinum* has a world-wide distribution. It is an unusual fern in that it can become an invasive weed; its potentially prolific spore production (each fertile frond may yield 30 million spores) and robust rhizomes, which have the ability to withstand periodic burning, make it very difficult to eradicate. Livestock avoid eating the living plants which are poisonous, but Bracken remains toxic in hay and silage. Recent reports suggest that the spores may also be carcinogenic.

Bracken is most commonly found on the dry acid soils of heathland and abandoned farmland, in woods and on sand-dunes. In Co. Dublin, Bracken-dominated vegetation is widespread and ranges from almost sea level to about 500 m. It is particularly frequent in three areas of the county: on the mountains in the south (7 and 8), in coastal heathlands on the Howth peninsula and Ireland's Eye (5) and on the sand-dunes of the north coast, for example at Corballis and Portrane (3). In the uplands, it is often the dominant vegetation on the sides of sheltered valleys, stopping just short of the exposed ridges and wet moorland. Above Glenasmole (7), Bracken reaches its highest altitude in the ravines of Cot Brook and the River Dodder valley where associated ferns are Lady-fern *Athyrium filix-femina* and Lemon-scented Fern *Oreopteris limbosperma*. In places in the Glencullen valley (8), patches of Bracken grow with Green-ribbed Sedge *Carex binervis* and Wavy Hair-grass *Deschampsia flexuosa* among Heather *Calluna vulgaris* and Bilberry *Vaccinium myrtillus*. In a quite different kind of habitat, Bracken is a characteristic species under Larch *Larix* spp. in conifer plantations.

Bracken dies down in the autumn and so the most commonly associated plants are spring flowering species which appear before a dense canopy forms again in the summer. On the lower slopes of the sheltered valleys the herb layer, otherwise typically found in deciduous woodlands, includes Bluebell *Hyacinthoides non-scripta*, Wood-sorrel *Oxalis acetosella* and Common Dog-violet *Viola riviniana*. Later in the year only tall plants, or those with a climbing habit, can compete with the canopy. These include Honeysuckle *Lonicera periclymenum*, Brambles *Rubus fruticosus* agg. and Greater Stitchwort *Stellaria holostea*. The accumulation of plant litter under Bracken also inhibits the growth of other plants.

Pethybridge and Praeger (1905) surveyed the vegetation of the uplands in the southern part of the county at the beginning of the 20th century and mapped and photographed areas covered by Bracken. Moore (1960) resurveyed and compared the same areas. He noted that Bracken had spread extensively especially on rough grazing, in recently planted forest, and on abandoned farmland where it favoured areas which had been cultivated and where the A_o horizon (mixed mineral-organic matter near soil surface) had been broken up and mixed with the coarse glacial drift underneath. The invasive nature of Bracken can be clearly seen in former pastures and abandoned farmland in the Glenasmole valley. Here it is associated with acid grassland species such as Tormentil *Potentilla erecta*, Bent *Agrostis canina* and Heath Bedstraw *Galium saxatile*. Old cultivation patterns, including "lazy beds", can still be seen beneath Bracken, and arable species such as Corn Spurrey *Spergula arvensis* persist.

The coastal heathland of Howth Head sustains a most extensive Bracken community. After heathland has been burnt, a regular occurrence during dry summers, some of the first colonisers are Heath Groundsel *Senecio sylvaticus*, Rosebay Willowherb *Chamerion angustifolium* and English Stonecrop *Sedum anglicum*. They are quickly replaced by Bracken and a wider range of herbs before Bracken finally becomes dominant. The sheltered west side of Ireland's Eye (5) holds another example of a coastal Bracken-dominated community. Here its associates are the early-flowering Bluebell *Hyacinthoides non-scripta*, Primrose *Primula vulgaris* and Pignut *Conopodium majus*. Bracken does not grow on the rocky outcrops or amongst the bird colonies. It was formerly more widespread on Lambay Island (3) which is now farmed quite intensively.

Bracken forms extensive communities on the sand-dunes along the north coast of the county where it is accompanied by Harebell *Campanula rotundifolia*, Primrose *Primula vulgaris* and Red Fescue *Festuca rubra*. On older dunes which are lightly grazed, it forms a complete cover with Gorse *Ulex europaeus* and Bramble *Rubus fruticosus* agg., but it does not grow in short rabbit-grazed turf. In sheltered areas on the Portrane Peninsula, it grows among Marram *Ammophila arenaria* and Lyme-grass *Leymus arenarius*, almost on the shore.

Finally, Bracken is found elsewhere throughout the county on roadside banks, in fallow fields and wasteground. It also occurs occasionally in the inner city growing on old mortared walls and elsewhere.

HEATHLAND AND MOORLAND

Extensive areas of upland in south Co. Dublin in Districts 7 and 8 are covered with heath and moorland vegetation. Heathland occurs on the drier slopes and on Howth (5); elsewhere moorland is found where there is an accumulation of acid peat, leading to the development of blanket bog on the gentler slopes. Although the peat is generally relatively thin (< 2 m), it has been extensively cut for fuel, so that the natural vegetation patterns are replaced by a mosaic of regenerating wetter patches separated by drier banks of peat. Other expanses of moorland have been drained, fertilised and planted with coniferous trees. Only the most remote areas remain undisturbed.

Heathland   E. Nic Lughadha

On fairly well-drained acid soils, between about 65 and 450 m altitude, a type of vegetation called dwarf-shrub heath develops. A good example is to be found on Howth Head where Heather *Calluna vulgaris*, Bell Heather *Erica cinerea* and Western Gorse *Ulex gallii* are the most important species, though their proportions differ from site to site. This sort of heathland is also found in the south of the county, for example, on Three Rock Mountain and the south-facing slopes of Two Rock Mountain above the road through the Glencullen Valley, where Bilberry *Vaccinium myrtillus* may also be a component. Dwarf-shrub heath intergrades with acid grassland above the farmland to the south-east of the Glenasmole Reservoirs. In the Dublin mountains, Western Gorse *U. gallii* declines in frequency both below about 300 m, being replaced by Gorse *Ulex europaeus*, and above 400 m where it gives way, at least on reasonably well-drained slopes, to Heather *C. vulgaris*. Bracken *Pteridium aquilinum* does not usually invade heathland where Heather is well established.

In general, the appearance of heathland can be described as a mosaic of mats or tussocks of some or all of the shrubby species mentioned above. This is often interspersed with more open, grassy areas of Bent *Agrostis* spp. and Sheep's-fescue *Festuca ovina*, with occasional broad-leaved herbs such as Heath Bedstraw *Galium saxatile* and Tormentil *Potentilla erecta*. The extent of these grassy spaces and the composition and height of the Western Gorse and the heathers vary considerably with time. Much of this variation may be attributed to the effects of grazing and burning, the chief events which shape and maintain this type of vegetation. In the Dublin mountains some heathland is regularly, carefully and deliberately burned to promote the growth of grass, herbs and young nutritious shoots of gorse and heather for grazing. In contrast, on Howth Head, fires occur at irregular intervals and they may be intense and long-lasting. Unless exceptionally high temperatures are reached, both Heather *Calluna vulgaris* and Western Gorse *Ulex gallii* survive vegetatively and grow back slowly. Bell Heather *Erica cinerea*, on the other hand, re-establishes itself quickly, chiefly from seed, and usually becomes dominant in the years immediately following a fire. Sheep's Sorrel *Rumex acetosella*, Heath Milkwort *Polygala serpyllifolia* and Common Dog-violet *Viola riviniana* are often conspicuous during this time, as are the grasses and herbs listed earlier. These early colonisers are eventually crowded out by the developing Western Gorse and/or Heather which form dense mats up to about 30 cm tall. As time goes on the plants become taller and more leggy, but rarely exceed 80 cm. Where the common Gorse *Ulex europaeus* is present, it can reach heights of 2 m, forming miniature woodlands in disturbed heathlands. However, it is not a typical plant of dwarf-shrub heath communities, being more characteristic of poor grassland. Its occurrence in both habitats confirms that it is often difficult to draw a line between heathland and rough grassland.

Moorland   J. Reynolds and S. Reynolds
Moorland/blanket bog occurs where there is an accumulation of acid peat, with a calcifuge flora including the characteristic *Sphagnum* moss species. It should be noted that in the Systematic List in this *Flora*, a distinction has not been made between moorland and blanket bog and that the terms are often used interchangeably.

Moorland, usually found over 300 m in the county, is rarely dominated by a single species, but rather there is a mosaic of different dominants interspersed with patches of *Sphagnum* moss. On the drier expanses of moorland, Heather *Calluna vulgaris* is often abundant, even on deep peat. In the wetter areas, Heather and Bell Heather *Erica cinerea* decline in frequency and

Cross-leaved Heath *Erica tetralix* increases, together with Common Cottongrass *Eriophorum angustifolium*, Hare's-tail Cottongrass *E. vaginatum* and Deergrass *Trichophorum cespitosum*. Other commonly associated calcifuge species are Bilberry *Vaccinium myrtillus*, Heath Rush *Juncus squarrosus*, Purple Moor-grass *Molinia caerulea* and Green-ribbed Sedge *Carex binervis*. In wet flushes, where there is some mineral enrichment, a greater variety of plants is found including Bog Asphodel *Narthecium ossifragum*, Bog Pondweed *Potamogeton polygonifolius*, Bog Pimpernel *Anagallis tenella*, Common Butterwort *Pinguicula vulgaris*, Pale Butterwort *P. lusitanica* and Round-leaved Sundew *Drosera rotundifolia* as well as the sedges *Carex panicea, C. nigra* and *C. viridula* subsp. *oedocarpa*. The best developed blanket bog in Co. Dublin is in the southern part of District 7 on the slopes of Kippure and Seefingan. However, it is badly eroded on the ridge between the summits of the two mountains, leaving prominent peat hags. Elsewhere, extensive peat cutting has removed the bog surface and Soft-rush *Juncus effusus*, which thrives in disturbed wet ground, becomes a conspicuous component of the flora.

Among the mountain plants of south Co. Dublin, Crowberry *Empetrum nigrum* is widespread and Lesser Twayblade *Listera cordata* is quite common on Two Rock Mountain and Prince William's Seat (8). Several other species are rare: three Clubmosses, *Huperzia selago, Lycopodium clavatum* and *Diphasiastrum alpinum*, grow on peat near the summit of Seahan (7) and there are small patches of Bog-rosemary *Andromeda polifolia* near the summit of Kippure (7) and between Glendoo and Glencullen Mountains (8). Starry Saxifrage *Saxifraga stellaris*, still occurring by the Slade Brook and River Dodder above Glenasmole (7) and Cowberry *Vaccinium vitis-idaea*, still near the summits of Kippure and Seahan (7), were considered by Colgan (1904) to be the only true alpine plants in Co. Dublin. Cranberry *Vaccinium oxycoccos* persists in blanket bog on Glendoo (7) at about 575 m; it is more usually found in lowland bogs in Ireland.

WETLANDS

Lakes, Reservoirs and Ponds   D. Nash
Almost all of the standing waters of Co. Dublin, being usually reservoirs, quarry ponds, golf hazards or ornamental features, owe their origins to human activity. While many of the former quarry and estate ponds have disappeared or are no longer maintained, those that remain make a valuable contribution to the maintenance of the diversity of aquatic life in the county.

The largest area of open water is formed by the Bohernabreena reservoirs in Glenasmole (7) which were completed in 1887 for the Rathmines Town Commissioners. The reservoirs collect some water from the immediate sides of the valley but the main source of water is the River Dodder which has been diverted and canalised in order to keep the reservoirs topped up. The surface waters of the Upper (Southern) Reservoir have been found to have a mean pH value of 7.5 (A. McNally pers. comm.) and a low alkalinity value of *c.* 2 meq / litre (King and Nash 1994) and are quite low in nutrients. The Upper Reservoir, with a surface area of 23 hectares (Moriarty 1991), for the most part, has its margins lined with either stone or concrete. Levels are subject to fluctuation with water demand. Canadian Waterweed *Elodea canadensis* is very plentiful and other macrophytes (large submerged plants) found are Thread-leaved Water-crowfoot *Ranunculus trichophyllus*, Curled Pondweed *Potamogeton crispus*, Perfoliate Pondweed *P. perfoliatus*, Amphibious Bistort *Persicaria amphibia* and the Stonewort *Nitella opaca*. Shoreweed *Littorella uniflora*, a county rarity, grows extensively on its western side. The northern end has muddy and marshy margins with Lesser Spearwort *Ranunculus flammula*, Marsh Woundwort *Stachys palustris* and Willows *Salix* spp. Two species of Bulrush, *Typha latifolia* and *T. angustifolia*, occur between the reservoirs. The Lower (Northern) Reservoir, which has been partially drained, contains a wide range of plants such as Water-starwort *Callitriche* spp., Common Spike-rush *Eleocharis palustris*, Water Mint *Mentha aquatica*, Water-pepper *Persicaria hydropiper* and Marsh Yellow-cress *Rorippa palustris* growing on the exposed mud. Water Sedge *Carex aquatilis* grows at the south end, at its only site in the county.

The two Brittas 'Ponds' just north of Brittas (6), which no longer function as reservoirs, have low alkalinity levels similar to that for Bohernabreena. Both ponds are now shallow with low gradients. Shoreweed *Littorella uniflora*, at its second Dublin location, extends to a depth of 0.5 metres. Macrophytes are abundant. Three species of Pondweed, Curled Pondweed *Potamogeton crispus* and the very similar looking Smaller and Lesser Pondweeds, *P. berchtoldii* and *P. pusillus*, Canadian Waterweed *Elodea canadensis* and Spiked Water-milfoil *Myriophyllum spicatum* thrive there. Amphibious Bistort *Persicaria amphibia* is found both in water and on land. On the west side, in the shallow water and margins of the northern pond, Water-plantain *Alisma plantago-aquatica*, Water Horsetail *Equisetum fluviatile*, Bottle Sedge *Carex rostrata* and Common Spike-rush *Eleocharis palustris* grow. In summers, when the levels are low, Red Goosefoot *Chenopodium rubrum* and Marsh Yellow-cress *Rorippa palustris* are plentiful on the shores.

At Gollierstown (6), beside the Grand Canal, there are several quarry ponds from which limestone was hewn for the construction of canal bridges. The pond waters are generally clear, deep and calcareous and dominated by the Stoneworts *Chara hispida* and *C. globularis*. Other submerged plants include Mare's-tail *Hippuris vulgaris*, Canadian Waterweed *Elodea canadensis*, Spiked Water-milfoil *Myriophyllum spicatum* and the rare Fan-leaved Water-crowfoot *Ranunculus circinatus*. Aquatic plants with floating leaves include Broad-leaved Pondweed *Potamogeton natans*, Common Duckweed *Lemna minor* and Lesser Marshwort *Apium inundatum*. Branched and Unbranched Bur-reed *Sparganium erectum* and *S. emersum*, Reed Sweet-grass *Glyceria maxima*, Common Spike-rush *Eleocharis palustris* and Common Club-rush *Schoenoplectus lacustris* extend from the shore for a short distance until the water abruptly deepens. The variety of aquatic plants that are found along the shore line include Lesser Water-parsnip *Berula erecta*, Celery-leaved Buttercup *Ranunculus sceleratus*, Water Mint *Mentha aquatica*, Common Sedge *Carex nigra* and False Fox-sedge *Carex otrubae*.

Balrothery Reservoir (2), just off the main road to Belfast, is no longer used as a water source and has become shallower and eutrophic, and vegetation has advanced from its shores. Greater Duckweed *Spirodela polyrhiza* is found along the edges amongst the marginal plants, at its only extant station in Co. Dublin. Amphibious Bistort *Persicaria amphibia*, Lesser

Pondweed *Potamogeton pusillus* and Common Water-crowfoot *Ranunculus aquatilis* are found in open water. The latter plant bears a certain morphological resemblance to its close relative Brackish Water-crowfoot *R. baudotii* which is usually found closer to the sea.

The Phoenix Park (4) contains five ponds in areas freely accessible to the public: the Glen Pond in the Furry Glen, the Quarry and Machinery Ponds near Mountjoy Cross, the Citadel (Dog) Pond and the People's Garden Pond. All are at least partially surrounded by trees, which include Evergreen Oak *Quercus ilex*. The presence of shade and decaying leaf litter limits the range of aquatic species present. Common plants such as Yellow Iris *Iris pseudacorus*, Fool's Water-cress *Apium nodiflorum* and Common Reed *Phragmites australis* are found. The submerged plants include Canadian Waterweed *Elodea canadensis*, Lesser Pondweed *Potamogeton pusillus* and two species of Stonewort *Chara* spp. The floating Water Fern *Azolla filiculoides* was once recorded in the Machinery Pond but is no longer there. Sweet-flag *Acorus calamus*, also found in Luttrellstown Lake, and Sea Club-rush *Bolboschoenus maritimus*, normally a brackish water plant, grow in the People's Garden Pond and it must be assumed that these were planted.

Ponds are a usual feature of the coastal golf-courses in Dublin. Some of them were developed for the utilitarian purpose of providing a water supply for the greens during the summer months; others merely serve as hazards for the inaccurate golfer. These ponds tend to be small, alkaline and quite rich in nutrients (King and Nash 1994). Each of these and the other coastal pools from Elm Park (Donnybrook) (8) to Donabate (3) has its own unique combination of plants. Common plants include Stoneworts *Chara* spp., Water-plantain *Alisma plantago-aquatica*, Duckweeds *Lemna minor* and *L. trisulca*, Spiked Water-milfoil *Myriophyllum spicatum*, Pondweeds *Potamogeton natans* and *P. berchtoldii* and Horned Pondweed *Zannichellia palustris*. On the damp margins, which extend as water levels drop, Bog Pimpernel *Anagallis tenella*, Early Marsh-orchid *Dactylorhiza incarnata*, Marsh Helleborine *Epipactis palustris* and the scarce Variegated Horsetail *Equisetum variegatum* sometimes occur. Brackish Water-crowfoot *Ranunculus baudotii* has been found in temporary pools at Baldoyle (5), at Portmarnock and on Portmarnock Golf-course (5). The latter contains Grey Club-rush *Schoenoplectus tabernaemontani*, which also grows in the Portmarnock Raceway Pond.

Additional ponds and lakes worthy of mention are: Abbotstown Lake (4) where the Stonewort *Nitella opaca* may be found; a pond at Mount Argus (7) containing the rare Rigid Hornwort *Ceratophyllum demersum*; Hynestown Reservoir (1) with Trifid Bur-marigold *Bidens tripartita* on its shoreline at its only Dublin site; a tiny pond in a field at Ballinascorney Gap (7) with Greater Spearwort *Ranunculus lingua*, Curly Waterweed *Lagarosiphon major* and New Zealand Pigmyweed *Crassula helmsii*; and the lake in the National Botanic Gardens (4) which contains the only Dublin station for the Stonewort *Nitella gracilis*, the two Waterweeds *Elodea canadensis* and *E. nuttallii* and New Zealand Pigmyweed *Crassula helmsii*. The latter plant, which is a native of New Zealand and Australia, has been commonly used in aquaria and discarded or planted in ponds in the United Kingdom from where it has escaped, spread rapidly and choked waterways. It is now considered to be a nuisance plant that should be, if at all possible, eliminated. It is already known in Co. Down and may be poised to spread extensively in Ireland in a manner similar to that of Canadian Waterweed *Elodea canadensis* in the 19th century.

Rivers and Canals   D. Nash

The Liffey, Dodder, Tolka and Broad Meadow are the main Dublin rivers. The Liffey, which is a river of medium current, is the largest and the deepest waterway offering the greatest variety of aquatic and riparian vegetation. The other shorter rivers, especially the Dodder which rises in the Dublin mountains, are subject to relatively greater and more rapid fluctuations in water levels which limit the variety and range of instream vegetation. The Grand and Royal Canals were built in the early 19th century for the transport of goods and were used until the 1950s when they became no longer commercially viable. The canals connect the Shannon with Dublin and are topped up by water sources on their journeys. Plants which typically may be found in marshes and wet areas abound along the margins.

Biological surveys carried out by the Environmental Protection Agency (Clabby *et al.* 1991, 1994) demonstrate that the Dublin rivers may be classified as being either 'slightly' or 'moderately polluted' with a consequent abundance of vegetation. Work on the trophic status of the canals (Caffrey and Allison 1998) shows that approximately 30% of the feeder streams exhibit moderate to high levels of pollution as indicated by elevated levels of phosphorus, although levels drop quite rapidly from the point of confluence to values slightly in excess of 20 mg / litre.

The River Liffey rises in Co. Wicklow on the slopes of Tonduff Mountain and eventually enters Co. Dublin between Leixlip and Lucan. Upstream from the Islandbridge weir (4 and 7), the river supports a variety of plant communities. Along its banks are found the trees Alder *Alnus glutinosa*, Willows *Salix* spp., Ash *Fraxinus excelsior*, Sycamore *Acer pseudoplatanus* and a variety of planted exotics in the contiguous gardens and woodlands. The tall grasses, Reed Canary-grass *Phalaris arundinacea* and Reed Sweet-grass *Glyceria maxima*, grow along its margins and Indian Balsam *Impatiens glandulifera*, a naturalised introduction from the Himalayas, is a conspicuous feature especially at Islandbridge. Common Club-rush *Schoenoplectus lacustris* occurs in slow moving water near Lucan (4 and 6) extending almost to mid-stream. The Flowering-rush *Butomus umbellatus*, a rare plant in Dublin, is plentiful in the millrace at Palmerston (7) and here and there mainly along the southern margin of the river to Islandbridge. An interesting range of pondweeds is found - Curled Pondweed *Potamogeton crispus*, Small Pondweed *P. berchtoldii*, Broad-leaved Pondweed *P. natans*, the hybrid Willow-leaved Pondweed *P. x salicifolius* (flourishing in the absence of both of its parents, *P. lucens* and *P. perfoliatus*) and Fennel Pondweed *P. pectinatus*. The latter species, which thrives in more enriched waters, forms luxuriant rafts stretching from one bank to the other in some of the riffles near the Strawberry Beds. Canadian Waterweed *Elodea canadensis* and Spiked Water-milfoil *Myriophyllum spicatum* are found in the quieter or deeper waters. Yellow Water-lily *Nuphar lutea* grows in the more sheltered parts and Arrowhead *Sagittaria sagittifolia* is found above the Islandbridge weir. Two kinds of Bur-reed *Sparganium erectum* and *S. emersum* may be seen, often with their underwater leaves bent with the current. Thread-leaved Water-crowfoot *Ranunculus trichophyllus*, the only aquatic member of the genus recently seen in the Dublin section of the river, grows around and below the weir at Lucan. One of the characteristic Liffey Valley plants, Green Figwort *Scrophularia umbrosa*, may be found along the river banks.

The Broad Meadow River has its estuary just east of Swords (3). The summer levels are frequently very low, allowing the botanist to walk upstream in mid-channel. Drainage has severely canalised the river. The filamentous green algae *Cladophora* and *Enteromorpha* extend as far upstream as Fieldstown House (1). Common Water-crowfoot *Ranunculus aquatilis* together with Horned Pondweed *Zannichellia palustris* are plentiful along most of the river. Hemlock Water-dropwort *Oenanthe crocata* is occasionally seen. Feeder drains contain Branched Bur-reed *Sparganium erectum*, Plicate Sweet-grass *Glyceria notata*, Water-cresses *Rorippa* spp., Fool's Water-cress *Apium nodiflorum*, Brooklime *Veronica beccabunga* and Water Mint *Mentha aquatica*.

The Tolka, which has its source in Co. Meath, flows east and enters Dublin Bay at Fairview (5). Near Mulhuddart (4), it has luxuriant marginal vegetation which includes Common Club-rush *Schoenoplectus lacustris* and Reed Sweet-grass *Glyceria maxima* and, instream, Curled Pondweed *Potamogeton crispus*, Canadian Waterweed *Elodea canadensis* and Various-leaved Water-starwort *Callitriche platycarpa*. Thread-leaved Water-crowfoot *Ranunculus trichophyllus* occurs at Cardiff's Bridge, Cabra, and in a side channel at the National Botanic Gardens (4) together with Nuttall's Waterweed *Elodea nuttallii*. The latter, an alien of North American origin, was first reported from here in the 1970s (Scannell 1977). Small Pondweed, *Potamogeton berchtoldii* and Horned Pondweed *Zannichellia palustris* are occasionally found in the Tolka.

The Dodder begins its journey to the sea just below the summit of Kippure and has a rocky or scoured gravelly bed which presents little opportunity for aquatic plant growth, except on its margins. The yellow Monkeyflower *Mimulus guttatus* is scattered here and there from Glenasmole (7) downstream. Scattered plants of Hemlock Water-dropwort *Oenanthe crocata* and Marsh Yellow-cress *Rorippa palustris* are found. Occasional gravel islands occur and on these a variety of terrestrial and marsh plants grow. Bulrush *Typha latifolia* is found at Firhouse weir (7), and Horned Pondweed *Zannichellia palustris* - a plant tolerant of nutrient enrichment - makes its first appearance. The deeper waters below Orwell Bridge (7 and 8), the result of a weir, contain curled Pondweed *Potamogeton crispus*, Fennel Pondweed *P. pectinatus*, Branched Bur-reed *Sparganium erectum* and two Waterweeds *Elodea canadensis* and *E. nuttallii*. At Ballsbridge and below the railway line near Lansdowne Road Station (8), the banks have extensive stands of Indian Balsam *Impatiens glandulifera* and Reed Canary-grass *Phalaris arundinacea*.

The Deansgrange Stream and the Shanganagh River both join the sea south of Killiney (8). The latter has an extensive stand of Giant Hogweed *Heracleum mantegazzianum* along its banks at Loughlinstown (8) and the former has Nuttall's Waterweed *Elodea nuttallii* in Kilbogget Park (8) and on the edge of Killiney beach (Reynolds and O'Reilly 1986). The Cammock River, and the Slade which merges with it, rises in the foothills of the Dublin mountains and, having been culverted in several places, joins the Liffey at Heuston Railway Station (7). The Cammock (6 and 7) contains Stream Water-crowfoot *Ranunculus penicillatus* and the Protected Species Opposite-leaved Pondweed *Groenlandia densa* (Wyse Jackson 1988).

The Royal Canal joins Termonbarry, Co. Longford, with the Liffey at Spencer Dock (4 and 5) in Dublin City at its eastern end. Along its course it receives water from Lough Owel near Mullingar. Its waters are alkaline with a mean pH value of 8.0 and a moderately high alkalinity value of 4.2 meq/litre (Caffrey and Allison 1998). The flora of the canal has been much disturbed, especially during the decade from the late 1980s, by road building, dredging, the use of weedkillers and the deposition of refuse. A number of species found in the canal which appear to be migrants from the midlands include Greater Spearwort *Ranunculus lingua*. Tubular Water-dropwort *Oenanthe fistulosa*, once a common canal plant, has not been seen in Co. Dublin since its Clonsilla (4) site was destroyed by dredging in 1988. It is now rare in the canal west of Co. Dublin. Fan-leaved Water-crowfoot *Ranunculus circinatus* has been noted west of Clonsilla. Stoneworts *Chara* spp., *Tolypella intricata* and *Nitella opaca* were plentiful in the canal shortly after dredging (Nash and King 1993, King and Nash 1994) and before the application of herbicides. Most of these Stoneworts probably have their origins in the calcareous midland lakes. However the origin of *T. intricata*, a Red Data Book species (Stewart and Church 1992), in Ireland known only from canals, is obscure (Praeger 1934). Bulrush *Typha latifolia*, Sweet-grasses *Glyceria* spp., Bottle Sedge *Carex rostrata*, Yellow Iris *Iris pseudacorus* and Common Club-rush *Schoeneoplectus lacustris* are characteristic fringing plants. The Water-milfoils *Myriophyllum spicatum* and *M. verticillatum*, Mare's-tail *Hippuris vulgaris*, Curled Pondweed *Potamogeton crispus* and Horned Pondweed *Zannichellia palustris* form the submerged macrophyte community. Plants with floating leaves include Duckweeds *Lemna minor* and *L. trisulca*, Broad-leaved Pondweed *Potamogeton natans* and Yellow Water-lily *Nuphar lutea*.

The Grand Canal links the Shannon at Shannon Harbour near Banagher, Co. Offaly, to the Liffey at Grand Canal Harbour, Ringsend after encircling part of the south side of the city. Pollardstown Fen, Co. Kildare, is an important source of mineral rich water which is used to maintain water levels. The canal has a mean pH value of 8.1 and a moderately high alkalinity value of 5.0 meq / litre (Caffrey and Allison 1998). It has the richest flora of any of Dublin's waterways and contains representatives of almost all of the aquatic plants found elsewhere in the county. Rigid Hornwort *Ceratophyllum demersum*, an uncommon plant in Ireland first reported from Dublin by Scannell (1971), is the dominant species in Grand Canal Harbour. Opposite-leaved Pondweed *Groenlandia densa*, a Protected Species, is found westwards to the Naas road (and also in the Cammock River which runs along the canal for a short distance). The flowers of Canadian Waterweed *Elodea canadensis* and Spiked Water-milfoil *Myriophyllum spicatum* can sometimes be seen projecting from the water in summer, together with the white flowers of Fan-leaved Water-crowfoot *Ranunculus circinatus* which is found westwards from Baggot Street at least as far as Gollierstown. The Pondweeds include Small Pondweed *Potamogeton berchtoldii*, Curled Pondweed *P. crispus* and Fennel Pondweed *P. pectinatus*. Stoneworts are often plentiful after dredging and refilling of canal sections, and of particular note are *Tolypella intricata* and *T. prolifera*. Three species of Water-dropwort *Oenanthe crocata*, *O. aquatica* and *O. fluviatilis* may be seen. The latter two species, together with Arrowhead *Sagittaria sagittifolia*, are a few of the plants which most likely owe their presence to the canal link with the Shannon. Needle Spike-rush *Eleocharis acicularis* has been noted at Davitt Road, Drimnagh, and near Gollierstown, and the Flowering-rush *Butomus umbellatus* near the 12th lock at Ballymakaily.

Marshes and Fens   J. Reynolds and S. Reynolds

In his introduction to the *Flora of the County Dublin*, Colgan (1904) noted the absence in the county of extensive tracts of marsh. He did not distinguish between marshes and fens and named only three areas where marshes occurred: the Bog of the Ring in District 1, along the coast in District 2 and beside the Grand Canal near Hazelhatch in District 6. While there are luxuriant fringes of emergent plants along parts of the rivers and canals and around some reservoirs, there are no extensive areas of marsh associated with them. Bogs and marshes were already being drained in Colgan's time and land drainage since then has led to a further decrease in the wetlands of the county.

Marshes, which occur mainly on mineral soils, are seasonally flooded by surface water, while fens are kept wet all year by ground water relatively rich in mineral salts. Marshes are not homogeneous. At their wettest, they are often 'reed swamps' dominated by stands of tall grasses and at the other extreme, they merge into damp grassland. Near the coast, marshes may show a brackish influence and indeed may intergrade with saltmarsh. The periodic drying out of marshes prevents an accumulation of unrotted vegetation. In contrast, fens accumulate unrotted vegetation as peat due to the low oxygen content of the permanently waterlogged substrate. In the wetter parts of Ireland, fens are succeeded by rainwater-fed acid bog.

Descriptions of a selection of marsh sites and of the fewer fen sites follow, based on field work carried out mostly in 1990. Many of the plant species listed below, as well as a variety of Sedges *Carex* spp., are common to both marshes and fens.

In Co. Dublin, Common Reed *Phragmites australis* stands occur in the lowlands and are mainly found along the coast north of Howth. South of Killiney (8), near the mouths of the Shanganagh River and Deansgrange Stream, two small areas are dominated by Common Reed. On drier ground, tall plants of Common Nettle *Urtica dioica* and Rough Meadow-grass *Poa trivialis* grow among the Reed with Large Bindweed *Calystegia silvatica* climbing up their stems. In wetter areas, Common Reed grows with Reed Canary-grass *Phalaris arundinacea*. These Reed stands contain more species towards their margins, for example, False Fox-sedge *Carex otrubae*, Common Spike-rush *Eleocharis palustris*, Water Mint *Mentha aquatica* and Amphibious Bistort *Persicaria amphibia*, before grading into a marshy meadow. Near the mouth of the Mayne River, north of Baldoyle (5), Common Reed grows on intertidal mud with Sea Aster *Aster tripolium*.

A rather different community may be found at Booterstown (8) where the 4 hectare marsh, cut off from the sea by the building of the railway in the 19th century, has developed under the influence of two small freshwater streams entering at the northern end and tidal flooding from the south-east corner (Reynolds and Reynolds 1990). As one might expect, this marsh shows an intermingling of freshwater and saltmarsh plants, the distribution and variety of which change from year to year with changing proportions of fresh and saltwater. Near the main freshwater inflow are Fool's Water-cress *Apium nodiflorum*, Water-cress *Rorippa nasturtium-aquaticum*, Great Willowherb *Epilobium hirsutum*, Amphibious Bistort *Persicaria amphibia* and Water Horsetail *Equisetum fluviatile*, while at the seaward edge are Sea-milkwort *Glaux maritima*, Lesser Sea-spurrey *Spergularia marina*, Glasswort *Salicornia* spp., Sea-purslane *Atriplex portulacoides* and Common Saltmarsh-grass *Puccinellia maritima*. However, most of the marsh is covered by vegetation tolerant of brackish water, dominated by Sea Club-rush *Bolboschoenus maritimus*, Grey Club-rush *Schoenoplectus tabernaemontani*, Saltmarsh Rush *Juncus gerardii* and Sea Aster *Aster tripolium*. Two rare plants found here are Wild Celery *Apium graveolens*, in small numbers, and Borrer's Saltmarsh-grass *Puccinellia fasciculata*, a Protected Species. At Booterstown, *P. fasciculata* is more numerous when the mud is open and somewhat disturbed or poached.

One of the best lowland coastal marshes is an extensive area between Portmarnock and the railway in District 5. Here, towards the sea, the poorly drained rushy fields contain a number of shallow depressions where Grey Club-rush *Schoenoplectus tabernaemontani* is dominant, thus showing a maritime influence. Wild Celery *Apium graveolens* occurs near tidal drains and many common marsh and damp grassland plants are also present including Hard Rush *Juncus inflexus*, Marsh Ragwort *Senecio aquaticus*, Lesser Spearwort *Ranunculus flammula*, Ragged-Robin *Lychnis flos-cuculi* and Common Fleabane *Pulicaria dysenterica*. Further inland, the fields are bordered by freshwater marsh, the wetter parts with Bulrush *Typha latifolia*, Lesser Water-plantain *Baldellia ranunculoides*, Mare's-tail *Hippuris vulgaris* and Lesser Marshwort *Apium inundatum* among mature Alder *Alnus glutinosa* and Willow *Salix* spp.

The Bog of the Ring was considered the most interesting locality in District 1 by Colgan. This extensive fen is now largely destroyed, dissected by roads and drained by deep ditches cut through the peat and marl, with the resulting damp pasture dominated by Yellow Iris *Iris pseudacorus* and Soft-rush *Juncus effusus*. Along the streams, Purple-loosestrife *Lythrum salicaria*, Great Willowherb *Epilobium hirsutum* and Jointed Rush *Juncus articulatus* may also be found, while small wetter areas contain species such as Bottle Sedge *Carex rostrata*, Floating Sweet-grass *Glyceria fluitans*, Common Marsh-bedstraw *Galium palustre* and Brooklime *Veronica beccabunga*.

Two areas of fen are to be found in District 8. Ballybetagh Bog, at an altitude of about 230 m, lies at the head of a tributary of the Glencullen River. Several hectares of this fen have been partially drained. There are, however, still many large tussocks of the Greater Tussock-sedge *Carex paniculata* and between them are Common Sedge *Carex nigra*, Marsh Marigold *Caltha palustris*, Cuckooflower *Cardamine pratensis*, Marsh Cinquefoil *Potentilla palustris* and Bogbean *Menyanthes trifoliata*. The last two species are uncommon in the county. Just south of the fen, on the county boundary, an unimproved damp meadow contains a variety of Sedges *Carex* spp., Marsh-orchids *Dactylorhiza* spp. and their hybrids.

The second small area of fen, where Greater Tussock-sedge *Carex paniculata* is dominant, lies along another tributary of the Glencullen River at about 335 m on the northern slope of Glencullen Mountain below the forestry plantation. The soils are more acid and the flora is different from that at Ballybetagh. Where the tussocks grow close together in shallow flowing water, associated species are Purple Moor-grass *Molinia caerulea*, Sharp-flowered Rush *Juncus acutiflorus*, Common Marsh-bedstraw *Galium palustre* and Marsh Thistle *Cirsium palustre*. Where the tussocks are more widely spaced, other species may be found, including Bog Pondweed *Potamogeton polygonifolius*, Lesser Spearwort *Ranunculus flammula*, Marsh Violet *Viola palustris* and patches of Bog Moss *Sphagnum*.

Marshy areas are not well developed around the reservoirs in Co. Dublin, although some, such as those at Glenasmole (7) and Brittas (6), have an extensive littoral flora. Willows *Salix* spp. have colonised the head of the northern Glenasmole Reservoir and Lesser Bulrush *Typha angustifolia* occurs sparingly between the reservoirs. There is luxuriant emergent vegetation around the margins of the reservoirs at Balrothery (2) dominated by Bulrush *T. latifolia* and at

Knocksedan (3) by Branched Bur-reed *Sparganium erectum*. Small areas of marsh persist by some ponds, for example, beside an artificial pond at Gay Brook west of Malahide (5). That pond is bordered by Water Horsetail *Equisetum fluviatile*, Marsh Horsetail *E. palustre*, Marsh Willowherb *Epilobium palustre*, Water Mint *Mentha aquatica* and Silverweed *Potentilla anserina*. Both the Royal and Grand Canals bear persistent fringes of vegetation which extend into the inner city despite regular clearance, and good examples of bordering marsh may be found at Gollierstown and Hazelhatch on the Grand Canal in District 6.

One of the best marshy meadows is by the River Liffey at Palmerston (7). This species-rich meadow, between the millrace and the river, has several wetter areas dominated by Reed Sweet-grass *Glyceria maxima*, Yellow Iris *Iris pseudacorus* and Bulrush *Typha latifolia*. In many parts of the county, such marshy meadows grade into damp grassland. Some characteristic plants of these poorly drained fields are Wild Angelica *Angelica sylvestris*, Meadowsweet *Filipendula ulmaria*, Yellow Iris *Iris pseudacorus*, Creeping Buttercup *Ranunculus repens* and a variety of grasses including Creeping Bent *Agrostis stolonifera*, Yorkshire-fog *Holcus lanatus*, Crested Dog's-tail *Cynosurus cristatus* and Cock's-foot *Dactylis glomerata*.

WOODLANDS AND HEDGES

Woodlands
D. Kelly and M. Norton

Before the arrival of mankind, the area that is now Co. Dublin would have been largely covered by forest, except for the upper slopes of the mountains and a few low-lying wetlands. Most of the lowlands were cleared of forest in pre-historic times. The Pale of medieval times was the most intensively farmed region of Ireland, and timber was evidently scarce; in a law of 1534 A.D. it was "enjoyed that every husbande having a plough within the English pale shall sette by the year 12 ashes in the ditches and closes of his farm upon payne of 2d to be forfyte to the Deputy". In 1691, Dublin is described as being "A County very rich and fertile in Corn and Grass but destitute of Woods, so that they have a kind of fat Turff or Coal" (Eachard 1691).

Most of the broad-leaved woodlands in the county today are found in old estates, and date from the hey-day of private planting in the 18th and 19th centuries: the principal species planted were Pedunculate Oak *Quercus robur*, Beech *Fagus sylvatica* and Ash *Fraxinus excelsior*. Many of these woods have survived due to their amenity value, as private demesnes or public parks, or because of their location on steep slopes, unsuitable for agriculture or building. Nowadays, amenity woods and parks tend to be subjected to a combination of trampling, heavy grazing and excessive "tidying" (e.g. of fallen timber), so that the woodland flora is often greatly depleted. Broad-leaved woods generally have a canopy of tall trees and an understorey of shrubs or small trees such as Hazel *Corylus avellana*, Hawthorn *Crataegus monogyna* and Holly *Ilex aquifolium*. The understorey in old estate woods is prone to invasion by laurel-leaved evergreen shrubs that cast a dense shade and completely suppress both the ground flora and tree regeneration. Of these, Cherry Laurel *Prunus laurocerasus* occurs on a range of soils and is all too luxuriant in large estates such as Luttrellstown Demesne (4) and Marley Park (8). *Rhododendron ponticum* is a problem particularly in the upper part of Howth Demesne (5), where it is regenerating profusely and engulfing both woodland and heath vegetation.

Santry Woods (5) include some uncommon species that tend to be associated with old woodlands, most notably Hairy St John's-wort *Hypericum hirsutum* which is a Protected Species in Ireland under the Wildlife Act. Another unusual feature here is the wooded swamp, dominated by a mixture of Alder *Alnus glutinosa* and several species of Willow *Salix*, which has developed from a former ornamental lake.

Beech is an introduced tree that is an important component of many Dublin woods. It casts a deep shade and few species flourish under its canopy. Those that do include early flowering ("vernal") species, notably Ramsons *Allium ursinum* and shade-tolerant ferns, for example, Soft Shield-fern *Polystichum setiferum* which dominates the ground flora of the Beech wood at Knocksedan (3). A rare parasitic species, Toothwort *Lathraea squamaria,* can tolerate deep shade and occurs in abundance under Beech at St Catherine's (4). Beech saplings are themselves very shade-tolerant and so are well adapted to invading woodland dominated by other deciduous species. A good example of a regenerating Beech population may be seen by the Ward River at Knocksedan.

Elms have been widely planted, both the native Wych Elm *Ulmus glabra* and several introduced kinds. An old English Elm *Ulmus procera* in the courtyard of Howth Castle was said to have been planted in 1585 A.D. - one of the earliest records of tree planting in Ireland. Alas, the tree died of Dutch Elm Disease in the 1970s or 1980s as did most Elm trees in the county. Today, few mature Elms survive unscathed, although dead trunks often produce healthy re-sprouts or suckers, and self-sown saplings of Wych Elm continue to spring up in plenty (even in neglected corners of the inner city).

The most species-rich natural woodlands in the county today are found in steep-sided glens, usually on calcareous glacial drift in the Dublin Mountains (such as in Glenasmole) and along the banks of the River Liffey. The Liffey Valley woodlands, once contiguous, are now broken up into fragments, for example, St Catherine's Woods, Luttrellstown, Knockmaroon, St Edmundsbury and Fonthill. These include some of the tallest woodlands in the county. Here the canopy is formed by a mixture of native species such as Ash, Pedunculate Oak and Wych Elm. Introductions such as Beech and Sycamore *Acer pseudoplatanus* are also plentiful, while Horse-chestnut *Aesculus hippocastanum,* Lime *Tilia* x *vulgaris* and various conifers occur occasionally. Natural regeneration is patchy; where fallen trees create gaps in the canopy, the illuminated areas are invaded by Ash and Sycamore saplings. The ground flora of these woods includes a good number of very local woodland species. Yellow Archangel *Lamiastrum galeobdolon,* a characteristic plant of the county, is plentiful (in Ireland it is largely restricted to the counties Dublin, Wicklow and Wexford). Other uncommon species include Bearded Couch *Elymus caninus,* Wood Millet *Milium effusum,* Wood Fescue *Festuca altissima,* Thin-spiked Wood-sedge *Carex strigosa* and two parasitic species, Toothwort *Lathraea squamaria* and Ivy Broomrape *Orobanche hederae.* The Liffey Valley forms the headquarters in Ireland of Green Figwort *Scrophularia umbrosa* and Hairy St John's Wort *Hypericum hirsutum.*

Glenasmole (7), where the River Dodder reaches deep into the Dublin Mountains, contains some important fragments of woodland on steep slopes cut into limestone-rich glacial drift. These woods are generally of lower stature than those in the Liffey Valley but apparently spontaneous in origin and composed almost entirely of native species. The canopy is mainly composed of Hazel *Corylus avellana*, overtopped locally by taller trees, mostly Ash. This situation favours a rich ground flora; the spring-flowering herbs provide a medley of colours, including stands of Yellow Archangel *Lamiastrum galeobdolon*, Wood Anemone *Anemone nemorosa* and Woodruff *Galium odoratum*. Rarer species in the Glenasmole woods include Early-purple Orchid *Orchis mascula*, Broad-leaved Helleborine *Epipactis helleborine* and Hairy Wood-rush *Luzula pilosa*. Neither Narrow-Leaved Helleborine *Cephalanthera longifolia*, discovered there in the 1930s (Anon. 1961), nor the saprophytic Yellow Bird's-nest *Monotropa hypopitys*, have been re-found in recent years. The steep slopes are interrupted here and there by springs amid wet flushes. Here the vegetation is sometimes encrusted with calcareous tufa. A distinctive flora develops with Marsh Hawk's-beard *Crepis paludosa* and luxuriant stands of Great Horsetail *Equisetum telmateia*. Lugmore Glen (7), incised into limestone-rich glacial drift on a hill slope above Tallaght, is a delightful little Hazel wood with a rich ground flora similar to parts of Glenasmole.

Woods on acid soil are found over the siliceous rocks (granite and schist) which form the upland areas of the county. Small patches of broad-leaved woodland on acid soil occur scattered around the slopes of the Dublin Mountains, for example, The Scalp, The Dingle and Fitzsimon's Wood (8). The characteristic calcifuge (acid-loving) trees are Sessile Oak *Quercus petraea* and Rowan *Sorbus aucuparia*. There is, however, much variation from wood to wood - the canopy in The Dingle, for instance, is composed of a mixture of Grey Willow *Salix cinerea* subsp. *oleifolia*, Blackthorn *Prunus spinosa* and Holly *Ilex aquifolium*. The ground flora in woods on acid soil is relatively poor in vascular plants: Great Wood-rush *Luzula sylvatica*, Hard-fern *Blechnum spicant* and Wavy Hair-grass *Deschampsia flexuosa* are characteristic and locally plentiful.

Fitzsimon's Wood at Sandyford is probably the best example in the county of spontaneous woodland on acid soil. The woodland is dominated by the fast-growing Downy Birch *Betula pubescens*; young trees of Pedunculate Oak *Quercus robur*, Ash and Hawthorn are plentiful, with lesser quantities of Sycamore, Beech and Wild Cherry *Prunus avium* (the prevalence of Pedunculate Oak instead of the acid-loving Sessile Oak is an odd quirk of nature). There is a well developed understorey of Holly. The ground flora is very sparse, with little but Ivy *Hedera helix* amid Broad Buckler-fern *Dryopteris dilatata* and Navelwort *Umbilicus rupestris* on the granite boulders. Old maps show that woodland has long existed in the vicinity, but today there are very few mature trees or old stumps. Instead we can see all stages in a natural succession from grassland and heath through spiny scrub to woodland. Within stands of woodland an occasional gaunt-looking specimen of Blackthorn or Gorse *Ulex europaeus*, now dead or moribund, provides evidence of the pre-existing scrub vegetation that has been overtopped and suppressed by the growth of the trees.

Coniferous woodland is a newcomer to the Dublin landscape. The switch in emphasis among foresters from broad-leaved trees to conifers took place in the 19th century, and scattered stands of mature conifers survive from plantings in that century. However, the plantations which now cover the middle slopes of the Dublin Mountains are the result of State planting in the past half-century. The even-aged blocks of conifers are usually composed each of a single species: Sitka Spruce *Picea sitchensis* is by far the commonest species, followed by Lodgepole Pine *Pinus contorta* and the only deciduous conifers planted on a commercial scale, the Larches *Larix decidua, L. kaempferi, L. x marschlinsii*. In recent years there has been an increasing trend to plant fringing belts of other species around the main bulk of the plantations, including deciduous species such as Birch and Rowan. The dense year-round shade of most conifers, and the acid, slow-decomposing carpet of needles, result in an extremely limited ground flora, with little but the occasional starved-looking Wood-sorrel *Oxalis acetosella* or Bramble *Rubus* spp. The flora along paths and rides and in clearings in conifer plantations can be modestly diverse: typical species include Wood Sage *Teucrium scorodonia*, Foxglove *Digitalis purpurea*, Heath Bedstraw *Galium saxatile* and Rosebay Willowherb *Chamerion angustifolium*.

Hedges   D. Doogue

The hedged landscape of the Irish countryside results from a number of diverse but inter-related historical processes. The transformation from primeval woodland to planned "enclosed" farmland was seldom accomplished in a single step. Indeed many parts of the Irish countryside may have been cleared of woodland for much longer than is usually supposed. The long-standing open character of parts of the landscape is indicated by the physical and cultural prominence of standing stones (often glacial erratics), features of very limited territory-delimiting value in heavily wooded terrain. Cultural evidence is also afforded by the frequency of Irish place names derived from <u>Magh</u> (a plain) often anglicised to May-, Mo-, or Moy- and <u>Cluain</u> (a meadow) often anglicised to Clon- (Joyce 1901).

The process of hedgerow formation was linked to the need to define property limits and to restrict the movement of livestock in a mixed arable and pastoral agricultural economy. The patterns and character of hedgerow development were later to be heavily modified by the interplay between political and military conquest, agrarian reform and technological development. The broad chronology of the enclosure processes has been established (Aalen 1978). Suspected ancient earthworks, surmounted by hedgerows have recently been provisionally identified in the Naul Hills in Co. Dublin. However, it appears that most of the contemporary field network has been formed since the late 17th century (Aalen 1978).

In ancient Ireland where land was owned tribally, systematic enclosure was seldom initially necessary. Different enclosure/exclosure features such as <u>cora trí liag</u> (wall of three stones), <u>Clas</u> (trench and bank or <u>mur</u>) or <u>Nochtaile</u> (a bare fence which may have had a crest of Blackthorn - "<u>cir draigin</u>") are recorded. Blackthorn *Prunus spinosa* may also have been planted to strengthen the mur (Binchy 1978). Following the Norman conquest, the Gaelic system of communal land ownership was superseded by a scheme of feudal overlordship with the manor as the basic administrative unit. The lands of Kinsaley (Kinsealy, Co. Dublin) for instance are mentioned in a charter dating from *c.* 1170 (Otway-Ruthven 1951a, 1951b). By medieval times the townland was considered to be the fundamental unit of tenure, held by a single sub-tenant (Otway-Ruthven 1951a). The surviving evidence suggests that medieval landholdings were usually scattered, consisting of many small strips held in a number of different fields, mainly on the better soils. Medieval field patterns (strip holdings) survived as late as 1825 in Rathcoole and to a similar date in Dalkey, Saggart, and Clondalkin (Otway-Ruthven 1951a, 1965).

Evidence of planned living fences begins to emerge with the progress of the Tudor conquest. In 1534 the Ordinances for the Government of Ireland required the planting of Ash *Fraxinus excelsior* where land was ploughed. A memorandum from a book of information delivered by Robert Legge to Sir John Perotte, the Lord Deputy of Ireland, for the reformation of its civil government (1584) declared "It were very necessary at the Parliament some good act, order or provision were instituted and made here for enclosing of grounds within this land with hedges and ditches, planting such trees to make hedgerows as the people may conveniently get to plant, or else with some kind of thorns or fruit trees, as in Somersetshire and Devonshire they do".

Following the Cromwellian campaign, and particularly with the ascendancy of newer landowners, woodland and scrub clearance expanded. Piecemeal enclosure increased although the pattern varied between areas. Within the county great variation in field patterns was apparent. In the Manor of Maynooth, an area of mixed agriculture, the landscape consisted of small and medium-sized fields, irregular in outline and apparently the product, not of subdivision processes, but of the original primary piecemeal division of the area. Most boundaries were hedged and ditched, with no evidence of former open fields. A century later the basic pattern had remained unchanged. In striking contrast, at the southern end of the county in the Manors of Castledermot and Graney, Co. Kildare, most of the land in 1756 was laid out in huge fields. The only hedges were along townland boundaries. Eighty years later, the enclosure pattern in this area was virtually complete, most fields being by then less than 15 acres in extent, with both systematic and unsystematic enclosures discernible (Horner 1968).

It was not until the first half of the 18th century that Irish landscape painting had developed to the point where it constituted a reliable visual record of the countryside. A "View of Dublin from the Phoenix Park" dating from 1699 attributed to Thomas Bate shows a landscape devoid of hedges. However, a century later, William Ashford's "A View of Dublin from Chapelizod" (*c.* 1797) indicates clearly laid-out fields adjoining the River Liffey west of Dublin City, with cattle and horses grazing in fields hedged with shrubs and small trees (Kennedy 1993).

Immediately before the closure of the independent Irish Parliament (1801) a number of acts were introduced for the enclosure of commonage at Garristown, Co. Dublin and Dromiskin, Co. Louth (Aalen 1978). Agricultural "improvement" continued. As part of the new agricultural movement, organisations such as the (Royal) Dublin Society, which was founded in 1731, supported the establishment of base-line surveys of agricultural practices in rural Ireland by producing a series of statistical surveys of individual counties (*e.g.* Archer 1801). In upland Kildare quickset hedges formed inter-field divisions. It was proposed that Elm *Ulmus* sp., Ash *Fraxinus excelsior* and evergreen or other Privet *Ligustrum* spp. be planted as well as seedling Barberry *Berberis vulgaris* and that every farmer should have a nursery for thorn, crabs and trees (Rawson 1807). Quicks could be purchased from local nurseries (Feehan 1983).

The gradual establishment of a workable system of local government permitted the development or upgrading of a road system throughout the country. A deed of 1785 required a head-tenant "to keep the Dublin turnpike road well and sufficiently gravelled and to plant and prepare the road ditches with Ash and other timber planted at ten feet distances" (Andrews 1964). A committee of the House of Commons directed "That all pollards, bushes or other growth, standing or growing on banks, hedges, walls or other fences adjoining to the highways, be annually cut down before the 15th November" and "that no trees shall be planted or be permitted to stand or grow within thirty feet of any highway intended to be fenced out for the purposes of making any enclosure, except such trees as shall be actually standing or growing for the ornament or shelter of the house, building or court-yard of the owner thereof" (Greig 1818).

The establishment of the Congested Districts Board in the late 19th century and its successor, the Land Commission (1923), resulted in the acquisition, division and redistribution of major land holdings to small farmers. The Board built houses and constructed the outer farm boundaries, which were set with Whitethorn *Crataegus monogyna*. The pre-existing boundaries of the former estate were utilised and new internal divisions established (Nolan 1988).

The current trend towards removal of hedges and amalgamation of fields has not resulted in the dramatic transformations of the landscape as has occurred in parts of Britain (Hooper 1968, Baird and Tarrant 1973, Hickie 1985). This is in part attributable to the continued importance of livestock-raising in the Irish economy, assisted in recent times by European Union (EU) price-support mechanisms.

Several hedge-types of differing ages and mode of origin may thus be recognised in the Co. Dublin landscape: (a) planted hedges originating mainly from the agricultural improvement of 1750-1850, enclosing land formerly farmed as part of open field systems, (b) earlier planted hedges dating from private sporadic or piecemeal enclosure, and (c) more ancient hedges, many of which may have originated as strips of wildwood retained when forests were cleared. Within quite limited areas, even within townlands themselves, individual hedges can be found whose included trees, shrubs and woody climbers are very different from nearby and sometimes even adjacent hedges.

A growing appreciation of the importance of hedgerows as areas of nature conservation provoked a number of investigations in Britain in recent years. Local studies revealed that older hedges were much more species-rich than those associated with the enclosure movement. Mathematical formulae were developed suggesting that individual 30 yard lengths of hedge acquired on average one additional species per century. These theories were applied to Ireland with very limited success. The enthusiasm of hedge-daters waned a little, with the realisation that certain areas were far richer in hedge-forming species than others, for ecological rather than historical reasons. Lime-rich soils have many species that are unable to maintain a presence in base-poor, upland situations. No matter how old certain hedges are in these hilly areas, they are unlikely to acquire additional species, because the extra species are not present in the hinterland. However old hedges (or hedges on older boundaries) usually have more species than their newer counterparts, although whether these hedges have acquired these extra species with the passage of time, or have retained their original complement, is a matter for further study.

In Ireland certain trees, shrubs and woody climbers are largely confined to hedges that are formed on roadsides and townland boundaries - topographical features that are themselves usually older (Synnott 1973). It is often possible within a small area such as a townland to distinguish the straight planned hedges that may have been deliberately planted with (usually) Hawthorn from the much older and irregular townland matrix, whose hedges are not only more species-rich but contain species that do not spread easily into more modern hedges. These more ancient hedges give the truest expression of the background geographical distribution of the native species. To appreciate more fully the underlying natural patterns of localised species-composition it is necessary to ignore the veneer of recently-introduced trees and shrubs such as Sycamore *Acer pseudoplatanus* or Beech *Fagus sylvatica* as well as opportunist colonisers such as Elder *Sambucus nigra* or horticultural escapees, for example, Snowberry *Symphoricarpos albus*.

Farmers and other landowners were prepared to plant or promote species with ornamental or economic value. Wild Cherry *Prunus avium* was encouraged for its attractive flowers and seems to have been widely planted this century. Various forms of Wild Plum *Prunus domestica* occur, sometimes as two or three trees in a hedge near old settlements, more rarely as single-species hedges where they may persist as remnants of abandoned orchards. More interestingly the true Crab Apple *Malus sylvestris,* with glabrous leaves, pedicels and calyx, is very rare in the north of the county, while the cultivated Apple *Malus domestica* with pubescent leaves, pedicels and calyx, is common. However, several hedges near Balrothery and Ballyboghil have mixtures of hairy Apples together with almost glabrous trees that mimic *Malus sylvestris*. These may be descendants of older domestic apples that were planted in the hedge.

A separate group of hedge-forming native species can be distinguished in upland situations. These are very thin hedges, formed often on stone-faced raised banks, and dominated (if one ignores the almost ubiquitous Hawthorn) by Gorse *Ulex europaeus* with very few other species present - usually Mountain Ash *Sorbus aucuparia* and Broom *Cytisus scoparius*. Damper ground nearby will have hedges with Eared Willow *Salix aurita* and Downy Birch *Betula pubescens*. In striking contrast, in natural hedges on lime-rich lowland soils, Hawthorn is far less dominant while Hazel *Corylus avellana,* Spindle *Euonymus europaeus* and Guelder-rose *Viburnum opulus* are conspicuous. Hedges of this quality are rare in the Dublin area and are often associated with topographical features such as gravel ridges, suggesting that they are surviving remnants of the original scrub, most of which has long since been cleared.

The most recently-formed hedges are usually dominated by Hawthorn which may be planted directly into the soil or set into the side of earthen banks. These hedges are often colonised by Brambles *Rubus fruticosus* agg., Ash *Fraxinus excelsior,* Ivy *Hedera helix* and Elder *Sambucus nigra*. Many of the hedges on the periphery of the city are formed around a core group of naturally-occurring species, principally Blackthorn *Prunus spinosa*. These hedges are often quite dense and have been subsequently colonised by Sycamore *Acer pseudoplatanus* and Honeysuckle *Lonicera periclymenum*. Their less formal layout suggests that they were established before the systematic methodology of the enclosure movement, using whatever species were available locally.

The rarity of woodland elements in the herbaceous flora of north Co. Dublin is well-known. The same scarcity applies to species that are capable of forming hedges. The high agricultural potential and available markets for produce has resulted in a long history of intensive exploitation of north Co. Dublin resulting in the removal of most original woodland and scrub woodland, and the subsequent decline of many hedge-forming species. Goat Willow *Salix caprea,* the willow most tolerant of dry-ground conditions, is very rare and confined to a few species-rich hedges near Swords and Ballymun. Hazel is also very rare, as is Field-rose *Rosa arvensis*, an interesting problem that needs careful consideration by historical geographers. Holly *Ilex aquifolium* is usually a common species in hedgerows on higher ground but on more level ground in the north of the county it is usually associated only with the most species-rich hedges. Grey Willow *Salix cinerea* subsp. *oleifolia* will colonise many hedges - even planted ones - provided that there are drains or some open water available. Even if no open water is visible the presence of Grey Willow is indicative of the route of former open land drains or streams, long since piped or diverted.

The geographical distribution patterns of Wild Roses in Co. Dublin are fascinating (Doogue 1994). The relative scarceness of *Rosa arvensis* in the far north of the county may be attributed to the removal of the original woods. This species is still reasonably common along the Liffey and Tolka Valleys and other sheltered sunny situations but seldom occurs in open ground at even slightly higher elevations. A more bewildering case concerns the cluster of sites for Short-styled Field-rose *Rosa stylosa* in the Balrothery area. This is one of the rarest of Irish roses, and yet the material in the north of the county is extremely pure - unlike much of the reputed *R. stylosa* material from the rest of Ireland which is usually represented by hybrids between it and Dog-rose *R. canina.* Why should these plants, scattered over a couple of kilometres of hedge, survive here and be so rare elsewhere in Ireland? A third conundrum concerns the group of Downy roses - plants with resinous or turpentine-scented leaves, pedicels, and sepals, loosely referred to in the past as *R. mollis, R. villosa,* or *R. tomentosa.* On the hilly ground above the Bohernabreena Reservoir and in the Glencullen Valley, the very deep pink petals of *R. sherardii* are a conspicuous feature of roadside hedges in June. Similar plants re-appear along the network of minor roads running through the Naul Hills. Yet on the slightly lower ground in Districts 3 and 4, plants of this group are represented by another Downy Rose, usually with white petals with a discrete pink tip and bearing leaves with a different resinous scent. These are provisionally referred to *Rosa* x *scabriuscula,* a reputed hybrid between *R. tomentosa* and *R. canina.* However both these parent taxa appear to occupy quite distinct geographical areas and occur in rather different hedgerow community types. Determined Rhodologists will find grappling with the more complex relationship between reputed hybrids of *R. caesia* and *R. canina* and their putative parents of even greater interest. True *R. canina* is not as common as is usually believed, and most of the reputed hybrid plants are usually treated as if they were part of a broadly-defined *R. canina* complex. However, on the sides of the Dublin mountains and particularly in the Glenasmole Valley, individual rose bushes manifest the *R. caesia* influence in their ancestry in their more pruinose leaves, larger fruits and larger, hairier stylar clusters. It is tempting to speculate that in isolated parts of the foothills of the Dublin mountains, plants closely resembling *R. caesia* still survive, slightly beyond the topographical and ecological limits of the swarm of *R. canina* x *caesia* hybrids that predominates over most of the adjacent lowlands.

The rate at which hedgerows are being removed from the Irish landscape has been a matter of concern for some years and now needs to be assessed formally. Until recently, most of this destruction was propelled by a real or imaginary need to facilitate the movement of farm machinery and was usually directed at internal field boundaries. Nowadays however, with the movement of city-dwellers into the countryside, roadside hedges that have taken hundreds or possibly thousands of years to develop are being grubbed out by mechanical diggers in a few hours to be replaced by suburban intrusions such as *Chamaecyparis lawsoniana* and *Populus candicans 'Aurora'*. Unfortunately no inventory of hedges of high ecological significance has been compiled for the Dublin area. Consequently the planning authorities are not yet in a position to protect this major part of our heritage from these and other unwelcome developments.

WEEDS OF ARABLE LAND
P. Hodson

In Ireland, land was first brought into agricultural use by Neolithic farmers about 4,000 B.C. Botanical evidence from pollen analysis indicates that new plants, chiefly cereals and their weeds, were introduced at about the same time as areas of native woodland were being cleared (Mitchell 1986). Monk (1991) has reviewed the archaeobotanical evidence of field crop plants in Ireland in the period from 630-1000 A.D. The fact that the arable weed flora of Co. Dublin prospered until early this century is well documented in the botanical literature. Archaeobotanical evidence from Viking and Medieval Dublin (Mitchell 1987, Geraghty 1996) shows the close association of man with his accompanying flora. The main cereal crops under cultivation at the time appear to have been Wheat, Barley, Oats and possibly Rye, and examination of pit fills in the town showed that a range of weeds grew in association with them. Corncockle *Agrostemma githago* and Corn Marigold *Chrysanthemum segetum* were both abundant as weeds of cereal crops. Corncockle was also identified in the archaeological remains as finely ground fragments milled with grain. No effort appears to have been made to remove the Corncockle seeds which were large and farinaceous. It has since been discovered that the seeds contain saponin which is toxic to humans and animals, and the species was removed using modern seed cleaning methods. The decline of Corncockle was no doubt hastened by the fact that its seeds are viable for only a short period. Although still frequent elsewhere in Ireland at the end of the 19th century, it was by that time rare in Co. Dublin (Colgan and Scully 1898). The species had not been reported in the county since 1947, and was furthermore thought to be extinct in Ireland (Curtis and McGough 1988) until field work for this *Flora* produced a single record, albeit of possible garden origin, in District 8 in 1993. It is interesting to note that Corn Chamomile *Anthemis arvensis*, also considered to be extinct in Ireland, was recorded at the same time at the same location, and a couple of years earlier on a golf-links at Portmarnock where the ground had been disturbed.

The excavations of Medieval Dublin revealed the presence of other cereal crop weeds such as Corn Mint *Mentha arvensis*, Corn Spurrey *Spergula arvensis* and Narrow-fruited Cornsalad *Valerianella dentata*. The pit fills also showed that a number of arable weed species such as

Wild Radish *Raphanus raphanistrum* subsp. *raphanistrum,* Poppy *Papaver* spp., Scarlet Pimpernel *Anagallis arvensis* and Red Dead-nettle *Lamium purpureum* grew abundantly in the comparatively warm and enriched ground within the town. The large number of Fat-hen *Chenopodium* spp., Orache *Atriplex* spp. and Knotgrass *Polygonum* spp. seeds in the fills confirms that these were important food plants. Fat-hen and Orache were eaten in Dublin as leafy vegetables until well into the 18th century (Rutty 1772). Knotgrass was cultivated into medieval times and used in gruel or coarse bread for poorer people (Mitchell 1986).

Random sampling of arable land in Co. Dublin during the early 1990s has indicated that the typical arable weed flora is made up of three components in roughly equal measure i.e. annual weed species characteristic of the habitat, together with a number of perennial and annual ruderal (waste ground) species. The annual arable weed component includes a number of native species and species which may have been introduced with crops, such as Sun Spurge *Euphorbia helioscopia,* Common Hemp-nettle *Galeopsis tetrahit,* Common Poppy *Papaver rhoeas,* Fat-hen *Chenopodium album,* Charlock *Sinapis arvensis,* Small Nettle *Urtica urens,* Corn Spurrey *Spergula arvensis,* Field Pansy *Viola arvensis,* Knotgrass *Polygonum* spp. and Fumitory *Fumaria* spp. Some of the tilled ground and fallows along the north Co. Dublin coast still support an interesting arable weed flora including the rare Small-flowered Crane's-bill *Geranium pusillum,* Cut-leaved Dead-nettle *Lamium hybridum,* Northern Dead-nettle *L. confertum* and Prickly Poppy *Papaver argemone* (see District 2 Account for details). The perennial species found in arable land originate from diverse habitats. Examples include Common Nettle *Urtica dioica,* Silverweed *Potentilla anserina,* Creeping Bent *Agrostis stolonifera,* Common Couch *Elytrigia repens,* Field Horsetail *Equisetum arvense* and Field Bindweed *Convolvulus arvensis.* Many of these perennial species are well adapted to the arable habitat in possessing deep and fast-growing root systems and underground stems that are capable of vegetative regeneration from even small fragments. The annual species typical of ruderal habitats which are found in arable land include Groundsel *Senecio vulgaris,* Hedge Mustard *Sisymbrium officinale,* Common Chickweed *Stellaria media,* Cleavers *Galium aparine* and the alien Pineappleweed *Matricaria discoidea.*

Arable weed species generally display prolific seed production coupled with high rates of germination. One plant of Common Poppy *Papaver rhoeas,* for example, will produce 17,000 seeds on average, of which 65% may germinate within eight months of shedding (Salisbury 1964). This fecundity, combined with a rapid cycle from seed to flower, is most noticeably manifested by the Common Poppy when it becomes a feature of new roadway banks immediately after construction. So, the general reduction in the arable flora becomes all the more remarkable when this fecundity and their adaptability is taken into account. The seed bank in arable land has been estimated at up to half a million seeds per square metre (Hanf 1983) and the longevity of viable seed of arable weed species is well documented (Salisbury 1964). The seeds of some species, such as Wild Radish *Raphanus raphanistrum* subsp. *raphanistrum* remain viable even after subjection to the high temperatures encountered within manure heaps. Autumn germination is prevalent in arable weeds and some species, such as Shepherd's-purse *Capsella bursa-pastoris,* will flower at practically any time of the year, irrespective of day length. The ability to produce two, three or even more generations per year is characteristic of a number of species.

Nathaniel Colgan's *Flora of the County Dublin* (1904) provides a detailed account of the status of arable weeds before the 20th century revolution in agricultural practices that heralded their decline. Colgan's *Flora,* the *Supplement to Colgan's Flora of the County Dublin* (Anon. 1961) and this *Flora* provide 'snapshots' in time which illustrate the diminution of the arable flora over the course of almost 100 years. At the beginning of the 20th century, cornfields and potato fields still flourished in areas such as Howth, Kilbarrack and Glasnevin, and a number of arable weed species were so common that Colgan did not list individual sites for them. Two species, Green Field-speedwell *Veronica agrestis* and Grey Field-speedwell *Veronica polita,* provide graphic examples. Green Field-speedwell is now rare as a garden weed and in disturbed ground, and Grey Field-speedwell has suffered a similar fate. In contrast, Common Field-speedwell *Veronica persica,* a native of south-western Asia which reached Ireland before 1845 (Colgan and Scully 1898), became widespread and common in Ireland early in the 20th century. It has remained a very common weed of arable ground, gardens and waste ground in Co. Dublin.

The tale of Flixweed *Descurainia sophia* is another typical example of the 20th century decline of arable weeds. This crucifer was first reported from Dublin in the 18th century by Threlkeld (1726). He noted it as growing "...upon some of the low Thatched Cabbins at the End of *New Street,* near *Black Pitts.*" (These two streets are still extant, being located just south of St Patrick's Cathedral in the south of the city). Colgan found Flixweed in six of his eight Districts, reporting it as abundant in a number of coastal areas including "...on walls and thatched roofs in Rush village, 1893." According to the *Supplement,* it was "not nearly so common as in Colgan's time" and occurred in five Districts. This species is now only found occasionally in the coastal Districts of north Co. Dublin, where it is almost wholly confined to waste ground and sandy roadsides. One of its modern stations - a neglected barley field at Portrane - is reminiscent of its arable ancestry.

In 1926 there were 9,500 ha of ploughed land in Co. Dublin; by 1995 this had risen to 24,000 ha (Table 4). Paradoxically, however, conditions suitable to arable weed communities have diminished greatly through a combination of factors, the most important of which are:

- the mechanisation of farming which allows more intensive cultivation with more frequent weed disturbance
- modern seed cleaning methods which remove weed seeds from cereal crop seeds
- widespread and regular use of ever more effective systemic and selective weedkillers
- the decline in fallows
- more efficient land drainage
- the introduction of chemical fertilisers and lime which alter the nutrient levels and acidity of soil
- an increase in the average farm size and the emergence of extensive monocultures, particularly of cereal crops.

Political and economic factors combined during the first half of the 20th century to encourage rapid growth in Ireland's agricultural output. Mitchell (1986) draws attention to the fact that the demand for agricultural products generated by the First and Second World Wars led to increases in production at the expense of the reserve-fertility of Irish soils. After World War II chemical fertilisers were sold at subsidised prices to encourage farmers to replenish depleted soils. Since 1970 the European Union Common Agricultural Policy has been predominant. It is clear, therefore, that the factors which influenced the decline of suitable arable weed habitats were not only complex, but were exacerbated by the coincidence of pressures which were both internal and external to Ireland. Thus the arable weed flora is faced with a situation which has conspired to extinguish some species and push others into a variety of marginal habitats - the edges of fields beyond the reach of sprayers, disturbed ground, roadside verges, sandy ground near the coast, rocky seashores, derelict sites, gardens, disused quarries and rubbish tips. Henbit Dead-nettle *Lamium amplexicaule* is a good example of a marginalised arable weed. Outside District 2, it is rare in the county, found at nine sites in four Districts of which only one is on arable land.

In parallel with Great Britain (Stewart *et al.* 1994), the rate of disappearance of arable species has been dramatic with this group suffering a relatively high number of extinctions in Ireland. Of the 10 species listed in the *Irish Red Data Book* (Curtis and McGough 1988) as apparently extinct, five are arable species. A further four arable species are listed as nationally highly threatened. Rough Poppy *Papaver hybridum* was thought to be extinct in Ireland until it was found in a neglected barley field and on disturbed ground in north Dublin (District 3) during the course of field work for this *Flora*. Alongside the general decline in the arable flora, there are some interesting new arrivals to the county. Black-grass *Alopecurus myosuroides,* for example, was first noted in a cabbage field in north Dublin in 1985. Although classified as alien in Ireland, this species is a native weed of cereals in Britain where it has a largely southern distribution. Stewart *et al.* (1994) note that " In most fields the traditional weeds have been replaced by a group of species, including [Black-grass] *Alopecurus mysuroides* and [Cleavers] *Galium aparine*, which are resistant to herbicides or can take advantage of high levels of nutrients in fertilised fields". So it remains to be seen whether Black-grass becomes established in Co. Dublin.

The discovery of Sharp-leaved Fluellen *Kickxia elatine* on the edge of a potato field near the sea in south Dublin in 1984 significantly extended the range of this Protected Species in Ireland. The species was also recorded seven years later as a weed of cultivation in the National Botanic Gardens at Glasnevin. Before its discovery in south Dublin in 1984, Sharp-leaved Fluellen was previously known only from coastal locations in southern and western Ireland. At the south Dublin site, it grew within a field system which supported, in current terms, an unusually rich arable flora. Over thirty species were recorded in the vicinity, including a number of declining arable species such as Corn Marigold *Chrysanthemum segetum,* Field Woundwort *Stachys arvensis* and Dwarf Spurge *Euphorbia exigua*. It is most unlikely that the decline of arable weeds will be reversed unless there are major changes in agricultural management practices and land usage which would facilitate their revival. The current practice of spraying land, temporarily taken out of cultivation, with herbicide is not helpful. The introduction of creative measures, perhaps in conjunction with the agricultural "setaside" programme, are needed to conserve the traditional arable weed part of our floral heritage.

SUBURBAN AND URBAN HABITATS

S. Reynolds

One of the greatest changes in Co. Dublin since Colgan's *Flora* was published has been the immense expansion of Dublin City and suburbs. This has resulted in the loss of many natural habitats and their flora, including sites and plants referred to by Colgan. However, in modern Dublin there are pockets and corridors of semi-natural habitats in the parks, playing fields, cemeteries, grass verges and along railway lines, canals and rivers. Although many of these semi-natural habitats are managed (cleared, planted, mown, fertilized and sprayed with herbicide), they still contain species characteristic of wetland, grassland and woodland vegetation.

In the suburbs, fairly extensive areas of semi-natural grassland, hedgerow and woodland persist in the grounds of some private houses and schools and in public parks. Such areas are valuable refuges for native plants and other wildlife in an otherwise built-up environment. Re-seeded open spaces and grass verges are usually botanically uninteresting, but less-managed green spaces and many suburban lawns often contain a surprising variety of common plants, for example, Yarrow *Achillea millefolium*, Clovers *Trifolium* spp., Plantains *Plantago* spp. and Buttercups *Ranunculus* spp.. Other plants commonly encountered are Cat's-ear *Hypochaeris radicata*, Creeping Cinquefoil *Potentilla reptans*, Common Mouse-ear *Cerastium fontanum*, Selfheal *Prunella vulgaris* and Docks *Rumex* spp.. Less frequently, there may be Cowslip *Primula veris*, Field Wood-rush *Luzula campestris* and Cuckooflower *Cardamine pratensis*. However, not all such plants are native relicts from countryside habitats. On the grass median of the dual carriageway near Stillorgan (8), scattered plants of Chicory *Cichorium intybus*, possibly introduced with grass seed, have been seen. Slender Speedwell *Veronica filiformis*, introduced as a rockery plant into the British Isles from Turkey and the Caucasus, is now a common sight in lawns and on roadside verges in the spring. An invasive perennial which can regenerate from broken fragments, it was first noticed in Ireland in the 1930s (Bangerter and Kent 1957). The less showy Mind-your-own-business *Soleirolia soleirolii*, also an alien, is sometimes found in damper lawns.

The climate of urban areas is known to be somewhat different from that of the surrounding countryside (*e.g.* Sweeney 1987, Graham 1993). Two of the more important factors which affect plants are considered to be the higher temperatures and greater air pollution. The raised air temperatures may allow plants which originate in places with a warmer climate to thrive, for example, Oxford Ragwort *Senecio squalidus*, a native of central and southern Europe. It arrived in Cork in the early 1800s, rapidly established itself there and reached Dublin about 1890, probably introduced with old building and railway materials (Colgan 1904). Air pollution, whether gaseous - one of the most common substances is sulphur dioxide - or particulate in the form of dust, affects slow-growing broad-leaved plants more than plants, such as Common Chickweed *Stellaria media*, which continuously produce new leaves.

The flora of Dublin City and suburbs is made up of native plants and a high proportion of non-native or alien plants. Because of the artificiality of the habitats, many plants which are common in the countryside are uncommon in the city, and only one native species scheduled by the Wildlife Act (1976) occurs here - Opposite-leaved Pondweed *Groenlandia densa*, found in the Grand Canal, the Royal Canal and a tributary of the Cammock River (Wyse Jackson 1988, Dromey 1991). Dublin's alien plants are often garden escapes or discards, but others may have arrived with cargoes imported through Dublin Port (Reynolds 1996). Whereas some aliens, such as Sycamore *Acer pseudoplatanus* (from continental Europe, introduced several centuries ago) and Pineappleweed *Matricaria discoidea* (from North America, first recorded in 1894 on Howth) are now part of the permanent Irish flora, most do not become established. The *Flora of Inner Dublin* (Wyse Jackson and Sheehy Skeffington 1984) lists approximately 300 native and alien species and gives an account of the urban flora at that time and of various habitats and sites where plants may still be found.

Urban habitats are essentially artificial - buildings, walls, pavement and road edges, wasteground and derelict sites. Of these, wasteground and derelict sites provide the largest open spaces in Dublin city where plants can grow. A great assortment of annuals and perennials may easily be found at such sites, including Mugwort *Artemisia vulgaris*, Common Mallow *Malva sylvestris*, Beaked Hawk's-beard *Crepis vesicaria* and Hedge Mustard *Sisymbrium officinale* as well as Mayweeds *Tripleurospermum* spp., Thistles *Cirsium* spp., Spurges *Euphorbia* spp. and Willowherbs *Epilobium* spp.. Also common are the aliens Annual Mercury *Mercurialis annua* and Oxford Ragwort *Senecio squalidus* and plants that were originally garden escapes, for example, Snapdragon *Antirrhinum majus*, Purple Toadflax *Linaria purpurea* and Feverfew *Tanacetum parthenium*. Wastegrounds are the only areas where some sort of natural plant succession can occur in the city. They are first colonised by weedy pioneer species, for example, Red Dead-nettle *Lamium purpureum*, Groundsel *Senecio vulgaris* and Cleavers *Galium aparine*, which can establish themselves readily in open disturbed ground. If a piece of wasteground remains undeveloped for a few years, the pioneer species are replaced by taller grasses and other flowering plants and finally by shrubs and woody plants, such as the aliens Japanese Knotweed *Fallopia japonica*, Butterfly-bush *Buddleja davidii* and Sycamore *Acer pseudoplatanus*, and native Willows *Salix* spp. and Elder *Sambucus nigra*.

On two more permanent areas of reclaimed land, at Dublin Port and Ringsend Dump (between Ringsend and Sandymount), some 200 different kinds of plants were recorded for this *Flora*. Since infill comes from many sources, a variety of garden plants, ornamental and vegetable, appear along with other alien and native plants. The above two sites are interesting as there is always the chance of finding unusual and exotic species, for example, Small Melilot *Melilotus indicus*, Larkspur *Consolida ajacis*, Toothed Medick *Medicago polymorpha* and Cotton Thistle *Onopordum acanthium*. Distinctive plants on Ringsend Dump are Wild Teasel *Dipsacus fullonum* and Fennel *Foeniculum vulgare* which grow abundantly there. Patches of multi-coloured Sand Lucerne *Medicago sativa* subsp. *varia* have persisted for many years in this area. Two yellow-flowered members of the Cabbage family not commonly seen elsewhere in Ireland, Hoary Mustard *Hirschfeldia incana* and Bastard Cabbage *Rapistrum rugosum*, are very common at Dublin Port. They and other alien plants probably arrived as contaminating seeds in imported cereals and animal feed (Reynolds 1996). Many alien plants do not survive for long and so fail to spread and establish themselves (see Supplementary List in Systematic Section).

They may not be able to tolerate the combination of cold and wet conditions, or short summers may prevent the seed of more southern species from ripening, or the appropriate pollinators may be lacking. However, alien plants are worth reporting as some of them, for example the Fleabanes *Conyza* spp., may become more widespread (Reynolds 1997).

Less hospitable, and often temporary refuges for plants, are small pieces of ground around trees and lamp posts. Members of the Daisy family such as Dandelion *Taraxacum officinale* agg., Sowthistles *Sonchus oleraceus* and *S. asper* and Groundsel *Senecio vulgaris,* which all produce numerous plumed fruits, find a niche here, as does Common Chickweed *Stellaria media* which can produce more than one generation of fruiting plants a year. A characteristic plant of Dublin pavement edges, where there is some accumulation of soil and dirt, is the alien Wall Barley *Hordeum murinum*, which was already well established in the city at the turn of the century (Colgan 1904). In Ireland, it is found chiefly in east coast towns. Some plants can survive heavy trampling and grow in pavement cracks, for example, Annual Meadow-grass *Poa annua*, probably the most widespread wild grass in the world, Knotgrass *Polygonum aviculare*, Procumbent Pearlwort *Sagina procumbens* and Shepherd's-purse *Capsella bursa-pastoris*. The small annual Fern-grass *Catapodium rigidum* not only favours the base of walls but may also be found on wall tops.

Walls are considered the most extreme habitat of urban plants due to exposure, the scarcity of water and poor soil. Plants grow in the lime-rich mortar between the stones or bricks; an example is Pellitory-of-the-wall *Parietaria judaica* which grows on the walls bordering the Liffey. Red, pink and white-flowered Wall Valerian *Centranthus ruber*, originally introduced from the Mediterranean as a garden plant, has been a common feature in Dublin on wasteground rubble and city walls for the last hundred years. Ivy-leaved Toadflax *Cymbalaria muralis*, another garden escape and native in southern Europe, is similarly widespread. The native ferns Wall-rue *Asplenium ruta-muraria*, Maidenhair Spleenwort *A. trichomanes* and Intermediate Polypody *Polypodium interjectum* grow on relatively dry walls, whereas Hart's-tongue *Phyllitis scolopendrium* and Male-fern *Dryopteris filix-mas* prefer damper walls where there may be water seepage from broken gutters or downpipes. Occasional plants of Bracken *Pteridium aquilinum* may be seen on city buildings, or colonising rocks and infill by the Liffey near the East Link Toll Bridge.

Finally, one of Dublin's most characteristic species of wall and wasteground, Butterfly-bush *Buddleja davidii*, was introduced into the British Isles from China in the late 1800s. It produces numerous small narrowly-winged seeds which are readily dispersed by air and plants flourish where very little nourishment and water seem available. Apart from growing on walls and wasteground, Butterfly-bush adorns roofs and chimney pots and is now one of the most conspicuous and distinctive plants in Dublin City.

REFERENCES FOR PART I

Note: Abbreviations used for journal titles are as in the Bibliography (Appendix I).

Aalen, F.H.A. (1978). *Man and the Landscape in Ireland.* Academic Press, London.

Adams, J. (1908a). The new flora of burnt ground on the Hill of Howth: A Study of plant dispersal. *IN* **17**: 133-134.

Adams, J. (1908b). The burnt ground on Howth Head. *IN* **17**: 268.

Andrews, J.H. (1964). Road planning in Ireland before the railway age. *Irish Geography* **5**: 17-41.

Anonymous [Baily, K.S.] (1833). *The Irish Flora.* Hodges & Smith, Dublin.

Anonymous (1926-1995). Reports of the Central Statistics Office, Dublin.

Anonymous (1961). *A Supplement to Colgan's Flora of the County Dublin.* The Stationery Office, Dublin.

Anonymous (1983). *The Climate of Dublin.* The Meteorological Service, Dublin.

Archer, J. (1801). *Statistical Survey of County Dublin.* The Dublin Society. Hodges & Smith, Dublin.

Babington, C.C. (1859). Hints towards a *Cybele Hibernica. Natural History Review* **6**: 533-537.

Babington, C.C. (1881). *Manual of British Botany.* (8th edn). John van Voorst, London.

Baird, W.W. and Tarrant, J.R. (1973). *Hedgerow Destruction in Norfolk, 1946-1970.* University of East Anglia, Norwich.

Bangerter, E.B. and Kent, D.H. (1957). *Veronica filiformis* Sm. in the British Isles. *Proc. BSBI* **2**: 197-217.

Binchy, D.A. (Ed.) (1978). *Corpus Iuris Hibernica.* Ard Léinn, Baile Átha Cliath.

Booth, E.M. (1979). *The Flora of County Carlow.* Royal Dublin Society, Dublin.

Boyle, P.J. (1972). Spartina *in Ireland.* Unpublished Ph.D. thesis. National University of Ireland, University College, Dublin.

Boyle, P.J. (1976). *Spartina* M9. A variant *Spartina* in three regions north of Dublin. *The Scientific Proceedings of the Royal Dubl. Soc.* (series A) **5**: 415-427.

Boyle, P.J. (1977). *Spartina* on Bull Island. Pp. 88-92 in: Jeffrey, D.W. (Ed.). *North Bull Island Dublin Bay, a Modern Coastal Natural History.* Royal Dublin Society, Dublin.

Brück, P.M., Potter, T.L. and Downie, C. (1974). The Lower Palaeozoic stratigraphy of the northern part of the Leinster massif. *Proc. RIA* (B) **74**: 75-84.

Brück, P.M. and Reeves, T.J. (1976). Stratigraphy, sedimentology and structure of the Bray Group in County Wicklow and south County Dublin. *Proc. RIA* (B) **76**: 53-77.

Brunker, J.P. (1950). *Flora of the County Wicklow.* Dundalgan Press, Dundalk.

Caffrey, J.M. and Allison, J. (1998). Eutrophication in canals. Pp. 1-10 in: J.C. Wilson (Ed.). *Eutrophication in Irish Waters.* Proceedings of a conference held at the Royal Irish Academy, 21-22 March 1996.

Clabby, K.J., Lucey, J. and McGarrigle, M.L. (1991). *Interim Report on the Biological Survey of River Quality.* Environment Research Unit, Dublin.

Clabby, K.J., Lucey, J. and McGarrigle, M.L. (1994). *Interim Report on the Biological Survey of River Quality*. Environment Research Unit, Dublin.

Clapham, A.R., Tutin, T.G. and Warburg, E.F. (1952). *Flora of the British Isles*. (1st edn). Cambridge University Press, Cambridge.

Clapham, A.R., Tutin, T.G. and Warburg, E.F. (1962). *Flora of the British Isles*. (2nd edn). Cambridge University Press, Cambridge.

Colgan, N. (1894). *Carex axillaris* and *Filago minima* in Co. Dublin. *IN* **3**: 202.

Colgan, N. (1896). *Scrophularia umbrosa* (Dum.) in Ireland. *IN* **4**: 182.

Colgan, N. (1904). *Flora of the County Dublin: Flowering Plants, Higher Cryptogams and Characeae*. Hodges, Figgis & Co., Dublin.

Colgan, N. (1912). The burnt ground flora of Killiney Hill. *IN* **21**: 72-76.

Colgan, N. (1913). Further notes on the burnt ground flora of Killiney Hill. *IN* **22**: 85-93.

Colgan, N. and Scully, R.W. (1898). *Contributions towards a Cybele Hibernica*. (2nd edn). Ponsonby, Dublin.

Collins, T. (1985). *Floreat Hibernia*. Royal Dublin Society, Dublin.

Contejean, C. (1881). *Geographic Botanique - Influence du Terrain sur la Vegetation*. Paris.

Coxon, P. (1992). Dublin in the grip of an Ice Age: the Quaternary geology of the Dublin region. *Geographical Viewpoint* **20**: 35-52.

Curtis, T.G.F. (1991a). A site inventory of the sandy coasts of Ireland - their types and distribution. Pp. 6-17 in: Quigley, M.B. (Ed.). *A Guide to the Sand Dunes of Ireland*. European Union for Dune Conservation and Coastal Management, c/o Department of Geography, Trinity College, Dublin.

Curtis, T.G.F. (1991b). The flora and vegetation of sand dunes in Ireland. Pp. 42-66 in: Quigley, M.B. (Ed.). *A Guide to the Sand Dunes of Ireland*. European Union for Dune Conservation and Coastal Management, c/o Department of Geography, Trinity College, Dublin.

Curtis, T.G.F. and McGough, H.N. (1988). *The Irish Red Data Book. 1: Vascular Plants*. The Stationery Office, Dublin.

Curtis, T.G.F. and Sheehy Skeffington, M.J. (1998). The salt marshes of Ireland: an inventory and account of their geographical variation. *Biol. Env. Proc. RIA* (B) **98**.

D'Alton, J. (1838). *History of the County of Dublin*. Hodges & Smith, Dublin.

D'Arcy, C.F. (1934). *The Adventures of a Bishop*. Hodder & Stoughton, London.

Daultrey, S. (1995). Climate Variability in Ireland: Are There Signals Amongst the Noise? Pp. 37-51 in: Feehan, J. (Ed.). *Climate Variation and Climate Change in Ireland*. Environmental Institute, University College, Dublin.

Doogue, D.[A.] (1984). History of the flora. Pp. 5-24 in: Wyse Jackson, P. and Sheehy Skeffington, M. *The Flora of Inner Dublin*. Royal Dublin Society in association with the Dublin Naturalists' Field Club, Dublin.

Doogue, D.A. (1994). *The Composition of the Hedges of Leinster, Ireland, with particular reference to the Taxonomy and Ecology of the Genus* Rosa *Linnaeus*. Unpublished Ph.D. thesis. University of Dublin, Trinity College.

Doogue, D.[A.] and Parnell, J.[A.N.] (1992). Fragments of an eighteenth century herbarium, possibly that of Caleb Threlkeld in Trinity College, Dublin (**TCD**). *Glasra (new series)* **1**: 99-109.

Doogue, D.A. and Walsh, W. (1989). Some Liffey valley plants. Pp. 76-77 in: Healy, E., Moriarty, C. and O'Flaherty, G. (Eds). *The Book of the Liffey from Source to the Sea.* Wolfhound Press, Dublin.

Dromey, M. (1991). *Groenlandia densa* (L.) Fourr. in the Royal Canal, Dublin. *INJ* **23**: 383-384.

Dublin Naturalists' Field Club (1986). *Reflections and Recollections. 100 Years of the Dublin Naturalists' Field Club.* Dublin.

Eachard, L. (1691). *An Exact Description of Ireland.* Thos. Salisbury, London.

Feehan, J. (1983). *Laois - An Environmental History.* Ballykilcavan Press, Stradbally.

Ferguson, I.K. (1964). *A Study of the Taxonomy of* Salicornia *L. in Ireland.* Unpublished Ph.D. thesis. University of Dublin, Trinity College.

Fitzgerald, D. and Forrestal, F. (1996). Monthly and annual averages of rainfall for Ireland, 1961-1990. *Chronological Note* No. 10.

Forbes, E. (1846). On the connexion between the distribution of the existing fauna and flora of the British Isles and the geological changes which have affected their area. *Memorandum of the Geological Survey of the United Kingdom* **1**: 336-432.

Fraser, J. (1838). *Guide through Ireland.* William Curry Junior & Company, Dublin.

Gardiner, M.J. and Radford, T. (1980a). Soil associations of Ireland and their land use potential. Explanatory bulletin to Soil Map of Ireland 1980. *Soil Survey Bulletin* **36**: 1-143.

Gardiner, M.J. and Radford, T. (1980b). *Ireland - General Soil Map (2nd edn). Scale 1: 575,000.* An Foras Talúntais, Dublin.

Geraghty, S. (1996). *Viking Dublin: Botanical Evidence from Fishamble Street.* Royal Irish Academy, Dublin.

Graham, E. (1993). The urban heat island of Dublin city during the summer months. *Irish Geography* **26**: 45-57.

Greig, W. (1818). *Strictures on Road Police.* Archer, Dublin.

Hanf, M. (1983). *Weeds and their Seedlings.* BASF United Kingdom Ltd., England.

Hart, H.C. (1883). Notes on the flora of Lambay Island, County of Dublin. *Proc. RIA* (B) **3**: 670-693.

Hart, H.C. (1887). *The Flora of Howth.* Hodges, Figgis & Co., Dublin.

Hart, H.C. (1898). *Flora of the County Donegal.* Sealy, Bryers & Walker, Dublin; David Nutt, London.

Hickie, D.A. (1985). *A Hedge Study of North Co. Dublin.* Unpublished M.Sc. thesis. Environmental Science Unit, Trinity College, Dublin.

Hoare, P.G. (1975). The pattern of glaciation of County Dublin. *Proc. RIA* (B) **75**: 207-224.

Hoare, P.G. (1976). Glacial meltwater channels in County Dublin. *Proc. RIA* (B) **76**: 173-185.

Holland, C.H. (Ed.) (1981a). *The Geology of Ireland.* Scottish Academic Press, Edinburgh.

Holland, C.H. (1981b). Geology. Pp. 123-128 in: McBrierty, V.J. (Ed.). *The Howth Peninsula, its History, Lore and Legend.* North Dublin Round Table, Dublin.

Hooper, M. (1968). *The Rates of Hedge Removal. Symposium* No. 4: Nature Conservancy. Monks Wood Experimental Station, Peterborough.

Hoppen, K.T. (1970). *The Common Scientist in the Seventeenth Century*. Routledge & Kegan Paul, London.

Horner, A.A. (1968). *Aspects of the Historical Geography of parts of the Duke of Leinster's Estates in Co. Kildare c. 1750-1854*. Unpublished B.A. dissertation. Department of Geography, Trinity College, Dublin.

Horner, A.A. (1985). The Dublin region 1880-1982: an overview of its development and planning. Pp. 21-75 in: Bannon, M.J. (Ed.). *The Emergence of Irish Planning*. Turoe Press, Dublin.

Horner, A.A. (1994). Physical change and administrative response within the Dublin City Region during the twentieth century. *Acta Universitatis Carolinae Geographica* **26**: 27-143.

How, W. (1650). *Phytologia Britannica, Natales Exhibens Indigenarum Stirpium Sponte Emergentium*. Cotes, London.

Hudson, R.G.S., Clarke, M.J. and Sevastopulo, G.D. (1966). A detailed account of the fauna and age of a Waulsortian Reef Knoll Limestone and associated shales, Feltrim, Co. Dublin. *Scientific Proceedings of the Royal Dublin Society* (A) **2**: 251-272.

Jeffrey, D.W. (Ed.) (1977). *North Bull Island Dublin Bay, a Modern Coastal Natural History*. Royal Dublin Society, Dublin.

Jones, B.M.G. and Newton, L.E. (1970). The status of *Puccinellia pseudodistans* (Crep.) Jansen and Wachter in Great Britain. *Watsonia* **8**: 17-26.

Joyce, P.W. (1901-1913). *Irish Names of Places*. Vols. **1-3**. Phoenix Publishing Co., Dublin, Cork and Belfast.

Kennedy, B. (1993). *Irish Painting*. Town House, Dublin.

King, J.J. and Nash, D.W. (1994). The charophyta of County Dublin (H21). *Biol. Env. Proc. RIA* (B) **94**: 255-264.

Linnaeus, C. (1753). *Species Plantarum*. (1st edn). Stockholm. Facsimile edition of 1957. The Ray Society, London.

Linnaeus, C. (1754). *Flora Anglica*. (1st edn). Stockholm. Facsimile edition of 1973. The Ray Society, London.

Linnaeus, C. (1759). *Flora Anglica*. (2nd edn). Stockholm. Facsimile edition of 1973. The Ray Society, London.

Mackay, J.T. (1806). A systematic catalogue of rare plants found in Ireland. *Transactions of the Dublin Society* **5**: 121-184.

Mackay, J.T. (1825). A catalogue of the indigenous plants found in Ireland. *Transactions of the Royal Irish Academy* **14**: 103-198.

Mackay, J.T. (1836). *Flora Hibernica*. William Curry Junior & Co., Dublin.

Mackay, J.T. (1859). Additions to the plants of Ireland since the publication of "*Flora Hibernica*". *Proceedings of Dublin University Zoological and Botanical Association* **1**: 250-253.

Mackay, J.T. (1860). Additional plants for *Flora Hibernica*. *Proceedings of Dublin University Zoological and Botanical Association* **2**: 65-66.

Madden, B., Jennings, E. and Jeffrey, D.W. (1993). Distribution and ecology of *Zostera* in Co Dublin. *INJ* **24**: 303-310.

Matthews, J.R. (1937). Geographical relationships of the British flora. *Journal of Ecology* **25**: 1-90.

McConnell, B.J. and Philcox, M.E. (1995). *Sheet 16 Kildare - Wicklow 1: 100,000 Bedrock Map Series*. Geological Survey of Ireland, Dublin.

McConnell, B.J., Philcox, M.E., Sleeman, A.G., Stanley, G., Flegg, A.M., Daly, E.P. and Warren, W.P. (1995). *Geology of Kildare - Wicklow. A Geological Description to Accompany the Bedrock Geology 1: 100,000 Map Series, Sheet 16, Kildare - Wicklow*. Geological Survey of Ireland, Dublin.

McMullen, R.M. (1967). *Monotropa* in Dublin area. *INJ* **15**: 307.

McNamee, K.A. and Jeffrey, D.W. (1977). Ecophysiology of saltmarsh plants. Pp. 100-103 in: Jeffrey, D.W. (Ed.). *North Bull Island Dublin Bay, a Modern Coastal Natural History*. Royal Dublin Society, Dublin.

Mitchell, [G.]F. (1986). *The Shell Guide to Reading the Irish Landscape*. Country House, Dublin.

Mitchell, G.F. (1987). *Archaeology and Environment in Early Dublin*. Royal Irish Academy, Dublin.

Mitchell, [G.]F. and Ryan, M. (1997). *Reading the Irish Landscape*. Country House, Dublin.

Mitchell, M.E. (1974). The sources of Threlkeld's *Synopsis Stirpium Hibernicarum. Proc. RIA* (B) **74**: 1-6.

Monk, M.A. (1991). The archaeobotanical evidence for field crop plants in early historic Ireland. Pp. 315-328 in: J.M. Renfrew (Ed.). *New light on Early Farming*. Edinburgh University Press, Edinburgh.

Moore, D. and More, A.G. (1866). *Contributions towards a Cybele Hibernica, being Outlines of the Geographical Distribution of Plants in Ireland*. Hodges, Smith & Co., Dublin.

Moore, J.J. (1960). A re-survey of the vegetation of the district lying south of Dublin (1905-1956). *Proc. RIA* (B) **61**: 1-36.

Moore, J.J. (1977). Vegetation of the dune complex. Pp. 104-106 in: Jeffrey, D.W. (Ed.). *North Bull Island Dublin Bay, a Modern Coastal Natural History*. Royal Dublin Society, Dublin.

Moore, J.J. and O'Reilly, H. (1977). Saltmarsh: vegetation pattern and trends. Pp. 83-87 in: Jeffrey, D.W. (Ed.). *North Bull Island Dublin Bay, a Modern Coastal Natural History*. Royal Dublin Society, Dublin.

More, A.G. (1872). On recent additions to the flora of Ireland. *Proc RIA* (B) **2**: 256-293.

Moriarty, C. (1991). *Down the Dodder. Wildlife, History, Legend, Walks*. Wolfhound Press, Dublin.

Nash, D.W. (1995). Stations for *Senecio viscosus* L. in Ireland. *INJ* **25**: 59-66.

Nash, D.W. and King, J.J. (1993). The genus *Tolypella* in Co Dublin (H21). *INJ* **24**: 329-332.

Nelson, E.C. (1980). Walter's Wade's '*Flora Dublinensis*' - an enigmatic Irish botanical publication. *Long Room* **20-21**: 16-20.

Nelson, E.C. (1988). Introduction, pp. xiii-lii, [to] *The First Irish Flora. Synopsis Stirpium Hibernicarum. Caleb Threlkeld*. Facsimile edition. Boethius Press, Kilkenny.

Ní Lamhna, É. (1982). The vegetation of saltmarshes and sand-dunes at Malahide Island, County Dublin. *J. Life Sci. R. Dub. Soc.* **3**: 111-129.

Nolan, S.C. (1989). The style and timing of Dinantian syn-sedimentary tectonics in the eastern part of the Dublin Basin. Pp. 83-97 in : Arthurton, R.S., Gutteridge, P. and Nolan, S.C. (Eds). *The Role of Tectonics and Carboniferous Sedimentation in the British Isles*. Yorkshire Geological Society Occasional Publication **6**.

Nolan, W. (1988). New fields and farms: migration policies of state land agencies 1891-1980. Pp. 296-319 in: Smyth, W.T. and Whelan, K. (Eds). *Common Ground. Essays on the Historical Geography of Ireland*, presented to T. Jones Hughes. Cork University Press, Cork.

O'Reilly, H. and Pantin, G. (1957). Some observations on the salt marsh formation in Co. Dublin. *Proc. RIA* (B) **58**: 89-128.

O'Riordan, C. (1983). *The Natural History Museum, Dublin*. The Stationery Office, Dublin.

Otte, M.L. (1994). *A Re-evaluation of the Management Policy Concerning Spartina - grasses at the North Bull Island Saltmarshes*. Unpublished report for Dublin Corporation.

Otway-Ruthven, J. (1951a). The Organisation of Anglo-Irish agriculture in the Middle Ages. *The Royal Society of Antiquaries of Ireland* **81**: 1-13.

Otway-Ruthven, J. (1951b). Place-names in Ireland. *Irish Geography* **2**: 45-51.

Otway-Ruthven, J. (1965). The character of Norman settlement in Ireland. *Historical Studies* **5**: 75-84.

Perring, F.H. and Walters, S.M. (1962). *Atlas of the British Flora*. Nelson, London and Edinburgh.

Pethybridge, G.H. (1908). The new flora of the burnt ground on the Hill of Howth. *IN* **17**: 160.

Pethybridge, G.H. and Praeger, R.Ll. (1905). The vegetation of the district lying south of Dublin. *Proc. RIA* (B) **25**: 124-180.

Piper, R. (1970). *Glenasmole Orchids*. Unpublished manuscript, now held by the Department of the Environment, Dublin.

Praeger, R.Ll. (1901). Irish topographical botany. *Proc RIA* (series 3) **7**: i-clxxxviii; 1-410.

Praeger, R.Ll. (1907). Phanerogams and vascular cryptogams. In: Contributions to the natural history of Lambay, Co. Dublin. *IN* **16**: 90-99.

Praeger, R.Ll. (1908). Flora of burnt ground at Howth. *IN* **17**: 186.

Praeger, R.Ll. (1909). *A Tourist's Flora of the West of Ireland*. Figgis & Co., Dublin.

Praeger, R.Ll. (1932). Some noteworthy plants found in or reported from Ireland. *Proc. RIA* (B) **41**: 95-124.

Praeger, R.Ll. (1934). *The Botanist in Ireland*. Hodges, Figgis & Co., Dublin.

Praeger, R.Ll. (1951). Hybrids in the Irish flora: a tentative list. *Proc. RIA* (B) **54**: 1-14.

Rawson, T.J. (1807). *The Statistical Survey of Co. Kildare*. The Dublin Society, Dublin.

Ray, J. (1660). *Catalogus Plantarum circa Cantabrigiam Nascentium*. Cambridge and London.

Ray, J. (1724). *Synopsis Methodica Stirpium Britannicarum* (3rd edn). London. The Ray Society, London.

Reilly, P.A. (1993). The flowering plants and ferns of the Phoenix Park, Dublin. *Glasra* (new series) **2**: 5-72.

Reynolds, J.D. and Reynolds, S.C.P. (1990). Development and present vegetational state of Booterstown marsh, Co. Dublin, Ireland. *Bull. IBS* **13**: 173-188.

Reynolds, S.C.P. (1996). Alien plants at ports and in coastal habitats on the east coast of Ireland. *Watsonia* **21**: 53-61.

Reynolds, S.C.P. (1997). *Conyza bilbaoana* also in Ireland. *BSBI News* **74**: 44-46.

Reynolds, S.C.P. and O'Reilly, H. (1986). *Elodea nuttallii* (Planchon) H. St John in County Dublin. *INJ* **22**: 119-120.

Riely, J.O. and Page, S.E. (1990). *Ecology of Plant Communities*. Longman Scientific and Technical, Harlow.

Rohan, P.K. (1986). *The Climate of Ireland* (2nd edn). Meteorological Service, Dublin.

Rutty, J. (1772). *An Essay towards a Natural History of the County of Dublin*. Vol. 1: *Botany*. W. Sleater, Dublin.

Salisbury, E. (1964). *Weeds and Aliens* (2nd edn). The New Naturalist Series. Collins, London.

Scannell, M.J.P. (1971). *Ceratophyllum demersum* L. in County Dublin. *INJ* **17**: 61.

Scannell, M.J.P. (1977). *Elodea nuttallii* (Planch.) St. John in the pond at Glasnevin. *INJ* **19**: 130.

Scannell, M.J.P. and Synnott, D.M. (1972). *Census Catalogue of the Flora of Ireland.* The Stationery Office, Dublin.

Scully, R.W. (1916). *Flora of County Kerry.* Hodges, Figgis & Co. Ltd., Dublin.

Sell, P.D. and Murrell, G. (1996). *Flora of Great Britain and Ireland.* Vol. **5**. Cambridge University Press, Cambridge.

Sheehy Skeffington, M.J. and Wymer, E.D. (1991). Irish salt marshes - an outline review. Pp. 77-91 in: Quigley, M.B. (Ed.). *A Guide to the Sand Dunes of Ireland.* European Union for Dune Conservation and Coastal Management, c/o Geography Department, Trinity College, Dublin.

Sheppard, R. (1993). *Ireland's Wetland Wealth, the Birds of the Estuaries, Lakes, Coasts, Rivers, Bogs and Turloughs of Ireland.* Irish Wildbird Conservancy, Dublin.

Simms, G. (1982). *William Molyneux of Dublin.* Irish Academic Press, Dublin.

Smith, J.E. (1818). *Compendium Florae Britannicae.* (3rd edn). Longman, Hurst, Rees, Orme & Brown, London.

Smith, J.E. (1824-1836). *The English Flora.* Vols. **1-5**. Longman, London.

Sowerby, J. and Smith, J.E. (1790-1814). *English Botany.* Vols **1-36**. J. Davis, London.

Stewart, A., Pearman, D.A. and Preston, C.D. (1994). *Scarce Plants in Britain.* Joint Nature Conservation Council, Peterborough.

Stewart, N.F. and Church, J.M. (1992). *Red Data Books of Britain and Ireland: Stoneworts.* The Joint Nature Conservation Committee, Peterborough.

Sweeney, J.C. (1987). The urban heat island of Dublin City. *Irish Geography* **20**: 1-10.

Synnott, D.M. (1973). Hedge dating in Duleek. *Annala Dhamhliag* **3**: 21-24.

Synnott, D.M. (1990). The bryophytes of Lambay island. *Glasra (new series)* **1**: 65-81.

Threlkeld, C. (1726, re-issued in 1727). *Synopsis Stirpium Hibernicarum.* Davys, Norris & Worrall, Dublin.

Tutin, T.G., Heywood, V.H., Burges, N.A., Moore, D.M., Valentine, D.H., Walters, S.M. and Webb, D.A. (Eds). (1964-80). *Flora Europaea.* Vols **1-5**. Cambridge University Press, Cambridge.

Wade, W. (1794). *Catalogus Systematicus Plantarum Indigenarum in Comitatu Dublinensi Inventarum.* G. Sleater, Dublin.

Wade, W. (1804). Plantae rariores in Hibernia inventae. *Transactions of the Dublin Society* Vol. **4**: 1-214.

Walsh, L. (1978). *Richard Heaton of Ballyskenagh 1601-1666.* Parkmore Press, Roscrea.

Warburton, J. Whitelaw, J. and Walsh, R. (1818). *History of the City of Dublin.* Cadell & Davies, London.

Watson, H.C. (1847-1859). *Cybele Britannica.* Vols. **1-5**. Longman, London.

Watson, H.C. (1873-1874). *Topographical Botany.* T. Ditten, London.

Webb, D.A. (1953). *An Irish Flora.* (2nd edn). Dundalgan Press, Dundalk.

Webb, D.A. (1983). The flora of Ireland in its European context (The Boyle Medal discourse, 1982). *J. Life Sci. R. Dubl. Soc.* **4**: 143-160.

Webb, D.A. (1986). The hey-day of Irish botany, 1866-1916. *The Scottish Naturalist* **1986**: 123-134.

Webb, D.A. and Scannell, M.J.P. (1983). *Flora of Connemara and the Burren*. Royal Dublin Society, Dublin; Cambridge University Press, Cambridge.

White, J. (1808). *An Essay on the Indigenous Grasses of Ireland*. Graisberry & Campbell, Dublin.

White, J. (Ed.) (1982). *Studies on Irish Vegetation*. Royal Dublin Society, Dublin.

Whittaker, E.J. (1981). *A Seventeenth Century Flora of Cumbria. William Nicolson's Catalogue of Plants*. The Surtees Society, Gateshead.

Wyse Jackson, P.N. (1993). *The Building Stones of Dublin: a Walking Guide*. Country House, Dublin.

Wyse Jackson, P.N., Stone, J.J., Parkes, M.A. and Sanders, I.S. (1993). *Field Guide to the Geology of some Localities in County Dublin*. Department of Geology, Trinity College, Dublin; ENFO, Dublin.

Wyse Jackson, P.S. (1988). *Groenlandia densa* (L.) Fourr. in Dublin. *INJ* **22**: 457.

Wyse Jackson, P.[S.] and Sheehy Skeffington, M.[J.] (1984). *The Flora of Inner Dublin*. Royal Dublin Society in association with the Dublin Naturalists' Field Club, Dublin.

Wyse Jackson, P.S., Moriarty, C. and Akeroyd, J.R. (Eds) (1988). *In the Field of the Naturalists*. The Dublin Naturalists' Field Club, Dublin.

PART II

SYSTEMATIC SECTION
EXPLANATORY NOTES ON THE SYSTEMATIC
AND SUPPLEMENTARY LISTS

The Systematic and Supplementary Lists contain a summary of the results of the Dublin Naturalists' Field Club's (DNFC) survey of the flora of Co. Dublin. The survey was mainly carried out over a ten year period starting in 1983. Plants were recorded in each 1 km x 1 km square in the county, totalling some 1000 squares. To put these records in context, many historical records are included, particularly those of Colgan (1904) in his *Flora of the County Dublin* (= *Colgan*) and those in *A Supplement to Colgan's Flora of the County Dublin* (Anon. 1961 = *Suppl*). The latter publication contained the results of field work also carried out by Field Club members and the year of its publication, 1961, is used as the divide between 'recent' records (post-1961) and 'old' records (pre-1961) given in the Lists.

While no attempt has been made to incorporate all the plant records in the published literature since *Colgan* and *Suppl* in the text, additional references are given where they provide relevant or interesting information on the status, occurrence or history of a species in the county. The Bibliography in Appendix 1 contains a comprehensive list of publications and unpublished sources since *Colgan*.

PLANTS INCLUDED
The Systematic List includes vascular plants (Clubmosses, Horsetails, Ferns and Flowering Plants) which were found growing in the wild in Co. Dublin. The majority of these plants are native. If not native in the county, they are usually well established or, if occurring casually, can be found on a fairly regular basis. Also included in the Systematic List is a group of green algae, the Charophytes or Stoneworts, frequently collected with other aquatic plants. Approximately 1150 taxa are listed: 925 species (including 15 Charophytes), 52 subspecies, 76 hybrids, 32 microspecies of *Rubus fruticosus* agg. Bramble and 72 microspecies of *Taraxacum officinale* agg. Dandelion. During the Field Club's survey, 59 species and 11 hybrids previously recorded from the county were not re-found. Information for a further 189 taxa of casual plants not found on a regular basis and non-native plants (= alien plants) which were either not established in the wild or which were found infrequently during the main recording period is given in the Supplementary List which follows the Systematic List.

NOMENCLATURE
The scientific names, authorities, common names and the sequence of families, genera and species follow Stace (1991) with some exceptions. Nomenclature follows Edees and Newton (1988) for *Rubus fruticosus* agg., Dudman and Richards (1995) for *Taraxacum officinale* agg., and Allen (1950) and Moore (1979) for the Charophytes. The common names used in Stace (1991) are largely based on the work of Dony *et al.* (1986), as are the common names in Scannell and Synnott (1987). Additional common names given in Webb (1977) are included where in frequent use. Official names in the Irish language are not included and may be found in Scannell and Synnott (1987).

Allen, G.O. (1950). *British Stoneworts (Charophyta)*. Haslemere Natural History Society, Arbroath.

Dony, J.G., Jury, S.L. and Perring, F.H. (1986). *English Names of Wild Flowers*. (2nd edn). Botanical Society of the British Isles, London.

Dudman, A.A. and Richards, A.J. (1995). *Dandelions of the British Isles*. BSBI Handbook (unpublished draft).

Edees, E.S. and Newton, A. (1988). *Brambles of the British Isles*. The Ray Society, London.

Moore, J.A. (1979). The current status of the Characeae (Stoneworts) in the British Isles. *Watsonia* **12**: 297-309.

Scannell, M.J.P. and Synnott, D.M. (1987). *Census Catalogue of the Flora of Ireland*. (2nd edn). The Stationery Office, Dublin. (= CC2).

Stace, C.A. (1991). *New Flora of the British Isles*. Cambridge University Press, Cambridge. (= *Stace*).

Webb, D.A. (1977). *An Irish Flora*. (6th edn). Dundalgan Press, Dundalk.

Synonyms (scientific names which have been superseded or rejected) are given only where they were the scientific names used in *Colgan*, *Suppl* and *CC2* or, more rarely, in Webb (1977). They are placed in brackets, without authorities, after the scientific name, e.g. **Myosotis discolor** Pers. (*M. versicolor*) - the latter name was used in *Colgan*.

For hybrids, the parent species are given, followed by the hybrid name and authority in brackets, e.g. **Quercus petraea** x **Q. robur** (**Q**. x **rosacea** Bechst.).

STATUS
The status of a plant taxon, whether 'native', 'possibly introduced', 'probably introduced' or 'alien', refers to Ireland and follows *CC2* in the main. Where it differs, the status in Co. Dublin has been re-evaluated by the editors. In this *Flora*, the following definitions of status are used:

Native: plants which are indigenous to Ireland and for which there is no evidence that they arrived as a result of human activity.

Alien: plants which are definitely known to have been introduced as a result of human activity.

Possibly introduced: plants which may have been introduced as a result of human activity.

Probably introduced: plants for which there is a strong suspicion that they were introduced as a result of human activity.

Casual: plants which do not persist in a locality without re-introduction.

Naturalized: introduced plants which have become well established in the wild.

The above categories are not mutually exclusive; populations of certain species may be native in some places and result from human introduction in other places, e.g. **Lysimachia nummularia** Creeping-Jenny, native by rivers but a garden escape in the city. Of the 925 species in the Systematic List, some 699 are considered to be native, 31 possibly introduced, 53 probably introduced and 142 are aliens. Casual plants and alien plants which are not fully naturalized are included in the Supplementary List.

A plant species protected by the Wildlife Act (1976) and scheduled by the Flora Protection Order (1987) is described as a **Protected Species** (see Curtis and McGough 1988). The following 18 Protected Species have been recorded in Co. Dublin (the three not refound since 1961 are in brackets):

Centaurium pulchellum	Lesser Centaury
(Clinopodium acinos)	(Basil Thyme)
Filago minima	Small Cudweed
Galeopsis angustifolia	Red Hemp-nettle
(Gnaphalium sylvaticum)	(Heath Cudweed)
Groenlandia densa	Opposite-leaved Pondweed
Hammarbya paludosa	Bog Orchid
Hordeum secalinum	Meadow Barley
Hypericum hirsutum	Hairy St John's-wort
Kickxia elatine	Sharp-leaved Fluellen
(Mertensia maritima)	(Oysterplant)
Orchis morio	Green-winged Orchid
Ornithopus perpusillus	Bird's-foot
Papaver hybridum	Rough Poppy
Pseudorchis albida	Small-white Orchid
Puccinellia fasciculata	Borrer's Saltmarsh-grass
Saxifraga granulata	Meadow Saxifrage
Viola hirta	Hairy Violet

DISTRIBUTION

For the purposes of this survey, Co. Dublin was divided into eight Districts, five north of the River Liffey (Districts 1 - 5) and three south of that river (Districts 6 - 8). The Districts (Fig. 5) are the same as those described in *Colgan* and later used in *Suppl*. They were based on the baronial divisions of the county, but with some modifications to make the boundaries more readily identifiable in the field, for example, sometimes modified to follow streams or roads. Details of the boundaries are given at the beginning of each District Account in Part I.

The post-1961 record of a plant taxon in any of the eight Districts in Co. Dublin is indicated by the number(s) of the District(s) in which it occurs, and a bracketed number is used for pre-1961 records which were not refound, e.g. **Coeloglossum viride** Frog Orchid (1) (2) **5** (6) **7 8**, found in Districts 5, 7 and 8 since 1961, with pre-1961 records only for Districts 1, 2 and 6.

For less common species, details of habitat, location, recorder and year when found are given for each District in which they occur (see PLANT RECORDS below).

Maps are included for over 200 selected species, excluding rare species for which there are few records. The dots on the maps represent occurrence of the species in 2 km x 2 km (tetrad) squares. The distribution pattern of a particular species should be interpreted in conjunction with the geological and soil maps and with the habitat comments for that species. Records for the two most easterly tetrads on Howth Head are combined with those in their adjacent counterparts because of the small areas of land in the former.

FREQUENCY AND HABITATS

The frequency of a plant taxon refers to its frequency in Co. Dublin and/or in the habitat or habitats where it is found. The terms abundant, very common, common/frequent, occasional, rare, very rare and extremely rare are used. Some plants are widespread and common in the habitats in which they occur, e.g. **Galium saxatile** Heath Bedstraw. Other plants are found in a very specific kind of habitat e.g. **Papaver argemone** Prickly Poppy, occasional on sandy roadsides and in fallow ground. A particular species may be common in certain areas or habitats, but rare in others, e.g. **Senecio squalidus** Oxford Ragwort, common as an urban weed and rare elsewhere in the county. The Habitat Accounts are in Part I.

PLANT RECORDS

In general, if there are five or fewer records of a species for any one District, or if a species is rare in the wider Irish context, the individual records are cited and the following information is given: frequency, habitat(s), location(s), recorder(s) and year(s) when found. Historical information is included for many species, the main sources used being *Colgan* and *Suppl* as well as some herbarium records. This information provides a summary of the previously known distribution of a species which can be compared with the present known distribution. The phrase 'still at' indicates the confirmation of an earlier record. Additional references, mainly post-1961, are given where relevant.

Records published in the *Flora of Inner Dublin* (Wyse Jackson and Sheehy Skeffington 1984) are indicated by 'FID' and the reader is referred to that work for further information. The Inner City, as defined in *FID*, is as follows: starting at Ringsend where the Grand Canal joins the River Liffey, the boundary follows the Grand Canal west to Rialto, turning north-east along the route of the canal's infilled branch by Grand Canal Bank, north along Basin Street Upper and Steevens' Lane, across the Liffey, along Infirmary Road and the Broadstone railway line to Cabra, and returning by the Royal Canal to its junction with the Liffey at North Wall Quay.

New Irish and new Co. Dublin records are indicated by **NIR** and **NCR** respectively. **NDR** refers to a new record for a District. However, not all occurrences of such records are indicated, *i.e.* for some microspecies, recent taxonomic splits, hybrids and the casuals and aliens listed in the Supplementary List.

The contributors of plant records and their initials, abbreviations for herbaria and general abbreviations and terms used in the text are listed below. The abbreviations for the Major References cited in the Systematic List are also given below; all other references are in the Bibliography in Appendix I.

PLACE NAMES AND LOCATIONS

Place names generally follow the spelling on Ordnance Survey maps for Co. Dublin unless the commonly used form is different. Ordnance Survey grid references have not been included in the Systematic and Supplementary Lists, but may be found in the Topographical Index. Grid references for streets have not usually been included in the Topographical Index and the reader is referred to indexed street maps. Many of the locations mentioned in the text are in private ownership and permission for entry should be sought from the owner or occupier.

RECORDERS

An individual record concludes with the initials of the recorder(s) and the year(s) of the record, e.g. CB/91 refers to a record made by Catriona Brady in 1991. The initials used for the recorders are as follows:

AJR	=	John Richards	JRA	=	John Akeroyd
ALP	=	Anthony Primavesi	JS	=	Jonathan Shackleton
AN	=	Alan Newton	KF	=	Keith Ferguson
BB	=	Betty Blyth	MAF	=	Tony Farragher
BM	=	Brian Madden	MC	=	Marcella Campbell
CB	=	Catriona Brady	MD	=	Marie Dromey
CH	=	Christopher Haworth	MN	=	Margaret Norton
CM	=	Con Maxwell	MS	=	Maura (M.J.P.) Scannell
DA	=	David Allen	MSS	=	Micheline Sheehy Skeffington
DAS	=	David Simpson	MWJ	=	Michael Wyse Jackson
DAW	=	David Webb	NMcG	=	Noel McGough
DD	=	Declan Doogue	NS	=	Nick Stewart
DNFC	=	several members of the DNFC	PC	=	Peter Carvill
DK	=	Daniel Kelly	PG	=	Philip Grant
DN	=	David Nash	PH	=	Pauline Hodson
DS	=	Donal Synnott	PP	=	Peter Pitkin
EJ	=	Eleanor Jennings	PWJ	=	Peter Wyse Jackson
ENL	=	Eimear Nic Lughadha (E. Lowe)	RF	=	Rosaleen Fitzgerald
EMcA	=	Eveleen McAuley	RG	=	Roger Goodwillie
GS	=	Gerry Sharkey	RLP	=	Robert Lloyd Praeger
HJH	=	Howard Hudson	RMcM	=	Richard McMullen
HOR	=	Helen O'Reilly	SR	=	Sylvia Reynolds
JB	=	Jean Bobear	TC	=	Tom Curtis
JK	=	Jimmy King	TK	=	Terry Keatinge
JP	=	John Parnell	WAW	=	William Watts
JR	=	Julian Reynolds			

HERBARIA

The herbaria listed here contain collections of dried plants which include the voucher specimens from Co. Dublin cited in the Systematic and Supplementary Lists.

BEL	=	Ulster Museum, Belfast
BM	=	British Museum (Natural History), London
CAM	=	St John's College, Cambridge
DBN	=	National Botanic Gardens, Dublin
MANCH	=	Manchester Museum
OXF	=	University of Oxford, Botany School
TCD	=	Trinity College, Dublin, Botany Department

MAJOR REFERENCES

The following abbreviations are used for the principal publications and sources referred to in the Systematic List and text:

Brunker MS:	Annotated copies of *Colgan* in possession of DNFC members and other persons.
BSBI Atlas:	Perring, F.H. and Walters, S.M. (Eds) (1962). *Atlas of the British Flora.* Thomas Nelson & Sons, London.
CC1:	Scannell, M.J.P. and Synnott, D.M. (1972). *Census Catalogue of the Flora of Ireland.* The Stationery Office, Dublin.
CC2:	Scannell, M.J.P. and Synnott, D.M. (1987). *Census Catalogue of the Flora of Ireland.* (2nd edn). The Stationery Office, Dublin.
Colgan:	Colgan, N. (1904). *Flora of the County Dublin.* Hodges, Figgis & Co., Dublin.
Colgan & Scully:	Colgan, N. and Scully, R.W. (1898). *Cybele Hibernica.* (2nd edn). Ponsonby, Dublin.
Crit. Suppl:	Perring, F.H. and Sell, P.M. (1968). *Critical Supplement to the Atlas of the British Flora.* Thomas Nelson & Sons, London.
Cybele:	Moore, D. and More, A.G. (1866). *Contributions towards a Cybele Hibernica.* Hodges, Smith & Co., Dublin.
FID:	Wyse Jackson, P. and Sheehy Skeffington, M. (1984). *The Flora of Inner Dublin.* Royal Dublin Society in association with the Dublin Naturalists' Field Club.
Flora of Howth:	Hart, H.C. (1887). *The Flora of Howth.* Hodges, Figgis & Co., Dublin.
Ir. Flora:	Anonymous [Baily, K.S. = Lady Kane] (1833). *The Irish Flora.* Hodges & Smith, Dublin.
ITB:	Praeger, R.Ll. (1901). *Irish Topographical Botany. Proceedings of the Royal Irish Academy* (series 3) **7**: i-clxxxviii, 1-410.
Stace:	Stace, C.A. (1991). *New Flora of the British Isles.* Cambridge University Press, Cambridge.
Suppl:	Anonymous (1961). *A Supplement to Colgan's Flora of the County Dublin.* The Stationery Office, Dublin.

Full details of publications and their abbreviations referred to in the extracts from *Colgan* may be found in the Bibliography reproduced from that Flora in Appendix 2.

GENERAL ABBREVIATIONS AND TERMS

agg. = aggregate: a group of very similar species which are difficult to distinguish
auct. = *auctorum*: of various authors but not the original one
c. = *circa*: about
cf. = *confer*: comparable with
cm = centimetre
cv. = cultivar

et al. = *et alia*: and others

FID = *The Flora of Inner Dublin*; occurs in the inner city (see PLANT RECORDS and MAJOR
 REFERENCES above)

ha = hectare

hr = hour

ined. = *ineditus*: unpublished

km = kilometre

l = litre

m = metre

meq = milli-equivalent

mg = milligram

NCR = New County Record

NDR = New District Record

NIR = New Irish Record

op. cit. = *opere citato*: in the work cited

pro parte = in part

s.l. = *sensu lato*: in the broad sense

sp. = species (singular)

spp. = species (plural)

s.s. = *sensu stricto*: in the strict sense

subsp. = subspecies (singular)

subspp. = subspecies (plural)

taxon (plural taxa) = an undefined taxonomic grouping, such as a genus, species, subspecies,
 hybrid

tetrad = 2 km x 2 km square, based on Ordnance Survey grid

var. = *varietas*: variety

SUMMARY: ARRANGEMENT OF ENTRIES IN THE SYSTEMATIC LIST

Genus, species and authority **or** Hybrid - parent species given, with hybrid name and authority
 in brackets **or** Species and subspecies with authority

Synonym(s), without authority, in brackets

Common name

Status in Co. Dublin

Extract from *Colgan* for selected species

Extract from *Suppl* for selected species

Other pre-1961 records

District number(s) - where taxon found post-1961

District number(s) in brackets - taxon previously found in a District, but not refound post-1961

Frequency in Co. Dublin and/or in habitat(s) where found

Habitat(s) where found

Additional information and references (author(s) and publication date; full references in
 Bibliography in Appendix 1)

For less common species, following the District number, details of habitat(s), location(s),
 recorder(s) and year(s) when found

Map showing distribution - each dot represents occurrence in a 2 km x 2 km square

SYSTEMATIC LIST

CHAROPHYTA   (Stoneworts)

CHARACEAE

Little critical work has been done on the Stoneworts since the beginning of the 20th century. While there have been taxonomic changes, comparisons with earlier work can be generally and validly made. One new species has been recorded and three (including some considered by *Colgan* to be aliens in Dublin) have not been refound. Nomenclature essentially follows Allen, G.O. (1950) *British Stoneworts (Charophyta)*. Haslemere. James J. King and David W. Nash (1994) have published a comprehensive review of Charophyta of County Dublin.

Chara

C. aculeolata Kutz. *(C. polyacantha)*
Native
Colgan: 4. Royal Canal at Lucan, 1894 (Praeger) Top. Bot. First record in 1901; Top. Bot.

(4)

It may be extinct in the county.
_ _

C. aspera Deth. ex Willd.
Native
Colgan: Alien? 4. Royal Canal at Lucan in 1894 (Praeger) Top. Bot,

(4)

It may be extinct in the county.
_ _

C. contraria A.Br. ex Kutz.
Native

| 4 | 5 | 6 | 7 |

Scattered at various sites along the Royal Canal (4), especially from Clonsilla westwards; rare elsewhere.
4. Ornamental pond in the National Botanic Gardens, Glasnevin, T. Champ/84, NS/91. Pond in Luttrellstown Estate, DN/89.
5. Pond at the 5th green, Royal Dublin Golf-course, JK, DN/89. Wet pathway at Balscadden, DN/90. Reservoir near St Anne's Golf-course clubhouse, JK, DN/89.
6. Pond south of the Grand Canal at Gollierstown, DN/89.
7. Grand Canal between Suir and Herberton Roads, DN/89.
_ _

C. delicatula C.A. Agardh sensu J. Groves & Bullock-Webster, non Desv.
Native

| 4 | 5 | 6 | (7) |

4. Ornamental pond in the National Botanic Gardens, Glasnevin, T. Champ/84, NS/91. Royal Canal near Blanchardstown, NS/91.
5. In five different ponds on Portmarnock Golf-course, JK, DN/88, 89. Reservoir on Howth Golf-course, DN/90.
6. Pond on the north side of the Grand Canal at Gollierstown, MN/88.

C. desmacantha (H. & J. Groves) J. Groves & Bullock-Webster
(*C. aspera* var. *desmacantha*)
Native

Colgan: 4. In the Canal at Blanchardstown, 1889 (*Scully*) *Groves 1898* – and in the same canal near Lucan, 1895!

It may be extinct in the county.

C. globularis Thuill. *(C. fragilis, C. globularis* var. *capillacea)*
Native

Colgan: 2. Ponds at Lusk, 1900; 3. Pools by the Ward river above Swords, 1903; 5. At Howth, 1860 (*D. Moore*) *Groves 1895.* Pools near the Quarries, Sutton (*D. McArdle*) *Praeger 1895.*

Suppl: 2. Lily pond in garden, Kenure Park, Rush (A.W.S., 1923). 5. Water-hole on golf links, North Bull (1947). 8. S.W. bog at Ballybetagh (1946).

| (2) | (3) | 4 | 5 | 6 | 7 | 8 |

4. Quarry Pond in the Phoenix Park, PR/89. Royal Canal at Cross Guns Bridge, JK/90. Royal Canal at Liffey Junction, NS/91.
5. Ponds at the 2nd and 7th green at Portmarnock Golf-course, DN/88. 7th green at the Royal Dublin Golf-course, DN/88.
6. Two ponds north and south of the Grand Canal at Gollierstown, DN/89.
7. Grand Canal below Baggot Street Bridge and between Suir and Herberton Roads, DN/90.
8. Concrete reservoirs below the Owendoher River at Edmondstown, DN/90.

C. hispida L.
Native

Colgan: 1. Bog of the Ring, 1895: N.C. 2. In a bog near Balruddery (*Dr. Scott*) *Mack. Rar.* 4. Canal at Lucan, 1894. 5. At Raheny, 1893 (*Praeger*) *Groves 1895.* Pool near Feltrim, 1900; Raheny quarries, 1903; and 6. by the Grand Canal at Gollierstown, 1903: N.C.

Suppl: Occasional. 5. Pond at St. Anne's Clontarf (1956)

| (1) | (2) | 4 | (5) | 6 |

4. Two ponds in Luttrellstown Estate, DN, MN/89. Royal Canal west of Collins Bridge, MN/89, Royal Canal at Castleknock, NS/91.
6. Pond on the north side and two ponds on the south side of the Grand Canal at Gollierstown, MN/88 & DN/89.

C. rudis (A.Br.) Leonh.
Native

| 4 |

4. Royal Canal between Collins Bridge and Pakenham Bridge, JK, DN/91.

C. vulgaris L.
Native

| 2 | 3 | 4 | 5 | 6 | 7 | 8 |

---

var. **vulgaris**

| 2 | 3 | 4 | 5 | 6 | 7 | 8 |

At various sites in the Royal Canal (4) westwards from Clonsilla and in the Grand Canal from Baggot Street to the 7th lock; rare to occasional elsewhere.
2. Balrothery Reservoir, DD/88. Pond at Balbriggan Golf-course, T. Champ/91.
3. Cattle drinking trough at Turvey House, JK/88. Two ponds and a reservoir on the Island Golf-course, Malahide, JK, DN/89. Drain in the Ward River valley, JK/89. Tonelagee Reservoir, JK/89. Drain on Balcarrick Golf-course, T. Champ/89.
4. Lake at the National Botanic Gardens, Glasnevin, T. Champ/84. Machinery pond at Mountjoy Cross, Phoenix Park, DN, JK/88. Tracks and quarry lake at Huntstown, DN, MN/89.
6. North Brittas Pond, DN/88, 89. Grand Canal at the 12th lock, DN, MN/88, 89.
7. Wet area at the edge of the northern reservoir in Glenasmole, DN, MN/88, 89. Pond in Tymon Park off Wellington Lane, P. Fitzmaurice/88. Pool beside the River Dodder at Firhouse, DN/90.
8. Pool near the Sandyford Industrial Estate, SR/86. Pond at the Roadstone works at Ballycorus, SR/88. Reservoir at Leopardstown Racecourse, SR/87. Pool at U.C.D. (Belfield) near the car park, DN/89. Pond at the 11th tee at Elm Park Golf-course, DN/89.

---

var. **longibracteata** (Kutz.) J. Groves & Bullock-Webster

| 3 | 4 | 5 | 7 |

On various golf-courses in 5; rare elsewhere.
3. Dune-slack at Donabate, SR/87. Beaverstown Golf-course, JK, DN/89. 6th green on Corballis Golf-course, DN, JK/89.
4. Drain at Mulhuddart, JS, MN/87. Ditch by the Royal Canal at Cabra, DN, JK/89. Huntstown Quarry, NS/93.
5. Wet tracks at Feltrim Quarry, DN/89. Drain at Gay Brook, DN/89. Ornamental pond at Thormanby Road, DN/89. Ornamental pond in the south-east corner of St Anne's Park, Raheny, PG, DN/91. Two ornamental ponds at Santry Garda Station, JK/92.
7. New pond at Tymon Park, Wellington Lane, DN/88.

Nitella

N. gracilis (Smith) C.A. Agardh
Native

Colgan Native: 8. Near Ballybetagh, Glencullen, 1872 (D. Orr) Bab. Man. 8th Ed. & Groves 1895. Open to doubt, the authority for the station not being satisfactory.

| 4 |

4. Lake at the National Botanic Gardens, Glasnevin, MS/80. Some doubt exists as to the identity of plants from this site; some specimens have been determined as **N. mucronata** (A. Braun) Miquel; however, the balance of opinion suggests that the specimens are **N. gracilis**.

N. opaca (Bruz.) C.A. Agardh / **N. flexilis** (L.) C.A. Agardh
Native

Colgan: 4. In the Royal Canal near Lucan, 1900: N.C. 5. Hill of Howth, 1860 *(Moore) Groves 1895*. Near the Source of Ballsaggart stream, Howth, 1894; *Praeger 1895*. 6. In the Grand Canal above Clondalkin, 1902: N.C.

Suppl. 7. Abundant in Kimmage Millpond (J.P. Brunker, 1921). This pond has since been filled in.

| 4 | (5) | (6) | 7 | 8 |

Infertile specimens of these species were not identified to species level during the current survey but placed within this aggregate grouping.

4. Lake in the grounds of Veterinary Research Laboratory at Abbotstown, DN/90, (**N. opaca**). Royal Canal west of Drumcondra Bridge, NS/91, (**N. flexilis**).
7. West side of the southern lake in Glenasmole, DN/91 & DN, JK/92, (**N. opaca**). Grand Canal at Ranelagh and Davitt Road, JK/88. Grand Canal at Clondalkin near the M50 motorway, DN/91.
8. Pool at the head of a drain at the south end of Ballybetagh Bog, SR/86 & DN/89, (**N. opaca**); apparently now gone, DN/92. Ornamental pond at Johnstown Road Garden Centre, Cabinteely, DN/90, (**N. opaca**).

Tolypella

T. glomerata (Desv.) Leonh. (*T. nidifica* var. *glomerata*)
Native

Colgan: 4. Canal near Glasnevin, 1857 *(Moore) Groves 1890*. Abundant in the Royal Canal; and 7. In the Grand Canal near Dublin, 1890 *(Scully) Groves 1895*.

Suppl: 4 and 7. Still in both canals (J.P. Brunker, 1922).

| 4 | (7) |

4. Royal Canal west of Collins Bridge and west of Granard Bridge, and at Longford Bridge, JK, DN/91 & NS/91. Huntstown Quarry, NS/93.

T. intricata (Trent. ex Roth) Leonh.
Possibly introduced

Colgan: 4. Royal Canal and ditches near the Tolka: *Guide*. Royal Canal near Glasnevin, before 1860 *(Moore) Groves 1890* – Still there in 1896 *(F.W. Moore & D. McArdle) Cyb II*.

| 4 | 5 | 7 |

Scattered along the Royal Canal.
4. Scattered between Pakenham Bridge and the county boundary on the Royal Canal, DN, JK/91. From the North Strand to Longford Bridge on the Royal Canal, NS/91.
5. Royal Canal west of North Strand, NS/91.
7. Grand Canal, scattered between Rathmines and Clogher road, NS/93.

T. prolifera (Ziz ex A. Braun) Leonh.
Possibly introduced

Colgan: Alien? 4. Royal Canal near Glasnevin *(Moore) Groves 1890*.

| (4) | 7 |

7. Grand Canal just west of Portobello Bridge and at Parnell Road near Harold's Cross Bridge, DN/92.

LYCOPODIOPSIDA   (Clubmosses)

LYCOPODIACEAE

Huperzia

H. selago (L.) Bernh. ex Schrank & C. Martius (*Lycopodium selago*)
Fir Clubmoss   Native

Colgan: 5. On the moor a little north of the marsh near the summit of Howth: *Flor. Howth.* 7. On Seefingan mountain, 1882; sparingly on the northern slope of Seecawn mountain, 1892, and frequent on the upper western slopes, 1892-1903; in wet bog by the Cot Brook, Kippure, 1893, and above Piperstown, 1902; 8. Sparingly on the Three Rock mountain above Ballyedmonduff, 1900: *N.C.* Quite a rare species save on the mountains above the head waters of the Dodder. In District 8 it appears to be absent from large areas of elevated mountain bog and moorland.

Suppl: 5. Never re-found on Howth. 7. Still on N. slope of Seecawn (1955) and frequent on W. slope (1955). Still above Piperstown (1920-1950) and on Three Rock Mountain (1953).

Rare, on bare peat on moorland and in rough grassland. Not refound on Three Rock Mountain (8).

7. Still in various locations in the upper Glenasmole Valley although some populations may have been eliminated by the planting of conifers. Still on the west and north sides of Seahan (Seecawn) Mountain, ENL/83 & SR, DN, CB/90. West of Castlekelly, ENL/83. Beside the fork in the road east of Castlekelly, on the Featherbed/Piperstown road, DD, EMcA/83. Many scattered plants on gravel between granite outcrops on the summit of Kippure, CB, PH, SR/90.
8. Wet area in the Glencullen Valley opposite Walsh's Lane on the lower slopes of Two Rock Mountain, SR/87.

Lycopodium

L. clavatum L.
Stag's-horn Clubmoss   Native

Colgan: 6. Abundant on the summit of Slieve Thoul, Brittas, 1894-1902: *N.C.* 7. Kelly's Glen, Ballinascorney and other places on the Dublin mountains: *Ir. Flor.* Cruagh mountain, Feather Bed and Kelly's Glen, rare: *Kinahan 1854.* Abundant on open grassy slopes and amongst bracken on Glassavullaun mountain, Glenasmole, 1895-1900: *N.C.*

Suppl: 6. Not seen recently on Slieve Thoul. 7. At 1, 600 ft. on Seecawn (J.P. Brunker, 1935). On W. side of Ballymorefinn at the point where Brittas River emerges from the forestry plantation (A.W. Stelfox, 1951). Still in Kinahan's station on Featherbed Mountain, by Military Road about half a mile above Killakee (1954).

Very rare, in open ground in heathland. Not refound at the stations on Slieve Thoul (6) which includes Saggart Hill and is now largely planted with conifers, nor on Ballymorefinn and the Featherbed Mountain (7). Similarly, much of the formerly open grassy slopes on Glassavullaun Mountain, Glenasmole (7) where Colgan found this species are now densely invaded by bracken.

7. Summit of Seahan (Seecawn) Mountain, ENL, HOR/83.
8. Spoil heaps from old granite quarries on the north side of Prince William's Seat, TK/67.

Diphasiastrum

D. alpinum (L.) Holub (*Lycopodium alpinum*)
Alpine Clubmoss   Native

Suppl: 7. On or near the summit of Cruagh Mountain (W.B. Bruce in *I.Nat.,* XVI, 1907). Bruce's discovery was made when he was lost in a fog but his specimen is in the Herbarium of the National Museum [DBN]. He was never able to find the station again, and later searches by other botanists failed also. Most of the mountain is now covered by forestry plantations.

| 7 |

Extremely rare, in shallow pockets of bare peaty soil. Not refound on the summit of Cruagh Mountain (7).

7. A few plants on the west-south-west face of the summit of Seahan (Seecawn) Mountain, HOR/75, 76. One plant, west-north-west of the summit of Seahan Mountain, SR, CB, DN/90.

SELAGINELLACEAE

Selaginella

S. selaginoides (L.) P. Beauv.
Lesser Clubmoss   Native

Colgan: 2. Marshy ground by the sea between Skerries and Loughshinny, 1895: *N.C.* 3. Portrane: *Guide.* Frequent and in some spots abundant in damp hollows of the Portrane sandhills, 1904: *N.C.* 5. At Howth: *Wade Rar.* North side of Hill of Howth (*D. McArdle*) *Ir. Nat.,* 1893. Sandy low grounds at Portmarnock: *Flor. Hib.* abundant here in hollows of the sandhills, 1904! 6. Marshy pasture above Saggard chapel, 1894: *N.C.* North of Slieve Thoul, 1895: *Rev. C.F. d'Arcy.* 7. Moist banks of the Dodder near Rathfarnham and marsh south of Mount Pelier, 1893; in Lugmore Glen, 1903; 8. Ticknock, 1903; Prince William's Seat, 1901: *N.C.*
Suppl: 3. Still at Portrane and Donabate sandhills (1948). 5. Still in one small marsh on Howth Head (1943-1956). Still in Portmarnock sandhills (1955). 7. Roadside in Ballinascorney Gap (1942-1948).
DNFC Annual Report for 1968: 7. Report of discovery "near Tallaght" of a new station. No further details, but known to be Whitestown, Tallaght (fide DD).

| 2 | (3) | 5 | (6) | 7 | 8 |

Very rare, in boggy ground and marshes. Not refound in the dune-slacks of north Co. Dublin (3 & 5) where it was formerly recorded.

2. A few plants, still in a marsh by the coast, between Skerries and Loughshinny, RF/90.
5. Still on Howth at Central Marsh, PWJ/77 & PG/90.
7. Still in a marsh at Ballinascorney Gap, DD/92.
8. A single plant, at about 365 m on the north-east facing slope of Glencullen Mountain, SR/84, near *Colgan's* station on Prince William's Seat.

EQUISETOPSIDA   (Horsetails)

EQUISETACEAE

Equisetum

E. hyemale L.
Rough Horsetail   Native

Colgan: 4. "It is found in Finglass Brook": *Rutty's Dublin.* In Luttrell's-town woods *(Dr Scott) Mack. Rar.* Lower road going to
Lucan; banks of the Liffey opposite Woodlands: *Ir. Flor.* Banks of the Liffey from a little above Woodlands to near Lucan,
1893-1904: N.C. 7. At Killakee *(Greenwood Pim) Cyb. II.* Abundant along a roadside fence east of Mount Venus, 1902
(Mrs Praeger) Praeger 1904 & MS. 8. Near Whitechurch: *Kinahan 1854.*
Suppl: Confirmed only from 7. Roadside near Mount Venus (1956).

Rare, on shaded riverbanks. Mrs Praeger's 1902 record, from a roadside fence east of Mount
Venus, may well be the same as Kinahan's "near Whitechurch" record (8).
6. South bank of the River Liffey at Lucan, HOR/85, **NDR**. Lucan Demesne, JP/85.
6/7. South bank of the River Liffey near the Wren's Nest Weir, JP, JS/84 & MN, JS/85.
8. Beside a stream, north of Kilgobbin Church, PC/83.

- -

E. hyemale x **E. variegatum (E.** x **trachyodon** A. Braun*)*
Mackay's Horsetail   Native
Suppl: 8. By Bride's Glen stream near Ballycorus (A.A. Lisney, 1930).

Not refound at its station below the old lead works by the Bride's Glen stream at
Ballycorus (8) despite repeated searches by SR and HOR.

- -

E. variegatum Schleicher
Variegated Horsetail   Native

Colgan: 4. In the Dublin Canal *(Mr Moore) Phytol.,* 1842, p. 338. Along the Royal Canal east of Clonsilla station, abundant for a
considerable distance *(Moore);* sparingly on the bank of the same canal below the bridge at Cross Guns, *(More) Cyb.* All
along the canal from Lucan to Liffey Junction, and especially abundant below Clonsilla, where it spreads for more than a mile
in a continuous dark green belt, 1903: N.C. 7. Along the Dodder river at Rathfarnham and at Bohernabreena: *Colgan 1893.*
By the Dodder above Old Bawn, 1903: N.C. First record in 1842: *Phytologist l.c.* The above records all refer to the *var. majus*
Syme, here taken as type. The Co. Dublin plant was long erroneously regarded as identical with *var. wilsoni Newman* from
Killarney, and was recorded as such in *Cybele. Var. arenarium Newman.* 3. At Portrane *(Moore) Cyb.* Sandhills opposite
Malahide *(Scully) Cyb. II.* – probably the same station as the foregoing – frequent here in 1904! 5. Found on Portmarnock
sands by Dr Taylor: *Warburton 1818.* Frequent in damp hollows of Portmarnock sandhills, 1900: N.C. First found by Dr Taylor
and first recorded in 1818: *Warburton.* The sandhill variety is a very dwarf and slender plant quite procumbent in grassy and
moss grown hollows, and scarcely discoverable without careful search on hands and knees.
Suppl: 3. Still at Donabate (1944). Still abundant along the Royal Canal (1957). 5. Still at Portmarnock sandhills (1957). 7.
Still along the River Dodder above Oldbawn (1957).

Very rare, in dune-slacks and on canal banks. Most plants of this species growing in dune-slacks in the county are prostrate, unlike typical **E. variegatum** var. **variegatum**; these have been called **E. variegatum** var. **arenarium** Newman. However, near water holes and in some other sites erect plants are occasionally found (var. **variegatum**). This species was formerly abundant on the margins of the Royal Canal (4) and *Colgan* also recorded it from a number of localities along the River Dodder (7). However, today few suitable habitats remain there (the bank of the River Dodder at Oldbawn has now been graded and converted to amenity grassland); indeed the last records for the area date from 1928 (M.Buchanan at Oldbawn and J.P.Brunker at Bohernabreena). The dredging of the Royal Canal in 1988 at Clonsilla (4) has severely reduced, if not destroyed, populations of the species in this area.

3. Dune-slack on the Island Golf-course, Malahide, PR/83, 87. Abundant in a large dune-slack on Portrane Peninsula, PR, DD/90.
4. By the Royal Canal, west of Clonsilla, a site largely destroyed by dredging in 1988, JS/83 (var. **variegatum**).
5. South and west of the Causeway, North Bull Island, D.Jeffrey, PP/75. Dune-slacks at the south end of North Bull Island, DD/90. Beside a water hazard and in the dune-slacks on Portmarnock Golf-course, DN, RF/88. A single plant at the north end of Portmarnock sand-hills, DD/89. Marsh in Kilrock Quarries, PG/90.
8. Field between Barnaslingan Lane and Ballycorus, south-east of Kiltiernan, SR, HOR/84 (var. **variegatum**).

E. fluviatile L. (*E. limosum*)
Water Horsetail   Native

| 1 | | 2 | | 3 | | 4 | | 5 | | 6 | | 7 | | 8 |

Scattered but locally common in margins of canals, ditches, pools and lakes.

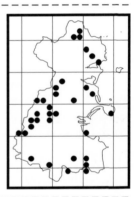

E. fluviatile × **E. arvense** (**E.** × **litorale** Kuehl. ex Rupr.)
Shore Horsetail   Native

Praeger, (1939): Edge of Royal Canal west of Lucan railway station.

| 1 | | 3 | | 4 | | 5 | | 6 | | 7 |

Rare, in drains on canal banks and in marshes.

1. Bog of the Ring, GS/88, **NDR.**
3. Malahide, RF/85, **NDR.**
4. On the banks of the Royal Canal, inner city stretch, DD, PWJ/81. On the banks of the Royal Canal, west of Ashtown and east of Kirkpatrick and Kennan Bridges, MN/88.
5. Near the railway at Portmarnock, DN/88, **NDR.**
6. North of Brittas, ENL/83, **NDR.** Scattered along the banks of the Grand Canal between Ballymakaily Mill and Hazelhatch, MN/88, 89.
7. Palmerston Marsh, DD/82, **NDR.**

FID.

E. arvense L.
Field Horsetail   Native

| 1 | 2 | 3 | 4 | 5 | 6 | 7 | 8 |

Very widespread. Common on waste ground, sand-dunes and roadsides.
FID.

E. sylvaticum L.
Wood Horsetail   Native

Colgan: 6. Sparingly by a stream north of Slieve Thoul, 1895: *Rev. C.F. d'Arcy.* 7. Kelly's Glen *(M.J. O'Kelly) Ir. Flor.* Frequent in the upper parts of Glenasmole (Kelly's Glen) along the Dodder affluents, as by the Slade, the Slade Brook and the Cot Brook, also frequently on banks by the upper channel of the waterworks at Castle Kelly, 1901; in upper Ballinascorney Glen, 1903: *N.C.* 8. Three Rock mountain, very fine and abundant: *Kinahan 1854.* On the north-east and south-east slopes of the Three Rock, 1893; abundant at the head of the Little Dargle and by the Glencullen river at Ballybrack, 1903: *N.C.*

| 6 | 7 | 8 |

Rare, in flushed grassland in upland areas.
6. Wet pasture on the slopes below Knockandinny Golf-course, JP/82 (apparently refinding C.F. d'Arcy's 1895 record from north of Slieve Thoul).
7. Still above the Cot and Slade Brooks and nearby on a boggy slope, west of Castlekelly, DD/82 & HOR/85.
8. By a stream on the east slope of Glendoo mountain, HOR, CB/86. Wet meadow by the Glencullen River, west of Boranaraltry Bridge, HOR/85. Roadside banks and adjacent fields near the top of the Ticknock road, SR, HOR/83. Still on the south-east slope of Three Rock Mountain near Ballyedmonduff and east of the Burrow Road, PC/75 & HOR/85. Barnacullia, PC/75.

E. palustre L.
Marsh Horsetail   Native

| 1 | 2 | 3 | 4 | 5 | 6 | 7 | 8 |

Scattered but locally common in marshy ground and on canal banks.
FID.

E. telmateia Ehrh. (*E. maximum*)
Great Horsetail   Native

| 1 | 2 | 4 | 5 | 6 | 7 | 8 |

Locally abundant, especially in parts of 1, 2, 7 & 8: associated with spring lines, seepage on slopes and damp woodland, ditches and field margins.
4. Harristown House, north of Finglas, MN/83, **NDR.**

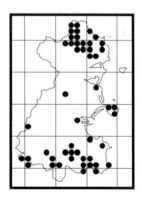

PTEROPSIDA   (Ferns)

OPHIOGLOSSACEAE

Ophioglossum

O. vulgatum L.
Adder's-tongue   Native

Colgan: 1. Abundant in the Naul Hills, as at Walshestown, near Nag's Head, near Clonany bridge, &c., 1895-1903; 2. South-east of Hollywood, near Ballough, near Kenure Park, &c., 1895; at Whitestown, Rush, 1903: N.C. 3. Remarkably abundant on the northern slope of Pilot's Hill, Lambay island: *Flor. Lambay.* Near the monument, Portrane, 1894 *(W.H. Bloomer) Colgan 1895.* Abundant by the Ward river above Knocksedan, 1896; south of Thomondtown, 1902: N.C. 4. Scribblestown, near the old orchard: *Wade Rar.* Lawn of the Observatory, Dunsink: *Ir. Flor.* Abundant by the Santry river near Sellick, 1895 and in marshy pastures at Dunsoghly castle, 1903: *N.C.* 5. At Stockoole (between Cloghran and St Doulough's) *Molyneux App. to Threlkeld.* Abundant at Stockhole and at St Doulough's, 1903; in Howth demesne, 1898; on Feltrim Hill, 1902: *N.C.* 6. On the southern slope of Slieve Thoul, 1895: *Rev. C.F. d'Arcy.* Near Athgoe, 1897; by the canal near Clondalkin, 1903: N.C. 7. All along the bluffs of the Dodder valley, very abundant at Kilnasantan (St Anne's), 1854: *Kinahan 1854.* Heights along the east side of Glenasmole, from a little above Friarstown to the head of the glen, 1895: *Dr E.J. McWeeney.* Abundant near Ballyfermot and in mountain pastures in Lugmore, 1895: &c.: N.C. 8. Bilalley Hill and also on the mountain side from Woodtown to Stackstown: *Wade Rar.* Near Glendruid and near Ticknock, 1895; near Ballinclea, 1902: N.C. Near Carrickmines, 1897: Scully. In profusion at Delbrook, Dundrum: *Tatlow 1898.* *DNFC Annual Report, 1907:* Jobstown.

(1) (2) **3** (4) **5** (6) **7** **8**

Very rare, in dune-slacks and damp grassland. *Colgan* listed over 30 sites for this species and the *Suppl* records it from all districts. At the beginning of the 20th century Adder's-tongue was most commonly found in damp lowland pastures. This type of habitat is now rare in the county due to pasture improvement and drainage.

3. Dune-slack at Malahide Island, PR/85.
5. Frequent in the Alder Marsh on North Bull Island, MS/65, DD/69 & ENL, MN/84. Portmarnock sand-dunes, 0.75 km east of the school, DD, ENL/86. A few plants in grazed pasture, west of Casana Rock, Howth, CB/92.
7. Still in Glenasmole at St Anne's Fields, HJH/77.
8. About 100 plants near the north end of Ballybetagh Bog, SR, JR/84. Foxrock Golf-course, M. Friel/86. Unimproved grassland in a garden on Torquay Road, Foxrock, W. O'Sullivan/90.

- -

Botrychium

B. lunaria (L.) Sw.
Moonwort   Native

Colgan: 3. Sandy pastures near the monument, Portrane, 1894: *Colgan 1895.* 5. On the Cosh, 1867: *Flor. Howth.* Hilly pasture east of Cabeena Lodge, Howth, 1897; 6. To the east of Brittas and on Glenanareen mountain, north of Slieve Thoul, 1895; on Knockandinny mountain, 1897: N.C. 7. "In the Pastures of Palmerstown": *Threlkeld.* "On a mountain S. of Templeogue, 1739": *Annot. in Threlkeld.* Abundant on the northern slopes of Mount Pelier at intervals, from 700 feet to the top, 1894; *Colgan 1895* perhaps the same locality as the preceding. Kelly's Glen: *Mack. Cat.* Kilnasantan, and bluffs along Kelly's Glen in patches. A fine sub-form with deeply incised fronds found here growing in patches distinct from the ordinary form, from 6 to 9 inches high, 1854: *Kinahan 1854*. Along Kelly's Glen, luxuriant about Saint Anne's, 1895: *Dr E.J. McWeeney*. At Piperstown, growing in granite freestone amongst stunted Ling, 1895; frequent in pastures, Lugmore, 1896: *N.C.* 8. At Kingston, 1853: *Rev. S.A. Brenan*. Near Balalley, 1894, and sparingly at Ticknock, 1895: *W.H. Bloomer*. Sparingly at Ballybrack, Glencullen, and abundant on the summit of Three Rock mountain, 1895: *N.C.* At Moreen, near Dundrum: *Tatlow 1898*. Above Glensouthwell, 1901: *Miss Helen Laird*.

Suppl: 6. Heath at Mountseskin (J.P. Brunker, 1919). 8. Ballybetagh Bog (1946).

DNFC Annual Report 1907: 7. Jobstown.

Brunker MS: 7. S. of Mt Pelier, 1919.

DNFC Annual Report 1953: 3. Ward River Valley.

Very rare. It was already a rare species at the turn of the 19th century. Formerly more common in upland, usually in base-poor pastures. Records in 1951 and 1952 (by MS) from wet pastures at Bohernabreena (7) possibly correspond to that of E.J. McWeeney who recorded the species in 1895 from St Anne's (7).

5. Four plants on unimproved grazed pasture west of Casana Rock, Howth, CB/92.
6. One plant in unimproved pasture between Brittas and Saggart Hill, south of Glenaraneen, PG/90.
7. In woodland on the east side of the southern reservoir, Bohernabreena, CB/93.

- -

OSMUNDACEAE

Osmunda

O. regalis L.
Royal Fern   Native

Colgan: 5. Several plants inaccessibly situated on the cliffs, Howth Head, indigenous *(Hart) Flor. Howth.*

A single plant, evidently the last survivor in the district, between the old mill and St Marnock's, Portmarnock, 1869: *Hart MS*. (7. Sparingly in Kelly's Glen: *Mack. Cat.* Upper end of Kelly's Glen in meadows: *Flor. Hib.* "Formerly found in Kelly's Glen, the station is now drained which perhaps accounts for its not being found there now": *Kinahan 1854*. 8. "In a moorish Ground in ye Millstone Glin near Ticknock": *Annot in Threlkeld* not later than 1740).

Suppl: 5. One plant observed regularly in Hart's original station from 1890 until 1902, and was there in 1910 (E.L. Drury). "There are now two very large Royal Ferns and three smaller ones on the cliff-face, all luckily out of reach" (Douglas Drury 1949 per E.L. Drury).

Brunker MS: 7. One small plant appeared '57 at NE abutment of Orwell Bge, Rathgar. No doubt derived from a garden higher up the river: but its survival is worth watching. Did not survive! '58.

(5) (7) (8)

Very rare or extinct. Not refound at its only "recent" station in the county on a cliff-face at Howth Head (5). A clump which was presumably planted has been found growing in wet ground at Howth House by CB/91. In Ireland this species is commonest in western bogs and very rare in the east. The species still occurs elsewhere on the east coast of Ireland on low cliffs (e.g. south of Wicklow town).

HYMENOPHYLLACEAE

Hymenophyllum

H. wilsonii Hook. *(H. unilaterale)*
Wilson's Filmy-fern   Native

Colgan: 7. Kelly's Glen: *Guide.* Abundant at the head of Glenasmole (Kelly's Glen) about 1845: *John Bain.* Very sparingly under a wet rock by the Cot Brook at the head of Glenasmole, 1883: *Rev. C.F. d'Arcy.* Still there in 1901! Ascends to 900 feet in Glenasmole. First record in 1878: *Guide* - but there can be little doubt that the record for *H. tunbridgense* in *Ir. Flor.* - "Kelly's Glen, Ballinascorney: *M.J. O'Kelly"* refers to this species. In proof of the former local abundance of this plant in the Dublin mountains, the late Mr John Bain, who succeeded Dr Mackay as curator of Trinity College Botanic Gardens, was accustomed to tell the following story: About the year 1845 he visited Glenasmole, or Kelly's Glen, as it was then called, in company with Dr Mackay and Dr Scouler, Professor of Mineralogy to the Royal Dublin Society. While Bain and Mackay botanised below Grierson's (now Cobb's) Lodge, Scouler pushed on up one of the forks of the river above the lodge, and after a short absence appeared running down the glen in great excitement. When he rejoined Mackay and Bain he exhibited himself to the indignant botanists with his shoulders "quite draped in a shawl of *Hymenophyllum*, the growth of a century," which he had ruthlessly torn from off a granite boulder. The well meant efforts of the Royal Dublin Society to foster botanical studies by a scheme of prizes for collections of rare plants, did much to bring the Filmy Fern to the verge of extinction in the county, as no such collection was deemed complete without this species.

7

Extremely rare, on shaded boulders in the mountains. One of the rarest Dublin species. C.F. d'Arcy's record for this fern from the Cot Brook (7) has never been reconfirmed.
7. Refound on a granite boulder at about 300 m in the River Dodder above Glenasmole, A.L.K. King/67 & C. Breen, DNFC/86.

- -

POLYPODIACEAE

Polypodium

P. vulgare agg.
Native

1	2	3	4	5	6	7	8

Common on old walls, banks and as an epiphyte on trees. *Colgan* and *Suppl* did not distinguish the species within this aggregate and therefore many of our district records are new.
FID.

- -

P. vulgare L.
Polypody   Native

(1)	2	6	7	8

Common on acid dry stone walls, hedgerow banks and rocks and also in woodland. First recognised from specimens collected from near the base of Three Rock Mountain (8) by R.Ll. Praeger in 1894 (**DBN**).

P. vulgare x interjectum (P. x mantoniae Rothm. & U. Schneider)
Native

| 2 | 4 |

Very rare.
2. Old bank in woods in Ardgillan Park, MN/90.
4. Wall of the bridge at Mulhuddart, RF/89.

- -

P. interjectum Shivas
Intermediate Polypody   Native

| I | 2 | 3 | 4 | 5 | 6 | 7 | 8 |

Common on old limestone walls throughout the county and in stabilised dunes on North
Bull Island, at Portmarnock and on Malahide Island. The first records for the county are
specimens collected in Ballybrack (8) by J.S. Jackson in 1962 (**DBN**).

- -

P. cambricum L. (*P. australe*)
Southern Polypody   Native

| 2 | 3 | 8 |

Extremely rare. First recognised from specimens collected from Dargle by Dr Steele in 1816
(**DBN**), although this may be a record for Co. Wicklow and not for Dublin.
2. Boulder, east of the bridge and below the waterfall in the Delvin River at Naul, DS/67.
3. Above Saltpan Bay, Lambay Island, DS/90.
8. Wood on the east side of Killiney Hill, HOR/85.

- -

DENNSTAEDTIACEAE

Pteridium
Three subspecies are recognised by *Stace*, but they have not been differentiated in this *Flora*.

P. aquilinum (L.) Kuhn (*Pteris aquilina*)
Bracken   Native

| I | 2 | 3 | 4 | 5 | 6 | 7 | 8 |

Common and sometimes dominant in poor upland grassland on acid ground, upland
woodland margins, hedgebanks and along canal banks, and on sand-dunes; less frequent in
the lowlands; occasional on old walls in the city.
FID.

THELYPTERIDACEAE

Phegopteris

P. connectilis (Michaux) Watt (*Polypodium phegopteris, Thelypteris phegopteris*)
Beech Fern   Native

Colgan: 7. On Seecawn mountain, Glenasmole, 1883 *(Rev. C.F. d'Arcy) Colgan 1893* in considerable quantity here in 1903!
At about 1,100 feet on Seecawn mountain. First found in 1883 by Rev. C.F. d'Arcy; first record in 1893: *Colgan 1893.*
At a meeting of the *Dublin Nat. His. Socy.* held in 1863, Mr William Archer is reported to have made the following
reference to this fern: "It would be interesting to botanists to know that, although nearly extinguished at Powerscourt
Waterfall, this beautiful plant still existed in the neighbourhood of Dublin" *(Proc. IV., p.60, 1865).* No locality is given,
however, and the word, "neighbourhood, " in this passage must clearly be taken in a very wide sense, so wide, perhaps
as to include the adjacent parts of Wicklow. Yet it is not improbable that Mr Archer may have been acquainted with
some station for this fern in the Dublin Mountains.
Suppl: 7. On the S. side of the gorge of the stream between Ballymorefinn and Corrig just below the waterfall (J.P.
Brunker, 1925-1955). This is possibly the same station as that of the Rev. C.F. D'Arcy "on Seecawn mountain, " as the
plant has not been re-found on the actual slopes of Seecawn.

Extremely rare.
7. Still on Seahan (Seecawn) Mountain where many plants occur below a waterfall in a shady river
    gorge, on the stream which flows between Corrig Mountain and Ballymorefinn Hill, HJH/87.

Oreopteris

O. limbosperma (Bellardi ex All.) Holub (*Lastraea oreopteris, Thelypteris limbosperma*)
Lemon-scented Fern   Native

Colgan: 7. "Abundant in the glen near Middleton Brook (the combined Cot and Slade brooks) where I first met it in
1854; Glenismaul more sparingly": *Kinahan 1854.* Frequent but nowhere abundant, along the Slade and Cot brooks,
1901; very sparingly near Cobb's Lodge, Upper Dodder, 1894; abundant on the slopes of Glassavullaun mountain and
along the lower reaches of the Slade torrent, 1895-1903; 8. A single plant on Glencullen mountain, 1894, and another in
1901: *N.C.* A single plant on Glendhu mountain about 1880 *(Rev. C.F. d'Arcy) Colgan 1895.* Ranges from 750 feet on
Glassavullaun mountain *(N.C.)* to 1,250 feet on Killakee mountain *(Praeger).*

Rare, on banks of mountain streams and in sheltered moorland.
7. Occasional in the upland parts of this district in sheltered gorges. Still on Corrig
    Mountain from 500 m to the summit, HOR/85. Sides of Seahan (Seecawn) and on the
    south and west sides of Glenasmole, ENL/83, HOR/85 & DNFC/87. Still frequent near the
    Slade Brook above Castlekelly, on the lower slopes of the north face of Kippure between
    240 and 280 m, SR, HOR/85.

ASPLENIACEAE

Phyllitis

P. scolopendrium (L.) Newman (*Scolopendrium vulgare*)
Hart's-tongue   Native

1	2	3	4	5	6	7	8

Common and extremely widespread in hedge banks, in woodland and on old walls in the lowlands. Often luxuriant in hedgerows, with **Polystichum setiferum**.
FID.

Asplenium

A. adiantum-nigrum L.
Black Spleenwort   Native

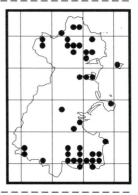

1	2	3	4	5	6	7	8

Occasional on old walls, not usually limestone, and stone-faced roadside banks on higher ground. Rarer in the lowlands and in 4 & 5.
4. Wall in Phoenix Park, JS/86.
5. Wall of the railway depot at Castleforbes Road, North Wall, PG/89.

A. marinum L.
Sea Spleenwort   Native

Colgan: 2. Sparingly on rocks and on the walls of the old church, St Patrick's island, Skerries, and 3. On the cliffs at Portrane, 1893: *N.C.* Isle of Lambay: *Newman 1840.* 5. "Crevices of the rocks abundantly at the south side of Howth near where passengers are landed from the packet in bad weather, in a kind of cave which is liable to be passed by": *Wade Rar.* Frequent from Kilrock to the Baily Lighthouse and at Drumleck: *Flor. Howth.* At the Cliffs, south side of Howth Head, 1901: *N.C.* 8. On the cliffs at and about Dunleary: *Wade Rar.* no doubt now extinct. Killiney Bay: *Newman 1840.* Near the Lead Mines at the base of Killiney Hill, in fair quantity, 1903: *N.C.* On Dalkey island, 1901: *E.D. Daly.*

2	3	5	8

Rare, on cliffs, rocks and old walls very near the sea.
2. A few plants still on the walls of the old church, St Patrick's Island, DD, NMcG/84.
3. A single plant on sea-swept cliffs at Portrane, DD/74.
5. Occasional in the spray zone along the cliffs from the Nose of Howth to Drumleck Point, and a single plant on the walkway from Howth Harbour to Howth Lodge Hotel, Howth Head, PG/90, CB/91.
8. A few plants still at Whiterock, Killiney, near the entrance to the lead mines, SR/87. Dalkey Island, M. Turner/54, (**TCD**).

A. trichomanes L.
Maidenhair Spleenwort   Native

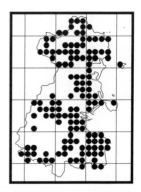

1	2	3	4	5	6	7	8

Common on old mortared walls especially in the lowlands.
FID.

A. ruta-muraria L.
Wall-rue   Native

1	2	3	4	5	6	7	8

Widespread and very common on old mortared and limestone walls throughout the county.
FID.

Ceterach

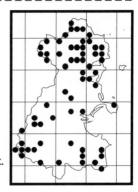

C. officinarum Willd.
Rustyback   Native

Brunker MS: Ascends to 1,000' at Ballinascorney Gap.

1	2	3	4	5	6	7	8

Occasional on old mortared walls. Widespread but rarely abundant.

WOODSIACEAE

Athyrium

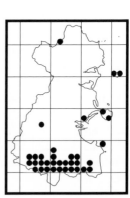

A. filix-femina (L.) Roth (A. *filix-foemina*)
Lady-fern   Native

Colgan: 1. Frequent in glens in the Naul Hills; and 2. Very sparingly on ditch banks between
Lusk and Man of War, 1903: *N.C.* 3. Near Raven's Well and north side of Knockbane: *Flor.*
Lambay. 5. Frequent on Howth Head, 1904: *N.C.*

In some of the narrow deep-cleft stream-courses in the coal measures of the Naul Hills this
fern grows in great luxuriance, fronds gathered here in 1903 measuring 4 feet in length: *N.C.*

1	(2)	3	5	6	7	8

Very common in sheltered situations in the mountains, in damp acid
ground in woodlands and in stream gulleys. Rare elsewhere but still present on the Naul Hills
(1), Lambay (3) and Howth Head (5). Colgan's record from ditch banks between Lusk and Man
O'War (2) has not been refound despite several searches.

DRYOPTERIDACEAE

Polystichum

P. setiferum (Forsskaol) Moore ex Woynar (*Aspidium angulare*)
Soft Shield-fern   Native

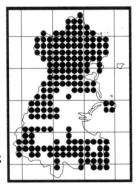

| 1 | 2 | 3 | 4 | 5 | 6 | 7 | 8 |

Very common and sometimes locally dominant in lowland hedgerows;
common in woodlands.

P. aculeatum (L.) Roth (*Aspidium aculeatum*)
Hard Shield-fern   Native

Suppl: I. Walshestown (Colgan in *I.N.* XVI, 1905). 7. By Old Mountseskin Road, one mile W. of Jobstown (R.W. Scully and
J.P. Brunker, 1919). Included only in Colgan's Appendix.

| 1 | (2) | 3 | 4 | (5) | 6 | (7) | 8 |

Rare in hedgerows and woodlands.
Colgan considered that early records for this species in the county were errors.
A Kinahan specimen (labelled var. ***viviparum***) mounted on a sheet of **Blechnum spicant,**
(TCD) may form the basis of the assertion that the species occurred in Dublin. Kinahan
also recorded this species on the Belgard to Tallaght road and near Ballyboden (Synnott
1968). O'Brien (1907) recorded **P. aculeatum** from the roadside south of Walshestown
House (1) and on a roadside leading to Nevitt from the Five Roads (2). This species has not
been refound in any of the above localities despite careful search.
1. Dry shaded roadside ditch, south-east of Ballymadun, DD/84.
3. Woods, south-west of the hospital at Portrane, PR/85.
4. Between the Royal Canal and railway, east of Leixlip where it is present both on the
    north side of the railway embankment and under Beech in a canal-side hedgerow due
    east, JS/84 & DN/87. One plant, in a dry ditch under Beech trees near the church, 3.5 km
    north-north-east of Mulhuddart, MN/84.
6. 2 km south-west of Rathcoole, HOR, PR, CB/86.
8. Roadside bank, Stepaside Lane, just south of Stepaside, SR, JR/84-92, **NDR**.

Dryopteris

D. filix-mas (L.) Schott (*Lastraea filix-mas*)
Male-fern   Native

| 1 | 2 | 3 | 4 | 5 | 6 | 7 | 8 |

Widespread and common in hedgerows and woodlands.
FID.

D. affinis (Lowe) Fraser-Jenkins (*D. borreri, D. pseudomas*)
Scaly Male-fern   Native

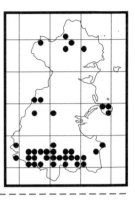

I		2		4		5		6		7		8

Most frequent in the mountains; rare in the north of the county in
woodlands and hedgerows on base-poor substrates. Not
distinguished in *Colgan* nor in the *Suppl.*
4. By the inner city stretch of the Royal Canal at Sheriff Street,
DNFC/80.
FID.

D. aemula (Aiton) Kuntze (*Lastraea aemula*)
Hay-scented Buckler-fern   Native

Colgan: 7. A few weak plants in the Cot Brook glen at the foot of a cascade; also in a glen in Feather Bed mountain, very
weak and straggling: *Kinahan 1854.* "I know of but two localities in which it occurs in Dublin, Howth and Glassavullaun
in Dodder valley": *Kinahan 1858.* This critical species is doubtfully entitled to a place in the county flora. I have sought
for it without success in all of the stations given above and although an apparent confirmation for the Howth Station
was given in the *Flora of Howth, 1887,* where the plant is entered as "Common in the woods of Howth demesne," this
record was withdrawn by Mr Hart as erroneous in 1897 *(Journ. of Bot., p.347).* Yet in spite of the absence of any recent
record it seems inadvisable to reject the plant, since it is abundant in the Wicklow mountains, 12 miles from the Dublin
border, and has been deliberately recorded for Dublin by a competent authority.

Never refound in Kinahan's stations (7), which may have referred to depauperate **D. dilatata**.

D. dilatata (Hoffm.) A. Gray (*Lastraea dilatata, D. austriaca*)
Broad Buckler-fern   Native

Colgan: 1. Frequent in the Naul Hills, 1903; 2. Abundant in the upper wood at
Gormanstown and sparingly south-east of Hollywood, 1894; sparingly between Lusk
and Man of War, 1902; frequent in and around Kenure Park, 1900: *N.C.* 3. Sparingly in
Salt Pan bay, Lambay island: *Flor. Lambay.* In Portrane demesne, 1894; 5. Frequent on
Howth Head, 1904: *N.C.*

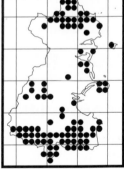

I		2		3		4		5		6		7		8

Occasional in shady hedgerows and woodlands. Commonest on
base-poor substrates. Often in coniferous woodland. Frequent in
6, 7 and 8; rare elsewhere.
3. Still on Lambay Island, DD/91.
4. St Catherine's Woods, MN/84, **NDR**.
5. Santry woods, DN/88. Ben of Howth, DN/89. Malahide near
Gay Brook, DN/89. Hedgerow at Portmarnock, DN/88. Malahide Castle,
DD/83. Redrock, ENL/83. Howth Demesne, ENL/84.

BLECHNACEAE

Blechnum

B. spicant (L.) Roth
Hard-fern   Native

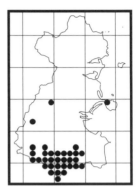

Colgan: 1. Sparingly at Garristown Bog, 1893; frequent and locally abundant in and around the Naul Hills, 1900-03; 5. Sparingly in the central parts of Howth Head, 1903: *N.C.*
Suppl: Naul Hills, Howth and common on mountains.

(1)	4	5	6	7	8

Common in wet acidic habitats on peat or mineral soil; very rare elsewhere.
4. Rock outcrop at Abbotstown, MN/88, **NDR**.

AZOLLACEAE

Azolla

A. filiculoides Lam.
Water Fern   Alien

3	4	7	8

Rare, in ponds and canals.
3. Farm pond at Turvey Bridge, PR/84.
4. Island Pond in Phoenix Park, JS, MN/81, 83, **NCR**. Ponds in the National Botanic Gardens, Glasnevin, MN/90, NS/92.
7. Grand Canal from Dolphin's Barn to Leeson Street Bridge, MWJ/84.
8. Many plants, not known to have been deliberately introduced, in two small artificial ponds at Sandyford and Stillorgan, SR/92.

MAGNOLIOPSIDA   (Flowering Plants)

MAGNOLIIDAE (Dicotyledons)

NYMPHAEACEAE

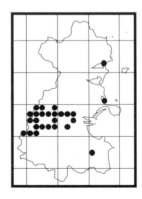

Nuphar

N. lutea (L.) Smith
Yellow Water-lily   Native

Colgan: 1. Curragha Bog: *Ir. Flor.-* not seen recently. 3. In a pond at Ballisk near Donabate, 1893-1902, perhaps introduced: N.C. 4. In pools near Glasnevin Bridge: *Wade Dubl.* Abundant in the Royal Canal from Lucan to Liffey Junction, 1893-1903; 6. In the

Grand Canal at intervals from Hazelhatch to Clondalkin, and 7. From Ballyfermot down to Richmond, 1892-1903: *N.C. Suppl:* 1. Bog of the Ring (1947). 4. Island Pond Phoenix Park (1956). 5. Santry Court Lake (1950). This has now been drained.

(1) | 3 | 4 | 5 | 6 | 7

Common in canals and rivers.

It occurs in the Royal and Grand Canals and the Rivers Liffey and Tolka. Possibly planted in ornamental ponds at Ballisk (3), Leopardstown (8) and perhaps elsewhere.

FID.

CERATOPHYLLACEAE

Ceratophyllum

C. demersum L.
Rigid Hornwort   Native

7

Common in the Grand Canal but very rare elsewhere.

7. Frequent along the Grand Canal, especially from Clondalkin to Ringsend, MS/70-83, JS/75 & DN/90. Pond at Mount Argus Church, DN/90. Originally planted but now spreading into the stream from a small pond at Stone Cross, Ballinascorney, JP, MWJ/88.

FID.

RANUNCULACEAE

Caltha

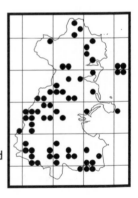

C. palustris L.
Marsh-marigold   Native

1 | 2 | 3 | 4 | 5 | 6 | 7 | 8

Occasional on margins of rivers, canals, ponds and other muddy and wet habitats, mainly lowland. It is becoming rarer as more wetland areas are drained.

Anemone

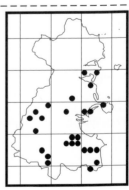

A. nemorosa L.
Wood Anemone   Native

Colgan: 4. "In Katherine's Wood, May, 1739": *Annot. in Threlkeld*-in profusion here in 1904! At Scribblestown, and abundant in Woodlands, 1900: *N.C.* 5. Kilmere wood and Santry wood: *Ir.Flor.* Common in woods, Howth: *Flor.Howth.* 6. Abundant in glens above the Embankment, Saggard, 1894, in profusion in Lucan Demesue, 1904; 7 and 8. Frequent in the upland glens: *N.C.* To 1,000 feet on Two Rock and 1,200 feet on Seecawn. Apparently quite absent from, and certainly very rare in, the northern half of the county.

Common, in base-rich deciduous woodland in the south of the county
and in the River Liffey Valley; usually in damp and shaded areas.
3. South-west of the hospital woods, Portrane, PR/84.
4. Tolka Lodge, Finglas, DD/66.
5. Howth Demesne, PG, DN/91. Santry Woods DN/89. St Anne's Park, Raheny, PG/87, 88.

A. apennina L.
Blue Anemone   Alien
Brunker MS: 2. Milverton, Skerries. 8. Rathfarnham Demesne.

Rare in woodlands. In Beech Park (4), Howth Demesne and St Anne's Park, Raheny (5);
grounds of Prospect House, Firhouse (7); woods at U.C.D. (Belfield), Leopardstown
Racecourse and by the Stillorgan Reservoirs (8).

Clematis

C. vitalba L.
Traveller's-joy   Alien

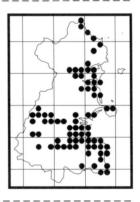

| 1 | 2 | 3 | 4 | 5 | 6 | 7 | 8 |

Occasional in hedgebanks, waste ground and sand-hills.
A garden escape, most frequent in the outer suburbs of the city
and the Liffey Valley.
FID.

Ranunculus

R. acris L.
Meadow Buttercup   Native

| 1 | 2 | 3 | 4 | 5 | 6 | 7 | 8 |

Widespread and extremely common in pastures, meadows and grassy roadsides.
FID.

R. repens L.
Creeping Buttercup   Native

| 1 | 2 | 3 | 4 | 5 | 6 | 7 | 8 |

Widespread and common especially in damp grassland and on roadsides.
FID.

R. bulbosus L.
Bulbous Buttercup   Native

| 1 | 2 | 3 | 4 | 5 | 6 | 7 | 8 |

Common on calcareous soils and on sand-dunes. Often found at relatively high altitudes in the county on glacial drift.
FID.

- -

R. parviflorus L.
Small-flowered Buttercup   Probably introduced

| (5) | (7) | (8) |

Probably extinct. Not refound between Baldoyle and Howth (5), at Greenhills (7), nor near Milltown and Bray (8). Although not seen for many years in Co. Dublin, it has been found recently in south-east Ireland.

- -

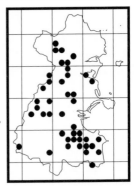

R. auricomus L.
Goldilocks Buttercup   Native

| 1 | 3 | 4 | 5 | 6 | 7 | 8 |

Occasional on shady roadsides and in base-rich deciduous woodlands, but very rare in the county north of the Broad Meadow River.

- -

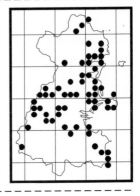

R. sceleratus L.
Celery-leaved Buttercup   Native

| 1 | 2 | 3 | 4 | 5 | 6 | 7 | 8 |

Occasional in ditches, pools and on marshy ground. Frequent by the coast; local elsewhere. Rare in the uplands.
FID.

- -

R. lingua L.
Greater Spearwort   Native

Colgan: (1. In Curragha bog: Ir. Flor. not seen recently. The bog is now almost completely drained and the plant is probably become extinct). 2. In a marsh drain near Balrothery, 1902: Colgan 1903. 4. In the Royal Canal, 1886: Herb. Scully - abundant here from above Lucan to below Ashtown, 1903! Frequent in bog drains at Dunsoghly, 1903: N.C. (5. Ditches along the shore at Raheny: Ir. Flor. - not seen recently). 8. Pool near Stillorgan railway station, 1902: Praeger. First record in 1833: Ir. Flor., the earlier record in Wade Dubl., 1794 marshy meadows at Scribblestown being probably referable to R. flammula.

| (1) | 2 | 4 | (5) | 7 | (8) |

Occasional to rare in different parts of the Royal Canal where it still survives in undredged sections between Lucan and Phibsborough (4); very rare elsewhere.

2. Still in a pond north of Balrothery, DN/92.

4. Still at Dunsoghly, in drainage ditches on the site of the old marsh, MN/83.

- -

R. flammula L.
Lesser Spearwort   Native

| I | 2 | 4 | 5 | 6 | 7 | 8 |

Occasional in marshes and on canal, river and pond margins.

- -

R. ficaria L.
Lesser Celandine   Native

| I | 2 | 3 | 4 | 5 | 6 | 7 | 8 |

- -

subsp. ficaria

| I | 2 | 3 | 4 | 5 | 6 | 7 | 8 |

Very common in shady habitats, woodlands and hedgerows; very rare in gardens.
FID.

- -

subsp. bulbilifer Lambinon (subsp. *bulbifer*)

| I | 2 | 3 | 4 | 5 | 6 | 7 | 8 |

Very common in shady habitats, gardens, disturbed roadsides, hedgerows and woodlands.
FID.

- -

R. hederaceus L.
Ivy-leaved Crowfoot   Native

| I | (2) | (3) | (4) | 5 | 6 | 7 | 8 |

Occasional in peaty pools and muddy ditches in 1, 6, 7 and 8. Although this species has been recorded from all districts in the past it was never common in the lowlands and has not been seen there recently.

5. Wet field at Kilrock, Howth, DN/88. Pool, west of Drumleck Point, DD, ENL/85.

- -

R. omiophyllus Ten. (*R. lenormandii*)
Round-leaved Crowfoot   Native

Colgan: 7. On Knockanavea, by the Military road, Feather Bed mountain, on Glendhu mountain, on Seecawn mountain, above

Piperstown, and in several stations by the upper Dodder, 1892-1903; 8. Roadside runnels in Glencullen, 1895; abundant in a marsh south of the Dingle, Glenamuck, 1902; in a muddy ditch at Ballyedmonduff, 1903: N.C. Two Rock Mountain, 1899 (N.C.) *Top. Bot.* Ranges from 400 feet at Glenamuck to 1,600 feet on Feather Bed mountain. Though usually sub-terrestrial in the county, this species is truly aquatic in the Glenamuck station, where it develops floating root fibres fully a foot in length. The plant attains in Co. Dublin its northern limit for Ireland.

| 7 | 8 |

Occasional in upland drains. Frequent in the Glenasmole Valley and the Featherbed (7); rare elsewhere.

8. Wet coarse sand beside the Wicklow Way in the Glencullen Valley, SR/88. East of Boranaraltry Bridge, HOR, EMcA/83. Still on the lower slopes of Two Rock Mountain in the Glencullen Valley, SR/87. Still near Ballyedmonduff, east of the Burrow Road, near a stream, HOR, EMcA/83.

R. baudotii Godron
Brackish Water-crowfoot   Native

Colgan: 3. Pond near Ballisk, Donabate, 1895: N.C. 5. At Portmarnock, 1883-87, and on Ireland's Eye, 1888: *Herb. Vowell.* At Portmarnock, 1900 *(Praeger) Top. Bot.* Ponds near Baldoyle Station: *Flor. Howth.* Very abundant in pools near the northern end of Baldoyle race-course, 1902: N.C. Var. CONFUSUS (Godron). - 5. Ponds by the sea between Sutton and Howth, 1882 *(Vowell) Herb.* and *Journ. Bot.,* 1882, p. 347- and in 1894!
Suppl: 5. Still on Ireland's Eye (1941).

| (3) | 5 |

Extremely rare, in brackish ponds.

5. Still at the north end of Baldoyle Race-course in pools, south of the Mayne River, DN/91. Still in pools at Portmarnock in the Brickfields, DN/91. In a water hazard on Portmarnock Golf-course, DN/91.

R. trichophyllus Chaix
Thread-leaved Water-crowfoot   Native

Colgan: 1. To the west of Ballyboghil, 1893; 3. By the Ward river near Knocksedan, 1895; near Donabate, 1899; 4. Quarry holes near Forest, 1894: N.C. 5. Marsh near the summit of Howth: *Flor. Howth* and in 1902! 6. Pool at the Rectory, Newcastle Lyons *(More) Cyb.* Near Johnstown 1897; in the Grand Canal near Lucan, 1900; 7. By the Dodder near Old Bawn, and quarry holes near Robin Hood, 1894: N.C. 8. Pools at Foxrock: *Vowell.* At Stillorgan, 1886: *Praeger.* The variety with floating leaves, *R. godronii* (Gren.) of *R. drouetti* (Godr.) has been found in the following stations: 1. Quarry pools near Hollywood, Naul Hills, 1894: N.C. 8. Near Foxrock *(Vowell) Journ. Bot.,* 1882, p. 370.
Suppl: 1. Bog of the Ring (1955). 2. Sparingly in a ditch between the Convent and windmill, Skerries (1918). Dried up floor of Balrothery Lough (1934). 4. Tolka above Cardiff's Bridge (J.P. Brunker, 1920). Half-mile S. of Dunsoghly (1937). 5. Cloghran (1935). St Doolagh's Quarries (1954). 7. Head of Upper Reservoir, Glenasmole (1957). R. Poddle at Firhouse (1957).

| (1) | (2) | 3 | 4 | 5 | 6 | 7 | 8 |

Occasional in pools, reservoirs and slow-moving streams. It is reputed to be the most pollution-tolerant of the aquatic buttercups.

3. Knocksedan Reservoir, PR/85. Broad Meadow River near the waterworks north of Swords, SR/89. Marsh by the Portrane Road, PR/90.
4. Field drain, west of Jamestown Road, just east of Finglas, DD/66. Luttrellstown, JS, MN/83. Ditch in the Phoenix Park, PR/86 & NS/92. Ditch, east of Clonee, MN, JS/87. Occasional in the River Tolka between Cardiff's Bridge and Glasnevin, MN/88.

5. Pond at Feltrim Hill Quarry, DN/88. Marshy ground, 1 km west-north-west of Portmarnock, DN/88. By a pond near the extreme eastern end of St Anne's Park, Raheny, PG/87, 88. Pools at Portmarnock Brickfields, DN/90, 91. Pond in Howth Demesne, north-north-east of Howth Castle, CB/91.
6. At the south end of Brittas Ponds, DD/83. By the weir on the River Liffey at Lucan, DN/90.
7. Northern end of the southern reservoir, Glenasmole, JP, DD/83, RMcM/85 & DN/90.
8. Shallow muddy pond to the north-west of Sandyford Industrial Estate, SR/86. Shanganagh River, west of the railway and south-east of Loughlinstown, SR/85, 89.

- -

R. aquatilis L. (*R. heterophyllus*)
Common Water-crowfoot   Native

Colgan: 1. Quarry holes near Hollywood, 1894; abundant in pools at the Bog of the Ring, 1895; 2. South of Nag's Head and at Lusk commons, 1895; Ballycummin, north of Lusk, 1902; 3. Sparingly near Balcarrig, Portrane, 1904; 4. Near Glasnevin, 1894; and abundant in quarry holes at Dunsoghly and Kildonan, 1895: *N.C.* 5. Pond at Corr Castle, Howth: *Flor. Howth.* 7. Ditches and quarry holes near Ballymount 1894; 8. Near Shanganagh, 1893; near Balalley, 1894; abundant in pools at Loughlinstown, 1902: *N.C. Var.* TRIPHYLLOS (*Wallr.*) 5. Near Baldoyle (*Dyer & More*) *Cyb. II.*
Suppl: 5. Near Baldoyle (1957). 7 Pools by Dodder above Oldbawn (1919). Abundant at head of Upper Reservoir, Glenasmole (1956). 8. Ballybetagh Bog (1946).

Occasional in pools, reservoirs and slow-moving streams. Many of the sites where this species was once recorded have been drained or filled in.
1. Hynestown Reservoir, GS/84.
2. Common in shallow water at the east side of Balrothery Lough, DD/84: some plants there are close in morphology to **R. baudotii**.
3. Marsh, 1 km west of Portrane, PR, DD/86. Broad Meadow River, near Lispopple Bridge, Roganstown Bridge and near the waterworks north of Swords, SR/89.
4. River Tolka just north of Ashtown, MN/83.
5. Still in Corr Castle pond, DD/82. Pool in a wet field at the north end of Portmarnock Golf-course, DNFC/88 & DN/88. Pond on Portmarnock Raceway, DN/88. Pond in the old garden in Howth Demesne, PG, DN/91.
7. Southern reservoir in Glenasmole, DD, EMcA/83 & RMcM/85. Pond at Delaford, DK/c.65.
8. Wet ditches, south of Ballybetagh Bog, SR, JR/87. Artificial pond at the south end of Leopardstown Racecourse, SR, HOR/83.

- -

R. peltatus Schrank
Pond Water-crowfoot   Native

Colgan: 4. "It grows in the middle of the *Liffy* between the Barracks and Island Bridge; its specious white Flowers look very charming as it floats upon the rolling Streams of the *Aon na Liffy*": *Threlkeld.* In the Liffey near Chapelizod: *Rec. Add.* and in the same river below Woodlands, 1900: *N.C.* 6. In the Liffey above Leixlip bridge, 1895; watercourse by the Grand Canal above Clondalkin, 1900; abundant in the Swift Brook below Brittas Ponds, 1894; and 7. Above the Ponds by the Ballinascorney road, 1895: *N.C.* Usually lowland, but ascends to 750 feet above Brittas. The finest of the County Dublin Water Ranunculi, and still, as in Threlkeld's day, a remarkable plant in many reaches of the Liffey. *Var.* TRUNCATUS (*Hiern*). 5. In pits and ditches at Portmarnock brickfields, 1894: *N.C.*
Suppl: 3. Broad Meadow Water at Lissenhall Bridge (1942). 7. Old city watercourse at Templeogue (1947). 7 and 8. Dodder at Orwell Weir and at Milltown Common (1946).

(5)

Our concept of this species is not comparable to that of previous workers on the Dublin flora. Both *Colgan* and *Suppl* records for **R. peltatus** can largely be referred to **R. penicillatus**. Records of **R. peltatus** var. **truncatus** Hiern from pits and ditches at Portmarnock Brickfields cannot be confirmed either. Today this site is occupied by **R. aquatilis, R. trichophyllus** and **R. baudotii**.

R. penicillatus (Dumort.) Bab. (*R. pseudofluitans*, *R. peltatus* pro parte)
Stream Water-crowfoot   Native

(4) (5) 6 7

Occasional in fast-flowing streams. Now replaced in the River Liffey in Co. Dublin by **Potamogeton pectinatus** which may be more tolerant to pollution caused by agricultural run-off.
6. Stream in Corcagh Demesne, JP/83 (now gone, JP/88). Stream to the east of Crooksling Glen, JP/84. Upper reaches of the Cammock River, south and east of Casement Aerodrome, JP/85, 86. Grand Canal (Webster 1988).
7. Below a bridge over the Cammock River, c. 300 m north-east of Clondalkin, MWJ/87 & DN/90. Small river, midway between Brittas and Aghfarrell, PWJ, MWJ/86 & DN/90. Still in the stream above Brittas Ponds by the Ballinascorney Road, DD/92.

R. circinatus Sibth.
Fan-leaved Water-crowfoot   Native

Colgan: 4. River Tolkay between Drumcondra and Cardiff's Bridge: Ir. Flor. Royal Canal, Blacquiere Bridge, 1858: Herb. R. Barrington. In the Liffey near Chapelizod (More) Cyb. Pools by the Tolka at Cardiff's Bridge, and abundant in the Royal Canal from Lucan to Dublin city, 1903; 6. Abundant in the Grand Canal from Hazelhatch to Clondalkin, and 7. From Clondalkin to James's Street Harbour and Ringsend Basin, 1903: N.C. In the flowering season, especially towards the end of June, this is a most conspicuous feature in the Royal Canal flora, where it spreads for miles along the still marginal waters in a broad band of white.

4 6 7

Extremely rare except in the Grand Canal.
4. Royal Canal between Collins Bridge and the county boundary, JK, DN/91.
6/7. Scattered along the length of the Grand Canal from Gollierstown eastwards to Baggot Street and in a quarry pond beside the canal at Gollierstown, MN/87 & DN/89, 90.

Aquilegia

A. vulgaris L.
Columbine
A rare but persistent garden escape. Found at various sites in 5 and 6.
This species has been recorded in the wild in Dublin for 200 years, sometimes well naturalized.

Thalictrum

T. minus L. (*T. dunense*)
Lesser Meadow-rue   Native

Colgan: 2. South of Loughshinny, 1882: *Hart MS.* Sandhills at Rush, 1891 *(Miss A.G. Kinahan) Cyb II.* 3. At the north end of Portrane peninsula, 1900-02: *Colgan 1903.* 5. "Found it but sparingly on Ireland's Eye, Howth; beyond the Sheds of Clontarf by the side of a ditch going to the Warren House": *Wade Rar.* Sandy shore on Ireland's Eye, 1892: *N.C.* By the side of the road near Baldoyle: *Mack. Rar.* On Portmarnock sandhills: *Mack. Cat.* Sandy banks near Robb's Walls, Malahide, 1897 *(Miss S. Colgan) Cyb. II.* - still there in considerable quantity, 1902!
Suppl: 2. Still at Rush *(1950).* 5. Almost obliterated at Robswalls by the building of the new road, but plants survive between the new and old roads (1957).

| 2 | (3) | 5 |

Very rare, in stable sand-dunes.
2. Still at Rush, by the caravan park, DD/85. Near Barnageeragh, RF/86.
5. Still above the beach on Ireland's Eye, ENL/85. Still on sand-hills at Portmarnock, HJH/83 & DD/91-94. Still at Robswalls at Malahide, HJH/85 & DD, DNFC/97.

PAPAVERACEAE

Papaver

P. somniferum L.
Opium Poppy   Alien

| 1 | 2 | 3 | 4 | 5 | 6 | 7 | 8 |

Occasional on waste ground in urban situations.
FID.

P. rhoeas L.
Common Poppy   Probably introduced

| 1 | 2 | 3 | 4 | 5 | 6 | 7 | 8 |

Common in most ruderal habitats; rare in the uplands.
FID.

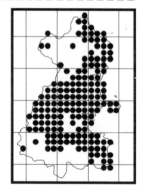

P. dubium L.
Long-headed Poppy   Probably introduced

| 1 | 2 | 3 | 4 | 5 | 6 | 7 | 8 |

subsp. **dubium**

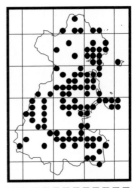

| 1 | 2 | 3 | 4 | 5 | 6 | 7 | 8 |

Common on waste ground.
FID.

---

subsp. **lecoqii** (Lamotte) Syme (*P. lecoqii*)

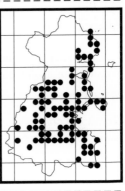

| 2 | 3 | 4 | 5 | 6 | 7 | 8 |

Occasional on waste ground. Common on calcareous ground in the lowlands.
FID.

P. hybridum L.
Rough Poppy   Probably introduced

Colgan: 2. About Rush: *Ir. Flor.*, 1833-and in 1902! At Skerries: *Rec. Add.* On the railway north of Balbriggan, 1894: 3. Frequent in sandy fallows and in cornfields Portrane peninsula, 1893-1902: *N.C.* "In fields between the old church of Kilbarrick and Sweetman's house on the road to Howth, where it was observed several years since by Mr Underwood and others": *Mack. Rar.* Old gravel pits near Raheny: *Mack. Cat.* Roadsides between Baldoyle and Portmarnock: *Ir. Flor.* Cornfields at the Cliffs, the Needles and Drumleck: *Flor. Howth.* Cornfields near Baldoyle, 1892, and frequent on the new tram line between Raheny and Sutton, 1900: *N.C.* At St Doulough's, 1894: *Praeger.* The rarest of the Co. Dublin poppies, and confined to the coast or its neighbourhood northward of the Liffey mouth.

| (2) | 3 | (5) |

Extremely rare. An endangered species in Ireland, legally protected under the Wildlife Act of 1976.
3. Disturbed ground in a housing estate to the west of Malahide, RF/85. Still on the margin of a barley field on the Portrane Peninsula, PR/85.

P. argemone L.
Prickly Poppy   Probably introduced

Colgan: 2. Abundant in sandy ground at Rush, 1893-1902; at Rogerstown, 1900; on the railway at Skerries and beyond Hampton Hall, 1894: 3. Frequent in sandy fallows to the north of Portrane peninsula, 1895-1902: *N.C.* 4. Near the Observatory (*Mr Brinkley*) Templeton MS. 5. Cornfields near Kilbarrick Church: *Mack. Cat.* By the shore at Kilbarrick, 1901; cornfield near Baldoyle, 1892; by the railway at Sutton and on sandy banks at Portmarnock, 1895; sandy ground at Greenfields, Sutton, 1900: *N.C.* 7. At the Green Hills: *More MS.* 8. "On a bank near Merrion shoar, 6/9 1740": *Annot. in Threlkeld.* Old gravel pits near Ball's Bridge: *Flor. Hib.* At Cabinteely (*Rev. S. Madden*) *Cyb.* Frequent along the railway below Killiney Hill, 1894-1902: *N.C.*

| 2 | 3 | (4) | 5 | (7) | (8) |

Occasional on the north coast on sandy roadsides and fallows. Apparently extinct inland in localities from which it was formerly recorded.

2. Common on sandy roadsides between Rogerstown and Rush, DD/82, 87.
3. Embankment by the road to the coast from Corballis where the road runs parallel to the coast, PR/83, 84. Still occasional on tracks and roadsides on the Portrane Peninsula, PR, DD/85, 91.
5. Still on waste ground and on the railway line at Sutton Station, DD/82, ENL/83 & NS/92. Kilbarrack Graveyard, PG/91. A few plants on the pathway leading to the Martello Tower in Howth Village, CB/92.

- -

Meconopsis

M. cambrica (L.) Viguier
Welsh Poppy   Introduced in Co. Dublin

| 7 | 8 |

Occasional on shady roadsides or tracks in woodlands. Most frequent in 7. Although a native in upland areas of the adjoining Co. Wicklow, all Dublin plants are probably of garden origin.
FID.

- -

Glaucium

G. flavum Crantz
Yellow Horned-poppy   Native

Colgan: 2. Along the shores at Rush, Skerries, and Balbriggan: *Ir. Flor.* By the shore a mile and a half north of Skerries in quantity for about 100 yards and again sparingly north of Balbriggan near the Delvin river, 1893; 3. Abundant at the north-west extremity of Portrane peninsula, and again at the south-west extremity, in the latter station spreading for upwards of 100 yards, 1900-03: N.C. 5. "Upon the sandy Baich everywhere and in *Clantarff Island*": Threlkeld. Between the Sheds of Clontarf and Howth: *Wade Dubl.* Sparingly on the shore near Sutton station, 1893; near Kilbarrick, near Warren Lodge, near Greenfields, and on the Cosh, 1901: N.C. 8. Between Sandymount and Merrion and at Killiney Bay: *Wade Dubl.* Killiney Bay, 1857: *Herb. R. Barrington* - and in 1872: *Greenwood Pim.* This is uncertain in its appearances like many others of our sea beach species. There are no recent records for District 8.
Suppl: 2. Still at Skerries (1946). 5. Ireland's Eye (1950). 8. Still at Killiney (1954). On a new dune on S. side of South Wall between Pigeon House and pumping station (1956).

| 2 | 3 | (5) | (8) |

Very rare on shingle beaches. Not seen recently on Ireland's Eye (5). There are no recent records in 8.

2. Still on a rocky shore, 1.5 km north of Skerries, DD, ENL/84.
3. Still on the Portrane Peninsula where two plants were recorded on the gravel strand, south of Corballis, Malahide Island and a further seven plants in a clearing in sand-dunes nearby, PR/84 & DD/91.

Chelidonium

C. majus L.
Greater Celandine   Alien

Colgan: 1. Roadside hedge near Baldwinstown, and 2. South of Balbriggan, 1894-1902; 3. Well established on banks and old walls near the ruined Church of Killeek, Knocksedan, 1893-1903; 4. Sparingly in a hedge by the Liffey about a mile below Lucan, 1893-1904; and 5. Roadside ditch above the Watermill, Raheny, 1881-1902: *N.C.* At the railway bridge over Howth road, 1866-69: *Flor. Howth.*

DNFC Annual Report, 1953: 5. Dollymount and Watermill Lane.

Suppl: 2. Farm N. of Loughshinny (1918). 3. Still at Killeek (1956). 5. Still at Watermill Lane (1954). 7. Roadside between Rockbrook and Pine Forest (1957). 8. Roadside near Barnacullia (1955).

| 1 | 2 | 3 | 4 | 5 | 7 | 8 |

Rare, in hedgerows and on roadsides and ruined buildings.
1. Hedgerow south-west of Garristown, GS/84. Hedgerow north-west of Oldtown, GS/83. Hedgerow near Rowlestown House, GS/85. Hedgerow north of Ballyboghil, GS/85.
2. Hedgerow, east of Tobersool House, RF/86. Roadside verge, south of Clonard, DD/87. Hedgerow at Rathmooney, RF/87.
3. Still near Killeek, PR/84. Hedgerows in the Lispopple area, PR/85, 86. Near Burrow, Portrane, PR/85.
4. Still on a roadside near Lucan, JS/83.
5. Still at Raheny, in Watermill Lane, DD/76. Near Sutton Railway Station, DD, JP/82. Quarry at Corr Castle, PG, DN/89. Eastern corner of St Anne's Park, Raheny, PG/90-92.
7. Waste ground, 0.5 km south-west of Firhouse on the Brittas road, PWJ, MWJ/87. Still by a roadside wall, just south of Rockbrook, PWJ/86.
8. On an old wall by the Dundrum Road near Milltown Bridge, SR/85.

FUMARIACEAE

Pseudofumaria

P. lutea (L.) Borkh. (*Corydalis lutea*)
Yellow Corydalis   Alien

Colgan: 6. On the walls of Lucan Railway Station, 1896-1904; and 7. At Clondalkin station, 1904: *N.C.*
Suppl: Still spreading from Lucan and Clondalkin railway stations (1955).

| 5 | 6 | (7) | 8 |

Occasional as a garden escape.
5. One clump on the railway wall on the Burrow Road, between the Sutton and Howth railway stations, CB/91, **NDR**.
6. Wall of the railway cutting to the south of St Helen's, Lucan, close to where *Colgan* noted it, JP/84. Trackside near a farm south-west of Brittas, JP/86.
8. Wall in Goatstown Road, HOR/84. Wall at Glenageary, SR, HOR/85.

Ceratocapnos

C. claviculata (L.) Liden *(Corydalis claviculata)*
Climbing Corydalis   Native

Colgan: 8. On the road leading to the Dublin Mountains under the hedges above Dundrum, above the Little Dargle, car road to Kilmashogue: *Wade Rar.* On thatched cabins near the Little Dargle: *Mack. Cat.* Thatched cabins between Ballinteer and the Little Dargle: *Flor. Hib.* Byeways leading from Kilgobbin to the mountains: *Ir. Flor.* Abundant amongst gorse and broken granite rocks in the Dingle, Glenamuck, 1882-1902: *N.C.* Abundant amongst gorse and rocks on Ballybrack (Killiney) Hill: *Ir. Nat.,* 1894, p. 140. Abundant on the south and south-east faces of Killiney Hill, 1903, also in the woods of Victoria Castle, Killiney, 1901: *N.C.*

5	8

Very rare, in heathland but often abundant in such sites after gorse burning.
5. A large clump on recently burnt peat to the west of Baily Green, 0.5 km north of the Baily Lighthouse, Howth, CB/91, **NDR**.
8. Still on Killiney Hill, MS/67, DNFC/82, JP/83 & SR, HOR/85. Roches Hill, MD/89. East facing slope of Dalkey Hill, SR/91. The Dingle, DNFC/83. East side of The Scalp, TK/67.

Fumaria

F. capreolata L. subsp. **babingtonii** (Pugsley) Sell *(F. pallidiflora)*
White Ramping-fumitory   Possibly introduced

Colgan: 5. At Baldoyle: *Guide.* In potato fields and in hedgebanks near Howth village, 1882-1896; and 7. Potato fields at Killinardan, 1900: *N.C.* Near Bohernabreena, 1893: *Praeger.* 8. Hedgebanks near Bray River, 1890: *More.* Cultivated ground at Stepaside and Dundrum: *Praeger 1894.* Abundant on the gravel mound at the old church of Kilgobbin, 1895-1902; abundant on drift banks near Killiney railway station, and in potato fields at Ticknock and Ballyedmonduff, 1894; at Bray Harbour, 1903: *N.C.* Ascends to 750 feet at Ticknock, but usually lowland.
Suppl: 2. Roadside at Knock Cross, Balrothery (1950). 5. St Doolagh's Quarries (1950). 8. Roadside at Ticknock (1957).

2	5	7	8

Rare, in ruderal habitats.
2. Still at Balrothery in disturbed ground at the south-east corner of Balrothery Lough, DD/84.
5. Roadside south-east of Kilronan House, Cloghran, ENL/84. Greenhollows, Howth, ENL/82, 83. Garden weed in Shielmartin Park, Howth, DD/78.
7. Arable weed at Firhouse and at St Columba's College, DK/c.65.
8. Still at Kilgobbin, on gravel surrounding the ruined church and nearby as a garden weed, PC/71-79 & HOR/86. Near the bandstand on the south-east side of Sorrento Park, Dalkey, SR, HOR/83.

F. muralis agg. *(F. boraei, F. confusa)*
Probably introduced

1	2	3	4	5	6	7	8

Abundant on tilled and waste ground throughout the county. The distinguishing features of **F. bastardii** and **F. muralis** s.s appear less distinct in Ireland than in Britain. We have had to include such plants in **F. muralis** agg.
FID.

F. bastardii Boreau
Tall Ramping-fumitory   Probably introduced

| 2 | 3 | 5 | 6 | 7 | 8 |

Occasional in waste places and on tilled ground.

F. muralis Sonder ex Koch
Common Ramping-fumitory   Probably introduced

| I | 2 | 4 | 6 | 7 | 8 |

Specimens of this species were not determined to subspecific level.
FID.

F. purpurea Pugsley
Purple Ramping-fumitory   Probably introduced

Colgan: 2. In sandy fallows near Rush, 1902; *Colgan* 1903.

| I | 2 | 3 | 8 |

Very rare, in tilled and waste ground.
1. Potato field, west of Naul, GS/87, **NDR**. Potato field between Nevitt and Nag's Head, CB, PH/90.
2. Sandy soil around new houses between Ballykea and the crossroads to Loughshinny, DD/85. Still in sandy fallows at Rush, DD/86 where it was first found in the county by Colgan.
3. Roadside on the Portrane Peninsula, DD/84.
8. Disturbed ground at Ringsend Dump, SR/87. South of Pigeon House Road, east of Irishtown, SR, HOR/84, **NDR**. Waste ground, south of Nutgrove Avenue, south-west of Churchtown, HOR/84.

F. officinalis L.
Common Fumitory   Probably introduced

| I | 2 | 3 | 4 | 5 | 6 | 7 | 8 |

Common in dry waste places and tilled ground. Much material belongs to subsp. **wirtgenii** (Koch) Arcangeli.
Subsp. **wirtgenii** was first recorded by Akeroyd in 1977 in Trinity College (7).
FID.

F. densiflora DC. *(F. micrantha)*
Dense-flowered Fumitory   Probably introduced

Colgan: 4. In a field at Finglas Quarry: *Colgan 1895.* 5. In a cornfield at Portmarnock, 1890: *Druce 1891.*

| (4) | (5) |

Not refound at Finglas (4). The quarries in which it occurred were filled in around 1970. It has not been refound at Portmarnock (5).

ULMACEAE

Ulmus

There are divergent views on the taxonomy of elms. **U. glabra** is readily identified, but it was often not possible to distinguish between **U. procera** and **U. minor** during the survey especially because, since the outbreak of Dutch Elm disease, most of the populations have existed as hedgerow suckers.

U. glabra Hudson *(U. montana)*
Wych Elm   Native; planted

1	2	3	4	5	6	7	8

Occasional in hedgerows throughout the county. Appears to be native in the upland areas but elsewhere is probably planted or self-sown from planted stock.
FID.

- -

U. procera Salisb.
English Elm   Possibly introduced

1	2	3	4	5	6	7	8

Rare, in hedgerows. Now, due to the ravages of Dutch Elm disease over the past 20 years, it is very much less frequent. Mainly found as a suckering shrub.
Not included by *Colgan* but listed in the *Suppl* which treated this species in a broad way to include **U. minor**.
FID.

- -

U. minor Miller
Small-leaved Elm   Possibly introduced

1	2	3	4	5	6	7	8

Common in hedgerows but difficult to distinguish from **U. procera**.

- -

CANNABACEAE

Humulus

H. lupulus L.
Hop   Alien

Colgan: 4. In Saint Catherine's Wood, 1739: *Annot. in Threlkeld.* 5. Thoroughly established in hedges and waste ground at Drumleck: *Flor. Howth.* 7. Hedges near the ruins of Tymon Castle, 1882-97 *(N.C.) Cyb. II.* 8. Sparingly on a roadside bank by the Glenamuck road, Carrickmines, 1894-99: *N.C.* A relic of cultivation long persistent in some places...
Suppl: Still established at 7. Tymon Castle (1956). 8. Still by Glenamuck Road, Carrickmines (1917). Roadside at Barnacullia (1953).

(4)	(5)	7	8

Very rare.
7. Still in hedges at Tymon Lane, CB/90.
8. Roadside at Barnacullia, PC/88. Growing at Ringsend Park in an **Escallonia** hedge, SR, HOR/85. Naturalized at the top of the railway bank at the east end of Military Road, Ballybrack, SR/87.

URTICACEAE

Urtica

U. dioica L.
Common Nettle   Native

| I | 2 | 3 | 4 | 5 | 6 | 7 | 8 |

Widespread. Common on waste ground and roadsides.
FID.

U. urens L.
Small Nettle   Alien

| I | 2 | 3 | 4 | 5 | 6 | 7 | 8 |

Commonest in arable sandy soils in 2. Elsewhere it is occasional on waste ground or cultivated land.
FID.

Parietaria

P. judaica L. (*P. officinalis, P. diffusa*)
Pellitory-of-the-wall   Native

| I | 2 | 3 | 4 | 5 | 6 | 7 | 8 |

Occasional on old walls especially near the coast.
FID.

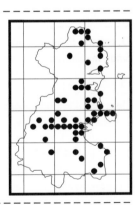

Soleirolia

S. soleirolii (Req.) Dandy (*Helxine soleirolii*)
Mind-your-own-business   Alien

| 4 | 5 | 7 | 8 |

Occasional as a garden weed or a garden escape close to human habitation.
FID.

FAGACEAE

Fagus

F. sylvatica L.
Beech   Alien
Commonly planted in all districts and occasionally self-seeding.
FID.

Quercus

Q. petraea (Mattuschka) Liebl.
Sessile Oak   Native; planted

| 2 | 5 | 6 | 7 | 8 |

Occasional in hedgerows and woods.
2. Roadside hedgerow, north-east of Ballyboghil, DD/84. Hedges along field margins, north-west of Ardla, possibly planted, DD/87.
5. At the edge of the demesne by the Howth Golf-course, DN/89.
6. Hedgerow, east of Esker, JP/87.
7. Small woodland fragment off the road opposite Woodtown Park, Stocking Lane, PWJ/87.
8. Fitzsimon's Wood, south-west of Sandyford, SR, HOR/84. Disused railway line, north-west of Sandyford Industrial Estate towards Dundrum, SR, EMcA/83. Ballybetagh Wood, SR, HOR/83. Hedge behind the Golden Ball at Kiltiernan, SR, HOR/85. The Scalp, DK/85. The Dingle, HOR/83. Cabinteely Park, Cornelscourt, HOR/84.

Q. petraea x **Q. robur** (**Q.** x **rosacea** Bechst.)
Native; planted

| 2 | 7 | 8 |

Occasional in hedgerows and woods.
2. Roadside hedgerow, south of Bettyville House, DD/85.
7. Roadside, 1 km east of Firhouse, MWJ, DAW/87.
8. Fitzsimon's Wood, south-west of Sandyford, SR, HOR/84. Hedge near the cromlech, Kiltiernan, SR, HOR/86. Hedge behind the Golden Ball, Kiltiernan, SR, HOR/85. Leopardstown Racecourse, SR/87. The Scalp, DK/85. Killiney Hill, SR/88. Hedge, south of Stepaside, SR/88. North of Glencullen Bridge, SR/88. Torca Wood, Dalkey, SR/89.

Q. robur L.
Pedunculate Oak   Native; planted

| 1 | 2 | 3 | 4 | 5 | 6 | 7 | 8 |

Occasional in hedgerows, parks and estates; often planted. It is not possible to determine which trees in Co. Dublin are native and not derived from planted stock.

BETULACEAE

Betula

B. pendula Roth *(B. verrucosa)*
Silver Birch   Native

Colgan: 2. In Gormanstown woods, 1895; 4. A couple of well grown young trees, obviously self-sown, on top of the Park wall at Island Bridge, 1902: *N.C.* 5. Frequent on Howth Head: *Flor. Howth.* 6. Frequent in Saggard Slade, and 8. At Ballycorus, 1901: *N.C.*

(2) 4 5 6 7 (8)

Rare as a native but widely planted and occasionally self-seeding.
4. By the Royal Canal, west of Clonsilla, JS/83.
5. River Tolka Basin, PG/90.
6. Lucan Demesne, JP/85.
7. Stream side below Cruagh Wood, above Rockbrook, PWJ, HOR/84.
FID.

- -

B. pendula x pubescens (B. x aurata Borkh.)

5

It may be under-recorded in Co. Dublin.
5. Birch scrub east of Black Linn, Ben of Howth, DK/94.

- -

B. pubescens Ehrh.
Downy Birch   Native

Colgan: 3. Sparingly near Portrane, 1900; 7. Frequent by the Cot Brook and Slade Brook, Kippure, 1901; and 8. Frequent on Killiney Hill, 1902: *N.C.*
Suppl: 7. Ballinascorney at c. 1,000 ft. on cliffs (A.W. Stelfox, 1923). Still there (1958). Still by the Cot and Slade Brooks, Glenasmole (1957). 8. Still at Killiney (1956).

(3) 5 6 7 8

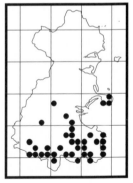

Frequent in the foothills and mountains (7 & 8) and on Howth (5). Very rare elsewhere as a native, but often planted. Often in woodlands, in scrub at the margins of conifer plantations and moorland, and by drains. Some of the specimens in 5 (Howth) and 8 (Fitzsimon's and Ballybetagh Woods, and Killiney Hill) resemble subsp. **tortuosa** (Ledeb.) Nyman (subsp. **carpatica** (Willd.) Asch. & Graebner).
FID.

Alnus

A. glutinosa (L.) Gaertner
Alder   Native

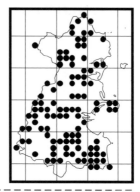

1	2	3	4	5	6	7	8

Common along all the river margins in the county and in hedgerows with adjoining streams. It appears to have been planted in some of its sites in the north of the county.
FID.

Corylus

C. avellana L.
Hazel   Native

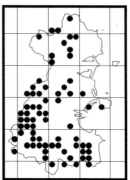

1	2	3	4	5	6	7	8

Widespread and frequent in lowland hedgerows and deciduous woodlands. Rare near the coast.
FID.

AIZOACEAE

Carpobrotus

C. edulis (L.) N.E. Br.
Hottentot-fig   Alien

2	5

Very rare on maritime cliff-tops, but widespread along sections of the Howth cliffs where it is locally dominant.
2. Rockabill, TC/90.
5. Howth Head, T. Crawford/No date. Doldrum Bay, near the Needles, Howth Head, DN/89, Lion's Head, Howth, DN/90. On the side of the cliffs, west of Drumleck Point, DN/90.

CHENOPODIACEAE

Chenopodium

C. bonus-henricus L.
Good-King-Henry   Alien

Colgan: 2. Near the church at Lusk, 1893; abundant in waste places and by the roadside at Balrothery, 1894-1902; 3. Roadsides near the ruined church of Killeek, Knocksedan, 1893-1903: *N.C.* 4. "In the Town of *Glasnevan* near *Sir John Rogerson's House*": *Threlkeld.* Near Glasnevin Bridge: *Wade Dubl.* Finglas Bridge and Cardiff's Bridge: *Ir. Flor.* By an old castle (Dunsoghly) a few miles north of Dunsink, 1894; *Praeger.* 5. At Artane: *Wade Dubl.* 7. "It grows beneath *Island Bridge* in the Pasture near the River": *Threlkeld.* Near Drimnagh Castle, 1893; by the wall of Tallaght monastery, 1894-95: *N.C.* 8. Carrickmines bridge and Dalkey: *Wade Dubl.* Near the ruins of Carrickmines Castle, 1902, and near Loughlinstown, 1895: *N.C.* At Little Bray, 1886: *Praeger.* At Old Connaught *(More) Cyb. II.* This plant was much grown as a pot-herb in old times, and in some of the stations just recorded in the neighbourhood of ruins has probably maintained itself for centuries. *Suppl:* 2. Still at Lusk Church (1956) and Balrothery (1947). 3. Still at Killeek (1953). 7. Lane from Jobstown to Knockannavea, quarter of a mile above the cross-roads to Oldbawn (1949-1957).

Very rare. Formerly associated with old ruins, many of which have been restored, re-pointed or tidied-up in recent years.

3. Lambay Island, M. Jebb/90s.

6. Building site beside the road leading to Athgoe Castle, JP/84, **NDR**.

C. rubrum L.
Red Goosefoot   Native

Suppl: 1. Naul Reservoir (1939). 2. Very abundant in the dried-up bed of Balrothery Lough (1934). 3. Still near Donabate (1949). Pond at Ballisk (1949). 5. On site of Carrickhill (1942). E. end of St Nessan's Bay, Ireland's Eye (1931). 6. Grand Canal N. of Milltown (R.W. Scully, 1918). 7. Roadside between Saggart and Tallaght (R.W. Scully, 1918). Tymon Castle (J.P. Brunker, 1931). Still by road near Oldbawn (1921).

| 1 | 2 | 3 | 4 | 5 | 6 | 7 | 8 |

Occasional on silage pits, manure heaps, muddy shores and by reservoirs.

1. Hynestown Reservoir, GS, DD/84, 85.
2. Old manure heap just west of Raheny, DD/84. Manure heap north of Rush Railway Station, DD/84. Compost heap north-west of Rush, DD/84.
3. Knocksedan Reservoir, MN/89.
4. Surrounding a cattle drinking hole, near Barberstown House, MN/84. Manure heap near the Custom House, MN, DN/87. Disturbed pathway by the Royal Canal, south-west of Pakenham Bridge, MN/89. Flower bed at the National Botanic Gardens, Glasnevin, DN/91.
5. South-west of Peafield, ENL/84. Still on Ireland's Eye, in a wet depression, ENL/84. Hollows in a limestone-gravel infill at the River Tolka Basin, PG/90. In a salt pan on the southern part of North Bull Island, PG/90.
6. At the south end of Brittas Pond, ENL/83; abundant there and completely covering the exposed mud floor of the reservoir, together with **Gnaphalium uliginosum** and **Rorippa palustris**, DD/88, 89. Common at the north end, JP, S. Waldren/94.
7. Cattle track in a field near Ballycullen, south-west of Templeogue, DK/84.
8. Manure heap in Ringsend Park, SR, HOR/85.

C. album L.
Fat-hen   Possibly introduced

| 1 | 2 | 3 | 4 | 5 | 6 | 7 | 8 |

Extremely widespread and very common in ruderal sites and as a weed of agricultural land.
FID.

Atriplex

A. prostrata Boucher ex DC. *(A. hastata)*
Spear-leaved Orache   Native

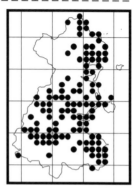

| (1) | 2 | 3 | 4 | 5 | 6 | 7 | 8 |

Common in a variety of coastal habitats, rarer as a colonist inland
and there confined to ruderal habitats.
FID.

A. glabriuscula Edmondston *(A. babingtonii)*
Babington's Orache   Native

| 2 | 3 | 5 | 8 |

Occasional on stony and shingle beaches.

A. littoralis L.
Grass-leaved Orache   Native

Colgan: 2. Near Balbriggan *(Moore) Cyb.* 3. On Lambay island: *Flor. Lambay.* 5. In a muddy soil at the south-west side of
Howth: *Wade Rar.* Abundant on the south-west shore of Howth Head from Greenfields to St Lawrence Cottage,
Sutton, and sparingly at Kilbarrick; also frequent on roadsides near Baldoyle, and abundant along the shore from
Baldoyle to near Portmarnock, 1903; on the shore at North Bull, 1895, and in sandy fallows there, 1903; on the new
tram track at Raheny, 1900, and near St Fintan's, 1904: *N.C.*
Suppl: 3. N. side of Swords estuary, W. of the railway embankment (1948). 5. Still near Baldoyle (1955) and on North
Bull (1955).

| 2 | 3 | 5 |

Common in the north of the county on stony and muddy shores. Now common in 2 & 3 on
the stony parts of the Malahide and Rogerstown estuaries where the sea is impounded by
railway embankments. Also common on North Bull Island (5).
2. Common along the shore between Rogerstown and Balleally, DD/84, 87.
3. Common along the back strand, Corballis, PR/83 & PR, DD/85.
5. Along the coast at Sutton, ENL/83, 84, CB/91 & PG/91. Shore, north of Baldoyle, ENL/84
   & CB/91. Beach at the south end of Portmarnock Peninsula, DN, RF/88.

A. patula L. (*A. erecta*)
Common Orache   Possibly introduced

| 1 | 2 | 3 | 4 | 5 | 6 | 7 | 8 |

Frequent in ruderal habitats.
FID.

- -

A. laciniata L. (*A. farinosa*, *A. sabulosa*, *A. maritima*)
Frosted Orache   Native

Colgan: 2. On the shore at Knockingan near Balbriggan (*Dr Scott*) *Mack. Rar.*, 1806 still there, a little south of the Delvin river,
1900! Between Balbriggan and Skerries, 1882: *Hart MS.* At Skerries, 1892 (*D. McArdle*) *Cyb. II.* and in 1902! Sparingly near
Rogerstown, 1902: *N.C.* 3. Sandy shore at Portrane (*More*) *Rec. Add.* Sparingly towards the southern end of Portrane peninsula,
1900, and by the shore below the new lunatic asylum, 1901: *N.C.* 5. At the south-west side of Howth: *Wade Rar.* abundant here
near Greenfields, Sutton, 1904! Between Howth and Baldoyle: *Ir. Flor.* At Portmarnock; on the Cosh, Howth; and on Ireland's
Eye: *Hart 1897.* Frequent along the shore from Portmarnock Point to Malahide, 1902; on the North Bull, especially towards the
northern end, 1904; 8. Sparingly on the South Bull, or Shelly Bank, beyond the Pigeon House, 1902: *N.C.*

| 2 | 3 | 5 | 8 |

Frequent along the north coast of the county, on shingle and sand; rare in 8.
8. Still on sand, east of the Pigeon House, SR/83. North end of Sandymount Strand,
    DNFC/83. Near the Martello Tower at Killiney, SR/83.

- -

A. portulacoides L. (*Obione portulacoides*, *Halimione portulacoides*)
Sea-purslane   Native

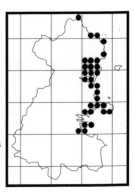

Colgan: 2. Frequent on Shennick's island and sparingly on the shore at Skerries, 1902;
sparingly between Balbriggan and the Delvin river, 1900; abundant for 2 miles in salt
marshes along the north side of Rogerstown creek, 1902: *N.C.* 3. Rocks on the south
side of Portrane and flat shore at north end of Portrane (*More*) *Rec. Add.* frequent herein
both stations, 1903! In great profusion near the head of the Rogerstown creek, and
frequent all round the Malahide creek, 1902: *N.C.* 5. Among the rocks of Howth facing
Dublin Bay, July 31st, 1799: *Templeton MS.* frequent here in 1904, as at the Martello tower,
Sutton, at Drumleck, &c.! Abundant in salt marshes between Baldoyle and Portmarnock,
1903: *N.C.* 8. "On ye Rocks towards Dunlary, July, 1734": *Annot. in Threlkeld.* Sparingly on cliffs
below Killiney Hill, 1902: *N.C.*

| 2 | 3 | 5 | 8 |

Common in salt-marshes and estuaries in the north of the county
and on sea-cliffs at Howth and Donabate, rarely on drift banks near the sea. Rare in 8.
8. On and at the west end of the South Wall, SR, JR/85. Booterstown Marsh, SR, HOR/85.
    Sparingly on walls at and north of Merrion Gates SR/85.

- -

Beta

B. vulgaris L.

| 2 | 3 | 4 | 5 | 8 |

subsp. **maritima** (L.) Arcang. *(B. maritima)*
Sea Beet   Native

| 2 | 3 | 5 | 8 |

Scattered along the coast on rocks, cliffs and walls.

----

subsp. **vulgaris**
Root Beet

| 4 |

Occasionally occurs as a relic of cultivation.
FID.

Salicornia
Colgan recognised only one species of **Salicornia**, *S. herbacea*.

S. pusilla J. Woods
One-flowered Glasswort   Native

| 3 | 5 |

Rare in salt-marshes.
3. South end of Malahide Island, PR/88, **NDR**.
5. North Bull Island, MS & C.A. Stace/75, **NDR**.

S. ramosissima J. Woods
Purple Glasswort   Native

| 2 | 3 | 5 |

Common in salt-marshes.
2. Bare mud, south of Balleally, DD, JP/82 & DD/87.
3. Estuarine mud at Raheen Point, Donabate, PR/83.
5. North and south of the Causeway, North Bull Island, and on the adjoining mainland,
   ENL/84, 85 & ENL, HOR/85.

S. europaea L.
Common Glasswort   Native

| 2 | 3 | 5 | 8 |

Common in salt-marshes.
2. Mud pans in the upper reaches of the salt-marsh at Rush, KF/61. Muddy foreshore at
   Balleally Dump, DD/87.

3. Raheen Point, Donabate, PR/83.
5. Common on North Bull Island, ENL, HOR/83. I km north-west of Redrock, Howth, ENL, HOR/83.
8. Booterstown Marsh, SR, HOR/85. Sparingly, in cracks on the South Wall, east of the Half Moon Bathing Place, SR/87.

S. nitens P. Ball & Tutin
Shiny Glasswort   Native
Recorded for Co. Dublin by Ferguson (1962) but not encountered during the present survey.

S. fragilis P. Ball & Tutin
Yellow Glasswort   Native

2	3	5

Very rare, in salt-marshes.
2. Levees and closed communities in the mid and lower zones of mature salt-marsh at Rush, KF/61, **NDR**.
3. South end of Portrane Peninsula, PR/87, **NDR**.
5. On the edge of the salt-marsh, south of the Causeway on North Bull Island, KF/61, **NDR** & ENL, HOR/85.

S. dolichostachya Moss
Long-spiked Glasswort   Native
Suppl: 2 and 3. Donabate estuary (O'Reilly and Pantin in *Proc. R.I.A.*, 58 B5 [1957]). 3 and 5. Malahide Estuary (O'Reilly and Pantin, *op. cit.*, 1957). 5. Bull Island marsh (1940). Baldoyle marsh (1957).

2	3	5	8

Common in salt-marshes.
2. Soft open mud in the lower zones of the salt-marsh at Rush, KF/61.
3. Salt-marsh, Portrane Peninsula, PR/87.
5. In a salt-marsh and on the mudflats on North Bull Island, KF/61 & HOR, ENL/84-86. Occasional on mudflats at the southern end of North Bull Island, PG/90.
8. Booterstown Marsh, SR/89, **NDR**.

Suaeda

S. maritima (L.) Dumort.
Annual Sea-blite   Native

2	3	5	8

Common in salt-marshes and estuaries; very rare in 8.
8. Booterstown Marsh, SR, HOR/85.

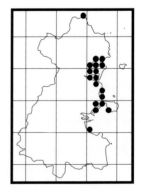

Salsola

S. kali L. subsp. **kali**
Prickly Saltwort   Native

| 2 | 3 | 5 | 8 |

Occasional on sandy and stony beaches; rare in 8.
2. On stable sand at the mouth of the Delvin River, DD/82. On fine shingle at Cardy Point, DD/87. Along the foreshore at Rogerstown, DD/83. On the shore below Hand Park, Rush, DD/87.
3. Occasional on beaches at Donabate and Portrane, PR/85, 87.
5. Along the foreshore of North Bull Island, DNFC/84, ENL, CB/85 & PG/92. Along the peninsula to Portmarnock Point, HJH/83, DN, RF/88 & DN/89. On the strand at Sutton, DNFC/88. Hole-in-the-wall beach, Sutton, ENL/84.
8. Sand to the east of the Pigeon House, SR, HOR/83.

PORTULACACEAE

Montia

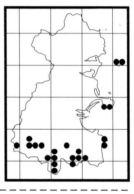

M. fontana L.
Blinks   Native

| (1) | 3 | 5 | 6 | 7 | 8 |

Occasional in muddy, acid ground on peat or mineral soil and in short turf.

---

subsp. **fontana**

| 7 |

Recently identified from specimens collected by H.G. Carroll in 1869 from Three Rock Mountain (8) (**DBN**).
7. South end of the southern reservoir in Glenasmole, CB, SR/90.

---

subsp. **variabilis** Walters

| 8 |

8. On granitic gravel by the Wicklow Way, south of Boranaraltry Bridge and on mud at Walsh's Lane south-east of Ballybrack, Glencullen Valley, SR, CB/89. In short turf on granite outcrop on the south-east slope of Dalkey Hill, SR/89, 91.

---

subsp. **minor** Hayw. (subsp. *chondrosperma*)

| 8 |

Recently identified from specimens collected by R.Ll. Praeger in 1894 from Dundrum (8) (**DBN**).
8. In short turf on granite outcrop, east-south-east of the church on Dalkey Island, SR/91.

CARYOPHYLLACEAE

Arenaria

A. serpyllifolia L.
Thyme-leaved Sandwort   Native

| 2 | 3 | 4 | 5 | 6 | 7 | 8 |

Common on walls and sandy ground.
subsp. **serpyllifolia**

| 2 | 3 | 4 | 5 | 6 | 7 | 8 |

Common in sand-dunes, sandy areas inland and occasionally on old walls.
FID.

---

subsp. **lloydii** (Jordan) Bonnier (subsp. *macrocarpa*)

| 2 | 3 |

Very rare on sandy and stony ground on the upper parts of seashores.
2. Rogerstown Harbour, DD/88, 89, **NCR.**
3. Lambay Island, DD/91.

---

subsp. **leptoclados** (Reichb.) Nyman (*A. leptoclados*)

Suppl: 5. Ireland's Eye (1945).

| 2 | 3 | 4 | (5) | (7) | (8) |

2. Walls between St Maur's G.A.A. Club and Rush, DD/87. Waste sandy ground, north-west of Rush Golf-course, DD/87.
3. Old walls in Swords, DD/86. Sand-hills just north of Portrane, DD, PR/87. Open sandy ground just north of Burrow, north of Portrane, DD, PR/87.
4. Disused quarry, south of Clanaboy House, Lucan, MN/88.

Moehringia

M. trinervia (L.) Clairv. (*Arenaria trinervia*)
Three-nerved Sandwort   Native

Colgan: 6. By Mount Seskin road and above the embankment, Saggard, 1895; roadside banks north of Athgoe Castle, 1904; abundant in Lucan woods, 1897; near Neillstown, 1900; 7. Roadsides near Woodtown, 1894; and at Ballynamanach, near Tallaght, 1895: *N.C.* 8. At Old Connaught: *Ir. Flor.* 1833 and in 1900! At Monkstown, *circa 1883:* *J. Bain.* Abundant at Kingstown, near the Scalp, 1894; near the old mill, Kiltiernan, 1895: *N.C.*

| 6 | 7 | 8 |

Occasional in woodlands on the south side of the River Liffey Valley and in the foothills of the mountains (7 & 8); rare in 6.
6. By the River Liffey at Lucan and St Edmundsbury, MN, HOR, PR/83.

7. Off the Mount Seskin road at Tallaght; on a track through woods in the Glenasmole Valley; Killakee woods; hedges and woods above Rockbrook; River Liffey Valley about 1 km east of the Hermitage Golf-course and north of Fonthill House, MN/90.
8. Larch Hill, west of Kilmashogue Mountain; St Enda's Park, east of Ballyboden; grounds of St Gerard's School, west of Bray; at Fern Hill, south of Sandyford; in woodlands near the Leopardstown Racecourse, SR, HOR/85-90.

Honckenya (*Honkenya*)

H. peploides (L.) Ehrh. *(Arenaria peploides)*
Sea Sandwort   Native

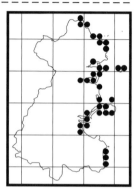

| 2 | 3 | 5 | 8 |

Frequent in fore-dunes and on shingle, especially along the seashore upper drift lines.

Minuartia

M. hybrida (Villars) Schischkin (*Arenaria tenuifolia*)
Fine-leaved Sandwort   Probably introduced

| (6) |

Not refound on the railway line at Hazelhatch (6) though now present on the same line not far to the west, in Co. Kildare.

Stellaria

S. media (L.) Villars
Common Chickweed   Native

| 1 | 2 | 3 | 4 | 5 | 6 | 7 | 8 |

Extremely widespread and common in a wide variety of ruderal habitats.
FID.

S. pallida (Dumort.) Crepin (*Alsine pallida, S. media* var. *boraeana, S. apetala*)
Lesser Chickweed   Native

| 2 | 3 | 4 | 5 | 6 | 7 | 8 |

Occasional in sand-hills and on old walls.
2. Rogerstown Boat Club, DD/83. Old walls by the sea in Skerries village, DD/82, 83. St Patrick's Island, Skerries, DD/83. Open dune grassland on the beach south of Rush, DD/83.

3. Short dune grassland above the back strand at Corballis, DD, PR/83. Sandy ground near the sea on Lambay Island, DD/82.
4. At the base of Dunsoghly Castle walls, MN/91, **NDR.**
5. Stapolin housing estate, north of Baldoyle, ENL/84. Disturbed ground between Howth and Deer Park golf-courses, ENL/84. Sea wall just west of Howth Railway Station, DD, ENL/88. Overgrown tarmacadam path in St Anne's Park, Raheny, PG/92. Malahide Esplanade, DD/94.
6. Wall on the Brownsbarn to Saggart road, west of Fortunestown, JP/84. Old railway platform at St Helen's, south of Lucan, JP/84. West of Clondalkin, JP/83. Wall by the main street at Lucan Demesne, MN/88.
7. Lawn on the south side of College Park, T.C.D., DD/89, **NDR.** Steps of Royal Irish Academy, MS/90.
8. Formerly on the West pier at Dun Laoghaire, but no longer there in 1985, HOR/83. Roadside opposite the Martello Tower at Ballybrack, SR/87. Base of a wall near the underpass just north of Killiney Railway Station, SR/86. South of the obelisk, on Killiney Hill, JP, DD/83. Base of the wall around the tower on Dalkey Hill, SR/86.

S. holostea L.
Greater Stitchwort   Native

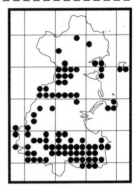

| 1 | 2 | 3 | 4 | 5 | 6 | 7 | 8 |

Common in base-rich woodland and hedgerows. Rare in the extreme north of the county.
1. North-west of Oldtown, GS/86.
FID.

S. palustris Retz.
Marsh Stitchwort   Native

Colgan: 1. In Curragha Bog: Wade Rar. 7 or 8. Wet slopes of the Dublin mountains (Moore) Cyb. Curragha Bog is now drained away, and this species, assuming it to have been correctly recorded by Wade, must have long since become extinct there. The later record is of much higher authority, and though the plant has not since been observed anywhere in the mountains, it seems hardly permissible to exclude it from the flora, since there is nothing in its Irish distribution to render its occurrence in Dublin improbable.

| (1) | (7) | (8) |

Not rediscovered in the Dublin Mountains (7 or 8) where it was noted in *Cybele*.

S. graminea L.
Lesser Stitchwort   Native

| 1 | 2 | 3 | 4 | 5 | 6 | 7 | 8 |

Common on roadside verges, in hedgerows and grassland.

S. uliginosa Murray *(S. alsine)*
Bog Stitchwort   Native

| 1 | 2 | 3 | 4 | 5 | 6 | 7 | 8 |

Common in streams and marshes in the south of the county;
occasional elsewhere.

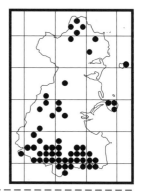

Cerastium

C. arvense L.
Field Mouse-ear   Native

| 2 | 3 | 5 | (8) |

Rare, on sandy roadside banks and in sand-dunes. Not refound along
the railway line between Merrion and Booterstown (8) *(Colgan)*.
2. Sandy roadside banks near the boat club at Rogerstown and
scattered from there to Rush on low earthen banks and in dune
grassland, DD/83.
3. At the north-west corner of Lambay Island, DD/82.
5. Feltrim Hill, DD/66. Sand-dunes mid-way along the western side
   of Portmarnock Peninsula, DD/82, 88. Scattered in Portrane
   sand-hills, DD/82. Cliffs at the Baily, Howth, MWJ/88 & CB/91.
   Sandy soil near the roundabout at the end of the causeway on North Bull Island, MWJ/84. By
   the green, north of the Alder Marsh on North Bull Island, PG/87.

C. tomentosum L.
Snow-in-summer   Alien

| 1 | 3 | 4 | 5 | 7 |

Occasionally naturalized on walls and banks. A garden escape, not included in *Colgan, Suppl*
or *CC2*.

C. fontanum Baumg. subsp. **vulgare** (Hartman) Greuter & Burdet
(C. triviale, C. vulgatum, C. fontanum subsp. *triviale)*
Common Mouse-ear   Native

| 1 | 2 | 3 | 4 | 5 | 6 | 7 | 8 |

Widespread and common in grasslands, waste ground and sand-dunes.
FID.

C. glomeratum Thuill. *(C. viscosum)*
Sticky Mouse-ear   Native

| 1 | 2 | 3 | 4 | 5 | 6 | 7 | 8 |

Widespread and common in gravelly or well-drained soils and particularly in poached, poorly drained soils at the entrance to cattle-pastures.
FID.

C. diffusum Pers. *(C. tetrandrum)*
Sea Mouse-ear   Native

| 2 | 3 | 5 | 7 | 8 |

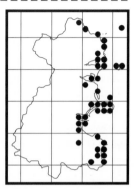

Common in sandy and gravelly places and in short turf on cliffs, chiefly by the sea. Very rare inland.
7. A single plant growing on the pavement, Clarendon Street, MWJ/93.

C. semidecandrum L.
Little Mouse-ear   Native

| 2 | 3 | 5 |

Occasional in sand-dune grassland.
2. Sandy ground at the south end of Rush Golf-course near Rogerstown, DD/83.
3. Sandy grassland near the entrance to the Island Golf-course, DD, PR/82. Sandy hollows at the north end of Portrane Peninsula, DD/83.
5. At the south end of the North Bull Island and 100 m north-east of North Bull Island Interpretive Centre, DD/83 & MWJ/88. Sand-hills to the east of Portmarnock, ENL/84. Frequent on thinly vegetated low dunes in Portmarnock sand-hills, DD/89.

Sagina

S. nodosa (L.) Fenzl
Knotted Pearlwort   Native

Colgan: All districts. Moist sandy places and marshy ground; frequent and locally abundant. An abundant species in the damp flats and hollows of the sandhills at North Bull and Portrane.

Suppl: Abundant on sandhills. Frequent elswhere.

| (1) | 2 | 3 | (4) | 5 | (6) | 7 | (8) |

Still frequent in dune-slacks at Donabate (3) and on North Bull Island (5); very rare elsewhere. This species has declined markedly since the 1960s.
2. Flushed grassland below a rock outcrop at Cardy Point, DD/87.
5. Edge of a pond in the western half of Portmarnock Golf-course, DN/89. Wet slope near the beach just west of Drumleck Point, DN/89. Wet field at Kilrock, DN/89.
7. Flush at 350 m altitude, 0.5 km north-east of Cunard, CB/89.

S. procumbens L.
Procumbent Pearlwort   Native

| I | 2 | 3 | 4 | 5 | 6 | 7 | 8 |

Common on damp pathways and muddy areas in damp pastures.
FID.

S. apetala Ard. (incl. *S. ciliata*)
Annual Pearlwort   Native

| I | 2 | 3 | 4 | 5 | 6 | 7 | 8 |

Frequent in dry ground.
S. ciliata, distinguished by both *Colgan* and *Suppl*, is now no longer considered a distinct taxon.
FID.

S. maritima G. Don
Sea Pearlwort   Native

| 2 | 3 | 5 | 8 |

Occasional on maritime walls and rocks, car parks near the sea and in salt-marshes.

Scleranthus

S. annuus L.
Annual Knawel   Probably introduced

Colgan: 1. Abundant in a cornfield near Damastown, Naul Hills, 1902: *Colgan 1903.* 5. Dry sandy fields between Baldoyle and Howth: *Ir. Flor.* Roadside and on light soil near Warren Lodge and Kilbarrick, occasionally: *Flor. Howth.* 7. Gravelly banks of the Dodder above Templeogue: *Mack. Cat.* Sparingly on gravelly tracks by the Dodder at Castle Kelly, Glenasmole, 1894-1900: *N.C.*

| (1) | (5) | (7) |

Formerly on sandy or gravelly ground; not seen recently.

Spergula

S. arvensis L.
Corn Spurrey   Probably introduced

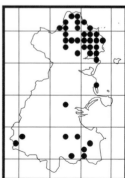

| I | 2 | 3 | 4 | 5 | 6 | 7 | 8 |

Occasional on base-poor arable ground in 1, 2 and 8; rare elsewhere.
4. Bank of the River Tolka in the National Botanic Gardens, Glasnevin,
   MN/87.
5. Sand-hills at Portmarnock, ENL/84, abundant there, DD/94.
   Alexandra Basin, Dublin Port, SR/89.

7. Allotments on the banks of the Grand Canal near Dolphin's Barn Bridge, MSS, PWJ/81. Irish Times Car Park, Hawkin's Street, PC, PWJ/79. Farm track at Ballymorefinn, SR/87. Exposed bed of the south end of the northern reservoir in Glenasmole, MN/88.

FID.

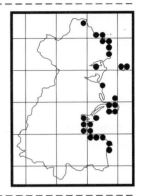

Spergularia

S. rupicola Lebel ex Le Jolis *(S. rupestris)*
Rock Sea-spurrey   Native

| 2 | 3 | 5 | 8 |

Common in salt-marshes, on rocky coasts and walls by the sea.

S. rupicola x **S. marina (S.** x **symeana** Druce)
Native

| 8 |

8. Growing with both parents east of the Half Moon bathing place, on the South Wall, SR/88. This was its first Irish record (Reynolds 1989a).

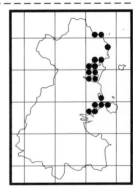

S. media (L.) C. Presl *(S. marginata)*
Greater Sea-spurrey   Native

| 2 | 3 | 5 |

Common in salt-marshes and muddy estuaries.

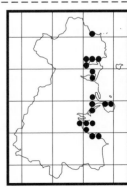

S. marina (L.) Griseb. *(S. salina)*
Lesser Sea-spurrey   Native

| 2 | 3 | 5 | 8 |

Common in salt-marshes; also on paths and gravel.

S. rubra (L.) J.S. & C. Presl
Sand Spurrey   Native

Colgan: 4. Along the canal from Dublin to Castleknock; and 5. About Clontarf and Ballybough Bridge: *Ir. Flor.*

| (4) | (5) | 8 |

Extremely rare.

8. Gravel track on north-east facing slope of Three Rock Mountain above Barnacullia, PC/76, 88 & SR, DD/91.

Lychnis

L. flos-cuculi L.
Ragged-Robin   Native

| (1) | 2 | 3 | 4 | 5 | 6 | 7 | 8 |

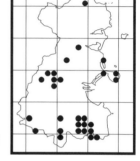

Occasional in the uplands in marshes and damp grassland; rare elsewhere.

2. West of the Corn Mill, near Balbriggan, DD/87.
3. Marshy ground in River Valley, Swords, PR/89.
4. Marsh at St Margaret's, MN/82. By Luttrellstown Lake, MN/89. Marsh by River Tolka at Blanchardstown, MN/83. Marshy ground by the Royal Canal at Ashtown and Castleknock, MN/85.
5. Wet field off Thormanby Road, Howth DN/89. Plentiful in Portmarnock Brickfields, DN/90.

Agrostemma

A. githago L. *(Lychnis githago)*
Corncockle   Alien

Suppl: Rare. 3. Still at Portrane and Donabate (1947). 7 Near Greenhills (J.P. Brunker, 1917). Near Mt St Joseph's, Clondalkin (J.P.B., 1920). Near outer gate of waterworks, Glenasmole (1946). Now very rare, probably due to the use of cleaner seed for crops.

| (2) | (3) | (4) | (5) | (7) | 8 |

Almost extinct.

Formerly a weed of cultivated ground, recorded at Rush (2), Portrane (3), Finglas (4), Howth, Portmarnock, Kilbarrick and Sutton (5), Greenhills (7) and Ticknock and Salthill (8). It was most abundant as a weed of legume crops. It is now almost extinct in the county other than as a garden plant due to efficient agricultural seed cleaning techniques, herbicides and changing farming practices.

8. East side of River Dodder between Sandymount and Irishtown (near the junction of Newbridge Avenue and Lansdowne village), possibly of garden origin, DN, SR/93.

Silene

S. vulgaris Garcke subsp. **vulgaris** (*S. cucubalus*)
Bladder Campion   Native

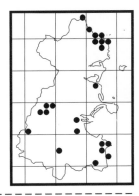

| (1) | 2 | 4 | 5 | 6 | 7 | 8 |

Occasional on sandy ground inland and railway banks; rare in 5.
5. Railway embankment at North Strand, PG/90.

S. uniflora Roth (*S. maritima, S. vulgaris* subsp. *maritima*)
Sea Campion   Native

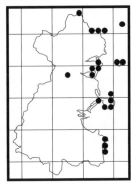

| 2 | 3 | 5 | 8 |

Common in various habitats in the spray-zone on coasts throughout
the county, though rarer in 8 than in the north. However, plants
apparently referable to this species grow on the parapet of
Knocksedan Bridge (3) which is more than 4 km from the sea.

S. noctiflora L. (*Melandrium noctiflorum*)
Night-flowering Catchfly   Alien

Suppl: 3. Burrow, Portrane (1953). 7. Waste ground at Inchicore (C.B. Moffat, *I.N.*, XXXIII, 1924).

| (3) | (7) |

Probably extinct. It was last seen on the western side of Portrane Peninsula (3) by J.P. Brunker
in 1953.

S. latifolia Poiret subsp. **alba** (Miller) Greuter & Burdet
(*Lychnis vespertina, Melandrium album, S. alba*)
White Campion   Native

Colgan: An abundant weed in sandy fallows at Sutton, Baldoyle, Portmarnock, Portrane,
Rush, and Skerries, 1902, becoming rarer further north: N.C. (7. At Inchicore railway
works, 1900: *R.A. Phillips.* Near the 5th Lock, Grand Canal, 1902 and 8. Casual near
Ballycorus lead-works, 1895: *N.C.*). A characteristic plant of the Dublin sea coast;
hardly more than casual in its inland stations.

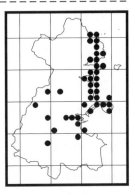

| 2 | 3 | 4 | 5 | 7 | 8 |

Common near the sea. Occasional inland and often as a casual.
FID.

S. latifolia × **S. dioica** (**S.** × **hampeana** Meusel & K. Werner;
Melandrium album × *M. dioicum, Lychnis* × *intermedia*)
Native

Suppl: 2. Lowther Lodge S. of Gormanston (1946).

| (2) | 3 |

3. Sandy ground by the gate of the caravan park field, east of Corballis, PR/84, **NDR.**

- -

S. dioica (L.) Clairv. *(Lychnis diurna, Melandrium dioicum)*
Red Campion   Native

Colgan: 3. Very abundant on Lambay island, especially among thickets or brambles: *Flor. Lambay* and in 1896 *(Praeger)*
Top. Bot. 4. Sparingly in Saint Catherine's Wood, 1895-1896: N.C. 5. Woods in Howth Demesne; at Carrickbrack; and in
sandy places amongst brambles on Ireland's Eye: *Flor. Howth.* 6. Abundant in Crooksling glen above the Embankment,
near Saggard, 1894-1903: N.C. 8. By the river above the bridge at Bray, 1895: *W.H. Bloomer.*
Suppl: 3. Still abundant at Lambay (1954). 5. Still at Ireland's Eye (1956) and Howth Demesne (1950). 7. Kimmage
rubbish dump (1948). Lugmore Glen, near Jobstown (1956).

| 3 | 4 | 5 | 6 | (7) | (8) |

Rare, in woodland margins and under brambles near the coast.
3. Still under brambles on Lambay Island, DD/91. Sand-hills, near Malahide Point, PR/83.
4. On a path at the edge of St Catherine's Woods, JS, MN/84 & DN/92. One plant beside the
   entrance gate of Beech Park at Clonsilla, JS/87.
5. At the eastern and north-eastern side of St Anne's Park, Raheny, PG/87, 88.
6. Still on Crooksling Hill, on the east side of the road, above The Embankment, DD/68,
   JP/82, 92 & MN/90.

- -

Saponaria

S. officinalis L.
Soapwort   Alien

| 2 | 3 | 4 | 5 | 6 | (7) | 8 |

A garden escape or throw-out that is occasionally established in most districts, usually as
the double-flowered form. A long-established plant in the county.
FID.

- -

POLYGONACEAE

Persicaria

P. amphibia (L.) Gray *(Polygonum amphibium)*
Amphibious Bistort   Native

| I | 2 | 3 | 4 | 5 | 6 | 7 | 8 |

Frequent in wetlands, by canals, in marshes and on damp arable land; often locally abundant.
FID.

P. maculosa Gray *(Polygonum persicaria)*
Redshank   Native

| 1 | 2 | 3 | 4 | 5 | 6 | 7 | 8 |

Widespread and very common in ruderal habitats throughout the county.
FID.

P. lapathifolia (L.) Gray *(Polygonum lapathifolium)*
Pale Persicaria   Possibly introduced

| 1 | 2 | 3 | 4 | 5 | 6 | 7 | 8 |

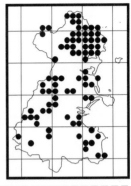

Frequent in tilled fields and waste ground. Widely distributed. Very
much commoner now than in Colgan's time.
2. Potato fields, north of Lusk, DD/82, **NDR.** Common throughout
   this district.
FID.

P. hydropiper (L.) Spach *(Polygonum hydropiper)*
Water-pepper   Native

| 1 | 2 | 4 | (5) | 6 | 7 | 8 |

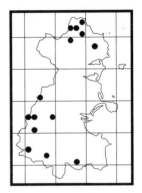

Common in muddy ground in the Naul Hills (1); rare elsewhere.
4. Two plants, on the bank of the River Tolka below Damastown,
   MN/88, **NDR.** Banks of the River Liffey at Lucan and at
   St Catherine's Estate, MN/89, 90.
6. Brittas Ponds, DNFC/89.
7. Palmerston Marsh, MN, ENL/85. West side and south end of
   the northern reservoir in Glenasmole, SR/89.
8. Muddy ditch by Walsh's Lane south-east of Ballybrack in the
   Glencullen Valley, SR, JR/86.

Polygonum

P. oxyspermum Meyer & Bunge ex Ledeb. subsp. **raii** (Bab.) D. Webb & Chater *(P. raii)*
Ray's Knotgrass   Native

Colgan: 2. Shore near Skerries, 1893; between Skerries and Loughshinny, 1894: *N.C.* North of Balbriggan: *Praeger* 1894.
and in 1900! 3. On Lambay island: *Flor. Lambay.* 5. Seashore at Sutton; between Baldoyle and Howth; plentiful on
Ireland's Eye: *Flor. Howth.* Sparingly near Malahide and on the North Bull, 1902: *N.C.* 8. Sea coast near Sandymount: *Flor.
Hib.* Killiney Bay (as *P. maritimum* Ray, Synop.): *Brit. Flor.,* 1842 and in 1901! Sparingly on the South Wall beyond the
Pigeon House, 1902, and frequent on the new railway embankment north of Bray river, 1903: *N.C.*

| 2 | (3) | 5 | (8) |

Extremely rare on shingle and sandy shores. Not seen recently on Lambay Island (3), nor on the
shore at Baldoyle, Malahide or North Bull Island (5), nor at Sandymount or north of Bray (8).

2. Still north of Balbriggan on a sandy shore near the mouth of the Delvin River, DD/82, 87.
Five plants, still above and below Holmpatrick Bridge, Skerries, DD/83, 87.
5. Still at the eastern end of the Hole-in-the-Wall beach (Claremont Strand), Sutton ENL/84.

P. arenastrum Boreau
Equal-leaved Knotgrass   Native

1	2	3	4	5	6	7	8

Common and widespread in the lowlands, especially on trampled ground, on road and path sides, waste ground, cultivated land and occasional on stony sea-shores.
FID.

P. aviculare L.
Knotgrass   Native

1	2	3	4	5	6	7	8

Common in the same habitats as **P. arenastrum**.
FID.

P. cf. **rurivagum** Jordan ex Boreau
Probably introduced

2	6

Extremely rare in cultivated land. Plants apparently conforming to **P. rurivagum**, which is not recorded from Ireland, occur both in Counties Dublin and Wexford often on base-poor soils. However we are not convinced that they are all identical to that taxon and further research is required to clarify their identity.
2. Many plants in a field, 0.25 km east of Nevitt, DD/89.
6. A few plants in allotments, south-south-east of Esker, JP/87.

Fallopia

F. japonica (Houtt.) Ronse Decraene (*Polygonum cuspidatum, Reynoutria japonica*)
Japanese Knotweed   Alien

1	2	3	4	5	6	7	8

Widely distributed throughout the county, often as a garden weed or in neglected waste ground. Also introduced to rural parts with garden rubbish or dumped soils.
FID.

F. sachalinensis (F. Schmidt ex Maxim.) Ronse Decraene
(*Polygonum sachalinense, Reynoutria sachalinensis*)
Giant Knotweed   Alien

5	7	8

Very rare, on waste ground and river banks.
5. Abandoned garden, west of Drumleck Point, Howth Head, DN/89.
7. Grassland at the road junction 100 m east of Clondalkin Round Tower, and by the River Dodder just east of Milltown, MWJ/87.
8. Ringsend Dump, SR/86.

F. convolvulus (L.) A. Löve *(Polygonum convolvulus)*
Black-bindweed   Possibly introduced in Co. Dublin

| 1 | 2 | 3 | 4 | 5 | 6 | 7 | 8 |

Frequent in ruderal habitats and tilled fields.
FID.

Rumex

R. acetosella L.
Sheep's Sorrel   Native

| 1 | 2 | 3 | 4 | 5 | 6 | 7 | 8 |

Common in heathland, upland grasslands and occasional in mature sand-dunes. Now spreading into gardens and flower beds with pot plants which have been grown in peat based composts. All material from Co. Dublin probably belongs to subsp. **pyrenaicus** (Pourret) Akeroyd.
FID.

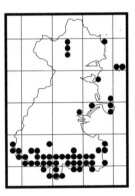

R. acetosa L.
Common Sorrel   Native

| 1 | 2 | 3 | 4 | 5 | 6 | 7 | 8 |

Widespread and common in damp grassland and by roadsides.
FID.

R. hydrolapathum Hudson
Water Dock   Native

Colgan: 3. Frequent and luxuriant by the Broad Meadow Water at Rowlestown, 1894 and above Fieldstown, 1903: *N.C.* 5.Near Malahide *(More)*; ditches between Raheny and Baldoyle *(Moore) Cyb.* Probably at one time more abundant in the county, before the marsh lands were reduced by drainage.

Suppl: 1 and 3. Frequent along the Broad Meadow at Rowlestown and Fieldstown (1948) - apparently its only present station in the county.

| (1) | (3) | (5) |

Not refound at any of its former sites. The Broad Meadow River was deepened in the 1960s.

R. crispus L.
Curled Dock   Native

| 1 | 2 | 3 | 4 | 5 | 6 | 7 | 8 |

---

subsp. **crispus**

| 1 | 2 | 3 | 4 | 5 | 6 | 7 | 8 |

Widespread and common on roadsides, in agricultural land and waste ground.
FID.

---

subsp. **littoreus** (J. Hardy) Akeroyd [incl. var. **trigranulatus**].

| 2 | 3 | 8 |

Frequent on shingle and sandy shores.
2. Cardy Point, DD/87. Barnageeragh, DD/90. Shenick's Island, DD/88.
3. Lambay Island, DD/91.
8. Mud in Booterstown Marsh, SR/88. Stony beach, south of Killiney, SR/88.

R. crispus x **R. obtusifolius (R.** x **pratensis** Mert. & Koch)**
Native

| 1 | 3 | 8 |

Occasional on waste ground and roadsides. Probably under-recorded.
1. North-west of Ballymadun, GS/86. At Moorepark, GS/86. At and to the east of Oldtown, GS/85, 86. West of Ballyboghil, GS/87. Rowlestown, GS/85. Beshellstown, GS/87. Bog of the Ring, GS/87.
3. Dump in a quarry near Donabate Railway Station, JRA/82.
8. Ringsend Dump, SR/86.

R. conglomeratus Murray
Clustered Dock   Native

| 1 | 2 | 3 | 4 | 5 | 6 | 7 | 8 |

Occasional in wet or damp ground especially in drains and ditches, and by pools and lakeshores. Throughout the county, though rare in the north.
FID.

R. sanguineus L.
Wood Dock   Native

| 1 | 2 | 3 | 4 | 5 | 6 | 7 | 8 |

Widespread. Common in damp shaded woods and hedges, roadside verges and waste ground.
FID.

R. pulcher L.
Fiddle Dock   Alien

Brunker MS: 3. Portrane, nr old Colgan station (no date).

(3) (8)

Previous records from between Portrane and Donabate (Phillips 1924) (3) and those in *Colgan* have not been reconfirmed.

R. obtusifolius L.
Broad-leaved Dock   Native

| 1 | 2 | 3 | 4 | 5 | 6 | 7 | 8 |

Extremely widespread. Very common on waste ground, roadsides and in pastures.
FID.

R. maritimus L.
Golden Dock   Native

Colgan: 1. On Curragha bog, near Garristown *(Mr L. Ogilby)*; abundant in this ... locality *(Moore) Cyb.* "Abundant by the stream through the bog at Garristown, 1882-83. It extends for two or three miles, ceasing before Coghills (Cockle's) bridge" *(Hart) Flor. Howth App.* The two localities above given are probably identical. Doctor Moore failed to find the plant at Garristown in 1876, and in the *Catalogue of the Phanerogamic Plants of Dublin and Wicklow*, compiled by him conjointly with Mr A.G. More in 1878, it is entered for Garristown bog only, and set down as "now apparently extinct." Three searches made by *N.C.* in 1893, 1894, and 1902, along the stream or ditch draining the bog, were equally unsuccessful, yet, having regard to the great abundance of the plant here in 1883, and to the well-known irregularity of its appearances, it would seem rash to exclude it as extinct. In their Flora of the Bavarian river-basins of Wornitz and Altmuhl (1848), Schnizlein and Frickhinger speak of this as an unstable plant, often found very sparingly where the year before it has grown in profusion. In 1851 it appeared in abundance on the bed of a dried up pond at Meudon near Paris, no trace of it having previously been seen about the pond or in its neighbourhood.
Suppl: Very rare. Investigations in 1923 (A.W. Stelfox), 1930 (H.J. Hudson) and 1954 have not led to the re-discovery of this species at Garristown, where further drainage operations have been carried out. 3. In the dry bed of a recently cleaned pond at Beaverstown House, Donabate (1949), covering about 200 sq. yards. Still there in 1956, around the edge of the pond.

(1) (3)

Probably extinct. Despite repeated searches of Garristown (1) over the last 100 years it has not been seen there since.

PLUMBAGINACEAE

Limonium

L. humile Miller *(Statice rariflora)*
Lax-flowered Sea-lavender   Native

| 2 | 3 | 5 | (8) |

Common in salt-marshes and on sea-cliffs, but absent from the south Dublin coast.

L. binervosum (G.E. Sm.) Salmon *(Statice occidentalis)*
Rock Sea-lavender   Native

| 2 | 3 | 5 | 8 |

Common in salt-marshes and on sea-cliffs.
2. Common in Rogerstown Estuary, DD/87.
3. Malahide Island (Ní Lamhna 1982b, Doyle 1982). Portrane Peninsula, DD, PR/83.
5. Upper parts of the cliff at Drumleck Point and just to the west, DN/89. Still on Howth on a low rocky cliff 50 m from the Baily Lighthouse, MWJ/88, where it was first reported by Baker (1954). Southern end of Portmarnock Golf-course, DN, RF/88. Salt-marsh on North Bull Island, PG/88.
8. Killiney Bay, SR, HOR/83, 85. On sea-railway wall between Merrion Gates and Booterstown Station, DN/94.

L. procerum (Salmon) Ingrouille
Native

| 3 | 5 | 8 |

Rare, in salt-marshes. Probably under-recorded. Material from the sites listed below has been described as **L. procerum** var. **hibernicum** Ingrouille (Ingrouille and Stace 1986).
3. Edge of the salt-marsh at Donabate, M.J. Ingrouille/80. Dune-slack on the edge of the salt-marsh at Portrane, M.J. Ingrouille/79.
5. Salt-marsh on North Bull Island, M.J. Ingrouille/80.
8. Killiney, M.J. Ingrouille/80.

Armeria

A. maritima (Miller) Willd.
Thrift, Sea Pink   Native

| 2 | 3 | 5 | 8 |

Very common in upper parts of salt-marshes, coastal cliffs and banks by the sea.

CLUSIACEAE (*GUTTIFERAE*)

Hypericum

H. androsaemum L.
Tutsan   Native

| I | 2 | 3 | 4 | 5 | 6 | 7 | 8 |

Occasional in damp shady sites, especially in deciduous woodland and tall hedgerows.
FID.

H. hircinum L.
Stinking Tutsan   Alien

| 4 | 7 | 8 |

Rare, on stonework by waterways.

4. Now abundant on stonework of the Royal Canal, from Cross Guns Bridge, where it was first recorded by DS/70, to Drumcondra, DK/90, **NCR**.
7. Walls by the River Dodder at Lansdowne Road, Ringsend, MWJ/81.
8. Walls of the River Dodder near Londonbridge Road, Ringsend, HOR, SR/85, DD/87. Clonskeagh Bridge, DK/90.

- -

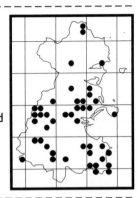

H. perforatum L.
Perforate St John's-wort   Native

| 2 | 3 | 4 | 5 | 6 | 7 | 8 |

Occasional in calcareous grasslands, quarries, gravel-pits, sand-dunes and on railway embankments.
FID.

- -

H. maculatum Crantz *(H. dubium)*
Imperforate St John's-wort   Native

Suppl: 5. North Bull, near second water-hole E. of "The Farm" (1945-1957).

| 3 | (5) |

Not refound on North Bull Island (5).
3. Derelict flower-bed east of Knocksedan Bridge, RF, DD/84, **NDR.**

- -

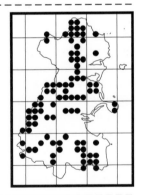

H. tetrapterum Fries
Square-stalked St John's-wort   Native

| 1 | 2 | 3 | 4 | 5 | 6 | 7 | 8 |

Occasional on riversides, in marshes and damp woodland.

- -

H. humifusum L.
Trailing St John's-wort   Native

Colgan: 1. Sparingly near Streamstown, Naul Hills, 1903; 3. Frequent in sandy fallows, Portrane, 1900: N.C. 5. Roadside near Glenaveena; stony ground below Muck Rock: *Flor. Howth.* Heath near Shielmartin, Howth, 1894; above the Broad Strand, 1900; abundant amongst fired gorse on the east side of Howth Head, 1902; 6. On Slieve Thoul, Brittas 1895; 7. Above Rockbrook, in Glendhu, and on granite freestone at the head of Glenasmole, 1892; frequent on Glassavullaun mountain, 1901; 8. Near Ballycorus, 1893; in Glencullen, 1901, and sparingly at Killiney, 1903: N.C.

| (1) | (3) | 5 | (6) | (7) | 8 |

Extremely rare, in heathland and dry banks in the uplands.

5. Still on Howth where a few plants grow near Heather Cottage, East Mountain, Howth, CB/91.
8. Grassy slope in Kelly's Glen, SR/87. Still in Glencullen near the river north-west of Glencullen Bridge, SR, HOR/84. South end of Ballybetagh Bog, JP/83.

H. pulchrum L.
Slender St John's-wort   Native

Colgan: 1. Sparingly in and around the Naul Hills, as near Balrickard and Hollywood, 1892; east of Nag's Head, 1902; on Knockbrack, 1903; 2. North of Lusk and by the railway between Rush and Skerries, 1894: *N.C.* 3. On the west side of Lambay: *Flor. Lambay.* 5. Frequent on Howth Head, 1903: *N.C.* 6, 7, and 8. Abundant in the mountains.

| 1 | 2 | 3 | 4 | 5 | 6 | 7 | 8 |

Occasional on well drained soil and banks in the uplands; relatively common in 8; rare elsewhere. Much less common now than at the turn of the century.
4. In grassland near the 'Rabbit Warren', Luttrellstown, MN/88, **NDR.** River Liffey Valley opposite Stewart's Hospital, MN/91.
5. Field behind Kilrock Quarries, Howth, PG/87, 88. On the western side of Portmarnock Golf-course, DN, RF/88.

FID.

H. hirsutum L.
Hairy St John's-wort   Native

Colgan: 4. In Luttrell's town wood (Woodlands), Mr Brinkley: *Templeton MS.* Abundant in Woodlands, 1901 and in Saint Catherine's wood, 1895-1904; banks by the Tolka above Blanchardstown, 1903: *N.C.* At Knockmaroon, 1866: *Hart MS.* and in 1895! 5. Santry: *Ir. Flor.* no recent record. 6. About Leixlip Waterfall, in the woody ground on the south side of the river, 1799: *Templeton MS.* Wood at Salmon Leap, abundant: *Mack. Cat.* Abundant here, above and below the Leap, 1904, also frequent in Lucan demesne below Leixlip bridge, 1895-1904: *N.C.* 7. Hedges near Drimnagh: *Colgan 1893.* Sparingly in Lansdown Valley, 1895: *N.C.*

| 4 | 5 | 6 | 7 |

Occasional on trackways and open sites in deciduous woods. Locally frequent along the River Liffey in 4, 6 & 7. Almost unknown in Ireland outside of the River Liffey Valley and legally protected under the Wildlife Act of 1976 as a rare and endangered species.
4. Barnhill Bridge over a disused branch of the Great Southern Railway, MN/83. St Catherine's Woods, MN/84, Lucan Quarry, MN, PR/85 & PR/90. By the River Liffey at Knockmaroon, MN, ENL/85. Two plants in the woods at Luttrellstown, MN, JS/85, 86. Especially common in a newly cleared mound near the 'Rabbit Warren' at Luttrellstown, MN/90. As a weed in the National Botanic Gardens, Glasnevin, DS/91.
5. East side of Santry Woods, DD/89.
6. Beech woods at Lucan demesne, HOR, MN/85. Below Saint Edmundsbury, JS, MN/85.
7. Woodland at Palmerston Marsh, MN, ENL/85. Banks of the River Liffey, north of King's Hospital School, MN/90.

H. elodes L.
Marsh St John's-wort   Native

Colgan: 8. Abundant in marshes near the foot of Kilgobbin mountain: *Wade Dubl.* Foot of the Three Rock mountain and above Marlay: *Ir. Flor.* On the south-east slope of the Three Rock, near Ballyedmonduff, and abundant in marshes north-west of Glencullen chapel, 1900; marshes on Prince William's Seat, 1901; in the Dingle, Glenamuck, 1895: *N.C.*

8

Locally abundant in flushed areas in mountain bogs, very rare elsewhere.

8. Plentiful in the Glencullen Valley and south facing slopes of Two Rock Mountain; scarce on the north facing slope of Three Rock Mountain, SR/83-87. A few plants still at Ballyedmonduff, on the south-east slope of Three Rock mountain, JR/92.

- -

MALVACEAE

Malva

M. sylvestris L.
Common Mallow   Possibly introduced

I	2	3	4	5	6	7	8

Frequent on waste ground, roadsides and gravelly sand usually near the sea and/or near habitation. *FID.*

- -

M. neglecta Wallr. *(M. rotundifolia)*
Dwarf Mallow   Alien

Colgan: In all of the following inland stations the plant occurs in the neighbourhood of dwellings or ruins 3. Near the old church of Killeek, 1894; 4. By the Canal near Cross Guns, 1903; 7. At Tallaght, 1892; Rockbrook, 1893-1903; Ballyfermot, 1895-1903; Island Bridge, 1902: 8. Carrickmines, 1895; and near Loughlinstown, 1903: *N.C.*
Suppl: 1. Bridge at Bog of the Ring (1956). 4. Near Lucan Bridge (1953). 7 By Dodder above Firhouse (1922-1957), Milltown (1948).

(1)	2	(3)	4	5	6	(7)	8

Waste places and paths near the sea. Often associated with old ruins inland.

2. Lusk Graveyard, DD/82.
4. By the estate gate immediately west of Lucan Bridge, MN, GS/85. Still by the Royal Canal near Cross Guns Bridge, DD/68-88.
5. By the North Bull Island Causeway, PG/87, 88. East end of Howth Harbour, DD/70-89.
6. Roadside 1.5 km west of Rathcoole, JP/86, **NDR.**
8. East side of the River Dodder near Ringsend Bridge, SR, HOR/85. Graveyard at Booterstown, HOR/85. Ringsend Dump, SR/86. Disused pasture near Bishop's Lane, west of Kiltiernan, HOR/85. Sorrento Park, Dalkey, SR, HOR/83. Park, south of Coliemore Harbour, SR, JR/90. Old Connaught Cross Roads, DNFC/84.
FID.

- -

Lavatera

L. arborea L.
Tree-mallow   Native; planted

Colgan: 2. Banks by the shore at Skerries, 1902; at Rush and Loughshinny, and 3. Occasional on field banks and near dwellings in Portrane peninsula, 1903: *N.C.* 5. On Ireland's Eye, an island near Dublin *(Mr Molden) Templeton MS.* not later than 1800. "On Ireland's Eye, where I have measured a plant 5 feet high": *Wade Rar.* abundant here on cliffs at the north-east end,

1899! In two Places, difficult to reach except from a boat, on the east side of Howth, between the Baily Lighthouse and Piper's Gut: *Flor. Howth*. Banks at Balscaddan, Howth, 1899; near Sutton coastguard station, 1902: *N.C.* 8. "On Ringsend shoar, 6/9, 1740": *Annot. in Threlkeld*. On the south-eastern side of Killiney Hill: *Ball 1839*. Abundant on cliffs at Sorrento, and on cliffs and railway cuttings at Vico near the base of Killiney Hill, frequent on rocks below Dalkey coastguard station, and sparingly at Sandycove harbour and on the sandy shore at Ballybrack, 1903: *N.C.* Though the Tree Mallow is frequently grown in cottage gardens along the coast, as at Skerries, Balscaddan, and Killiney, the cultivated plants are perhaps derived from neighbouring native stations, in some of which the species has since become extinct. On the isolated "stacks" of Ireland's Eye the plant has all the appearance of a native, and in its county headquarters about Killiney Bay it reproduces itself most freely, seedlings appearing frequently by roadsides and in cultivated ground, as well as on the cliffs and railway banks.
Suppl: 3. Roadside by old church at Killossery (1948).

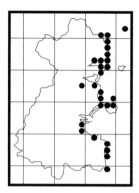

| 2 | 3 | 5 | 8 |

Occasional in ruderal places by the sea and on maritime rocky cliffs. Now more common as a synanthrope than in its native cliff habitat. Frequently cultivated as a garden plant in the Rush and Skerries regions (2) from whence it escapes onto waste ground.

DROSERACEAE

Drosera

D. rotundifolia L.
Round-leaved Sundew   Native

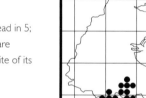

Colgan: Abundant in the mountain bogs in 7 and 8; frequent on Howth Head in 5; very rare in the northern parts of the county, for which the only records are Garristown Bog and Lambay *(Ir. Flor.)*; apparently quite absent from 6 in spite of its large area of mountain ground.

| (1) | (3) | 5 | 7 | 8 |

Common on wet peaty ground (usually mountain blanket-bog).
Not refound in Garristown Bog (1), which is now drained, nor on Lambay Island (3).
5. Still on Howth in the Central Marsh, PG/90.

VIOLACEAE

Viola

V. odorata L.
Sweet Violet   Probably introduced in Co. Dublin

Colgan: 2. Roadside near Balrothery, 1894; ditch bank east of Ballough, 1895; 3. Near Forest and between Donabate and Turvey, 1894; near Lissen Hall, 1894-1902; at Rowlestown, 1903: *N.C.* 4. Between Finglas and Cardiff's bridge: *Ir. Flor.* Hedgebank south of Kingstown cross-roads, 1895; by the roadside between Lucan and the Royal Canal in fair quantity, 1895-1903: *N.C.* 5. Plentifully in ditch banks at Goose Green, near Richmond: *Wade Dubl.* Near Raheny and beyond Drumcondra, 1895; 6. Near Newcastle and Neillstown, 1894; and 7. Well established in considerable quantity in hedgebanks near Tymon Castle, 1883-1900: *N.C.* 8. Roadside near Harold's Grange, 1884-94; by the old church of

Kilgobbin, on roadsides near Kiltiernan, and abundant along the roadside and in woods at Kilbogget, 1903: N.C. In many of the above stations, and in others that might be mentioned, the Sweet Violet occurs but sparingly, and in all it is more or less obviously introduced. Its long persistence in some stations entitles it, however to a place in the county flora. The form with violet coloured flowers is the only one which occurs wild in the county.

Suppl: 1. In wood N.E. of Killossery Bridge (1947). 3. Killeek churchyard (1936). Forrest Road, Cloghran (1935). Knocksedan (1947-52). Roadside at Kilsallaghan (1948). 7. Greenhills (1955), Woodtown (J.P. Brunker, 1919). Roadside near Tibradden House (1957). 8. Riverside near Carrickmines railway station (the white form) (1943).

(1) | 2 | 3 | 4 | 5 | 6 | 7 | 8

Rare, in roadside hedges and planted woodlands.
2. Still near Balrothery on roadside verges at the Man O' War Inn, DD/85. Near the shore between Rogerstown and Balleally, DD/84.
3. Balheary House, PR, DD/84.
4. At the Lucan end of St Catherine's, MN/85. Woods at Luttrellstown, JS/83 & MN/85. Tolka River Valley at Blanchardstown, DD/82.
5. Woodland at Clontarf Castle, ENL/85. North-eastern part of St Anne's Park, Raheny, PG/87, 88.
6. East across the valley from Verschoyles Hill, JP/86.
7. Roadside hedge at Aghfarrell, JP, DAS/84.
8. Roadside between Old Connaught and Old Conna Hill, DNFC/84. Wood by the Shanganagh River at Loughlinstown, SR, HOR/83.

- -

V. hirta L.
Hairy Violet   Native

Colgan: 2. Amongst furze on a bank by the Rogerstown estuary, near Ballayley, 1902: N.C. 3. Sandhills at Portrane *(More) Rec. Add.* Abundant in many parts of the Portrane peninsula, 1903: N.C. In several places on Lambay island: *Flor. Lambay.* 4. In the Phoenix Park and on Knockmaroon Hill, 1799: *Templeton MS.* In the Phoenix Park, near Chapelizod, 1900 *(N.C.) Top. Bot.* 5. In hilly and bushy pastures near the shore at Raheny: *Wade Dubl.* Among the sandhills at Baldoyle (Portmarnock): *Templeton MS.* abundant here in 1902! On the east side of Howth: *Ir. Flor.* abundant here on drift banks below the Old Baily, 1900! On the Cosh, Sutton, 1873 *(Greenwood Pim) Cyb. II.* and in 1901! On Feltrim Hill 1869: *Hart MS.* very abundant here in furze brakes and clefts of the limestone, 1904! 7. Abundant at the Green Hills, 1893-1900: N.C. A characteristic species of Co. Dublin, where it reaches its northern limit for Ireland.

(2) | 3 | 4 | 5 | (7)

Very rare, in sand-dunes and calcareous grassland. Legally protected under the Wildlife Act of 1976 as an endangered species in Ireland.
3. Sandy banks at the Island Golf-course, PR/88. Sand-dunes at the northern tip of Portrane Peninsula, DD/83, PR/90.
4. Calcareous grassland at the Magazine Fort in the Phoenix Park, PR/82. Scrub east of the Furry Glen, PR/91.
5. Feltrim Hill, M.I.Rix, S.J.Dickinson/67. Sand-hills in the lee of the main dunes on Portmarnock Peninsula, ENL/84 & DD/88.

- -

V. riviniana Reichb.
Common Dog-violet   Native

1 | 2 | 3 | 4 | 5 | 6 | 7 | 8

Common in hedgerows and sand-dunes; rare in coastal grassland. White-flowered forms occur at the Furry Glen in the Phoenix Park (4) (JS, MN/83) and very large-flowered forms in Santry Woods (5) (DD/82).

One of the morphological characteristics that distinguishes this species from the next is a distinct pale spur with a furrow and notch at its apex. In many Dublin plants these characteristics are not clearly seen.

V. reichenbachiana Jordan ex Boreau
Early Dog-violet   Native

| (2) | 3 | 4 | 5 | 6 | 7 | 8 |

Not rediscovered at Gormanstown Woods (2) where it was recorded by *Colgan*. Occasional in woodlands and hedgerows. White-flowered forms occur near Malahide (5). Plants with a narrow dark spur and rudimentary calycine appendages are rare.

V. canina L.
Heath Dog-violet   Native

| 2 | 3 | 5 |

Occasional in sand-dunes.
2. Still present in small quantity in sand-hills at Rush where *Colgan* notes it was abundant at the beginning of the century, DD/87.
3. Locally frequent on stable sand-dunes on the east side of Malahide Island at the Island Golf-course, DD/92.
5. Sand-dunes on North Bull Island, S. Clark/63. North and east of the Causeway, North Bull Island, ENL, MN/84 & ENL, CB/85. Locally common and forming large stands on Portmarnock sand-hills, ENL/84.

V. palustris L.
Marsh Violet   Native

| (5) | 7 | 8 |

Still common in wet acid upland areas. Not refound on Howth (5).

V. lutea Hudson
Mountain Pansy   Native

Colgan: 6. On the Hill of Lyons (Moore) Cyb. Near Brittas, 1880 (Charles Dickson) Cyb. II. In a glen on Slieve Thoul, near Brittas, 1897 (N.C) Top. Bot. 7. Heath near Ballinascorney (T.H. Corry) Journ. of Bot., 1882, p.222. Pastures about a mile east of Brittas ponds, and heath near the top of Mount Seskin, 1895; near the top of Lugmore, amongst gorse, 1896: N.C. Ranges from about 750 feet near Brittas to 1000 feet on Mount Seskin. First found by Charles Dickson in 1880; first record in 1882: Journ. of Bot. l.c. Threlkeld's record under Viola montana lutea grandiflora: "Fetch'd from the Hill of Hoath," more probably refers to V. Curtisii.

| 6 | 7 |

Extremely rare, in upland grassland. It was once a conspicuous feature of Dublin grassland in which it occurred amongst scattered bushes of gorse. Most of its former range is now occupied by improved sheep-grazed pasture.
6. Roadside east and north of Aghfarrel, Brittas, W. Bradley/82.
7. Upland heathy grassland just west of Tallaght Hill, JP, DD/83.

V. tricolor L.
Wild Pansy   Native

Colgan: 4. Cultivated grounds about Glasnevin and Finglas: *Ir. Flor.* Fallow land east of Clonsilla, 1895 *(N.C) Cyb. II.* 6. Cornfield near Newcastle, 1894; and 7. Fallow land at Piperstown, 1897 *(N.C) Top. Bot.* Ascends to 950 feet at Piperstown. This, the typical large-flowered plant with petals much exceeding the sepals, appears to be quite rare in the county.

| 1 | 2 | 3 | 4 | 5 | 7 |

---

subsp. **tricolor**

Suppl: 2. Wheatfield at Milverton, Skerries (J.P. Brunker, 1918). 3. Stubble near railway bridge at Rogerstown (1949).

| 1 | 2 | (3) | 4 | 7 |

Very rare, in arable ground.
1. Disturbed ground at Ballyboghil, DD/84, **NDR.**
2. Garden nursery, north-east of Gracedieu, DD/84.
4. Beside a newly laid path by the lake at Luttrellstown, MN/88. Abundant in strawberry fields north of Broghan Bridge, DD/78.
7. Old quarry by the roadside past the school on the Piperstown road, PWJ and Diane Wyse Jackson/84.

---

subsp. **curtisii** (E. Forster) Syme (*V. curtisii*)

| 2 | 3 | 5 |

Common in sand-dunes.

V. arvensis Murray
Field Pansy, Heartsease   Native

| 1 | 2 | 3 | 4 | 5 | (6) | (7) | 8 |

Occasional in arable land and on waste ground.

CUCURBITACEAE

Bryonia

B. dioica Jacq.
White Bryony   Alien

| 5 |

First recorded from near the Baily Lighthouse, Howth in *Colgan & Scully* by Miss A. Kinahan, and now widely established on the south side of Howth Head.
5. Along a wall and hedge near Whitewater Brook and naturalized along roadsides above Doldrum Bay, and on a cliff path at the end of Ceanchor Road, Howth, ENL/84 & DN/89. Hedgerow north-west of Redrock, Howth, DN/88. Exposed cliff face on the south side of Howth Head, J. Mulryan/75.

SALICACEAE

Populus

P. tremula L.
Aspen   Introduced in Co. Dublin

Colgan: 3. In hedges near Rathbeal and Little Forest, 1903: *N.C.* 7. Kelly's Glen: *Flor. Hib.* 8. Two or three trees near a farm house by the river above Bride's Glen, 1902: *N.C.*

Brunker MS: 4. Damastown, '57.

| (3) | 4 | 6 | 7 | 8 |

Occasionally self-sown. *Colgan* believed that this species could be native in mountain glens, especially along the upper Dodder river, but despite repeated searches by Colgan and others it has not been found there.

4. Near the Ordnance Survey Office, Phoenix Park, JS/83.
6. Roadside at Colganstown House, JP/87. Just west of Newcastle, JP/87. Tallaght Quarry, JP/83.
7. Banks of the River Poddle, south of Kimmage Cross Roads, PWJ/86.
8. Near the old church at Kilgobbin, PC/83. Ringsend Dump, PWJ/83. Roches Hill, SR/89.

- -

Salix

S. pentandra L.
Bay Willow   Introduced in Co. Dublin

Colgan: 2. In swampy ground south of Balrothery, 1902: *N.C.* 4. In woods at Luttrell's town; 5. At Santry; and 7. In moist hedgerows around Chapelizod: *Wade Dubl.* 8. Along the river near the head of Kelly's Glen, Kilmashogue, 1882, and abundant here in 1903, not only as a full-grown tree, but also forming thickets in swampy ground along the river in association with Alder and *Salix aurita* and looking quite wild: *Colgan 1904.* This handsome willow has no claim to be considered native anywhere in Co. Dublin. It is spreading, however in the Kelly's Glen station, though no doubt originally introduced there as in all other stations in the county, and seems to be worthy of admission to the flora as a naturalised species.

| 2 | (4) | (5) | (7) | 8 |

Rare, in ditches and marshy ground.
A.W. Stelfox noted that all the plants in Kelly's Glen were male, **(DBN)**. The Luttrellstown record (4) of Wade, made before 1794, may refer to the next taxon.
2. Three plants in a field drain at Haystown, DD/86.
8. Still at the south end of Kelly's Glen, between Kilmashogue and Tibradden Mountains, HOR/86 & SR/87.

- -

S. pentandra × S. fragilis (S. × meyeriana Rostk. ex Willd.)

| 4 |

Extremely rare, in damp woodland. Wade recorded **S. pentandra** from Luttrellstown (4); possibly in error for this hybrid.
4. On marshy ground at Luttrellstown near the lake, MN/88.

S. fragilis L.
Crack-willow   Alien

| 3 | 4 | 5 | 6 | 7 | 8 |

Occasional in hedgerows, on river and canal banks. Commoner in the south of the county.
Not in *Colgan* or *Suppl.*

---

var. **russelliana** (Smith) Koch

| 3 | 4 | 5 | 8 |

3. Marsh at Knocksedan Bridge, MN/90.
4. Frequent in the River Liffey and Tolka valleys and along the Royal Canal, MN/89.
5. Beside the River Tolka at Drumcondra, DN/88.
8. At the south-east corner of Leopardstown Racecourse, SR/88.

---

var. **decipiens** (Hoffm.) Koch

| 4 | 6 |

4. By the lake at Luttrellstown, MN/88. Royal Canal and River Tolka about 1 km east of
   Blanchardstown and River Tolka, north-west of Ashtown, MN/88.
6. Hedgerow, west of Rathcoole, JP/86.

S. alba L.
White Willow   Alien

| 4 | 6 | 7 |

Occasionally planted in the county usually near water: frequent near the River Liffey (4 & 6),
occasional along the River Dodder Valley and rare in Glenasmole (7).

S. triandra L.
Almond Willow   Probably introduced

| 4 | 6 |

Rare, but possibly becoming more widespread. Recent records may relate to descendants of
planted individuals; *Colgan* considered this species as always of planted origin in the county.
Not noted in *CC2*.
4. Banks of River Liffey at the Wren's Nest, MN/88.
6. Lucan, HOR/85.

S. purpurea L.
Purple Willow   Possibly introduced

| 4 | (5) | 7 |

Frequent and well established on the Royal Canal (4) where it does not appear to have been
planted. Not refound at Portmarnock (5) where it may have been planted.
4. Scattered and locally frequent along the Royal Canal, at Cabra, Ranelagh Bridge, east of
   Kirkpatrick Bridge, and between Clonsilla and the county boundary, MN/87, 88.
   Streamside at Dunsoghly, MN/88.
7. By the River Dodder at Templeogue, DK/91.

S. viminalis L.
Osier   Alien

| 1 | 2 | 3 | 4 | 5 | 6 | 7 | 8 |

Occasional on riverbanks and in hedgerows. Probably originally planted but now sometimes apparently self-sown. Only included in the appendix in *Colgan* but without details of distribution. At that time the species was considered to have been planted throughout the county and never naturalized.
FID.

S. viminalis x **S. caprea (S.** x **sericans** Tausch ex A. Kerner)
Probably introduced

| 2 | 4 | 5 | 6 | 7 | 8 |

Occasional in hedgerows and on canal, stream and river banks.
2. Hedgerow by a stream at the Corn Mill near Balbriggan, DD/87. Roadside hedges at Raheny, east of Lusk, DD/87. Roadside drain, near St Maur's G.A.A. Club, Rush, DD/87.
4. Roadside hedge, south and 1 km east of Pakenham Bridge, MN/87, 88. By the Royal Canal at Ashtown, MN/88. On various sites by the River Tolka; east of Clonee, below Cardiff's Bridge, at Finglas Bridge and around Blanchardstown, MN/88. Disused branch of the Great Southern Railway line at Barnhill Bridge, MN/88. By the River Liffey at the Strawberry Beds, MN/91.
5. Reclaimed land near Dublin Ferryport, DN/88.
6. Field margin and in a ditch by a stream, just east of Newcastle, JP/87. Field margin, south-south-west of Brittas, JP/86. Streamsides, west of Athgoe Castle, JP/88.
7. South end of the southern reservoir at Glenasmole, MN/88.
8. South end of Kelly's Glen, between Kilmashogue and Tibradden Mountains, SR/87.

S. caprea L.
Goat Willow   Native

Colgan: 3. Sparingly in hedges near Lubber's Wood, and 6. In copses in Crooksling Glen, 1903; 7. One tree near the head of Killakee river, 1894, another above Cobb's Lodge, Glenasmole, and a few in Ballinascorney Glen, 1896: N.C. Frequent in hazel copses on both sides of Glenasmole above Bohernabreena bridge, 1903: *Colgan 1904.* 8. Several trees along the Little Dargle river, 1893; sparingly by the Ballycorus river, 1902: N.C.
Suppl: 4. Road S. of St Margaret's (1948). 7. Bank of Brittas River above Aghfarrell (1953). Slade of Ballymaice (1947).

| 1 | 3 | 4 | 5 | 6 | 7 | 8 |

Occasional in woodland, hedgerows, on river and canal banks, and urban waste ground.
1. Garristown, GS/88, **NDR**.
3. Still in roadside hedges at Lubber's Wood, DD/85.
5. Waste ground, south-west of Alexandra Basin, Dublin Port, SR/88, **NDR**. Near former papermill at Portmarnock, DN/89.
FID.

S. caprea x **S. cinerea (S.** x **reichardtii** A. Kerner)
Native

| 2 | 5 | 6 | 7 | 8 |

Occasional in hedgerows.

2. Newlawn House, DD/85.
5. Reclaimed land near Dublin Ferryport, DN/88. Waste ground, south-west of Alexandra Basin, SR/88.
6. South-east of Esker, JP, ENL/87. Slade Valley, MN/90.
7. Near Fort Bridge and just further south, PWJ/86, DN/88 & MN/89.
8. Coast below Killiney Railway Station, SR/86. South-east margin of Leopardstown Racecourse, SR/88. Abandoned railway-line at Sandyford Industrial Estate, SR, JR/88. Edge of the wood on the east side of The Scalp, SR/88. Druid's Glen, SR, MN/90.

S. cinerea L. subsp. **oleifolia** Macreight (*S. atrocinerea*)
Grey Willow, Rusty Willow, Sally   Native

| 1 | 2 | 3 | 4 | 5 | 6 | 7 | 8 |

Frequent on damp ground throughout the rural parts of the county, mainly in hedgerows, by roadsides and on river banks.
FID.

S. cinerea x **S. aurita** (**S.** x **multinervis** Doell)
Native

| 3 | 7 | 8 |

Rare.
3. Marsh on the Portrane Peninsula, MN/87.
7. Hedgebank on the west side of Cruagh Wood, PWJ/84. Along the roadside, west of the reservoirs at Glenasmole, MN/89.
8. North slope of Three Rock mountain, SR/88. Below the cromlech, west of Kiltiernan, SR/88.

S. aurita L.
Eared Willow   Native

| 1 | 4 | 5 | 6 | 7 | 8 |

Common in the mountains but very rare elsewhere.
4. By the Royal Canal, north-west of Cabra, MN/88. Ditch at Dunsoghly, MN/88.
5. North Bull Island, DNFC/85, DN/90. Portmarnock Golf-course, DN/90.
FID.

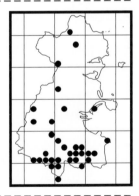

S. aurita x **S. repens** (**S.** x **ambigua** Ehrh.)
Native

| (7) |

Not refound on Mountpelier (7).

S. repens L.
Creeping Willow   Native

Colgan: 1. Sparingly in Garristown Bog, 1892; and 3. Abundant in the sandhills at Portrane, 1904: *N.C.* 5. In the sands at the Burrow of Portmarnock: *Wade Dubl.* in profusion here in 1904! Sparingly at the extreme northern end of the North Bull, 1900; and 8. Near Glencullen bridge, 1893: *N.C.*

Suppl: 1. Not confirmed from site of Garristown Bog. 3. Still abundant at Portrane (1957). 5. Still at Portmarnock (1957) and sparingly on the North Bull (1956). 8. Still in Glencullen (1950).

| (1) | 3 | 5 | 8 |

Common in dune-slacks. Very rare elsewhere. Abundant on Portmarnock Peninsula (5). The site at Garristown Bog has been drained for many years.

3. In a dune-slack and by a path through the golf-course, mid-way along Malahide Island Peninsula, PR/85.
5. Still in the Alder Marsh and elsewhere on North Bull Island (Anon 1917c), ENL, MN/84 & MS/85, 86.
8. Field in the Glencullen Valley, south of the main road through the valley just beyond Boranaraltry Lane, SR/87. Sparingly on peaty ground near the cromlech, west of Kiltiernan, PC/77.

BRASSICACEAE (*CRUCIFERAE*)

Sisymbrium

S. irio L.
London-rocket   Alien

Colgan: 3. Sparingly in the main street of Swords, 1893-1902: *N.C.* 4. Beside walls going to Glasnevin: *Ir. Flor.* Common about Glasnevin: *Cyb.* Corey Lane, Glasnevin *(Rev. H.G. Carroll) Herb. S & A. Mus.* Sparingly on Cabra Road, 1893; at the northern end of Chapelizod Bridge, 1902: *N.C.* 5. Common about Clontarf: *Cyb.* Annesley bridge and Dye House Lane, Clontarf, 1866: *Hart MS.* Roadside, Drumcondra, 1872: *(W.R. McNab) Herb. S & A. Mus.* A few plants by the shore below Claremont, Howth: *Flor. Howth.* Roadside east of Sutton railway station: *Praeger 1895.* 7. Kimmage Road and South Circular Road, 1892 *(More) Cyb II.* Kimmage Road, 1901: *H.W.D. Dunlop.* By the Dodder river at Rathgar and roadside near Kingsbridge *(Scully) Cyb. II.* Roadsides near Templeogue Bridge, 1893; near Templeogue Mill near Blue Bell, and near Inchicore, 1894; in Dublin city, on ruined walls in Clanbrasil Street, 1894; at Mount Brown, 1894-1902, at Marrowbone Lane, 1900, and at Island Bridge, 1902: *N.C.* Cottage roof in Chapelizod, 1903: *Scully.* 8. At Sandymount, 1849: *Herb. Dr W. Steele.* Abundant at Sandymount and Ball's Bridge, *circa 1865: John Bain.* Waste ground by the beach at Sandymount, and frequent along the branch railway to Ball's Bridge show yard, 1902: *N.C.* On the railway at Sidney Parade, 1867 *(W.G. Smith) Herb. Glasnevin* and at Salthill, 1858: *Herb. R. Barrington.* On the railway at Kingstown, 1893 *(N.C) Cyb. II.* At intervals along the railway from Merrion to Near Westland Row, and in waste ground near Merrion station, 1903: *N.C.* Roadsides south of Rathfarnham, Milltown, and Clonskeagh *(More) Rec. Add.* At Windy Harbour, 1900 *(Praeger) Top. Bot.* First record in 1818 *(Warburton):* it is probable, however, that the much earlier record in *Threlkeld,* 1727, under *Eruca sylvestris vulgatior* "It grows upon Walls as between *Dolphin's Barn and Cork Bridge"* should be referred here. This species, amongst the rarest of British as of Irish plants, is in Ireland confined to Co. Dublin, where it was formerly abundant in and around the city. Templeton in his *MS. Flora* not later than 1820, and Mackay in his *Flora Hibernica,* 1836, speak of it as common about Dublin; but of late it has become quite rare, though continuing to appear in small quantity in many stations. Its favourite habitat is along unpaved footways at the base of walls, and its increasing rarity is no doubt mainly due to the general introduction of concreted foot pavements throughout the surburban townships. *Suppl*: 2. Foot of wall at Loughshinny Harbour (1953). 4. By Liffey at foot of Knockmaroon Hill, Rectory Yard, Finglas (J.P. Brunker, 1921). 5. Still sparingly at Cosh, Sutton (1954). Still a few plants about Swords Castle (1956). 7. Mount Argus spoilbanks (1948), now gone. By Grand Canal at Ballyfermot (1930). 8. A few plants at Ballybrack Martello Tower (A.W. Stelfox, 1919). Still on path by railway near Lansdowne Road railway station (1948).

| 2 | (3) | 4 | (5) | 7 | 8 |

Extremely rare, at the base of walls, on railway lines and wasteground. It is now much rarer than at the turn of the century. Many of its former sites have been built on, tidied or sprayed.
2. Still at Loughshinny, in the harbour, RF, DD/85.
4. Still in Chapelizod Village, near the bridge on the steps of a derelict building, MN/86.
7. Several plants in Camden Place off Harcourt Street, MWJ/92.
8. Waste ground at the end of point at Ringsend, MS/76. Still at Sandymount, on the east side of the railway at Serpentine Avenue, SR/87.

S. altissimum L. (*S. pannonicum*)
Tall Rocket   Alien

Colgan (Appendix): 5. Rubbish heaps near Manure Works, East Wall. Along new electric tram line from St. Anne's, Dollymount, to beyond Raheny, 1900; a few seedlings on the same line near the Long Lane Sutton, 1901: *Colgan 1903*. *Brunker MS*: 4. By Liffey near foot of Knockmaroon Hill; Near Woodlands; Custom House Docks. 5. N. Bull; Road along the Cosh, Sutton. 7. Roadside near Robinhood, '18; Ballyfermot Bge, Grand Canal. 8. Dumps at South Wall, '52

| 3 | (4) | 5 | (7) | 8 |

Rare, in disturbed sandy ground.
3. Sandy ground at Portrane Village, PR, DD/83, 89.
5. Royal Dublin Golf-course and the Causeway, North Bull Island, DD/83, ENL, MN/84 & MC/91. Disturbed ground at the south end of Portmarnock Golf-course, DN/89. Roadside, north of the North Bull Wall on Clontarf Road, PG/87, 88. On a railway embankment at Fairview, DNFC/84. On waste ground in Dublin Port, SR/90.
8. Eastern part of Ringsend Dump, SR, HOR/83. Waste ground behind the west pier at Dun Laoghaire, SR, HOR/84.

S. orientale L. (*S. columnae*)
Eastern Rocket   Alien

| 2 | 3 | 4 | 5 | 6 | 7 | 8 |

Occasional in disturbed ground in the city and suburbs and along the coast; rare elsewhere. It is a relatively recent arrival in the county. Praeger (1946b) noted that this species had recently been reported from Dublin .
2. Rogerstown Village, DD/82, **NDR**.
3. Waste ground in Corballis sand-hills, DD, PR/87, **NDR**.
6. Open ground in Lucan Demesne, JS/83, **NDR**.
FID.

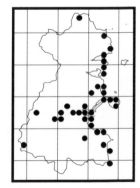

S. officinale (L.) Scop.
Hedge Mustard   Native

| 1 | 2 | 3 | 4 | 5 | 6 | 7 | 8 |

Extremely widespread in ruderal habitats.
FID.

Descurainia

D. sophia (L.) Webb ex Prantl (*Sisymbrium sophia*)
Flixweed   Possibly introduced

Colgan: 2. Sparingly at Lough Shinny and near Lusk and on walls and thatched roofs in Rush village, 1893; near Skerries, and abundant near Rogerstown harbour, and in sandy fallows near Rush, 1902: *N.C.* 3. Sandhills by the creek at Donabate *(More) Rec. Add.* Abundant in sandy fallows, both in the northern and southern parts of the Portrane peninsula, 1902: *N.C.* 4. About Glasnevin: *Ir. Flor. & (Moore) Cyb.* 5. About Drumcondra and Portmarnock: *Ir. Flor.* About Kilbarrick *(Moore) Cyb.* Abundant on the new tramway track at Raheny and Kilbarrick, 1900; abundant about Sutton, 1901; and frequent at Portmarnock, 1902: *N.C.* Abundant between Sutton and Baldoyle; a weed in potato gardens at Howth village; on Ireland's *Eye: Flor. Howth.* 7. "It grows among Rubbish and upon some of the low Thatched Cabbins at the End of *New Street,* near *Black Pitts*": *Threlkeld.* A rare plant in its inland stations in the county, but abundant and often luxuriant in many places along the coast from Sutton to Skerries, plants gathered at Rush measuring 3 feet 6 inches in height. The species finds its Irish headquarters in Co. Dublin, and outside of it appears to be quite rare or of only casual occurrence in the country.
Suppl: 2. Still about Rush (1941). 3. Still at Portrane (1939). 7. Rubbish dump at Kimmage (1948). 8. One plant by roadside at Ballybrack (R.W. Scully, 1918). Apparently not nearly so common as in Colgan's time, whereas *Sisymbrium altissimum* and *S. orientale,* included only as casuals in his Appendix, have now become widespread in the county, S. of the Ward River.

| 2 | 3 | (4) | 5 | (7) | (8) |

Occasional on sandy roadsides and fallow ground near to the north coast. *Colgan* recorded this species from a number of sites in 5. Very little fallow land remains now in this district.
2. Still scattered around Rush in waste ground and on sandy roadsides at Rogerstown Harbour, DD/82, 87. Sandy disturbed soil, between Ballykea and Loughshinny cross-roads, DD/85. Sandy waste ground, west of Rush golf-course, DD/87.
3. On disturbed ground beside the right-of-way on the Island Golf-course, Corballis, PR/85. Still at Portrane, in a neglected barley field and on a path in the sand-hills to the south-east, PR/85.
5. Roadside at Alexandra Basin, Dublin Port, SR/89.

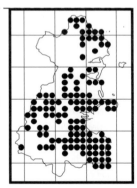

Alliaria

A. petiolata (M. Bieb.) Cavara & Grande (*Sisymbrium alliaria*)
Garlic Mustard   Native

Colgan: Widespread on the limestone in the southern districts, and especially abundant along the Liffey valley from Knockmaroon to Lucan. Quite rare to the north of the Ward River, being apparently absent from District 3. and only noted near the Naul in District 1 and near Balrothery in District 2.

| 1 | 2 | 3 | 4 | 5 | 6 | 7 | 8 |

Common throughout the south of the county; rarer in the north. It is most frequent on damp shady road-side banks. It occasionally persists in shady parts of large and old suburban gardens.

Arabidopsis

A. thaliana (L.) Heynh. *(Sisymbrium thalianum)*
Thale Cress   Native

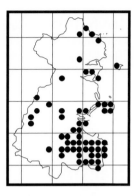

Colgan: 2. Sparingly on the wall of Balrothery churchyard, 1894: *N.C.* 3. Banks above the sea at Broad Bay and at Gillap, Lambay island: *Flor. Lambay.* 5. Banks over the sea, Howth, 1839 *(Moore) Herb. Glasnevin.* Plentiful on the south side of Howth: *Guide.* Banks by the roadside and elsewhere about Drumleck: *Flor. Howth.* Banks above the sea at north side of the Baily *(McArdle)* Praeger 1895. 8. Old walls near Stepaside: *Mack. Cat.* Walls near the Scalp, 1893: *Vowell.* Walls near the old church of Kiltiernan, and walls and banks on the east slope of Carrickgollagher, 1895; banks near Ballybetagh, 1901: N.C. A garden weed at Easton Lodge, Monkstown, 1875: *Greenwood Pim.*

| 2 | 3 | 4 | 5 | 6 | 7 | 8 |

Common in gardens and waste ground. Becoming increasingly frequent as a garden weed as it is distributed with container-grown plants from garden centres. It is common in the city and suburbs in pavement cracks and on gravel. Much commoner today than at the turn of the century. Most frequent in the south-eastern part of the county, northwards to Howth, and in scattered sites in Malahide and from Skerries to Balbriggan.

4. Chapelizod, DD/76, **NDR**.
6. St Helen's, Lucan, JP/85, **NDR**.
FID.

Erysimum

E. cheiranthoides L.
Treacle Mustard   Alien

| 5 | 7 | 8 |

Very rare, on waste ground.
5. Alexandra Basin, Dublin Port, SR/88.
7. Near the River Dodder, upstream from Templeogue, DK/91.
8. Behind the west pier at Dun Laoghaire; SR, HOR/84, **NDR**. This site was cleared in 1985.

E. cheiri (L.) Crantz *(Cheiranthus cheiri)*
Wallflower   Alien

Colgan: 2. Banks by the sea near the Martello Tower, Skerries, and 3. On old ruins at Swords, 1902: *N.C.* 4. Long established on the old Castle of Dunsoghly, 1894: *(N.C.) Cyb.II.* 5. By the railway close to Howth Station and on cottages in Howth village: *Flor. Howth.* 7. "In the Brow going up to the Hospital of *Kilmainham*": *Threlkeld.* Abundant on the walls, the roof, and the turrets of Drimnagh Castle, 1900: *N.C.* 8. Abundant on old walls near Milltown Bridge: *Wade Dubl.* Walls near Clonskeagh Bridge on the Dodder, 1892; thoroughly established on the cliffs at Sorrento and near the bathing-place at Vico, Killiney Bay, also on rocks in the railway cutting below Khyber Pass, and abundant on steep drift banks near the gasworks, Kingstown, 1903: *N.C.* A conspicuous ornament of the old Castles of Dunsoghly and Drimnagh in the month of May. The plant appears here and in the Kingstown station with pure yellow flowers, as a reversion, no doubt, from the cultivated variety with streaked petals.

| 2 | 3 | 4 | 5 | 6 | 7 | 8 |

Rare, on old walls, ruins, waste ground and sea-cliffs.

2. Still on old walls and ruins on the foreshore at Skerries Village, DD/82.
3. Still on old walls opposite the Co. Council yard at Swords, PR/90.
4. Still on Dunsoghly Castle, DD/74. Old wall of a house on Berkley Road, Phibsborough, DNFC/79. Cross Guns Bridge, MN/87.
5. Waste places on reclaimed land on the north side of Dublin Port, DN/88.
6. Lucan Demesne, JS/85, **NDR**.
7. Waste ground between Greenhills and Walkinstown where it is probably a recent garden discard, PWJ, SR, HOR/84.
8. Cliffs, south of Coliemore, HOR/83. Still on cliffs at the north end of Killiney Bay, SR, HOR/85.
FID.

Hesperis

H. matronalis L.
Dame's-violet   Alien

1	2	3	4	5	6	7

Occasional in rural ruderal habitats; an escape from gardens.
FID.

Barbarea

B. vulgaris R. Br.
Winter-cress   Native

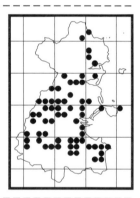

1	2	3	4	5	6	7	8

Occasional; roadsides, ruderal habitats and river banks.
FID.

B. intermedia Boreau
Medium-flowered Winter-cress   Alien

4	6	7	8

Very rare.
4/6. Bank of the River Liffey near Lucan, C. Shackleton/76, (**TCD**), **NCR**.
7.   By River Dodder between Templeogue and Rathfarnham bridges, HOR, SR/84.
8.   Roadstone Works at Ballycorus, SR, JR/84. Edge of Burton Road on Dalkey Hill, SR/89.

B. verna (Miller) Asch.
American Winter-cress   Alien

5

Rare, on waste ground.
5. Roadside at Greenhollows, Howth, DD/83. Building site at Doldrum Bay, Howth, ENL/84.

Rorippa

R. nasturtium-aquaticum (L.) Hayek (*Nasturtium officinale* pro parte)
Water-cress   Native

| I | 2 | 3 | 4 | 5 | 6 | 7 | 8 |

Very common in muddy, slow-moving streams and drains.
FID.

- -

R. microphylla x **R. nasturtium-aquaticum** (**Rorippa** x **sterilis** Airy Shaw)
Hybrid Water-cress   Native

| I | 2 | 3 | 4 | 5 | 6 | 7 | 8 |

Common in similar habitats to **R. nasturtium-aquaticum**. Often occurs in the absence of either parent.
FID.

- -

R. microphylla (Boenn.) N. Hylander ex A. & D. Löve
(*Nasturtium officinale* pro parte, *Nasturtium microphyllum*)
Narrow-fruited Water-cress   Native

| I | 2 | 3 | 4 | 5 | 6 | 7 | 8 |

Very common in similar habitats to **R. nasturtium-aquaticum** but less frequent.
FID.

- -

R. palustris (L.) Besser *(Nasturtium palustre)*
Marsh Yellow-cress   Native

Colgan: 1. On the margins of Curragha Bog and in stagnant pools about Greenoug: *Wade Rar.* At the Bog of the Ring and near Baldwinstown cross-road: *Colgan 1893*. Baldwinstown crossroad, 1902! 2. On the banks of a reservoir near Balbriggan (Dr Scott) *Mack. Rar.* At the Lough, Balrothery, and to the north of Lusk: *Colgan 1893*. 3. Muddy ground by the Broad Meadow Water above Fieldstown, 1903: *Colgan 1904*. 4. Islands in the Liffey at Island Bridge, 1866: *Hart MS.* 8. On the railway east of Blackrock station, 1892: *Scully.* Sparingly at both sides of Blackrock station and in a wall at Kingstown terminus, 1903: *N.C.* This species varies in size from 3 inches on muddy pond margins at Balrothery to 18 inches in railway drains at Blackrock. *Suppl: (as R. islandica).* 3. Killeek Reservoir (1953). 4. By R. Tolka below Cardiff's Bridge (1922). 6. Abundant on dried mud, Lower Pond, Brittas (1955).

| I | (2) | (3) | 4 | 5 | 6 | 7 | 8 |

Common in 4 & 5 along the River Tolka Valley from Mulhuddart eastwards to Dublin Port, on exposed mud of riverbanks, ponds and reservoirs; rare elsewhere.
1. Mud at Hynestown Reservoir, GS/84.
4. River Liffey at St Catherine's, MN/85. Drained section of the Royal Canal, 1 km east of Blanchardstown and on muddy margins of the Royal Canal at Cabra, MN/88 & DK/91.
5. Redrock, ENL/83, **NDR**.
6. Banks of the River Liffey at Lucan Demesne, JS/85. South end of Brittas Ponds and abundant there in 1990, DNFC/82, 90.
7. Abundant on the exposed drained lake bed of the northern reservoir in Glenasmole, MS/75, MN/88 & SR/89. River Dodder, east of Oldbawn, SR/89. Palmerston Marsh, DN/90.
8. River Dodder, east of Lansdowne Road Railway Station, SR/87. Bank of a stream at Cork Abbey, north of Bray, SR, HOR/85.

R. sylvestris (L.) Besser
Creeping Yellow-cress   Probably introduced in Co. Dublin

| 2 | 6 | 8 |

Rare.

2. Garden centre car park at Blake's Cross, DD/82, **NCR**.
6. On a newly sown area of lawn, by a footpath at Dodsboro housing estate, south-west of Lucan, MN/89.
8. Bank of the River Dodder near Rathfarnham Bridge, SR, HOR/84. Damp hollow in a field at the rear of Churchtown Fire Station, HOR/85.

R. amphibia (L.) Besser *(Nasturium amphibium)*
Great Yellow-cress   Native

Colgan (Appendix): 4. By the side of the pond opposite the Zoological Gardens, Phoenix Park: *Flor. Hib.* Apparently extinct in this the only recorded station for the county.

Suppl: 1. Two plants at Decoy Bridge, Bog of the Ring (1955). 1 & 3. Sparingly by Broad Meadow Water, Rowlestown to Balheary (1950).

| (1) | (3) | (4) |

Armoracia

A. rusticana P. Gaertner, Meyer & Scherb. *(Cochlearia armoracia)*
Horse-radish   Alien

| 2 | 3 | 4 | 5 | 6 | 7 | 8 |

Occasional on roadside verges, grassland and waste ground. Most frequent near the coast. Does not set seed in Ireland but spreads from root fragments.
FID.

Cardamine

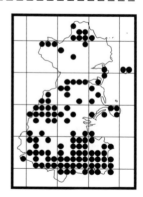

C. pratensis L.
Cuckooflower, Lady's-smock   Native

| 1 | 2 | 3 | 4 | 5 | 6 | 7 | 8 |

Occasional in damp meadows, marshes and canal banks.
FID.

C. flexuosa With.
Wavy Bitter-cress　　Native

| 1 | 2 | 3 | 4 | 5 | 6 | 7 | 8 |

Widespread and common in muddy and damp shady habitats; an increasingly frequent garden weed, distributed with garden centre plants.

- -

C. hirsuta L.
Hairy Bitter-cress　　Native

| 1 | 2 | 3 | 4 | 5 | 6 | 7 | 8 |

Widespread and common in similar habitats to **C. flexuosa** but also on drier soils and in sunnier situations; a common garden weed.
FID.

- -

Arabis

A. hirsuta (L.) Scop.
Hairy Rock-cress　　Native

Colgan: 5. On the old roof of St Doulough's church: *Mack. Cat.* On the top of the tower of St Doulough's 1890: *F.W. Burbidge.* On the walls of the priory of St Doulough's and on the rock at Feltrum Hill: *Ir. Flor.* Abundant and luxuriant on several walls about St Doulough's, 1903; sparingly on rocky banks at the eastern end of Feltrim Hill, 1904: *N.C.*
First record in 1825: *Mack. Cat.* An earlier record in *Mack. Rar.,* 1806: "Sandy fields near the seashore between Balbriggan and the Nanny Water," probably belongs to Co. Meath. At St Doulough's the plant attains to 20 inches in height.
Suppl: 5. Still on Feltrim Hill although its area has been much reduced (1956).

| (5) |

Not refound recently near St Doolagh's Quarries (5). Not seen since 1956 at Feltrim Hill (5).

- -

Erophila

E. verna agg. (*Draba verna*)
Native

| 1 | 2 | 3 | 4 | 5 | 6 | 7 | 8 |

Common on the coast on sand-dunes; rare inland.

- -

E. majuscula Jordan (*Draba verna* var. *majuscula*)
Hairy Whitlowgrass　　Native

| (6) | 8 |

Extremely rare. It has probably been under-recorded as it can be difficult to distinguish from other **Erophila** species.
8. By the Martello Tower at Ballybrack, HOR/85. Shallow turf over granite on Dalkey Hill and Killiney Hill, HOR/85, 87 & SR/88, 89.

E. verna (L.) DC.
Common Whitlowgrass   Native

| 3 | 4 | 5 | 7 | 8 |

Occasional; mainly on dry sandy soils and walls.
3. Beach at Portrane, PR/88.
4. Limestone outcrop by the Royal Canal west of Kennan Bridge, Clonsilla, CB, SR/90 & DN/91.
5. Sand-dunes on North Bull Island, SR, DD/88. Road to Feltrim Hill Quarry, DN/89. Sand-dunes at Portmarnock, DN/89. Wall on the eastern side of Baldoyle Race-course, DN/91. Wall beside Howth Castle, PG, DN/91.
7. On cement rendering on a path at Woodlawn Park Grove, south-west of Firhouse, JP/84.
8. Tarmacadam path of Roman Catholic church and gravel of ruined Church of Ireland church at Glencullen, HOR/87 & SR/89. Overgrown tarmacadam track on the west side of Leopardstown Race-course, SR/85, 87-89. Sand to the east of the Pigeon House, SR/88. Dalkey Island, SR/91.

E. glabrescens Jordan
Glabrous Whitlowgrass   Native

| 8 |

Extremely rare. Probably under-recorded.
8. Summit of Sorrento Park, Dalkey, HOR/87, **NCR**. Gravel car park near Woodbrook Golf-course, SR/87-89.

Cochlearia

C. anglica L.
English Scurvygrass   Native

Colgan (Appendix): 5. Muddy places on the North Wall: *Ir. Flor.* and 8. Banks of the Dodder near Haig's distillery: *Mack. Cat.* By railway on the south side of Killiney Hill *(Moore) Cyb.*
Suppl: 2. By mouth of Delvin River (1946). 3. Near Seatown, Swords (1957). 5. North Bull (1950).

| (2) | (3) | 5 | (8) |

Very rare, in salt-marshes. Very rarely found as the pure species, much more commonly as a back-crossed hybrid with **C. officinalis**. *Colgan* believed (probably correctly) that previous records of this species in Co. Dublin were referable to forms of **C. officinalis**.
5. North Bull Island, PWJ/78, 83.

C. anglica × C. officinalis (C. × hollandica Henrard)

| 5 |

Rare, in salt-marshes but much commoner than **C. anglica**, with which it is easily confused.
5. North Bull Island, with **C. anglica**, PWJ/78, 83. Portmarnock, DD/88. Mouth of the Mayne River, DD/92.

C. officinalis L.
Common Scurvygrass   Native

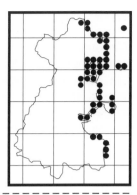

| 2 | 3 | 5 | 8 |

Common on maritime rocks and cliffs and in the upper portions of salt-marshes. **C. officinalis** subsp. **scotica** (Druce) P.S. Wyse Jackson (**C. scotica** Druce) has been recorded, in error, in Perring and Walters (1976) from north Co. Dublin.

- -

C. officinalis × C. danica

| 5 |

Rare. Both parents are highly variable species and hybrids between them are not easy to distinguish. The hybrids are more or less fertile and hybrid swarms may occur, as they do elsewhere in Ireland.
5. Ireland's Eye, PWJ/79.

- -

C. danica L.
Danish Scurvygrass   Native

| 2 | 3 | 4 | 5 | 6 | 8 |

Frequent; sandy soils and walls near the sea; rare inland on railway lines.
2. Pier at Rush, DD/82, **NDR**. Skerries near Holmpatrick, DD/85.
3. Still on the pier at Lambay Island, DD/91.
4. Beside the railway line west of Clonsilla, L.K. Shackleton/76, **NDR,** DN/96.
6. Railway ballast south of St Helen's, Lucan, JP/84, **NDR**.
FID.

- -

Capsella

C. bursa-pastoris (L.) Medikus
Shepherd's-purse   Native

| I | 2 | 3 | 4 | 5 | 6 | 7 | 8 |

Extremely common and widespread on waste ground, arable land and as a garden weed.
FID.

Thlaspi

T. arvense L.
Field Penny-cress   Probably introduced

Colgan: 2. Abundant in a sandy field at Rush, 1894: *Colgan 1895.* 3. At the Castle, Lambay island: *Flor. Lambay.* 4. About Glasnevin and Finglas Bridge: *Ir. Flor.* 5. Lately found on Howth by Captain Pratt: *Mack. Cat.* Fields on the neck of Howth, 1866; plentiful about Inisfallen and Hillside above Howth village, 1881-82; Balscaddan and about the Red Park: *Flor. Howth.* Potato field above Howth village, 1896 *(Miss S. Colgan) Cyb. II.* Sparingly at Baldoyle, 1866: *Hart MS.* frequent here in cornfields, 1900! At Raheny: *Ir. Flor.* 7. Sparingly at Bohernabreena, 1893: *Colgan 1895.* 8. In fallow fields at Bray: *Wade Dubl.*

| 2 | 3 | 4 | 5 | 7 | 8 |

Frequent in 2; rare elsewhere, on waste and disturbed ground and on roadsides.
3. Waste ground at Coolquoy, Slane Road, PR/87.
4. Cross Guns Bridge, DD/87. People's Garden, Phoenix Park, PR/89. Vegetable garden near St Margaret's Church, MN/89. Roadside north of Lucan, DD/86. Disturbed ground on a roadside at Packenham Bridge, DD/86.
5. Near Alexandra Basin, Dublin Port, SR/88-91. Waste ground at the River Tolka Basin, PG/90. By the dual carriageway east of Dublin Airport, SR/90. Disturbed pasture to the south-east of the car park at the summit of Howth Head and at the harbour, CB, PG/91.
7. Along the banks of the Grand Canal at Wilton Place, MN/83. Soil heap in agricultural land near Lugmore Glen, MN/90.
8. Disturbed ground near the Conference Centre and at the north-west corner of U.C.D. Belfield SR, HOR/84 & DK/90. Abandoned railway line at Foxrock Railway Station, SR/84. Old walled garden east of Sandyford, PC/78, 79. By the Stillorgan Road, north of Stillorgan, SR/89. Disturbed soil in a walled garden at St Philomena's Home, near Stillorgan, SR/91. Sandyford Industrial Estate, SR, JR/93.

- -

Lepidium

L. heterophyllum Benth. *(L. hirtum, L. smithii)*
Smith's Pepperwort   Native

Colgan: 1. In several stations in and around the Naul Hills, as at Streamstown, Walshestown, Balrickard, and Mullahow, 1903; 2. Sparingly near Clonard and south of Balbriggan, 1893-95; 5. Frequent on Howth Head, 1902: *N.C.* 6, 7 and 8. Frequent in the mountains: *N.C.*

| 1 | 2 | 5 | 6 | 7 | 8 |

Common in shallow acid soils in the uplands (7 & 8); occasional on disturbed ground in the north of the county; rare elsewhere.
1. Roadside banks, north-east of Naul, GS/83, 85. South-west of Balrothery, GS/85.
2. Still at Clonard, DD/87. Hedgerow at Turkinstown, RF, DD/86 & RF/87. On a wall, west of the Inn, Man O' War, DD/85. Still south of Balbriggan on waste ground by the shore at Fancourt, Balbriggan, RF/87.
5. Scattered along the cliff path, Howth, PG/87, 88. Rocky outcrops between Sutton House and Redrock, Howth, CB/91.
6. By the roadside on the north-east side of Knockandinny Golf-course, JP/82.
7. Shingle banks of the River Dodder, north of Fort Bridge, CB/91.

L. draba L. subsp. **draba** *(Cardaria draba)*
Hoary Cress   Alien

Colgan: 4. A casual on the Midland railway beyond Liffey Junction: *Praeger MS.* In profusion, spreading for about 100 yards in waste ground and on the banks of a railway siding near the mills at Cross Guns, Royal Canal, 1903 *(F.C. Crawford & N.C.) Colgan 1903.* In fair quantity in waste ground by the East Road, Dublin Harbour, 1903: *N.C.* No doubt originally introduced with grain; now fully established.

Suppl: Rare. 3. S. end of Portrane Head (1955). 4. Still in profusion at Liffey Junction (1956). 5. Rubbish dump near Howth station (1942). Roadside near Mayne Bridge, Portmarnock (1950). 7. By a lane near Whitehall, Crumlin (1943). 8. Roadside S. of Stepaside (R.W. Scully, 1918).

2	3	4	5	6	(7)	8

Occasional on roadsides and waste ground.
2. Shore north and south of Balbriggan, RF/86, 87. Skerries Railway Station, DD, EMcA/85.
3. South end of the cliff walk just east of Portrane, PR/84.
4. Still by the old mill on the Royal Canal at Cross Guns Bridge, MN/88.
5. By a gateway and field edge at Baldoyle Racecourse, DNFC/84, DN/90. By the Causeway on North Bull Island, Raheny and nearby at St Anne's Park, Raheny, PG/87, 88. Bank of the Royal Canal in the railway depot on North Wall Quay, DN/88.
6. Beside the railway line south of St Helen's, Lucan, JP/84. Flat grassy verge, near Casement Aerodrome, HOR/85, MN/90. Compost heap at Weston Aerodrome, JP/89.
8. By a car park near the Stillorgan Shopping Centre and nearby in a field beside Glenalbyn swimming pool, SR/83. By a stream in Wyattville Estate, Cabinteely, HOR/85. On a bank in Blackrock Park, SR/83. In park at north end of Sandymount Strand, SR/94.

Coronopus

C. squamatus (Forsskål) Asch. *(Senebiera coronopus)*
Swine-cress   Possibly introduced

I	2	3	4	5	(6)	(7)	8

Occasional on the coast and throughout 5; rare inland on waste and tilled ground.
1. Cultivated field, east of Oldtown, GS/86.
2. Bettyville House, north-east of Ballyboghil and nearby at the edge of a vegetable field, south of Bettyville House, DD/84, 85.
3. Between Turvey House and Turvey Bridge, PR/83. Disturbed ground at Swords, PR/85.
4. Ditch in the Phoenix Park near the former Papal Nunciature, JS/86. Farmyard, west of Cappagh Hospital, MN, JS/86. Waste ground by the Ashbourne Road, Finglas and on Mellows Road, MN, PR/85. By the lock gate of the Royal Canal, east of Blanchardstown, MN/86. By the Cabra Gate of the Phoenix Park, MN/86. By the new airport road at Harristown, 1 km south of St Margaret's, MN/90.
8. Muddy field at Kilgobbin, PC/72-79, 88. Walled garden of St Philomena's near Stillorgan, SR/91. Ballyogan tiphead, east of Stepaside, SR/93.

FID.

C. didymus (L.) Smith (Senebiera didyma)
Lesser Swine-cress   Probably introduced

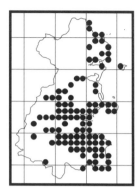

| 2 | 3 | 4 | 5 | 6 | 7 | 8 |

Frequent in ruderal habitats. Greatly increased since the turn of
the century when it had only been recorded in the south of the
county. Rare in 3 & 5.
3. Waste ground in Swords Village, PR, DD/86, **NDR**.
5. Waste ground north of Baldoyle Village, DD/84, **NDR**.
FID.

- -

Diplotaxis

D. muralis (L.) DC.
Annual Wall-rocket   Probably introduced

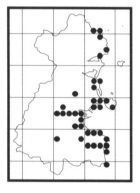

Colgan: 2. Gravel pits by the railway at Skerries, 1892 *(Dr McWeeney) Ir. Nat.*, 1892, p.93
and in 1902! Frequent along the railway from Rush to about a mile north of Balbriggan,
1894; occasional in fallows at Rush, 1903; 3. Along the railway at Donabate 1894-1902;
and abundant in sandy fields at Portrane, 1903: N.C. 5. On sandy ditchbanks at
Portmarnock, 1837 *(J. Johnstone) Mackay 1859* frequent here in sandy fallows 1902!
Sandy banks at Baldoyle, plentifully *(Moore) Cyb.* At intervals along the railway from
Raheny to Howth, 1901-03; on the shore at Sutton, 1901 and on wall-tops, roadsides
nd waste ground near the station, 1903; abundant on roadsides near Kilbarrick, 1902: N.C.
8. At Sandymount, 1886: *Herb. Vowell.* Bath Avenue, Irishtown, 1888; *More MS.* In the garden of Marine Hotel, Kingstown,
1898; on the railway at Merrion and Lansdown Road, 1901; in the public park at Kingstown, 1901-03; and abundant on the
branch railway from Lansdown Road to Ball's Bridge, 1902: N.C. On the railway about a quarter of a mile north of Bray river,
1895: W.H. Bloomer abundant here in 1900! and about a mile farther north on same line, 1903! A characteristic Co. Dublin
species, now spreading rapidly through Ireland along the railways. *Var. BABINGTONII Syme.* 2. Banks by the sea at Rush, 1903; and
3. Gravelly banks by the sea to the north of Portrane peninsula, 1900-02: N.C. 5. Near Sutton, 1891 *(Levinge) Cyb. II.* At Sutton,
1901, and at Portmarnock, 1902: N.C. This is a robust perennial plant reaching to 3 feet in height at Rush, but is rather a state
than a true variety.

| 2 | 3 | 4 | 5 | 7 | 8 |

Rare except in 8 where it is common along the coast: railway lines, waste ground and walls.
2. Still in the gravel pits at Skerries Railway Station and nearby, DD/84. Common at
   Rogerstown and Rush, DD/85.
3. Still in Portrane on waste ground on the foreshore, PR, DD/86.
4. By the Navan branch of the railway at Clonsilla where it has been known for many years
   (*Suppl*), HJH/83. Waste ground near the Mater Hospital, DNFC/81. By the gates of the
   Phoenix Park near the north Circular Road, MN/87. Roadside verge by the River Tolka
   west of Finglas Bridge, MN, JS/84.
5. Railway sidings at Sutton Station, DD/67. Base of wall in Howth Village, ENL/86. Waste
   ground at Dublin Port, SR/90. Frequent at Black Banks, Raheny, PG/89-92.
7. Building site off Baggot Street, PWJ/80. By the River Dodder south-west of Firhouse,
   SR/89. Waste ground 200 m north-east of Charlemount Street Bridge, MWJ/92.
FID.

Brassica

B. napus L.
Rape   Alien

| 6 | 7 | 8 |

Occasional on waste ground. Most specimens of this species were not determined to subspecific level. Subsp. **oleifera** (DC.) Metzger (Oilseed Rape) is the commonest form in the county.
6. Clondalkin Common, JP/83, **NCR**.
7. North-west of Ballyfermot, PWJ/86.
8. North-east of Foxrock Church, SR/85. Irishtown, SR/89. Near the sewage works east of the Pigeon House, SR/89.

- -

B. rapa L.
Turnip   Probably introduced

| 1 | 2 | 3 | 4 | 5 | 6 | 7 | 8 |

Common and widespread on waste and tilled ground.
FID.

- -

B. nigra (L.) Koch
Black Mustard   Native

Colgan: 2. Common at Rush and Skerries: *Ir. Flor.* Cultivated fields at Rush, 1894; banks and field borders at Windmill Lane, Skerries, 1893-1903: *N.C.* 3. Common at Swords, and 4. At Finglas and Glasnevin: *Ir. Flor.* 5. Portmarnock sands: *Mack. Cat.* High banks above the harbour, Howth village, *Flor. Howth.* Near the shore at Sutton, 1903: *Miss M.C. Knowles.* 7. Fields near Chapelizod: *Mack. Cat.* At Milltown, 1866: *Hart MS.* Abundant at Rathgar quarry, 1902, *Praeger.* This species appears to have been formerly common in many stations, though now become rare.

| (2) | (3) | (4) | (5) | (7) |

Not recently recorded. *FID* records are referable to **Hirschfeldia incana** (L.) Lagr.-Fossat with which **B. nigra** can be easily confused except when in fruit.

- -

Sinapis

S. arvensis L. *(Brassica sinapis)*
Charlock   Possibly introduced

| 1 | 2 | 3 | 4 | 5 | 6 | 7 | 8 |

Common in ruderal habitats and tilled ground.
FID.

- -

S. alba L. *(Brassica alba)*
White Mustard   Alien

Colgan: 2. About Rush and Skerries: *Ir. Flor.* Abundant in cultivated land at Skerries and at Ballough near Lusk, 1902: *N.C.* 3. At Swords, and 4. At Finglas and Glasnevin: *Ir. Flor.* 5. Plentiful at Portmarnock: *Flor. Hib.* At Raheny, Howth and Sutton, 1894 and at Baldoyle, 1903: *N.C.* 8. At Dalkey quarry, 1880: *Miss E. Malone.* In several places about Dundrum, 1894: *Praeger.* At Kiltiernan, 1893; a garden weed at Sandycove, 1900; and abundant in cultivated land at Ballybrack, 1903: *N.C.* This is apparently an increasing species in the county as elsewhere in Ireland.

2 (3) 4 5 8

Rare on roadsides and in ruderal habitats; occasional on tilled ground in the Skerries and Rush regions (2).
4. Scattered by the base of Knockmaroon Hill and one plant at the top, MN/88. One plant at Dunsink tiphead, SR, JR/93.
5. Abundant in an abandoned vegetable plot, All Hallow's College, Drumcondra, DD/92.
8. Playing-field south of Blackrock, SR, HOR/87. Waste ground, north-east of Foxrock Church, SR/85. Sandyford Industrial Estate, SR/93.

Erucastrum

E. gallicum (Willd.) O. Schulz
Hairy Rocket   Alien

4 5 8

Rare on roadsides and waste ground.
4. Finglas Industrial Estate, DD/88.
5. One patch on a sandy verge opposite St Fintan's Cemetery and in a garden in Carrickbrack Road, Howth, CB/91.
8. One plant on waste ground at Pottery Road, north-east of Cabinteely, SR/84, **NCR**.

Hirschfeldia

H. incana (L.) Lagr.-Fossat (*Brassica adpressa*)
Hoary Mustard   Alien

Colgan (Appendix) (as **Brassica adpressa**): 5. A single plant at Portmarnock, 1867 (*Hart*) *Rec. Add.* Along the roadside near Sutton station, (1890) (*Cecil Butler*) *Cyb.II.*

2 4 5 7 8

Common in waste places, on roadsides and disturbed ground especially in built-up areas; rare elsewhere. Although there is a specimen from the Dublin Port area in 1968 (**BEL**), **H. incana** was not generally recognised in Dublin until 1983 (Rich 1988), and records in *FID* for the similar looking **Brassica nigra** refer to this species. The appressed fruits of **H. incana** have slightly swollen tips whereas those of **B. nigra** have slender tips.
2. Waste ground, west of Lusk Village, DD/84.
4. Weedy field, east-north-east of Belgree House on the county boundary, MN/86. Quarry below Clanaboy House, Lucan, MN/87.
5. Abundant at Dublin Port, SR/91-95.
7. Many plants by the River Dodder between Oldbawn and Firhouse, SR/89.
8. Many plants at Ringsend Dump, DNFC/83-96. Sandyford Industrial Estate, SR, HOR/85. Ballyogan tiphead, SR/93.

Cakile

C. maritima Scop.
Sea Rocket   Native

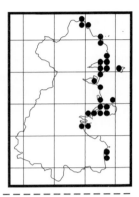

Colgan: Wide-spread along the coast from the Delvin river south to Killiney; rare over wide intervals but abundant in many stations, as on the South Bull, Dublin Harbour, the Velvet Strand, Portmarnock, &c., and becoming a common weed of cultivation in sandy fallows at Rush and Portrane.

2	3	5	8

Occasional in fore-dunes.

Rapistrum

R. rugosum (L.) Bergeret
Bastard Cabbage   Alien

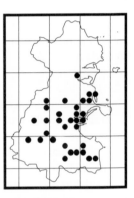

3	4	5	6	7	8

Frequent on wasteground in built-up areas; rare elsewhere. First recorded in 1921 (Grierson 1922); subsequent records given in Wyse Jackson (1981) and *FID.*
3. **Roadside verge of the Belfast road, north of Balheary House, PR/87.**
4. **Dunsink tiphead, MN/85, SR, JR/93. Chapelizod, A. Newmann/73.**
5. **Sea-wall, Clontarf, PC/73.**
8. **Kilmashogue Lane, SR/87. Reclaimed land on the north slope of Ticknock, SR/88. Irishtown, PC/77. Near Stepaside, PC/72. Milltown Bridge, PC/75-78. Ringsend Dump, PWJ/81.**

FID.

Crambe

C. maritima L.
Sea-kale   Native

Colgan: 5. Near Warren House on the road leading to Howth: *Wade Dubl.* Sea coast between Malahide and Baldoyle: *Mack. Cat.* South side of Howth, along gravelly shore: *Ir. Flor.* Seashore at Sutton *(Levinge) Cyb. II.* On the gravelly strand of Ireland's Eye, 1894: *Praeger 1895.* 8. "Upon the Sea Beach near Dunlary": *Threlkeld.* At Merrion and Dunleary: *Wade Dubl.* Railway bank near Killiney 1868. Herb. R. Barrington. Rutty in his *Natural History of the County of Dublin,* 1772, says of this species: "It is found on our shore and is in request as a kale," and in the Appendix to *Warburton's Dublin, 1818,* it is said to be "found on every part of the coast." From these and other early records it is clear that the plant was formerly frequent on the shores of Dublin Bay. Of the few recent records some, or perhaps all, may refer to survivals of or outcasts from cultivation, but as the plant is very uncertain in its appearances it seems inadvisable for the present to reject it as certainly extinct.

5 8

Extremely rare on shingle beaches. Recorded from Howth, between Malahide and Baldoyle, and Sutton (5), and Merrion and Dun Laoghaire (8) in the early 1800s but extinct in all these sites now. Some of the earlier records may refer to garden outcasts. Though not seen recently in many of its former localities, it may reappear from dormant seed.

5. Still on Ireland's Eye, DD/74, 81.

8. On the beach south of Killiney, RG/66; now believed to be of garden origin.

Raphanus

R. raphanistrum L.

2 3 4 5 (6) (7) 8

---

subsp. **raphanistrum**
Wild Radish   Alien

2 3 4 8

Very rare, on arable land and waste ground.

2. Arable field at Reynoldstown, RF/87.

3. Disturbed soil east of Donabate Village and on sandy fallows on the backstrand midway along western side of Malahide Island, DD, PR/87. Waste ground and hedgerows near Donabate, PR, DD/87.

4. Beside the gate of the U.C.D. boat club on Conyngham Road, MN/87.

8. Disturbed ground by Murphystown Road, south-east of Sandyford, SR/88. Disturbed ground, east of The Scalp, SR/87.

FID.

---

subsp. **maritimus** (Smith) Thell. (*R. maritimus*)
Sea Radish   Native

Colgan: 2. Frequent on sandy banks at Rogerstown harbour, and in sandy lanes and fallows and on the shore at Rush, 1893-1903; 3. Sandy fields to the north of Portrane peninsula, 1894: *N.C.* 5. Along the banks of the sea under Mr Hannington's at Howth: *Ir. Flor.* Shore betwen Greenfields and Sutton; banks by the sea at the Needles and Earlscliffe: *Flor. Howth.*

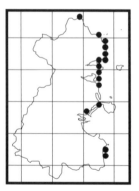

2 3 5 8

Locally common on sand-dunes and seashores.

Plants intermediate between the subspecies have been recorded from the shore east of Ballealy (2), DD/87 and at Rogerstown (2), DD/94.

RESEDACEAE

Reseda

R. luteola L.
Weld   Native

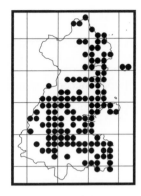

| 1 | 2 | 3 | 4 | 5 | 6 | 7 | 8 |

Common on waste ground and in gravelly places.
FID.

R. alba L.
White Mignonette   Alien

| 5 | (8) |

Extremely rare on sandy ground. This species was first recorded from sandy banks at Portmarnock (5) before 1824 by J.T. Mackay, (Parnell and Webb 1991). Though the area is now a golf-course, **R. alba** persists in fallow-type ground, usually springing up in abundance where sods have been removed. Formerly recorded on the banks of the Dodder and near Dundrum (8) but not seen there this century.

5. Still at Portmarnock on disturbed ground just inside the entrance to Portmarnock Golf-course, DD/71, B. Prendiville/85, DN/88 & DD/94. Gone from sites in Sutton and Howth where it was recorded last century.

R. lutea L.
Wild Mignonette   Probably introduced

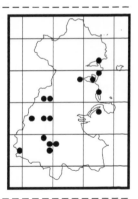

| 2 | 3 | 4 | 5 | 6 | 7 | (8) |

Common in sandy fallows near the sea; rare on sandy ground inland.

EMPETRACEAE

Empetrum

E. nigrum L.
Crowberry   Native

| 7 | 8 |

Widespread in moorland and heathland above 300 m.

ERICACEAE

Rhododendron

R. ponticum L.
Rhododendron   Alien

5	7	8

Occasional in moorland and woodland margins. A relatively recent escape which is now well established. It is beginning to take over parts of the moorland on Howth (including the Central Marsh) (5).

5. Spreading from Howth Demesne on to the Ben of Howth and from a garden on to East Mountain, DD/82 & CB/91.
7. Near the northern reservoir in Glenasmole, PR, MN/83. Near Castlekelly by the Cot and Slade brooks at an altitude of 250-300 m, HOR/85. Sides of the River Dodder below the gorge (spreading from the grounds of Glenasmole Lodge), and on a north facing slope of Kippure, SR, HOR/85.
8. Self-sown into an old granite quarry on the south side of the Glencullen Valley, SR, CB/88.

Andromeda

A. polifolia L.
Bog-rosemary   Native

Colgan: 7. Bogs along the Military Road leading from Roebuck to Lough Bray: *Ir. Flor.* Feather Bed mountain, 1871 (probably the same station as the preceding): *Hart MS.* and in 1903: *Praeger 1904.* Side of Kippure *(Hart) Guide.* Between the summit of Kippure and the highest point of the Military Road between Lough Bray and Killakee *(Hart) Flor. Howth.* frequent here in 1902, in a wet level bog on Kippure, west of the main fork of the Dodder! On Glendhu mountain, 1903: *Praeger 1904.* 8. Frequent in a wet bog above the Glencullen quarries on Prince William's Seat, 1901: *Colgan 1903.* On the ridge west of Prince William's Seat, 1903: *Praeger 1904.* Ranges from 1,300 feet to 1,500 feet on Kippure.

7	8

Extremely rare, in deep mountain blanket-bog.
7. Two small plants, still on the north-west face of Kippure near the summit at approximately 670 m, HOR/85.
8. In a bog south-west of Boranaraltry Bridge, between Prince William's Seat and Glendoo Mountain at about 500 m, C. Breen/93.

Calluna

C. vulgaris (L.) Hull
Heather, Ling   Native

(1)	3	5	6	7	8

Common in heathland and moorland on Howth and in the mountains. The fragment of peat-bog at Streamstown, Naul Hills (1) where it was recorded by Colgan in 1900-03 has been cleared. Now much rarer on Lambay Island (3) than it was at the turn of the century.

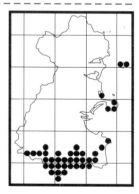

5. Sand-hills, in a depression with **Schoenus nigricans** and several pine trees, mid-way along western side of Portmarnock Peninsula, DN/88.

- -

Erica

E. tetralix L.
Cross-leaved Heath   Native

| 7 | | 8 |

Common in moorland in the mountains. Not on Howth.

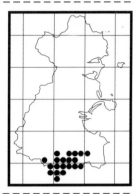

- -

E. cinerea L.
Bell Heather   Native

Suppl: 5. A large patch on the Royal Dublin golf links near the club-house, North Bull (1950).

| 3 | 5 | 6 | 7 | 8 |

Common in heathland and, more rarely, moorland on Howth and in the mountains. Now much rarer on Lambay Island (3) than it was at the end of the 19th century. Formerly recorded on a rocky knoll at Balcarrig (= Balcarrick), Portrane (3) (*Colgan*) but not refound recently.

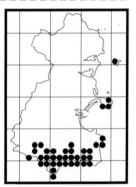

- -

Vaccinium

V. oxycoccos L. *(Oxycoccus palustris)*
Cranberry   Native

Colgan: 7. In a boggy hollow on the northern face of Glendu mountain, 1901: *Colgan 1903* the only definite County Dublin locality on record. At 1,900 feet on Glendhu mountain, the highest station at which the species has hitherto been observed in Ireland.
Suppl: 7. Abundant above the Upper Dodder on wet slopes opposite Castlekelly (A.W. Stelfox, 1922). N. side of Kippure and Seefingan (J. O'Callaghan, *I.N.,* XX, 1911).

| 7 |

Extremely rare, in mountain blanket-bog.
7. Still on Glendoo mountain, widespread on the north slope and flat summit, CB, SR, RF/89.

- -

V. vitis-idaea L.
Cowberry   Native

Colgan: 7. Plentiful on the Dublin mountains near Lough Bray: *Flor. Hib.* On Kippure mountain inside the Dublin boundary, *circa 1880 (Hart) Flor. Howth & MS.* probably the same locality as the preceding. Abundant over a considerable area near the summit of Kippure, 1893: *N.C.* Sparingly on the northern slope of Seecawn, 1900: *Colgan 1903.* Between Kippure and Seefingan and tolerably abundant on Seefingan, 1903: *Praeger 1904.* Ranges from 2,050 feet on Seecawn to 2,450 feet on Kippure.

$\boxed{7}$

Rare, in heathland.

7. Still on Kippure, on the summit and slope to the north-east, CB, SR/90. Still on Seahan (Seecawn) mountain, just east-north-east of the summit, DN, CB, SR/90.

- -

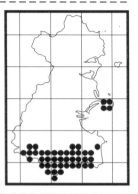

V. myrtillus L.
Bilberry, Frochan   Native

$\boxed{5}$ $\boxed{6}$ $\boxed{7}$ $\boxed{8}$

Very common in heathland and moorland.

- -

MONOTROPACEAE

Monotropa

M. hypopitys agg. *(Hypopithys multiflora)*
Yellow Bird's-nest   Native

Colgan: 4. Under beech trees, Saint Catherine's County Dublin *(Dr Wade) Mack. Cat.* and *Flor. Hib.* Not seen recently, though repeatedly sought for at Saint Catherine's. There is, however, no conclusive reason for rejecting Wade's locality, which was accepted by Mackay in his *Catalogue* of 1825 and repeated eleven years later in his *Flora Hibernica.* The station is a most appropriate one, and Wade appears to have been acquainted with the species. Its Irish distribution, so far as at present known, is no doubt western rather than eastern; yet on the whole, and in spite of the absence of any record of later date than 1836, the exclusion of the plant from the county flora does not appear to be justifiable.

$\boxed{(4)}$ $\boxed{7}$

Not refound at St Catherine's (4).

- -

subsp. **hypophegea** (Wallr.) Holmboe

$\boxed{7}$

Extremely rare.

7. Under hazel scrub on a bank rising steeply on the east side of the River Dodder at the Bohernabreena end of Glenasmole, RMcM/66. This is the only recent record for the species and subspecies in the county (**DBN**).

PRIMULACEAE

Primula

P. vulgaris Hudson
Primrose   Native

| 1 | 2 | 3 | 4 | 5 | 6 | 7 | 8 |

Common in hedgebanks and woodlands; occasional in coastal grassland. In most populations of primrose, individuals are of two types - pin, with long styles and short anthers, and thrum, with the reverse characters. These characters are important as they control the breeding biology of the species; seeds are usually only set when the different morphs cross with each other. In one population of **P. vulgaris** at Ballymaice occasional individuals have been found which are neither pin nor thrum but appear to be homomorphic, *i.e.* they have styles and anthers of the same length. This is an extremely rare phenomenon only known to occur in a few populations in the British Isles.
FID.

- -

P. vulgaris x P. veris (P. x polyantha Miller; *P. x tommasinii, P. x variabilis*)
Native

| 1 | 2 | 4 | 5 | 6 | 7 | 8 |

Occasional on roadside banks and woodland margins.
1. Roadside bank at Commons Upper, GS/86. Soil dumped after ditch clearing, north of Rowlestown, GS/83.
2. Woodland at Milverton, RF/86. 0.5 km north of Lusk Village, DD/86.
4. One plant near the Abbotstown Gates just south of Abbotstown, MN/83.
5. Field at the edge of Santry Woods, DNFC/85. Eastern part of St Anne's Park, Raheny, PG/87, 88. Howth Demesne, PG, DN/91. Sutton Cemetery, CB/91.
6. Upland pasture on Verschoyles Hill, SR/86.
7. Wood by the Slade River at Ballymaice, MWJ, JP/88.
8. One plant on the bank of the old railway line north-west of Sandyford Industrial Estate, SR, JR/84. One plant in a field beside the Bride's Glen River south of Laughanstown, SR, HOR/87.

- -

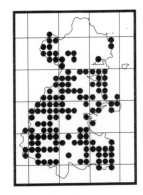

P. veris L. (*P. officinalis*)
Cowslip   Native

| 1 | 2 | 3 | 4 | 5 | 6 | 7 | 8 |

Occasional in pastures, sand-dunes, calcareous grassland and roadside banks. In many places this species has disappeared due to changes in pasture management and is now largely confined to ungrazed roadside banks.
FID.

Lysimachia

L. nemorum L.
Yellow Pimpernel   Native

I	4	5	6	7	8

Occasional in damp, shaded habitats. Locally frequent in the River Liffey Valley and in the mountains and their foothills; common in 8.
1. Baldwinstown, GS/86, **NDR**.
5. Santry Woods, DD/82. Woodland beside the Deer Park Golf-course, CB/92.
7. Hazel scrub in Lugmore Glen, Tallaght Hill, MN/90. Hazel scrub on the eastern slope above the River Dodder between Ballymaice and Fort Bridge, and above the northern reservoir in Glenasmole, MN/90.

- -

L. nummularia L.
Creeping-Jenny   Native; introduced

4	7	8

Rare, on river banks and in marshes. Invades and then appears to become an established component of the vegetation in river valleys.
4. River Tolka Valley north-west of Ashtown, MN/85.
7. Palmerston Marsh, MN, ENL, CB/85. Woods by the Slade River at Ballymaice, JP, MWJ/88. On a roadside grassy patch near Wilton Place, a garden escape, K. Duff, PWJ/80.
8. Garden escape, in the woods at Mount Merrion, SR/84.
FID.

- -

L. vulgaris L.
Yellow Loosestrife   Native

Colgan: 2. Quarry hole near Stamullen Bridge, on the Delvin river, in small quantity: *Colgan 1893.* (8. In marshy situations about Loughlinstown and Old Connaught: *Ir. Flor.* not seen recently.)

Suppl: 2. Extinct in 1917 - "the quarry at Stamullin has been long filled in" (C.E. Maconchy).

(2)	(8)

Not refound in either of its localities. Occasional garden escapes or discards of this species are found in the county.

- -

Anagallis

A. tenella (L.) L.
Bog Pimpernel   Native

(I)	2	3	4	5	6	7	8

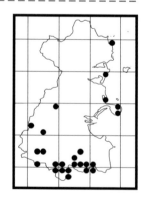

Occasional in marshes and flushed areas in the uplands and in dune-slacks. **A. tenella** was considered to be so common that *Colgan* did not cite localities. Although still widespread in the mountains, it is now confined in the northern parts of the county to fragments of marsh or dune-slacks.

210

2. Marsh on the coast between Loughshinny and Skerries, DD/84.
3. Dune-slack at Corballis, PR/86.
4. Marsh by the River Tolka at Blanchardstown, MN/83, 84.
5. Dune-slacks on Portmarnock Golf-course, DN/89. Marsh south of Kilrock Quarries, Howth, PG/88. Redrock, Howth, PG/88. Wet field beside Thormanby Road, Howth, DN/89.

A. arvensis L. subsp. arvensis
Scarlet Pimpernel   Native

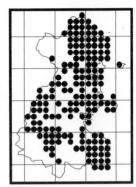

| 1 | 2 | 3 | 4 | 5 | 6 | 7 | 8 |

Common in dry sandy ground near the coast and on waste ground inland. A blue-flowered variant has been found as a weed in a vegetable garden, west of Shankill, CM/88 & SR/88, 89.
Subsp. **caerulea** Hartman, also with blue flowers, was recorded at Ballyogan tiphead, SR, JR/93.
FID.

Glaux

G. maritima L.
Sea-milkwort   Native

Colgan: Very rare in District 8, where it has been observed by N.C. in only two stations, on the South Wall, beyond the Pigeon House, growing sparingly in the joints of the granite causeway, 1902, and in fair quantity by the salt ditch near Booterstown railway station in 1904.

| 2 | 3 | 5 | 8 |

Abundant in the upper parts of salt-marshes on the north Dublin coast; rare in the south; also in dune-slacks and on shingle ridges.
8. Booterstown Marsh, DD/82. Dalkey Island, DN, DD/91.

Samolus

S. valerandi L.
Brookweed   Native

| (1) | 2 | 3 | 4 | 5 | (6) | (7) | 8 |

Occasional on low and wet cliffs, on shores and in dune-slacks in the north of the county. Rare inland.
2. 1 km south of Balscadden, MAF/92.
3. Edge of a pond on the east side of the Island Golf-course, DN/89. Base of a cliff north of the Martello Tower at Portrane, PR/89.
4. Ditch 1 km west of the Ward, JS/87. Pond in the Phoenix Park, MN/87. Marsh at Luttrellstown, JS, DD/83. Bank of a pond in the National Botanic Gardens, Glasnevin, MN/84.
8. Booterstown Marsh, RG/70; not refound recently.

CRASSULACEAE

Umbilicus

U. rupestris (Salisb.) Dandy *(Cotyledon umbilicus, U. pendulinus)*
Navelwort, Pennywort   Native

Colgan: 1. Clay banks above the Lough, Balrothery, and 2. Sparingly in rocks at the Naul, 1893. 5. On Ireland's Eye, 1896; abundant on Howth Head, 1904; 6. Roadside near Athgoe and near Johnstown, and hills above Saggard Slade, 1904: N.C. – 7 and 8. Abundant in many places in the non-calcareous uplands.

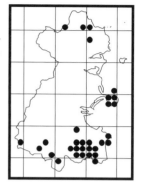

| 1 | 2 | 5 | 6 | 7 | 8 |

Common on acid rocks and walls and as an epiphyte; rare in the north except on Howth Head and absent from the lowlands.
1. Still at Naul, DD/84.
2. Still on stone-faced hedgerow banks at Balrothery Lough, DD/84. Shaded roadside banks at Rathmooney, DD/84.

Sedum

S. acre L.
Biting Stonecrop   Native

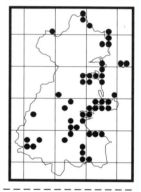

| 1 | 2 | 3 | 4 | 5 | 6 | 7 | 8 |

Common in dune grassland; rare inland and there usually on walls. *FID.*

S. album L.
White Stonecrop   Alien

| 1 | 2 | 3 | 4 | 5 | 6 | 7 | 8 |

Occasional on old walls. Described in *Suppl* as "spreading rapidly" and at that time (1961) not recorded from 1 and 5.

S. anglicum Hudson
English Stonecrop   Native

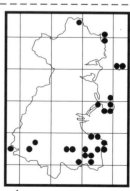

| 2 | 3 | 5 | 6 | 8 |

Occasional in 8 and on Howth (5) on very shallow base-poor soils in acid heathland; rare elsewhere, often on walls.
2. Rock outcrop 0.25 km south of Clonard, DD/87. Still on St Patrick's Island, DD/84.
3. Still on the west side of Lambay Island, but very much reduced since the time of Praeger's vegetation survey in the early part of the 20th century, DD/82.
6. Walls by the road near Knockandinny, JP/82, **NDR**. Walls by the road 1 km north-north-east of Castlewarden House, JP/87. Wall at Fortunestown, E. Parnell/84.

SAXIFRAGACEAE

Saxifraga

S. stellaris L.
Starry Saxifrage   Native

Colgan: 7. At the sources of the Dodder, Dublin mountains: *Flor. Howth.* By the Slade Brook, upper Dodder, in oozy
Sphagnum plashes, sparingly in two places, 1894-1901; about a dozen plants on wet rocks in the bed of the main stream
near Cobb's Lodge, 1896, and more abundantly higher up the stream, 1902: *N.C.* By a spring on Seecawn, 1903: *Praeger*
1904. Ranges from 900 feet to 1,800 feet on Kippure. This species appears to be altogether confined to Dublin to the
upper confluents of the Dodder on the northern slopes of Kippure and Seecawn. It varies much according to station. Of
weak straggling growth in oozy *Sphagnum* beds, where its usually barren patches simulate the Hypnoid Saxifrages in
habit, it becomes a robust plant with dense rosettes of broad leaves when growing on rocks in the stream beds.

7

Extremely rare, on moist rocks in rivers.
7. Still by the Slade Brook in flushes at about 270 m, HOR/85. One plant on a rock in the
   River Dodder gorge east of Glenasmole Lodge at about 250 m, and on mossy rocks near
   a small waterfall at about 300 m, SR, HOR/85 & C. Breen/86.

- -

S. umbrosa L. x S. spathularis Brot. (S. x urbium D.A. Webb)
Londonpride   Alien

6	7

Rare on shady banks.
6. Naturalized downhill from St Brigid's Home in Crooksling Glen, JP/84 & DK/92.
7. Numerous plants naturalized on a wooded slope in the north-east part of Massey Woods,
   SR, JR/94.

- -

S. granulata L.
Meadow Saxifrage   Native

Colgan: 5. On dry sandy ditch banks between Baldoyle and Portmarnock: *Mack. Cat.* Near Kilbarrick church: *Ir. Flor.,* 1833
and in 1866: *Hart MS.* On the race-course of Baldoyle, in damp mossy pasture, abundant over a space of some 30
yards in length, 1885-1902: *N.C.*
Suppl: 5. Last seen at Kilbarrick in 1919. A house was built on the spot in 1920. Not re-found on Baldoyle racecourse.

5

Extremely rare on sand-dunes. An endangered species in Ireland, legally protected under the
Wildlife Act of 1976. Not seen at Kilbarrack since 1919, nor has it been refound at Baldoyle
Racecourse (5) *(Colgan).* A double-flowered variant occurs near the Knockmaroon Gate in
Phoenix Park (4) and in St Anne's Park, Raheny (5).
5. Sand-hills, east of the Royal Dublin Golf-course on North Bull Island, BB/76, 89.

- -

S. tridactylites L.
Rue-leaved Saxifrage   Native

Colgan: 2. Abundant in sandy fallows and in sandhills at Rush, 1903; 4. Sparingly on walls near Lucan, 1893-1900: *N.C.* 5.
"On the sandy Banks near the *Brick-fields": Threlkeld.* On Feltrim Hill: *Flor. Hib.,* 1836 very luxuriant here in 1903! At the
eastern end of the Cosh: *Flor. Howth.* Abundant in sandy fallows, Portmarnock, 1902; in the old quarry at Cloghran, and

on the Rock, Corballis, 1903: 6. Rocks by the Liffey above Leixlip, 1894; on Leixlip Bridge and walls above it and on roofs and walls at Lucan, 1904: *N.C.* 7. "Upon Mr *Grosvenor's* Malt-house and some Houses in Cavan Street": *Threlkeld.* In Long Lane, between Camden Street and New Street: *Wade Dubl.* On wall-tops at Mount Brown and near Templeogue and in gravel pits near Green Hills, 1894: *N.C.* Near Tymon, 1902: *W.H. Bloomer.* 8. Near Sandymount: *Wade Dubl.* Beyond Dundrum: *Ir. Flor.* Wall-tops, Dundrum, 1894: *N.C.*

| 2 | 3 | 4 | 5 | 6 | 7 | 8 |

Rare in sandy soils and on dry wall tops. Occasional in sand-dunes.
2. Railway line, 1.5 km south of Skerries, DD/86. Still locally abundant in sandy fallows at Rush and Rogerstown, DD/92.
3. Still in sand-hills west of Corballis House, PR/89.
4. Old railway sidings by the Royal Canal west of Clonsilla Railway Station, JS, MN/88. Still sparingly on walls on and west of Lucan Bridge, MN/88. Lucan Quarries, ENL/90. Railway line off Fassaugh Road, inner city, PR/81.
5. Portmarnock sand-dunes, DD/89. Sand-dunes on North Bull Island, ENL, DD/84.
6. Roadsides at Lucan, HOR, CB/85. On the railway line, near St Helen's, Lucan, JP/84.
7. Shallow soil in the quarry at the top of Ballinascorney Gap, JP/90.
8. Car park on the western side of Leopardstown Racecourse, SR/90. Thousands of plants on limestone chippings, Ringsend Dump, SR/93.
FID.

- -

Chrysosplenium

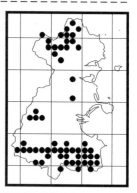

C. oppositifolium L.
Opposite-leaved Golden-saxifrage   Native

| 1 | 2 | 3 | 4 | 5 | 6 | 7 | 8 |

Common in wet ditches, stream sides and damp deciduous woodland. Frequent in the south and parts of the north, local elsewhere.

- -

Parnassia

P. palustris L.
Grass-of-Parnassus   Native

Colgan: 2. Frequent on drift banks and in marshy ground by the shore from Skerries to Balbriggan, 1893; 3. Abundant by the Ward River below Chapelmidway, 1894; abundant in a marsh near Raheen Point, Portrane, and in many of the hollows of the sandhills, 1903: *N.C.* 4. Abundantly in the Earl of Bective's grounds at Scribblestown and behind the Observatory: *Wade Dubl.* By the Tolka river above Blanchardstown, 1895: *N.C.* 5. In marshes at Howth: *Wade Dubl.* Near Cannon Rock, Howth, 1893, and in the central marsh, 1903: *N.C.* Low sandy ground at Portmarnock: *Mack. Cat.* 6. Abundant in marshes by the canal at Hazelhatch and in wet pastures above Saggard, 1894; 7. At Ballinascorney and by the Dodder at Newtown, 1894; abundant along the Dodder from Old Bawn to Bohernabreena, and in Lugmore, 1903: *N.C.* "It grows in the wet ground under *Inisacore Hill."Threlkeld.* 8. Plentiful round Kilgobbin: *Wade Dubl.* In Kelly's Glen, and at Ticknock, 1903; abundant on drift banks near Glencullen bridge, 1893, &c.: *N.C.* Ascends to 950 feet at Ticknock and to 1,000 feet on Knockanavea. The plant of the sandhills is often dwarfed to 2 inches in height.
DNFC Annual Report for 1953: Oldbawn, J.P. Brunker.

(2) (3) **4** **5** (6) **7** (8)

Very rare, in marshes and dune-slacks. Much rarer than at the turn of the century. In *Suppl* it is described as "frequent". Many of its former dune-slack sites now seem to be too dry to support it. The dwarf coastal ecotype, var. **condensata** Travis & Wheldon, has been reported from herbarium material of unknown collection date from near Malahide (Gornall 1988).

4. Marsh by the River Tolka at Blanchardstown, DD/76.
5. Still in a dune-slack just north of the old golf-course at Portmarnock, MWJ/85 & DN/91.
7. Marsh 300 m north-west of St Ann's Chapel, Glenasmole, DNFC/88. Just south of Stone Cross, Ballinascorney Gap, DN/89.

ROSACEAE

Filipendula

F. ulmaria (L.) Maxim. *(Spiraea ulmaria)*
Meadowsweet   Native

1 **2** **3** **4** **5** **6** **7** **8**

Very common in damp meadows, on roadsides, riversides and canal banks.
FID.

Rubus

There are many Bramble forms in Ireland that cannot be matched with any species yet named. Among the more common of these in Co. Dublin are:

(i)   a member of Series **Vestiti** with broad, white petals, common in 6, 7 & 8 as well as abundant in 2 at Five Roads.
(ii) a densely glandular bramble with narrow pink petals, common in 6 with some material in 7 & 8.
(iii) a member of Series **Radulae** with narrow pink petals, red styles and tiny rachis prickles, locally abundant in woods in 4 & 8 but also occurring in 7 around Glenasmole.

Subgenus Cylactis (Raf.) Foche

R. saxatilis L.
Stone Bramble   Native

Colgan: 7. Kelly's glen (Moore) Cyb. 8. On Kilgobbin mountain to the west of Kilgobbin, sparingly: Wade Rar. This species has not been seen recently, though frequently sought for in the mountain districts, but the authority for the Kelly's glen record is too good to permit of the plant being excluded from the Dublin flora. Wade, too, though an unsafe authority for some genera, was well acquainted with this species in the limestone districts of West Ireland, so that his Kilgobbin record cannot be lightly dismissed.

(7) (8)

Probably extinct. Not seen for a century in Dublin.

Subgenus **Idaeobatus** Foche

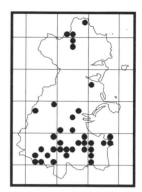

R. idaeus L.
Raspberry   Native

| 1 | 2 | (3) | 4 | 5 | 6 | 7 | 8 |

Rare in the lowlands; commoner on higher ground: hedgerows, roadside banks and river valleys.
FID.

Subgenus **Rubus**

Section **Rubus**

R. fruticosus L. agg.
Brambles   Native

| 1 | 2 | 3 | 4 | 5 | 6 | 7 | 8 |

Widespread and abundant on roadsides, waste ground, woodland margins and especially in hedges. It is an aggregate of many microspecies most of which reproduce asexually. Collections of these were made *c.* 1900, but few specimens are preserved in herbaria and, of these, few can be matched with currently recognised species. Study of the group in Dublin revived with a visit by A. Newton in 1984 (Newton 1986), followed by more intensive work in 1987-1991 by D.E.Allen (Allen 1988a, 1988b, 1990, 1993, 1994) who was usually accompanied by the district recorders concerned. As little prior critical work has been done on the genus most of the district records are new to the county. However, we have not so indicated them in the text, confining ourselves to listing new county or Irish records. We have included records for re-determined specimens in **DBN** even where these are very old. Brambles are long-lived and the bushes may well still survive in their original locations.
FID.

Subsection **Rubus**

R. nessensis W. Hall

| 7 |

7. Two bushes above the east shore of the northern reservoir, Glenasmole, DA/88, **NCR**.

Subsection Hiemales

Series Sylvatici

R. albionis W.C.R. Watson *(R. macrophyllus var. schlechtendalii)*

| 1 | (2) | 5 | 7 | 8 |

A dominant member of the Wicklow Mountains **Rubus** flora; common in 8. Recorded by RLP/1894 from Kelly's Glen.
1. One bush in a hedge at Walshestown, DA/87.
5. A large patch in Malahide Castle grounds, DA/87. Still on Howth, widespread and especially abundant at Greenhollows, DA/87. Baskin Lane, Malahide Road, MC/91.
7. Glenasmole, AN/84, DA/87. Roadsides at Ballinascorney House, DA/88.

- -

R. leptothyrsos G. Braunthyrsos

| 7 |

A mainly Scottish species in Britain; in Ireland otherwise only known in west Connaught.
7. Track at the southern tip of the northern reservoir at Glenasmole, DA/88.

- -

R. lindleianus Lees

| 4 | 5 | 8 |

4. A patch amongst gorse and a bush by the lake in Phoenix Park, DA/88.
5. Two clumps in Malahide Castle plantations, DA/87. Howth Demesne, DA/87.
8. One bush at Boranaraltry Lane, Glencullen Valley, DA/87.

- -

R. purbeckensis W.C. Barton & Riddelsd.

| 5 | 8 |

Believed endemic to the seaboard of Wessex (south coast of England) until its discovery on Howth in 1987. Since found to be widespread in the east of Ireland, from Howth to Wexford.
5. At several places on Howth, especially abundant at Greenhollows, DA/87: it is presumably the *"R. leucostachys"* recorded in *Colgan* as abundant here. Baskin Lane, Malahide Road, MC/91. Recorded on the Hill of Howth "in abundance" (Allen 1988a).
8. Two bushes in a lane alongside a conifer plantation at Ballycorus, DA/87.

- -

R. pyramidalis Kaltenb.

| 8 |

8. North base of Three Rock Mountain, RLP/1893, (**DBN**).

- -

R. robii (W.C.R. Watson) Newton

| 6 |

An upland species in Britain almost confined to the Pennines. Known previously only from Armagh and Cavan.
6. A single bush on a roadside margin of Saggart Hill plantation at about 1,000 m, DA/91, **NCR**.

Series Rhamnifolii

R. amplificatus Lees

| 1 | 5 | 6 | 7 | 8 |

1. Common on acid ground near Hynestown Reservoir, DA/87. Hedges at Kitchenstown, DA/87. Hedges at Walshestown, DA/87.
5. Common in Howth Demesne, DA/87.
6. Frequent in Coolmine plantation, DA/91. By a conifer plantation east of Brittas, DA/88.
7. Glenasmole, AN/84, DA/87. Lugmore Glen, DA/91.
8. Foxrock, C. Waterfall/05. Killiney Hill, DA/87.

R. boudiccae A.L.Bull & Edees

| 1 |

A south of England species, but proving to be unexpectedly widespread in north Leinster and Ulster.
1. Scattered among gorse in acid ground near Hynestown Reservoir, DA/87, **NCR**. One bush in a hedge at Nag's Head, DA/87.

R. cardiophyllus Lef. & Mueller

| 2 | 5 | 7 | 8 |

2. Balbriggan, RLP/1894. Five Roads, DA/87.
5. Clontarf, RLP/1894. One bush on a cliff-top at the Baily, Howth, DA/88.
7. Upper Glenasmole, DA/87.
8. One bush in a lane leading to Ballycorus lead mines, DA/87.

R. incurvatus Bab.

| 5 |

5. A colony at Redrock, AN/84 & DA/87. A patch at Greenhollows, Howth, DA/87.

R. nemoralis Mueller

| 1 | 2 | 5 | 6 | 7 | 8 |

Probably widespread in the mountains.
1. One bush in acid ground near Hynestown Reservoir, DA/87.
2. Five Roads, DA/87.
5. At several places on Howth, DA/87.
6. By a conifer plantation, east of Brittas, DA/88.
7. By the northern reservoir in Glenasmole, DA/88.
8. Foxrock, C. Waterfall/08. Common on roadsides around Ballybetagh Bog, DA/87. One bush in a lane leading to Ballycorus lead mines, DA/87.

var. **microphyllus** (Lindeb.) W.C.R. Watson (*R. pistoris*)

| 5 |

5. Several places on Howth, DA/87.

R. polyanthemus Lindeb. *(R. pulcherrimus)*

| 1 | 2 | 5 | 6 | 7 | (8) |

Common in 2.
1. Acid ground near Hynestown Reservoir, DA/87.
5. Still on Howth and abundant in the demesne, DA/87. Cliff top at the Baily, Howth, DA/88.
7. Glenasmole, RLP/1893. Lugmore Glen, DA/91.

R. subinermoides Druce

| 7 |

A south-east of England species which occurs infrequently in south-east Ireland.
7. Kelly's Glen, Glenasmole, AN/84.

Series Discolores

R. procerus Mueller ex Boulay cv. Himalayan Giant (*R. armeniacus*)
Alien

| 5 | 7 | 8 |

5. A single plant in each of two places on Howth, DA/87. Waste ground, Ballymun Road, Drumcondra, DA/88.
7. One clump in Lugmore Glen, DA/91.
8. Adventive in a garden at Stillorgan, DA/91.

R. ulmifolius Schott *(R. rusticanus)*

| 1 | 2 | 3 | 4 | 5 | 6 | 7 | 8 |

Widespread. Abundant in hedgerows and in waste places. The commonest lowland bramble in the county.
FID.

Series Vestiti

R. lanaticaulis Edees & Newton

| 1 | 2 | 8 |

1. Hedges at Kitchenstown, DA/87.
2. Five Roads, DA/87.
8. Common on Killiney Hill, DA/87.

R. lettii Rogers

| 5 |

Until recently, believed endemic to the northern half of Ireland and the Isle of Man.
5. One clump in Howth Demesne, DA/87.

R. ordovicum Newton

| 3 | 5 | 8 |

Unknown elsewhere in Ireland and believed endemic to north-west Wales until 1987.
Probably an accidental introduction to the county.
3. One clump in the shrubbery at Newbridge House, DA/91.
5. Santry Court, DA/87. Outside Howth Demesne, DA/87. One bush on a roadside wall
   below Greenhollows, Howth, DA/88. Collected on Howth by RLP/1893.
8. In quantity along a lane leading to Ballycorus lead mines, DA/87.

R. vestitus Weihe

| 3 | 4 | 5 |

A species usually growing on basic soils which is unexpectedly rare in the northern half of
the county.
3. The prevailing bramble on Lambay Island, RLP/04. The Burrow, Portrane, DA/87.
   Shrubberies at Newbridge House, DA/91.
4. Locally common along the road and in the plantation at Luttrellstown, DA/87.
5. In two places on Howth, DA/87.

Series Mucronati

R. wirralensis Newton

| 1 |

1. 1 km east of Kitchenstown, GS, AN/84.

Series Anisacanthi

R. dentatifolius (Briggs) W.C.R. Watson

| 1 | 2 | 5 | 6 | 7 | 8 |

Common in 6, 7 & 8.
1. Abundant by Hynestown Reservoir and Nag's Head, DA/87.
2. Five Roads, DA/87.
5. Common in Malahide Castle plantations, DA/87.

R. infestus Weihe ex Boenn.

| 7 |

7. Kelly's Glen, Glenasmole, AN/84.

Series Radulae

R. adenanthoides Newton

| 5 |

A common species in the northern half of Ireland.
5. Several places on Howth, DA/87.

R. echinatoides (Rogers) Dallman

| 7 |

7. Cruagh Wood, AN/84.

R. echinatus Lindley

| 1 | 2 | (5) | 6 | 7 |

Prefers clayey soil. First collected by RLP/1893 from Howth (5).
1. Acid ground near Hynestown Reservoir, DA/87. Still in hedges at Walshestown, DA/87.
2. Near Balbriggan, RLP/1893. Hedges at Rogerstown, DA/87. Hedges at Lusk, DA/88.
   Hedge, south of Balscadden, DA/88. Balrothery, MC/90.
6. One bush in grounds of St Brigid's Home, Crooksling Glen, DA/88. Verschoyles Hill, DA/88.
7. Kelly's Glen, Glenasmole, AN/84.

R. rubristylus W.C.R. Watson

| 1 | 2 | 4 | 5 | 6 |

In Ireland this is a species largely confined to the north-east quarter, otherwise mainly in the
Isle of Man and the north Welsh marshes. Widespread and locally frequent in 1 & 2.
4. Phoenix Park, DA/87.
5. Locally common on the exposed cliff-top at the Baily, Howth, DA/87.
6. Common around Brittas, DA/91.

R. rufescens Lef. & Mueller

| 7 |

7. Kelly's Glen, Glenasmole, AN/84.

Series Hystrices

R. dasyphyllus (Rogers) E.S. Marshall

| 5 | 6 | 7 | 8 |

Common in 6, 7 & 8.
5. One bush in Malahide Castle grounds, DA/87.

Series Corylifolii

R. nemorosus Hayne & Willd. (*R. balfourianus*)

| I | 2 | 5 |

1. Hedges at Walshestown, DA/87.
2. Balbriggan, RLP/1893. One bush at Five Roads, DA/87.
5. Common in Malahide Castle plantations, DA/87. Still on Howth in open heath at Greenhollows, Howth, DA/87.

R. pruinosus Arrh. (*R. sublustris*)

| 2 | 7 |

2. Hedges at Lusk, DA/87. Lane north of Balbriggan, DA/87.
7. Kelly's Glen, Glenasmole, AN/84.

R. tuberculatus Bab. (*R. dumetorum* var. *tuberculatus*)

| I | 5 |

In Ireland it is mainly ruderal in occurrence and apparently confined to the Dublin area: probably adventive.
1. Acid ground near Hynestown Reservoir, DA/87.
5. Howth, DA/87. Recorded in 1895 by RLP from Raheny.

Section Caesii

R. caesius L.

| (1) | (2) | (3) | (4) | (5) | (6) | (7) | (8) |

Widely misinterpreted in the past and recorded from banks of the Royal Canal (5) in *FID*, in error for a white-flowered member of **Rubus** Section **Corylifolii**: members of this section are derived from hybridization with **R. caesius** and in some cases resemble it.

Potentilla

P. palustris (L.) Scop. (*Comarum palustre*)
Marsh Cinquefoil   Native

Colgan: 2. Ditches near Balrothery, 1902: N.C. 5. Howth: *Ir. Flor.* Boggy ground near Woodside, Howth: *Flor. Howth.* Marsh under Dung Hill, Howth, 1893; in the central marsh, Howth, 1903; 6. In Crooksling glen, and glen on Mount Seskin 1894;

222

abundant by the lower Brittas pond and marshy ground east of it, 1895; frequent to the north of Saggard Hill, 1902; and 7. Abundant in a marsh on the south east slope of Knockanavea, 1895: N.C.

Suppl: 7. Featherbed Mountain, W. of Military Road at circa 1, 300 ft. (1950).

2	5	6	(7)	8

Very rare on marshy and boggy ground.

2. Still at Balrothery Lough, in ditches, DD/90.
5. Still on Howth in a marshy place on the track to Balkill Road just outside the Deer Park, and south of the reservoir on Howth, ENL/83 & DNFC/91.
6. Still at Brittas Ponds, PH/92.
8. Damp heathy ground east of Ballyedmonduff, PC/77, **NDR**. Ballybetagh Bog and on the margins of marshy fields to the south, JP/83 & SR, JR/87.

- -

P. anserina L.
Silverweed   Native

1	2	3	4	5	6	7	8

Widespread and abundant on roadsides, seashores, marshy places, pastures and waste ground. FID.

- -

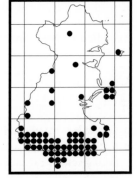

P. erecta (L.) Raeusch. *(P. tormentilla)*
Tormentil   Native

(1)	2	3	4	5	6	7	8

- -

subsp. **erecta**

2	3	4	5	6	7	8

Common in heathland and acid grassland on mixed mineral and peat soils on Howth and the uplands; very rare elsewhere.

2. Nag's Head, GS/85.
3. Lambay Island, SR, DD/91. Damp grassland by the Ward River 1 km west of Swords, DD/90.
4. Grassland above the woods and by the bank of the lake at Luttrellstown, MN/88, 89. Marshy field, north-west of Finglas, MN/84.
5. Alder Marsh on North Bull Island, PG/89.

- -

subsp. **strictissima** (Zimm.) A. Richards

5

5. Still on Howth at the Baily Lighthouse, DD/90. (There is a specimen from Howth collected by J.T. Mackay in the 19th century (**TCD**)).

P. erecta x **P. anglica** (**P.** x **suberecta** Zimm.)
Native

| 7 |

7. Roadside at Ballinascorney Gap, MN/89.

P. anglica Laich. *(P. procumbens)*
Trailing Tormentil   Native

Colgan: 1. Frequent near Mullahow; 2. At Mulheney, near Man of War, 1902; and 3. Near Donabate, 1901: *N.C.* 4. Phoenix
Park; and 5. Howth and Santry: *Ir. Flor.* 6. Roadside banks near Hazelhatch, 1895; and 8. Near Ballycorus, 1900: *N.C.*

| 1 | 2 | 3 | 4 | 5 | 6 | 7 | 8 |

Occasional in 2 & 8 on roadside verges; rare elsewhere.
1. Common in short grassland on the roadside verge at Winter Lodge, DD/87.
3. Embankment 1 km south-east of Thorntown Lodge, PR/87.
4. Calcareous grassland by the Royal Canal east of Kirkpatrick Bridge and north-east of
   Castleknock, MN/88. Above the 'Rabbit Warren' in Luttrellstown, MN/88.
5. Grassland at Redrock, Howth, CB/92.
6. Roadsides at Brittas, DD/83.
7. 2 km south of Rockbrook, PWJ, HOR, CB/85.
8. Still near Ballycorus chimney, DNFC/83. Coast east of Shankill, on a fallen clay cliff, SR/84.

P. anglica x **P. reptans** (**P.** x **mixta** Nolte ex Reichb.)
Native

Colgan: 7. By the Grand Canal near Herberton Bridge, 1888: *Herb. Scully.*

| 2 | 4 | 6 | 7 |

Occasional in 2 on roadside verges and waste ground where it sometimes forms extensive
stands.
4. Roadside verge north of Westmanstown, Lucan, MN/87. Disused part of Lucan Quarry,
   MN/88. Short grassland east of the Papal Cross in the Phoenix Park, MN/88. Astagob
   sand-pits, MN/88. Grassy bank in the Furry Glen, Phoenix Park, MN/91.
6. Roadside between Brittas and Glenaraneen, DD/90. Unimproved grassland in the Slade
   Valley, MN/90.
7. Wall between the two reservoirs in Glenasmole, MN/87. Lugmore Glen, MN/91.

P. reptans L.
Creeping Cinquefoil   Native

| 1 | 2 | 3 | 4 | 5 | 6 | 7 | 8 |

Widespread and common on roadsides, in meadows and pastures, sandy ground inland and
in ruderal habitats.
FID.

P. sterilis (L.) Garcke *(P. fragariastrum)*
Barren Strawberry   Native

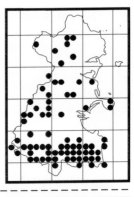

1		3	4	5	6	7		8

Common in shaded places: hedges, woods and banks in 6, 7 and 8, often on base-rich soils; rare and local in 1.

Fragaria

F. vesca L.
Wild Strawberry   Native

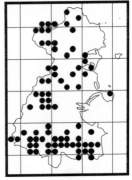

1	2	3	4	5	6	7		8

Common on roadside banks, in sand quarries and hedgerows.

Geum

G. rivale L.
Water Avens   Native

Colgan: 4. In Woodlands: *Mack. Cat.*, 1825 and in 1900 *(Miss Hunter) Top. Bot.* 5. In Santry wood towards the west: *Wade Dubl.* Santry and Kilmore woods: *Ir. Flor.* 6. Glens above the Embankment, Saggard, 1894: *N.C.* 7. Near Ballinascorney, 1876: *Greenwood Pim* and in 1903! In the Slade of Ballymaice, 1893, and abundant in Lugmore Glen, 1903: *N.C. Suppl:* Rare. 4. Still in Luttrellstown woods 1954. 6. Still in glen above Embankment (1956). 7. Still in Lugmore Glen (1955) and in Slade of Ballymaice (1957).

4	(5)	6	7

Very rare in damp shaded places.
4. Still in Luttrellstown, where a single plant was found between a stream and path just below the arch, JS/83.
6. Ditch near Athgoe Castle, JP, E. Parnell, DAS/84.
7. One plant in a wet flush north-east of Stone Cross, Ballinascorney Gap, CB/91.

G. rivale × G. urbanum (G. × intermedium Ehrh.)
Native

Colgan: 4. In Woodlands, 1880: *Hart MS.*

(4)	7

Extremely rare.
7. Near Aghfarrel, Brittas, JP/83, **NDR**.

- -

G. urbanum L.
Wood Avens   Native

1	2	3	4	5	6	7	8

Widespread and common on roadsides, in hedgerows and woodlands.
FID.

- -

Agrimonia

A. eupatoria L.
Agrimony   Native

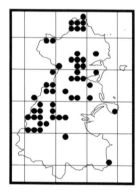

1	2	3	4	5	6	7	8

Occasional on roadside verges and banks on dry lime-rich sandy ground. Common in the lowlands; rare in 8. On higher ground in the north of the county confined to species-rich, sunny roadside banks, often as single specimens.
8. Limestone drift on the slope above Glencullen Bridge, JR/87. Grassy cliff on the east side of Woodbrook Golf-course, north of Bray, SR, HOR/84.

- -

A. procera Wallr. *(A. odorata)*
Fragrant Agrimony   Native

Colgan: 6. Sparingly amongst bushes on a grassy roadside at Castle Bagot, Milltowns, midway between Clondalkin and Newcastle, 1903, growing with the preceding species: *Colgan 1904.*
Suppl: 3. Lambay, abundant in bracken and brambles (Praeger, 1907).

(3)	5	6

Extremely rare in grassland. Not refound on Lambay Island (3). The distinction between this and the preceeding species is not always clear in Co. Dublin material. Plants in populations of **A. eupatoria** often resemble **A. procera** in the curvature of the spines on the calyx.
5. On a rock outcrop below the old church on Ireland's Eye, ENL, DD/82, **NDR**.
6. Banks of the Grand Canal at Gollierstown, JP, DD/89. This is close to Colgan's original station at Castle Baggot where it has not been refound.

Sanguisorba

S. minor Scop. *(Poterium sanguisorba)*
Salad Burnet   Native
DNFC Annual Report, 1954: 5. Feltrim Hill, H.J. Hudson.
DNFC Annual Report, 1956: 5. Carrick Hill, H.J. Hudson.

2	3	4	5	6	7	8

Occasional in the western part of the county; rare elsewhere: quarries, sandy ground and banks. Mainly a lowland species. Formerly more common and now much reduced due to habitat loss.
2. Embankment at Skerries Railway Station, RF/87.
3. Gravel quarries at Knocksedan, RF, DD/85.
5. East of The Summit on Howth Head, DN/90. St Doolagh's Quarries, HJH/83.

- -

Alchemilla Lady's-mantle

Although *Colgan* was aware of the considerable variation existing in this genus, it did not give localities for the segregates.

A. xanthochlora Rothm.
Native
Suppl: 7. Kelly's Glen at about 500 ft. (Colgan, 1903). Ballinascorney at 600 ft. (Colgan, 1903).

(7)

Not refound in Kelly's Glen or the Ballinascorney Gap (7).

- -

A. filicaulis Buser subsp. **vestita** (Buser) Bradshaw *(A. filicaulis)*
Native
Suppl: (as **A. vestita**) 3. Ward River valley above Swords (1953). 4. By River Tolka above Blanchardstown (Colgan, 1903). 6. Crooksling Glen (Colgan, 1903) - still there (1957). 7. Ballinascorney (Colgan, 1881). Glenasmole (Miss M. Buchanan, 1928). Killakee (1955). 8. Kiltiernan (Praeger, 1894).

(3)	4	6	7	8

Rare to occasional in short unimproved grassland.
4. Grassy bank by a tributary of the River Liffey west of Castleknock College, MN/84. Sparingly in grass by the Knockmaroon Gate in Phoenix Park, MN/85.
6. 2 km south-west of Rathcoole, HOR, PR, CB/86. West of the Brittas Inn and nearby at the extreme north end of Brittas Ponds, DD/82, 83. Upland pasture on Verschoyles Hill and nearby to the east, JP/86, SR, HOR/86. Beside the Tallaght to Clondalkin road, 1.75 km south of Clondalkin, JP/85.
7. Sand-hills near Aghfarrel, JP/83. Glen east of Tallaght Hill and nearby east of Kingswood, JP/83, 86. Grassland along the edge of the River Liffey, near King's Hospital School, SR, MN, ENL, RF/85. Scattered along the length of the Glenasmole Valley, DD/83, RMcM/83 & MN/90. East of Piperstown, PWJ/84. St Columba's College, DK/c.65. Dry pasture south of Rockbrook, PWJ, HOR, CB/86. Grassland at the west end of the Waterstown Dump at Palmerston, PH/91.
8. Ballyedmonduff, SR, HOR/86. Slope above Glencullen Bridge, SR/87. Beside Ballybetagh Bog, CB, SR/89.

A. glabra Neyg.
Native
Suppl: 6. Crooksling Glen (1954).

| 6 | 7 | 8 |

Frequent in 7 in unimproved upland pasture and on shady roadsides; rare elsewhere.
6. South-west of Rathcoole, HOR, SR, CB/86. Grassland around Brittas Ponds and nearby north of Monaspick, in Glenaraneen and on the north-west slope of Saggart Hill, DNFC/83, ENL/83 & JP/83-87. Ballinascorney Gap, DD/92.
8. Scattered in the Glencullen Valley. On the south-west slope of Two Rock Mountain, SR/84. Damp ditch south of Boranaraltry, HOR/85. Rock in the stream at the foot of Tibradden Mountain, HOR/85. Top of the Ticknock road, SR, HOR/83.

Aphanes

A. arvensis L. (*Alchemilla arvensis* pro parte)
Parsley-piert   Native

| 1 | 2 | 3 | 4 | 5 | 6 | 7 | 8 |

Frequent in 8 on shallow soils usually on limestone; uncommon elswhere. First recognised from a collection made by R.W. Scully in 1888 from Baldoyle (5) (**DBN**).
1. By the dam at Hynestown Reservoir, GS, DD/84.
2. Old walls in Rush village, DD/92.
3. Gravel path in the grounds of Newbridge House, PR/86.
4. Railway Embankment near Fassaugh Road, inner city, PR/81. Quarry near Cloghran House, MN/83. Limestone outcrop by the Royal Canal east of Kennan Bridge, MN/90. Disturbed ground by the road c. I km south-west of St Margaret's, MN/90.
5. Feltrim, DD/84. Bare rock at Redrock, Howth, DD/84.
6. Near the round tower west of Redgap, HOR, PR, CB/86. 2 km south-west of Rathcoole, HOR, PR, CB/86. Gravel in Tallaght Quarry, JP/83. Soil dump beside the road to the Belgard Roadstone Works, JP, D.Scott/85. Grassland at Fettercairn House, JP, DAS/85.
7. South-east of Mount Seskin, PWJ, MWJ/86. Roadside verge at Stone Cross, Ballinascorney Gap and off the road, due south, ENL/83, DD/83. Wall north of Piperstown, HOR/85. North-west corner of the northern reservoir in Glenasmole, HOR/85. East of Kingswood, Tallaght, JP/85.

A. inexspectata Lippert (*Alchemilla arvensis* pro parte, *A. microcarpa*)
Slender Parsley-piert   Native

| 7 | 8 |

Occasional on walls, roadside banks and trackways. Usually on base-poor soils. Widespread but local in 8. Not distinguished in either *Colgan* or *Suppl* and therefore new to the county. First recognised from a collection made by R.Ll.Praeger in 1894 from Dundrum (8) (**DBN**).
7. At various sites in the Glenasmole Valley. By the fork in the road, east of Castlekelly, DD, EMcA/83. On the roadside verge at Stone Cross, Ballinascorney Gap, DD/83. Granite

wall, above the Cot Brook near Glenasmole Lodge, HOR/85. Dry acid bank west of the southern reservoir in Glenasmole, MWJ, DAW/87. Forest track on north-west slope of Mountpelier, SR/90.

8. Short turf by a granite outcrop on Dalkey Island, CB, SR, DD, DN/91.

Rosa

Until recently little critical work has been undertaken on the genus **Rosa** in the county. *Colgan* recognised only four species. Recent work by DD has confirmed that hybridization is extensive between members of the genus within the county. The pattern of variation is further complicated by the presence of hybrids with **R. caesia**, which has not been recorded as a "pure" species.

R. arvensis Hudson
Field-rose   Native

| 1 | 2 | 3 | 4 | 5 | 6 | 7 | 8 |

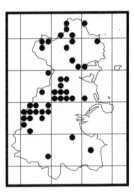

Common in the lowlands of 3, 4 and 6 in hedgerows, on roadsides and embankments; rare elsewhere.

1. A very large form in a roadside hedgerow at Dermotstown, DD/88.
2. Several plants on a bend in the road just west of the graveyard at Tobertown, DD/87.
5. Roadside hedge at Turnapin Bridge Lane, ENL/85. Black Banks, Raheny, PG/89-92.
7. Allagour in Glenasmole, DD/87.
8. Roadside hedge along Orwell Road, by Milltown Golf-course, SR/90. Field by Barnaslingan Lane, south-east of Kiltiernan, SR/92. Bank in Cabinteely Park, SR/90.

R. arvensis x **R. stylosa** (**R.** x **pseudorusticana** Crépin ex Preston)
Native

| 2 | 3 | 4 |

2. Lane north of Lusk, DD, ALP/91.
3. Chapelmidway, DD, ALP/91.
4. Hedgerow near Harristown House, DD/87. 1.5 km north of St Margaret's, DD/91.

R. arvensis x **R. canina** (**R.** x **verticillacantha** Mérat)
Native

| 4 | 7 | 8 |

Very rare.
4. Southern bank of the Royal Canal at Lucan, MN/88. St Margaret's, DD/91. Dunsoghly, DD/90.
7. Allagour, Glenasmole, DD/92.
8. Roadside hedge east of Loughlinstown, SR/90.

R. pimpinellifolia L. *(R. spinosissima)*
Burnet Rose   Native

| 2 | 3 | (4) | 5 | (6) | 7 | 8 |

Common in sand-dunes and coastal heathland in 3 and 5; rare
elsewhere. Scattered along the banks of the River Dodder between
Oldbawn and the Waterworks (7). Much commoner inland at the
beginning of the century than today. Many of the inland stations have
been lost due to sand-quarrying and intensive agriculture.
8. Limestone drift below the railway line at Killiney, SR, HOR/83.
    Whiterock, SR/85. East facing slope of Dalkey Hill,
    Elinor Reynolds, SR/91.

R. pimpinellifolia × **R. sherardii** (**R.** × **involuta** Smith)
Native

| 7 | 8 |

7. Still in Glenasmole, where it was first collected by A.W. Stelfox in 1921 (Anon. 1921b),
    (**DBN**), below Ballymorefinn, DD/87. By the River Dodder above Oldbawn, DD/90.
8. Abandoned railway line at Cabinteely, DD/88.

R. pimpinellifolia × **R. rubiginosa** (**R.** × **cantiana** (Wolley-Dod) Wolley-Dod; *R. moorei*)
Native

| (7) |

Found originally by A.W. Stelfox in 1921 (Anon. 1921b). Plants which appear similar to
R. × **cantiana** but which are probably of more complex hybrid origin occur in the upper
Glenasmole Valley (7).

R. stylosa Desv.
Short-styled Field-rose   Native

| 1 | 2 |

Very rare in roadside hedges.
1. Roadside hedge at Dermotstown, DD/88.
2. Roadside hedge, west of the Corn Mill, near Balbriggan, DD/87, **NCR**. Roadside hedge
    north-east of Dermotstown, DD/87, 88. Hedgerows, south-west of Clonard Cross, DD/87.

R. stylosa × **R. canina** (**R.** × **andegavensis** Bast.)
Native

| 4 | 6 | 7 | 8 |

Rare in hedgerows and scrub but common in Glenasmole (7).
4. By the Royal Canal north-west of Lucan, DD/86. By the River Tolka 1 km north of
    Blanchardstown, DD/88. On a disused branch of Great Southern Railway line at Barnhill,
    MN/88. Dunsoghly, DD/89. 2 km north of St Margaret's, DD/88.

6. Hedge near ruins, east of Grange Castle, JP, P.Chantaranothai/89. Bank of the Grand Canal 1.5 km north-east of Hazlehatch, MN/89.
8. Bank in Cabinteely Park, SR/90.

R. canina L.
Dog-rose   Native

| 1 | 2 | 3 | 4 | 5 | 6 | 7 | 8 |

Widespread and very common in hedgerows. All of the four major groups within this species recognised by *Stace* occur in the county and are, in decreasing order of frequency: the **Lutetianae**, the **Pubescentes**, the **Transitoriae** and the **Dumales**.
FID.

R. canina x **R. caesia** (**R.** x **dumalis** Bechst.)
Native

| 2 | 4 | 6 | 7 |

This category includes hybrids of both subspecies of **R. caesia** recognised in *Stace*.
2. South-west of Courtlough House, DD/89.
4. Harristown House, DD/86. Cappagh, DD/91.
6. Roadside at Glenaraneen, DD/92.
7. 1 km west of Castlekelly, DD/89. Roadside north of Friarstown, DD/92.

R. canina x **R. obtusifolia** (**R.** x **dumetorum** Thuill.)
Native

| 2 | 4 |

2. Loughshinny, DD/89.
4. 2 km north of St Margaret's, DD, ALP/91.

R. canina x **R. tomentosa** (**R.** x **scabriuscula** Smith)
Native

| 4 | 5 | 6 | 7 | 8 |

4. Hedge in Ballycoolin Road, west of Cappagh Hospital, DD/85. Road and fieldside hedges between Kilshane Bridge and Dunsoghly, and near Harristown House, DD/85, 86. Roadside hedge east of Broghan House, DD/87. Dunsoghly, DD/89.
5. Lane east of Feltrim Hill, DD/88.
6. Hedgerow at Aderrig, JP/87.
7. Hedge 300 m southeast of St Ann's Chapel, Glenasmole, DD/88.
8. Fieldside hedge south of Ballybetagh Bog, DD/87. Disused railway line east of Carrickmines, DD/88. East facing slope of Dalkey Hill, SR/91. Roadside hedge east of Loughlinstown, SR/90. Roadside hedge east of Ballycorus, SR/91.

R. canina × R. sherardii
Native

| I | 2 | 7 | 8 |

A specimen collected by Colgan from Streamstown (I) identified as **R. tomentosa** belongs to this hybrid taxon (**DBN**).
1. Balrickard, DD/85.
2. East of Nevitt, DD/85.
7. Cunard, Glenasmole, DD/86.
8. Hedges near Ballybetagh Bog, DD/87. Glencullen, DD/85 & SR/88.

R. tomentosa Smith
Harsh Downy-rose   Native

| (I) | (2) | (3) | (4) | (5) | (7) | (8) |

Most, if not all, of the records in *Colgan* for **R. tomentosa** and in *Suppl* for **R. villosa** L. refer either to **R. sherardii** or **R. × scabriuscula (R. canina × R. tomentosa)**. The **R. tomentosa** record for St Anne's Fields, Glenasmole (*Suppl*) may have been **R. canina × R. sherardii** which occurs in the vicinity. A specimen from Coolatrath (**DBN**) collected by Colgan in 1894 is morphologically very close to **R. tomentosa**. However, *Colgan* makes no mention of any member of the **R. tomentosa** group from this area. Coolatrath is situated very close to Dunsoghly where DD has found a number of shrubs of **R. × scabriuscula** but no **R. tomentosa**.

R. sherardii Davies
Sherard's Downy-rose   Native

| I | 2 | 3 | 6 | 7 | 8 |

Very frequent in hedgerows in I and 2 especially in the Naul Hills; rare elsewhere. Most of the earlier records of **R. tomentosa** refer to **R. sherardii**.
3. South bank of the Ward River I km west of Swords, DD/90.
6. Hedge west of Athgoe Castle, JP/88.
7. 350 m north-west of St Ann's Chapel, Glenasmole, DNFC/88. Gravel banks I km above Oldbawn, CB/90. Below Ballymorefinn, DD/89. Bohernabreena Waterworks, DD/86.
8. Occasional in the Glencullen Valley, SR, HOR/84, 85 & SR, JR/88.

R. sherardii × R. rubiginosa (R. × suberecta (J. Woods) Ley)
Native

| 2 |

Extremely rare in hedgerows.
2. Three plants in field hedges by the roadside just west of the Corn Mill, near Balbriggan, DD/87.

R. rubiginosa L.
Sweet-briar   Native

Suppl: 3. By railway at Corballis (1946). 5. Feltrim Hill (1932-1956). 7. About 600 yds S. of Bohernabreena Bridge by Waterworks road (1941).

| 2 | 3 | 5 | (7) | 8 |

Occasional in hedgerows and scrub.

2. Roadside hedges, north and south of Lusk, DD/84. Roadside verge and in fields near Palmerstown House, RF/85.
3. At the south end of Malahide Island, DD, PR/88. Still by the Railway at Corballis, DD, PR/88.
5. Still at Feltrim in a lane, east of Feltrim Hill, DD/90.
8. Field of gorse near Rathmichael House, west of Shankill, SR/87. By the Bray Road, north-west of Loughlinstown, DD/86. Roadside hedge, east of Loughlinstown, SR, DD/90.

Prunus

P. spinosa L.
Blackthorn, Sloe   Native

| 1 | 2 | 3 | 4 | 5 | 6 | 7 | 8 |

Widespread and common in hedgerows and scrub.

P. domestica L. *(P. insititia)*
Wild Plum, Bullace   Probably introduced

| 1 | 2 | 3 | 4 | 5 | 6 | 7 | 8 |

Common in roadside hedges in 2; occasional elsewhere. Sometimes highly persistent - for example, it may still be found in Santry Woods (5) from where it was first noted before 1833. Fairly widely planted in 2 & 3. Only included in the Appendix in *Colgan*. It is not always easy to distinguish **P. domestica** from **P. spinosa** in Dublin.

P. avium (L.) L.
Wild Cherry   Native; possibly introduced

| 1 | 2 | 3 | 4 | (5) | 6 | 7 | 8 |

Occasional in hedgerows. In many of its sites it appears to have been planted.
In (5) it was recorded as frequent near Stockhole in 1903 (*Colgan*).

P. laurocerasus L.
Cherry Laurel   Alien
Commonly planted in woods in the River Liffey Valley (4, 6, 7) and in the mountains of 6 & 7. Especially common in Massey Woods (7). Also frequent in large estates in 8. Although plants flower copiously along woodland margins and to a lesser extent in the interior of the woods, few seedlings are seen. Despite this, the species appears to be spreading in estate woodland and on the margins of coniferous plantations. Its growth habit, dominance over large areas, and ability to exclude native shrubs and herbs has led to the impoverishment of the flora of demesne woodlands.

Malus

M. sylvestris (L.) Miller *(Pyrus malus, Malus pumila)*
Crab Apple   Native

6	8

Very rare, in hedgerows.
6. Hedges, east of Milltown House, JP/89. Hedge by ruins, east of Grange Castle, JP,
   P. Chantaranothai/89. South-west of Badgerhill, JP/86.
8. Carrickmines, HOR/85. East of Shanganagh Cemetery, SR/87.

- -

M. domestica Borkh.
Apple   Alien

1	2	3	4	5	6	7	8

Occasional in hedgerows. Many plants which have been included in this species have only
slightly hairy pedicels and calyx, and may therefore be confused with **M. sylvestris**. Not
recorded in *Colgan* or *Suppl.*
FID.

- -

Sorbus

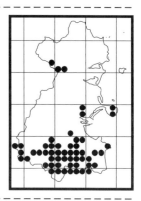

S. aucuparia L. *(Pyrus aucuparia)*
Rowan, Mountain Ash   Native

1	5	6	7	8

Occasional on acid soils in hedgerows, mountain sides and gullies;
rare in lowland hedgerows. Possibly planted in 1.
Widely grown in gardens.

- -

S. intermedia (Ehrh.) Pers.
Swedish Whitebeam   Alien

8

Very rare.
8. Several trees in Dalkey Quarry, on Roches Hill and Killiney Hill, DAW, PC/79, SR, HOR/85
   & SR/89. Edge of the churchyard at Kilgobbin, PC/83. Woodland, Barnacullia, PC/78.
   Roadside between Stepaside and Kiltiernan near Stepaside, PC/77.

- -

S. aria agg.
Native

Colgan: 4. Banks of the Royal Canal, near Pakenham bridge, 1894: *N.C.* 5. In the hedges to the west side of Howth: *Wade Rar.*
Found on the Hill of Howth by Mr Underwood, 1799: *Templeton MS.* North-east side of Howth, growing out of a rocky
mountain: *Ir. Flor.* Rocks high up on Dung Hill, Howth, perhaps the same locality as the preceding: *Flor. Howth.* Rock near the
summit of Ireland's Eye: *Praeger 1895.* Steep railway banks north of Killester, looking wild, and at intervals along the banks to

Malahide, 1894-1902; hedgerow near Feltrim, 1902; 6. Sparingly in a gravel pit near the Embankment, Saggard, 1895; sparingly in Crooksling glen, 1903; and 7. Several plants on the railway banks near Clondalkin station, 1902: *N.C.* 8. On the east side of the Scalp, 1871: *Hart MS.* Hedgerow between Carrickmines and Golden Ball, 1899: *N.C.*

Praeger (1946b): Frequent in old hedges, SE of Shankill Station and among native and planted trees at E base of Killiney Hill. *Suppl:* 1. Ditch near Walshestown (1955). 4. Quarry N.E. of Finglas Bridge (1940). 6. A seedling growing in the fork of a large willow tree by Grand Canal a little west of eleventh lock (1941) - still there (1956). Clonburris, Clondalkin (Miss Eileen Carey, 1956). 7. Friarstown Glen (A.W. Stelfox, 1923). By Middleton Brook above Castlekelly Bridge (1948). 8. Along the disused railway line and in hedges near Shankill (1953).

4	5

S. aria (L.) Crantz appears to be native only in Galway and the Burren, while **S. hibernica** has a more widespread but scattered distribution. The latter species was first recognised by Warburg in 1957. So while it is likely that most of the earlier records included in *Colgan* (as **Pyrus aria** Ehrh.) and *Suppl* (as **S. hibernica**) are referable to **S. hibernica**, it is not possible to confirm them. In this Survey the aggregate has been recorded in districts 4 and 5.

S. hibernica E. Warb.
Irish Whitebeam   Native

6	7	8

Rare in hedgerows and on rocky, usually calcareous ground. *Suppl* records have been included under **S. aria** agg.
6. Edge of the cliff above pools by Grand Canal at Gollierstown, MN/88 & DD, JP/89.
7. Roof of a ruin at Mount Venus; first seen by DK between 1960 and 1970; still there, DK/85.
8. Well established on Killiney Hill, DAW, PC/78. Western edge of the quarries on the north side of Killiney Hill, DAW/79. Several trees in Dalkey Quarry, SR, HOR/85. Hedges by fields to the north of Golden Ball, north of Kiltiernan, DAW, PC/78. Hedge to the west of the main road between Kiltiernan and The Scalp, DAW, PC/78. Several small trees in a roadside hedge, just east of Ballybetagh Bog, SR/84. Bank of the disused railway line, north-west of Sandyford Industrial Estate, SR/88. Old railway bank, between the mouths of the Shanganagh River and Deansgrange Stream, SR/89.

Crataegus

C. monogyna Jacq. (*C. oxyacantha*)
Hawthorn   Native

1	2	3	4	5	6	7	8

Widespread and common in hedgerows.
FID.

FABACEAE (*Leguminosae*)

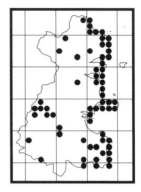

Anthyllis

A. vulneraria L.
Kidney Vetch   Native

I	2	3	4	5	6	7	8

Very common in maritime grassland and sand-dunes; rare inland,
and there confined to sandy and gravelly exposures. Plants
corresponding to var. **vulneraria** have been recorded from Lucan
Quarries (4) and to var. **langei** Jalas from Astagob and Clonsilla (4), MN/88.
FID.

- -

Lotus

L. corniculatus L.
Common Bird's-foot-trefoil   Native

I	2	3	4	5	6	7	8

Very common in pastures, dry banks, waste places and sand-hills. Unusually robust plants
approaching var. **sativus** Chrtkova occasionally occur as aliens on roadside banks.
FID.

- -

L. pedunculatus Cav. *(L. uliginosus)*
Greater Bird's-foot-trefoil   Native

Colgan: 1 and 2. Frequent and in some places abundant, as at Bog of the Ring; Garristown; several stations in the Naul Hills; near Lusk; Balrothery; Man of War, &c., 1893-1902; 3. At Turvey, 1893: *N.C.* 5. In Howth demesne: *Flor. Howth.* Sparingly on the south side of Howth Head, 1900; 6. On moist banks and in glens, west slope of Mount Seskin, 1895: *N.C.*

I	2	(3)	5	(6)	7	8

Frequent on damp roadside verges and marshes in 1 and 2; absent from the centre and
occasional in the southern parts of 7 and 8.
5. At Kilrock, Howth, PG/88.
8. By a stream below Ballyedmonduff, PC/73, **NDR.** West of Stepaside, HOR/83. Near the
   cromlech west of Kiltiernan, SR, HOR/86. In the Glencullen Valley and by the Glencullen
   River, SR, HOR/83, 84. North facing slope of Three Rock Mountain, HOR/83. Field near
   Rathmichael House, west of Shankill, SR/87.

- -

Ornithopus

O. perpusillus L.
Bird's-foot   Native

Colgan: 5. On bare sandy pasture fields on the south side of Howth a little above the cave where the *Asplenium marinum* grows; *Mack. Rar.* Sutton side of Howth, on a hanging bank beyond the Martello Tower: *Ir. Flor.* and in 1888: *Herb. Scully.* Sutton side of Hill of Howth in great quantity: *Flor. Hib.* Dry banks at Carrickbrack and on the seaward side of the road below it; between the Lighthouse and Glenaveena: *Flor. Howth.* In fair quantity on a rocky knoll north of the Red Rock, south side of Howth, 1902: *N.C.* Apparently much rarer now than it was in Mackay's time.

5

Extremely rare on shallow soil over rock by the coast. An endangered species in Ireland, legally protected under the Wildlife Act of 1976.

5. Still in short turf on rocky knolls near the Martello Tower at Redrock, Howth, ENL/84, HJH, DN/88 & CB/91. Howth, A.J. Craig/67.

Vicia

V. cracca L.
Tufted Vetch   Native

1	2	3	4	5	6	7	8

Common in hedgerows, roadsides, pastures and waste places.
FID.

V. sylvatica L.
Wood Vetch   Native

Colgan: 7. In a small wood on the banks of the Dodder near the Gap of Ballinascorney: *Mack. Cat.* Hazel copse by the Dodder above Bohernabreena bridge, 1894: *N.C.* 8. In hilly thickets between Dalkey and the Malpas obelisk: *Wade Dubl.* Thickets in Victoria Park on the east slope of Killiney Hill, and sparingly below the Park on banks between the railway and the sea, 1894-1904; in Killiney Castle grounds, 1902: *N.C.* This elegant species is remarkably luxuriant on Killiney Hill, where the trailing stems reach to 7 feet in length.

Suppl: 7. Slade of Ballymaice (1933) and by a small tributary of the Dodder opposite upper end of Glenasmole Lodge grounds (1943).

4	(7)	(8)

Extremely rare; on scrub margins and in gravel pits.

4. Abundant amongst scrub and on waste heaps in the disused part of Lucan Quarry, MN, PR/85, **NDR**.

V. hirsuta (L.) Gray
Hairy Tare   Native

Colgan: 1. Sparingly at Garristown and Hollywood, 1893; at Balrickard, 1895; 2. Sparingly near Balbriggan and Skerries, and abundant on Shennick's Island, 1893; by the railway between Rush and Skerries, 1894; amongst shingle on the shore at Skerries, 1902: *N.C.* 3. Lambay island: *Flor. Lambay.* Sandy fields at Portrane, 1895: *Scully.* 5. On the lands of Sutton and Howth: *Ir. Flor.* Plentiful on the south-east side of Howth; *Guide.* Bushy places above the Broad Strand, Howth, 1882; and 8. Cornfield near Loughlinstown, 1903: *N.C.*

Suppl: 3. Donabate Railway station (1945). 7. Cornfield at Oldbawn (1948).

(1)	2	3	4	5	6	(7)	8

Occasional near the coast, often on waste ground; very rare inland.

4. Quarry near Cloghran House, MN/82, **NDR**. Disturbed ground by the roadside c. 1 km south-west of St Margaret's, MN, DN/90.
6. Old garden at Wills Brook House, HOR/85, **NDR**.

V. tetrasperma (L.) Schreber
Smoth Tare   Probably introduced

(2) (4)

Probably extinct. Not seen recently. Last recorded in 1894 by the railway at Skerries (2) and in 1895 from Knockmaroon Hill (4) by Colgan (*Colgan & Scully*).

- -

V. sepium L.
Bush Vetch   Native

| 1 | 2 | 3 | 4 | 5 | 6 | 7 | 8 |

Abundant in roadsides, pastures, meadows and waste places. White-flowered variants have occasionally been found near Nag's Head (1), and at Clonsilla Railway Station and Dunsink Observatory (4), MN/85 & MN, JS/84.
FID.

- -

V. sativa L. *(V. angustifolia)*
Common Vetch   Native; alien

| 1 | 2 | 3 | 4 | 5 | 6 | 7 | 8 |

Common in hedgerows, roadside banks, sand-dunes. A white-flowered form has been recorded at the south end of Leopardstown Racecourse (8), SR, DK/86. Subsp. **nigra** (L.) Ehrh. is native and common; the alien subsp. **segetalis** (Thuill.) Gaudin has been noted at Ballyogan tiphead SR/93, and at Ringsend Dump, SR/94 (8).
FID.

- -

V. lathyroides L.
Spring Vetch   Native

Colgan: 3. Under Tinian Hill above the sea on the east side of Lambay: *Flor. Lambay.* 5. Sandy fields near Kilbarrick church: *Mack. Cat.* Sandhills at Baldoyle *(More) Cyb.* Sandy pasture near Portmarnock Point, 1885: *Vowell* and in 1901: *N.C.,* probably the same station as the preceding. On the Cosh, Howth, at the end nearest Baldoyle station and about the middle part: *Flor. Howth.* The records in *Ir. Flor.* for 4. "Gravel pits under Marine School, Phoenix Park," and for 5. "North Wall", and "Banks at the seashore from Clontarf to Howth," should probably be referred to immature states of *V. angustifolia.*
Suppl: 3. Corballis, Donabate (1952). 5. Still at Portmarnock (1957).

| 3 | 5 |

Rare, in mature sand-dunes.
3. Donabate, DS/63, C. Breen/91.
5. On low **Thymus** dominated sand-hills at Portmarnock, DD/83-89. East of The Farm and occasional in low sand-hills from the roundabout to the Alder Marsh, North Bull Island, DK/81, DD/83, MWJ/84 & ENL/85. South of the clubhouse on The Cosh, Sutton, DD/67.

Lathyrus

L. linifolius (Reichard) Baessler *(Lathyrus macrorrhizus, L. montanus)*
Bitter-vetch   Native

| 6 | 7 | 8 |

Occasional on river banks and shaded places in the Glenasmole Valley (7) and the Glencullen Valley (8).
6. Valley between Brittas and Saggart Hill, south of Glenaraneen, DD/90. A few plants on the slope of a wet gully on Saggart Hill, CB, PH/92.
7. In shaded areas between the two reservoirs in Glenasmole, DD/91.
8. At the top of the Ticknock road, SR, HOR/83. South of Ballybetagh Bog, SR, JR/87. Near the cromlech west of Kiltiernan, SR, HOR/86. Ballyedmonduff, SR, HOR/86. North of Glencullen Bridge, near Ballybrack and east of Boranaraltry Bridge in the Glencullen Valley, HOR/83, 85 & SR, HOR/84.

L. pratensis L.
Meadow Vetchling   Native

| 1 | 2 | 3 | 4 | 5 | 6 | 7 | 8 |

Widespread and common on roadside banks, sand-dunes and waste ground.
FID.

L. latifolius L.
Broad-leaved Everlasting-pea   Alien

| 5 | 8 |

Very rare, on sand-dunes and banks.
5. In mature sand-dunes at the south end of North Bull Island, DD/69, **NCR**. Naturalized at the east end of the Causeway on North Bull Island, DN/89.
8. Near Killiney Railway Station, on bank below railway, SR/92.

Ononis

O. repens L.
Common Restharrow   Native

Suppl: 1. Roadside between Primatestown and Garristown (1953).

| (1) | 2 | 3 | 4 | 5 | 6 | 7 | 8 |

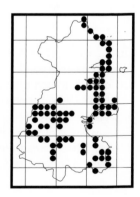

Common in sandy and gravelly ground by the coast; occasional in sandy ground inland. Material referable to var. **horrida** Lange, a form of **O. repens** with spines, persisted at Raheny Quarries (5) until 1966 (DD). It has been found in Dublin for several centuries and has also been found in Lucan Quarry (4) (MN, PR/85) and at Gollierstown (6) (JP, DD/89).

Melilotus

M. altissimus Thuill. *(M. officinalis* pro parte)
Tall Melilot   Probably introduced

2	3	4	5	7	8

Occasional in waste places. Mainly near the coast.
FID.

M. albus Medikus
White Melilot   Alien

5	7	8

Rare in sand-dunes and waste ground. Although clearly casual in most of its sites, it has persisted in closed sand-dune communities at North Bull Island for many years.
5. South end of North Bull Island, DD/69-91. Dublin Port, SR/91.
7. Scattered along the West Link motorway between Tallaght and the Naas Road junction, DD/92.
8. Southern edge of Ringsend Dump, DNFC/83. Waste ground near Ringsend Park, SR, HOR/85. Near the East Link Toll Bridge roundabout just east of Irishtown, SR/85.

M. officinalis (L.) Pallas
Ribbed Melilot   Probably introduced

(2)	3	4	5	(6)	8

Occasional in 3, 4 & 8; sometimes locally abundant in Dublin Port (5) and on Ringsend Dump (8). Occasional elsewhere on waste ground. *Colgan* and *Suppl* did not distinguish between **M. officinalis** and **M. altissimus** and therefore early records for this species are not comparable to ours.
5. Alexandra Basin, Dublin Port, SR/88.

M. indicus (L.) All. *(M. parviflora)*
Small Melilot   Alien

Brunker MS: 4. Near King James's Castle, Finglas, '22. Custom House Docks, '23. 5. Watermill Bridge, Raheny. 7. About 50 plants on footpath of new road to Inchicore Brickworks (*Ir. Nat.* 27, p.87). Tongue, '20. Victoria Quay, '21.

4	5	7	8

Rare on waste ground.
4. Finglas, F.H. Perring/62. Disturbed towpath by the Royal Canal west of Collins Bridge, MN/89. Dunsink tiphead, SR/93.
5. Dublin Port, SR/91.
7. On waste ground at Oldbawn Bridge, DD, JP/83. One plant, St Stephen's Green, MWJ/94.
8. Near Pottery Road, north-east of Cabinteely, SR/84. Beside Ringsend Park, SR, HOR/85. Ringsend Dump, SR/85, 87. South-west of the West Pier, Dun Laoghaire, SR/85.

Medicago

M. lupulina L.
Black Medick   Native

| 1 | 2 | 3 | 4 | 5 | 6 | 7 | 8 |

Widespread and very common on banks, waste ground and sandy places.
FID.

M. sativa L.
Lucerne   Alien

Colgan: 2. Well established on the sandhills near Rush *(Moore) Cyb.* Well established on Shennick's island, Skerries; sparingly on banks by the sea north of Rush, and in a pasture near Balbriggan, 1892; near the windmill, Skerries and to the south of Rush, 1902; 3. Pasture south-west of Swords, 1893; sandy fields and banks at Portrane, 1893-1903; near Donabate, 1902: *N.C.* 5. Sandy fields at Portmarnock, perfectly naturalised: *Mack. Cat.* and in 1866: *Hart MS.* Established in many places in north Sutton and about the railway at the Quarry: *Flor. Howth.* Field borders at Kilbarrick and at Sutton, 1893-1902; railway banks near Sutton, 1901: *N.C.*
Suppl: 2. S. side of Loughshinny Harbour (J.P. Brunker, 1918), still there in 1956. 4. Liffey Junction (1946). 5. North Bull (H.J. Hudson, 1932). Waste ground at Alexandra Road (1940-1954). Sutton Cross (1948). 7. Waste ground at Chapelizod (1952). 8. Above Vico bathing-place (J.P.B., 1919).

| 2 | 3 | 4 | 5 | (7) | 8 |

----

subsp. **sativa** (*M. sativa*)

| 2 | 3 | 4 | 5 | 8 |

Very rare on sand-hills and waste ground. Normally as a relic of cultivation.
2. Sand-hills to the west of Rush Golf-course, DD/89.
3. Scattered in fallow fields near Burrow, Portrane, PR/83.
4. Dry bank beside the Royal Canal at Cabra, DK/91.
5. Gravelly ground at Corr Castle, Howth, CB/91. Abandoned vegetable garden at All Hallow's College, Drumcondra, DD/92.
8. Ringsend Dump, near the seafront path, PWJ/83.

----

subsp. **varia** (Martyn.) Arcang. (*M.* x *varia, M. falcata* L. x *M. sativa, M. sylvestris*)

Colgan: 5. In considerable quantity on dry sandy banks at the southern end of Portmarnock sandhills, 1894-96 *(Praeger)*, and at Malahide, three and half miles to the northward, 1896 *(Prof. G.F. Fitzgerald): Ir. Nat.*, 1896, p.249. Well established in both the Malahide and Portmarnock stations, 1902, in the latter station spreading for about 80 yards: *N.C.*
Suppl: 2. Rush (M.J. Gorman, 1935). In some quantity on banks of a lane to the dunes, half-way from Rush to Rogerstown, also near the windmill at Rush (1943). 5. Still at both Portmarnock and Malahide Stations (1923-1956).

| 2 | 5 | 8 |

Very rare, on sand-dunes and on waste ground.
2. Still between Rogerstown and Rush on banks and roadsides, DD/89.
5. Near the clubhouse at Portmarnock Golf-course, DN, RF/88. Sandy roadside verge at Malahide, MN/83. South end of North Bull Island, MN/87.
8. Bank beside the seafront path on Ringsend Dump, SR/84. Ballyogan tiphead, east of Stepaside, SR, JR/94.

M. arabica (L.) Hudson (*M. maculata*)
Spotted Medick   Alien
Brunker MS: 2. "Clover Fields 'Brook End, Rush, '53. 4. "Custom House Docks, '23".

| (2) | (4) | 8 |

Extremely rare.
8. Grassland at Blackrock Park, V. Wolfe, MS/72.

Trifolium

T. ornithopodioides L. *(Trigonella ornithopodioides)*
Bird's-foot Clover   Native
Colgan: 5. Near the North Wall: *Wade Dubl.* Near the Light-house at Howth, 1843 *(Moore) Cyb. & Herb. Glasnevin.*
Forming the sod of an old grass-grown roadway between the Light-house road and the cliff path, Howth: *Hart 1897.*
Very abundant along the grassy margin of the Light-house road and along the old road leading thence, spreading for
fully 400 yards, 1902: *N.C.* 8. Found on the east side of Killiney Hill and near Bullock, 1806: *Mack. Rar.* On the south-east
side of Killiney Hill and near Bullock, abundant: *Flor. Hib.* not seen recently.
Suppl: 5. Still along the roadway to Baily lighthouse (1957). Between Sutton Martello Tower and Redrock (H.J. Hudson,
1932). Ireland's Eye (1952). 8. Over an area of a few square yards about 100 yards E.S.E. of the old church on Dalkey
Island, where one plant measured thirteen inches in diameter with fifty-three shoots (J.P. Brunker, 1919).

| 5 | 8 |

Very rare, on shallow soils over rock by the sea. Not refound on Ireland's Eye nor near the
Baily Lighthouse, Howth (5). However, its rediscovery at Killiney (8) where it had not been
seen since 1806 suggests that it may persist in small quantity in these areas.
5. Many plants on a rocky outcrop at Redrock, Howth, CB/91.
8. Still in the Killiney Hill area, in short turf over a granite outcrop on the south-east slope
   of Dalkey Hill, SR/91. Below the obelisk, near the wishing stone, on east side of Killiney
   Hill, SR, JR/93. Several plants on Dalkey Island, c. 40 m east-south-east of the church, SR,
   Owen Reynolds/93.

T. repens L.
White Clover   Native

| 1 | 2 | 3 | 4 | 5 | 6 | 7 | 8 |

Widespread and very common in grasslands and waste places. Introduced varieties in
pastures and planted on roadsides.
FID.

T. occidentale D.E. Coombe
Western Clover   Native

| 2 | 5 | 8 |

Very rare, on shallow calcareous soils overlying rock near the coast; first reported in Ireland in
1979 (Preston 1980). Skerries (2) is its most northerly known locality in Ireland (Akeroyd 1983).
2. Rocky promontory near Red Island, Skerries village, C.D. Preston, JRA/80, DD/82 &
   N.McGough/83.

5. Maritime grassland to the south and east of the Martello Tower at Redrock, JRA, C.D. Preston/79 & DNFC/82. The Cosh at Sutton, DD/83. Howth Head, JRA/79. On North Bull Island near the end of the Causeway, PG/93.
8. Rocky maritime turf near the landing area on Dalkey Island, JRA/78, 80, DNFC/83 & DD, SR/91.

T. hybridum L.
Alsike Clover   Alien

| 1 | 2 | 3 | 4 | 5 | 6 | 7 | 8 |

Occasional on waste ground and as a relic of cultivation.
FID.

T. fragiferum L.
Strawberry Clover   Native

Colgan: 2. Abundant along the south bank of the Delvin river, 1900: *N.C.* 3. Very plentiful near Swords, 1848 *(Moore) Herb. Glasnevin.* Abundant near Mullan, south of Donabate, 1903: *Scully & N.C.* 4. "In ye Deer Park, August, 1743": *Annot. in Threlkeld.* By the north bank of the Tolka above Mulhuddart bridge, 1893: *Colgan 1893.* By the Tolka at Glasnevin, 1902: *D. McArdle.* 5. Moist ground near Clontarf, 1799: *Templeton MS.* Abundant on a wet common at the waterfall between Drumcondra and Glasnevin Bridge: *Ir. Flor.* Salt marsh at Portmarnock: *Flor. Hib.* Between Baldoyle and Portmarnock: *Flor. Howth* and in 1901! Abundant along the shore north of Watermill Bridge, Raheny, 1892-1903; sparingly on North Bull, and abundant at Raheny Quarry, 1902: *N.C.* 6. By the Grand Canal, Hazelhatch, 1893: *Colgan 1893.* 7. By the Dodder above Donnybrook, 1902: *N.C.* 8. Side of Dublin Bay near Sandymount, 1799: *Templeton MS.* River bank, Shanganagh, 1858: *Herb. R. Barrington.* Shore at Ballybrack *(Moore) Rec. Add.* Very abundant by the Shanganagh river at Loughlinstown Commons, and again in moist ground near the mouth of the river at Ballybrack, 1901: *N.C.* The stations at Hazelhatch and Mulhuddart, distant, respectively, 12 and 8 miles from the nearest sea coast are amongst the most distinctly inland in which this species has been observed in Ireland. *Suppl:* 2. Coast, one mile N. of Loughshinny (1923 and 1941). 3. Newport House (1920-1957). 4. Blanchardstown (1942). 5. Yellow Walls, Malahide (1957).

| 2 | 3 | (4) | (5) | (6) | (7) | (8) |

Extremely rare, on grassland near the sea. Many of its former inland riverside sites have been lost through drainage and subsequent agricultural improvement
2. Still on rocks on the shore near the copper mine, 1.5 km north of Loughshinny, DD/83, 90.
3. Still near Mullan and Newport House. In low lying grassland near the sea at Keeling's Farm, east of Kilcrea House, PR/89.

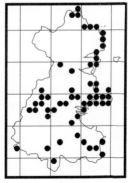

T. campestre Schreber *(T. procumbens)*
Hop Trefoil   Native

| (1) | 2 | 3 | 4 | 5 | 6 | 7 | 8 |

Occasional in sand-dunes and calcareous grassland.
FID.

T. dubium Sibth.
Lesser Trefoil   Native

| 1 | 2 | 3 | 4 | 5 | 6 | 7 | 8 |

Widespread and very common on paths, in waste ground, sand-dunes and pastures.
FID.

T. micranthum Viv. *(T. filiforme)*
Slender Trefoil   Native; probably introduced

Colgan: 1. Moist peaty ground at the northern end of the Bog of the Ring, 1903: *Colgan 1904.* 5. At Howth *(Moore) Cyb.*
Auburn and St Anne's, in closely mown grass plots: *Flor. Howth.* 8. Killiney Hill, 1859 *(Moore) Herb. Glasnevin.*
Suppl: 5. Howth *(I.N.* XXIX, 1920). Feltrim Hill (1938).

| (1) | 2 | 4 | 5 | 8 |

Very rare as a native in short grassland by the sea and as an introduction in lawns.
2. Rocks in permanent grassland above the spray zone along the shore between Skerries
   and Loughshinny, DD/83.
4. Lawn in the western part of National Botanic Gardens, Glasnevin, and by the herbaceous
   walk to the east, MS/80 & DN/89.
5. Patches in a lawn between Earlscliff House and Baron's Brae House at Drumleck Point,
   Howth, PG/91.
8. Near the obelisk on Killiney Hill, DD/67. Suburban lawn in Churchtown, MWJ/91. Suburban
   lawn, Orwell Gardens, Rathgar, MWJ/92.

T. pratense L.
Red Clover   Native

| 1 | 2 | 3 | 4 | 5 | 6 | 7 | 8 |

Widespread and abundant in meadows, pastures and on roadsides and waste ground.
FID.

T. medium L.
Zigzag Clover   Native

Colgan: 7. Roadside at Woodtown near Mount Pelier *(Scully) Cyb. II.* Covering some acres of pasture on the high drift banks
near St Anne's, Glenasmole, 1894-1900; in Glassamucky glen, Piperstown, and field banks above it, 1895; in Lugmore, 1896:
N.C. 8. Above the Little Dargle: *Ir. Flor.* and in 1903! In Kelly's glen, Kilmashogue, 1893: *Praeger 1894a.* By the railway between
Killiney and Bray: *Flor. Howth.* Sparingly near Ballycorus, 1894; abundant in Kelly's glen, 1903: *N.C.*
Suppl: 6. A large patch on roadside half a mile E. of the Embankment (R.W. Scully, 1918). 7. Slade of Ballymaice (1956).

| 2 | (6) | 7 | (8) |

Extremely rare in damp grasslands and on roadsides.
2. Ballast heaps at Skerries Railway Station, DD/90-92, **NDR.**
7. Still occasional in damp pastures above the reservoir in St Anne's Fields, Glenasmole,
   MS/68 & DD/83, 91. Roadsides near Fort Bridge, DD/90.

T. striatum L.
Knotted Clover   Native

Colgan: 3. Plentiful in several stations in Lambay island: *Flor. Lambay,* 1882 and in 1896: *Ir. Nat.,* 1896, p. 186. Rocky knolls,
Balcarrig, Portrane, 1894 *(N.C.) Cyb. II.* 5. Kilbarrick and Howth *(Moore) Cyb.* Abundant on Feltrim Hill *(More) Rec. Add.* and in

1900! Very sparingly at Carrigeen, Ireland's Eye: *Flor. Howth.* Plentiful above the Martello Tower, Sutton *(Miss R. Mahaffy)* *Praeger 1895.* 8. Killiney *(Moore) Cyb.* Steep banks above Strawberry Hill, Vico, 1901; on Knockachree, 1902; abundant on grassy banks near Dalkey church, 1898-1902: N.C. North of Bray railway bridge, 1872: *Herb. R.M. Barrington.*
Suppl: 5. Still on Ireland's Eye (1952) but no longer at Feltrim Hill where it was recorded until 1945.
Brunker MS: 8. Seen in 1960 at Colgan's Strawberry Hill, Vico station.

3	5	8

Very rare, in short grassland by the sea. Not found on Ireland's Eye (5) despite careful search.
3. Still in the north-west corner of Lambay Island, DD/82-92.
5. Sandy ground, between the clubhouse of the Royal Dublin Golf-course and North Bull Wall, ENL/83, 88. A few plants on rocky outcrops at Redrock, Howth, CB/92.
8. Near the Wishing Stone on the east side of Killiney Hill, DNFC/83.

- -

T. scabrum L.
Rough Clover   Native

Colgan: 2. Very abundant on the coast below Skerries, 1882 *(Hart) Journ. of Bot.,* 1883 frequent here in 1902! 5. Gravelly banks on the northern shores of Dublin Bay, 1799: *Templeton MS.* Sandy fields on the Sutton side of Howth: *Wade Rar.* Near Kilbarrick church: *Mack. Cat.* Near the sea from below Kilbarrick to Greenfields: *Flor. Howth.* On the North Bull *(D. Orr) Rec. Add.,* 1872 very abundant here at the southern end in 1903! Near Portmarnock, 1899: *Miss A.G. Kinahan.* Near Baldoyle, 1900: *N.C.* 8. About Sandymount *(Mr Molden) Templeton MS.* Killiney *(Moore) Rec. Add.* Steep banks above Vico, 1902: *N.C.* In the Park along the river at Bray *(More) Cyb. II.* This species reaches in Dublin its northern limit for Ireland.
DNFC Annual Report for 1907: 3. "Portraine....this being a new record for the district".
Suppl: 5. Still on North Bull (1957). Walltop E. of Portmarnock Bridge (1930). The erection of buildings has wiped out the stations at Sutton. 8. In the old battery on Dalkey Island (J.P. Brunker, 1919) also at Martello Tower and under E. wall of battery *(I. Nat., XVII,* 1908) - these steps were concreted in 1955, and the plant was obliterated.

2	(3)	5	8

Very rare, on shallow soils over rock by the coast.
2. Still at Skerries on shallow soil on a rock outcrop at Red Island, JRA/80 & DD/83.
5. Still at the southern end of North Bull Island, south of the clubhouse of the Royal Dublin Golf-course, ENL/85. One clump, in heavily rabbit-grazed turf, on a rocky outcrop at Redrock, Howth, CB/91.
8. Still on Dalkey Island, in maritime grassland near the landing area, at the Battery at the south end of the island, around the Martello Tower and on its top floor, JRA/80, DNFC/83 & DD, SR/91.

- -

T. arvense L.
Hare's-foot Clover   Native

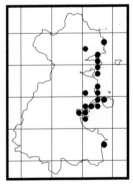

Colgan: 2. "The barren drifting sands all about Rush ... abound with the silky foliage of this trefoil": *Wade Rar.,* 1804 still abundant here in sandhills and fallows, 1903! 3. Lambay island: *Ir. Flor.* and *Flor. Lambay.* 5. Dry sandy pastures near Baldoyle and at Portmarnock sands, abundant: *Mack. Cat.* Sandbanks from Clontarf to Sutton: *Ir. Flor.* Frequent in sandy ground at Portmarnock, at Malahide, at Kilbarrick and at Sutton, 1902: *N.C.* Baily Lighthouse: *Flor. Howth.* Near Kilrock, Howth, 1894: *N.C.* 8. "I saw it once in the sandy Ground near Mirian": *Threlkeld.* Island of Dalkey: *Ir. Flor.* Lamb island, north end of Dalkey island, 1901; railway below Killiney Hill, 1902: *N.C.*
Suppl: 2. S. of Loughshinny Head (1918-1956). 3. Burrow, Portrane about 200 yards N. of village (J.P. Brunker, 1915, now abundant, 1956). 5. Common on North Bull (1920), abundant in 1955.

| 2 | 3 | 5 | 8 |

Locally common in sand-dunes. Never far from the coast but rarer in 8.

8. Still on banks near the footbridge below Killiney Hill, DD/74. On sandy ground near the South Wall and Pigeon House, HOR, SR/83. North slope of Ticknock, on dumped soil, SR/88.

Cytisus

C. scoparius (L.) Link *(Sarothamnus scoparius)*
Broom   Native

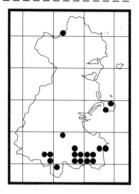

| I | 5 | 6 | 7 | 8 |

---

subsp. **scoparius**

| I | 5 | 6 | 7 | 8 |

Occasional in upland hedgerows and heathlands, mainly on Howth and the mountains, and near Naul.

---

subsp. **maritimus** (Rouy) Heyw.

Brunker MS: 5. At Kilrock and Drumleck, Howth,'54. Frequent on the east side of Howth near Casana's Rock,'46.

| 5 |

Extremely rare.

A prostrate form found in exposed coastal localities around Ireland. It retains its prostrate character in cultivation. Formerly recorded also on Killiney Hill (8) by A.G. More but not seen there recently.

5. Still on Howth in maritime heathland near Redrock, Howth, DD/66. Grassland near the Nose of Howth, DN/90. Not refound on Ireland's Eye (Hart 1887) where it was recorded first by More in 1872.

Ulex

U. europaeus L.
Gorse, Furze, Whin   Native

| I | 2 | 3 | 4 | 5 | 6 | 7 | 8 |

Virtually ubiquitous on higher ground. Rare as a native in the lowlands but extensively planted. Abundant in rough pasture, scrub and hedgerows. Occasional on waste ground. *FID.*

U. gallii Planchon
Western Gorse, Autumn Gorse   Native

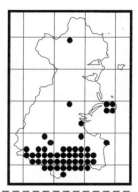

| 1 | | 4 | | 5 | | 6 | | 7 | | 8 |

Common on dry acid mineral soils (heathland) in the mountains
and at higher altitudes than the previous species; rare elsewhere,
especially in the north of the county.
1. Nag's Head, GS/85, **NDR**.
4. Ballygall Road East, Glasnevin, DD/67; now built over, **NDR**.

ELAEAGNACEAE

Hippophae

H. rhamnoides L.
Sea-buckthorn   Alien

Colgan: 2. Planted at Rush; *Rec. Add.,* 1872. Apparently spreading on the Rush sandhills, 1893 *(N.C.) Cyb. II.* A large thicket on
sandy bluffs above the beach at Rogerstown coast-guard station, with small scattered plants, apparently self-sown, in the
vicinity, some hundreds of seedling plants spreading for 45 paces along a sandy fallow near Rogerstown harbour, the seedling
obviously derived from a row of full-grown bushes capping an adjacent sand dike, also a large clump on a knoll and in
adjoining sandy hollows about 200 yards inland from the coast-guard station, with numerous seedlings appearing in the
neighbourhood of the mature plants, 1902: *Colgan 1904.* The Sea Buckthorn has been planted in many places through the
network of small carrot and parsnip plots which covered a large area of the landward side of the Rush sandhills. Here its far-
creeping roots serve as a binder of the sandy shelter dikes as it does of the shifting sand bluffs, by the coast-guard station,
and from these centres of distribution the plant will doubtless in time spread widely over the uncultivated part of the dunes.
As the result of storms, the roots of several mature plants were found laid bare along the sea face of the dunes here in
1902. Some of these roots, belonging to plants only 3 feet high, were found to measure fully sixteen feet in length. Though
usually a mere bush, the Buckthorn occasionally grows at Rush to the size of a small tree with a girth of 12 inches.
Suppl: 2. Still surviving in the sandhills at Rush (1957).

| 2 | | 3 | | 5 | | 8 |

Occasional in sandy places by the sea but locally dominant as between Rogerstown and Rush.
Also at a number of sites in 5 (originally planted but in many now naturalized and spreading;
near the Causeway, North Bull Island; at Sutton; south of Portmarnock; River Tolka Basin, and
Broad Strand, Howth); rare elsewhere. This species is reported to be dioecious. If the separation
of the sexes is absolute (*i.e.* plants are not incompletely dioecious) then the sex ratio of plants
at some sites (Rogerstown-Rush (2)) in Co. Dublin is strongly female biased. Populations of
established plants at Rogerstown-Rush appear to spread largely by extensive rhizome growth
rather than by seedling establishment.
3. Hedges and by roadsides in the Island Golf-course, PR/83, 85. Along the Burrow,
   Portrane, PR/83, 85.
8. Coast south of Killiney, apparently spreading from a nearby garden where it was planted
   in 1966. Now well established at the top of the shore, SR, HOR/83.

HALORAGACEAE

Myriophyllum

M. verticillatum L.
Whorled Water-milfoil   Native

Colgan: 4. Quarry holes about Finglas Bridge: *Ir. Flor.,* 1833 and in 1893! Banks of the Canal from Cross Guns to
Scribblestown: *Ir. Flor.* frequent all along the Royal Canal, 1901! 6. Frequent in the Grand Canal between Clondalkin
Bridge and Hazelhatch, 1902; and 7. Near Ballyfermot, 1903: *N.C.*
Suppl: 7. James's St. Harbour (1941).

4	6	(7)

Very rare in ponds and canals.
4. Pond at the National Botanic Gardens, Glasnevin, MN/86. Royal Canal 1 km east of
   Kennan Bridge and near Collins Bridge, and at the City Basin, MN/88, 89 & DN/90.
6. Grand Canal, 1.5 km north-east of Hazelhatch, DNFC/89.

- -

M. spicatum L.
Spiked Water-milfoil   Native

Colgan: 1. Deep ditches at Curragha: *Flor. Howth.* At the Bog of the Ring and 2. Abundant in Lusk Ponds and near Balrothery,
1902; 3. In the Broad Meadow Water near Lispopple, 1903; pond near Turvey, 1899; near Ballisk, Donabate, 1900; in the
Ward river below Brackenstown, 1903: *N.C.* 4. In Ponds, Phoenix Park: *Wade Dubl.* Ditches by the Royal Canal above Lucan
bridge, 1895, and near Blanchardstown, 1902: *N.C.* 5. At Clontarf: *Hart MS.* Pool by the sea at the Quarry, Howth: *Praeger
1895.* Pond near Feltrim Hill, 1900; 7. By the Dodder near Rathfarnham, 1893; and by the canal near Clondalkin, 1903: *N.C.*
Suppl: Still at 1. Bog of the Ring (1948), and 2. Balrothery (1950). 3. Killeek Reservoir (1953). 5. St Doolagh's Quarries
(1951). 7. Pond at Mount Argus (1946), now filled in.

(1)	2	3	4	5	6	7	8

Occasional; locally common in ponds, reservoirs and canals.
2. Balrothery Lough, DD/82.
3. Knocksedan Reservoir, PR, MN/85.
4. Royal Canal at Cross Guns Bridge and particularly plentiful north of Lucan, MN/88, 89.
   River Liffey west of Islandbridge, MN/88.
5. Park below the Ben of Howth, ENL/84. Ponds along the golf-course on Portmarnock
   Peninsula, DN, RF/88. Kilrock, Howth, PG/87, 89. Pond in the Royal Dublin Golf-course on
   North Bull Island, DN/88. Pond in public park, Thormanby Road, Howth, CB/92.
6. North and south ends of Brittas Ponds, DNFC/83, **NDR**. River Liffey at Lucan Demesne,
   HOR, MN, PR/85. Grand Canal 1.5 km north-east of Hazelhatch, MN/89.
7. Pond east of Aghfarrel, Brittas, JP, DAS/84. In a stream at the base of the valley south-
   south-west of Ballinascorney House, at c. 300 m, MWJ/87. Cammock River, below the
   bridge and c. 300 m north-east of Clondalkin Round Tower, MWJ/87.
8. Lake at the Roadstone Works at Ballycorus, SR, HOR/85, **NDR**.

LYTHRACEAE

Lythrum

L. salicaria L.
Purple-loosestrife   Native

I	2	3	4	5	6	7	8

Occasional in marshy meadows, wet ditches and on river and canal banks; rare in 8.

8. Stream north-west of Carrickmines, SR/87. Marsh below Barnacullia, PC, SR/88. Stream south of Kill of the Grange, SR/84.

L. portula (L.) D. Webb *(Peplis portula)*
Water-purslane   Native

Colgan: I. At the Bog of the Ring, 1893: *N.C.* 5. Howth: *Ir. Flor.* Near the signal station, Howth Head, 1902; on Ireland's Eye, 1899; 6. Sparingly at Brittas ponds, 1893; pools on Saggard Hill, 1902; 7. Abundant in bog pools at Piperstown, 1902; in profusion on the dried up bed of the upper reservoir, Glenasmole, 1901, the water having shrunk to a very low level by long drought; on Knockanavea, 1903; and 8. Pools on granite moorlands at Balalley, 1894: *N.C.*
Suppl: 3. Wet places by S. shore, Lambay (Praeger, 1907).

(1)	(3)	5	6	7	8

Very rare, on the margins of pools and reservoirs.

5. Still on Howth; in and completely covering a peaty pool, East Mountain, Howth, CB/92.
6. South end of Brittas Ponds, DD/83.
7. Mud adjoining shallow pools in the quarry at the top of the Ballinascorney Gap, DD/83. At the northern end of the southern reservoir in Glenasmole, DD/83.
8. East of The Dingle, HOR/84.

ONAGRACEAE

Epilobium

E. hirsutum L.
Great Willowherb   Native

I	2	3	4	5	6	7	8

Widespread and very common in ditches, drains, marshes, canal and river banks. White and salmon-flowered variants occasionally occur.
FID.

E. hirsutum × **E. ciliatum (E.** × **novae-civitatis** Smejkal)
Native

| 4 | 5 |

Rare.
4. Disused railway line near the North Circular Road at Cabra, DD/82.
5. Crescent Park, Fairview, DD/82, (Doogue *et al.* 1985).

- -

E. parviflorum Schreber
Hoary Willowherb   Native

| 1 | 2 | 3 | 4 | 5 | 6 | 7 | 8 |

Common in marshes, ditches, drains and damp waste ground.
FID.

- -

E. parviflorum × **E. ciliatum**
Native

| 8 |

Extremely rare.
8. Damp depression on the south-eastern edge of Leopardstown Racecourse, SR/88.

- -

E. montanum L.
Broad-leaved Willowherb   Native

| 1 | 2 | 3 | 4 | 5 | 6 | 7 | 8 |

Widespread and common in gardens, waste ground and woodland.
FID.

- -

E. montanum × **E. roseum (E.** × **mutabile** Boiss. & Reuter)
Native
Recorded from Co. Dublin in *CC2* on the basis of a record in Praeger (1951) but not seen
during this survey.

- -

E. montanum × **E. ciliatum**
Native

| 1 | 2 | 5 | 6 | 7 |

Rare, found in disturbed ground.
1. Hedgerow west of Palmerstown, GS/87.
2. Roadside near the County Council gravel pit at Wimbletown, DD/87. Dry drain south-
   east side of Milverton Estate, DD/87.
5. Garden at Drumcondra, DD/86, 87.
6. Shore of Brittas Ponds, MN/89.
7. Merrion Square, DD/83, 86. Weed in T.C.D. Botanic Garden, PWJ/83.

E. tetragonum L.
Square-stalked Willowherb   Alien

4	7

Extremely rare, in disturbed ground.
4. Damp pasture at edge of marsh at St Margaret's, MN/86. Disturbed pathway by the Royal
   Canal, west of Collins Bridge, MN/89.
7. A few plants on disturbed ground and in recently prepared flower-beds, T.C.D., DD/89, 90.
- -

E. obscurum Schreber
Short-fruited Willowherb   Native

I	4	5	6	7	8

Occasional in base-poor wetlands. Most common in 8.
FID.
- -

E. obscurum × **E. palustre** (**E.** × **schmidtianum** Rostkov)
Native

Praeger, 1951: No locality details.

I

I. Bog of the Ring, DD, GS/88.
- -

E. roseum Schreber
Pale Willowherb   Possibly introduced

Colgan: 8. Garden at Dundrum, common in 1897, very rare in 1900 (Praeger) Top. Bot.
Brunker MS: 7. Frequent, St James's Gate, '43.

4	6	(7)	(8)

Very rare on disturbed, sometimes damp, ground.
4. Near the sealion pond in the Zoological Gardens in Phoenix Park, MN/85. Flooded
   flower-bed in the National Botanic Gardens, Glasnevin MN/86. Broadstone link of the
   disused railway line, DD/83, **NDR**. Damp ground subject to flooding at the Hole-in-the-
   wall, Phoenix Park, DD/88. Damp ground by a disused branch of the Great Southern
   Railway at Barnhill Bridge, MN/88.
6. Bank of a wet ditch near Peamount Hospital, CB, SR/87, **NDR**.
- -

E. ciliatum Raf. *(E. adenocaulon)*
American Willowherb   Alien

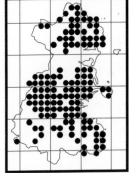

I	2	3	4	5	6	7	8

Common on dry waste ground, pathsides and as a garden weed.
Extremely widespread in the county following its relatively recent
introduction to Ireland and rapid subsequent spread (Doogue
et al. 1985).
FID.

E. palustre L.
Marsh Willowherb   Native

| I | 2 | 3 | 4 | 5 | 6 | 7 | 8 |

Occasional in marshes and on riversides. Most frequent in 8.

E. brunnescens (Cockayne) Raven & Engelhorn *(E. nerterioides)*
New Zealand Willowherb   Alien

Suppl: (as *E. pedunculare*) 5. Wall between railway and Burrow Road Station (1954).

| (4) | (5) | 6 | 7 | 8 |

Frequent in moist soils on paths and tracks in the mountains; rare elsewhere. Not refound at Cross Guns Bridge (4) (*FID*).
7. Wall in Lansdowne Road, Ballsbridge, MWJ/81, 89, **NDR**.
8. Gravel track in Glencullen Valley, HOR/83, **NDR**.
FID.

Chamerion

C. angustifolium (L.) Holub *(Chamaenerion angustifolium, Epilobium angustifolium)*
Rosebay Willowherb   Probably introduced

| I | 2 | 3 | 4 | 5 | 6 | 7 | 8 |

Common on road and tracksides in the uplands and on waste ground. Now common in the city centre on derelict building sites, tumbledown walls etc. Usually as isolated clumps in rural areas. Recorded in *Suppl* as "rare but increasing".
1. Roadside 1 km south of Garristown, GS/86, **NDR**.
2. Lusk Village, DD/85, **NDR**.
4. Castleknock, MN/86, **NDR**.
6. Waste ground near the old demesne in Clondalkin, JP/83, **NDR**.
FID.

Oenothera

O. glazioviana Micheli ex C. Martius *(O. erythrosepala)*
Large-flowered Evening-primrose   Alien

| 3 | 5 | 7 | 8 |

Rare, in sandy and waste ground near the sea. New to all of the following districts as this species was not recognised in *Suppl.*
3. Sand-hills mid-way along the eastern side of the golf-course on Malahide Island, A. Brady/69 (Brady 1974).

252

5. Railway embankment at Killester, DN/88.
7. Waste ground near the River Dodder at Firhouse, DK/83.
8. Ringsend Dump, DD, BSBI/86. Shore, south of Killiney, SR/85. Waste ground at Sandymount, MS/86. Ballyogan tiphead, east of Stepaside, SR, JR/93.

O. biennis L.
Common Evening-primrose   Alien

Suppl: 5. North Bull, about quarter of a mile short of the end (R.W. Scully and J.P. Brunker, 1922). Still on North Bull (1955).

| (5) | 8 |

Very rare, in waste ground.
8. Eastern edge of Ringsend Dump, SR, RF/86.
FID.

Circaea

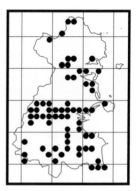

C. lutetiana L.
Enchanter's-nightshade   Native

| 1 | 2 | 3 | 4 | 5 | 6 | 7 | 8 |

Occasional in deciduous woodlands, shaded roadsides and hedgerows. Especially frequent in the River Liffey Valley. Formerly a common and troublesome garden weed. Less frequent in gardens today.
FID.

C. lutetiana × **C. alpina** L. (**C.** × **intermedia** Ehrh.)
Upland Enchanter's-nightshade   Introduced in Co. Dublin

| 4 | 7 |

Rare, as a weed in gardens.
4. National Botanic Gardens, Glasnevin, DS/73.
7. Garden weed at Rathgar, WAW/67.

CORNACEAE

Cornus

C. sanguinea L.
Dogwood   Native

Colgan: 1. Hedges near Wyanstown, stretching for about 300 paces, perhaps planted, but looking wild, 1902; 3. Several plants in a hedge by a lane leading from Donabate to Corballis, 1904; 4. Roadsides hedge between Ballymun and Coultry, in fair quantity, 1894: *N.C.* 5. Left hand side of the road going from Dublin to Cooluck, near Cooluck, 1799: *Templeton MS.* Abundant in hedges below Cooluck, scarcely indigenous: *Flor. Hib.* Copse by the Santry river below Santry demesne, frequent, 1895: *N.C.* Thickets between Howth Castle and the harbour: *Flor. Howth.* 6. Sparingly in the copse between Leixlip bridge and Salmon Leap, 1901; and 7. One bush on a roadside bank between Fir House and Old Bawn, 1892-1894: *N.C. Suppl:* 1. Wood at Westown, Naul (1953). 2. Milverton, Skerries (J.P. Brunker, 1911).

(1)	(2)	(3)	(4)	(5)	(6)	(7)

At least some of the records in *Colgan* for this species probably relate to **C. sericea** e.g. the copse by the Santry River below Santry Demesne (5) where it was recorded by Colgan in 1895. See Kelly (1990).

C. sericea L.
Red-osier Dogwood   Alien

4	5	7

Scattered along the River Liffey Valley in 4 and 7. Not recorded in *Colgan* or *Suppl.*
4. River Tolka north and west of Ashtown, MN/88. Luttrellstown, MN/88. Abbotstown, MN/88. Laneway at Phibblestown House, MN/88. Banks of the River Liffey between Palmerston Hospital and the People's Gardens in the Phoenix Park, MN/88 & DK/90. River Liffey at the Lucan end of St Catherine's, MN/85.
5. Well established in Santry woods, PWJ/82.
7. Banks of the River Liffey millrace, 2 km west of Palmerston, DNFC/85.

CELASTRACEAE

Euonymus

E. europaeus L.
Spindle   Native

Colgan: 1. Near Fanning's Walls, 1893: *N.C.*

Suppl: 4. Still at Luttrellstown (1953) and by Canal above Clonsilla (1958). 6. Glen above Embankment near Jobstown (1956). 7. Lugmore Glen (1956) and Glenasmole (A.W. Stelfox, 1952). *Brunker MS:* 7. One bush opp. Tynan Cottage, '59! Near Greenhills.

(1)	3	4	5	6	7	8

Occasional in hedgerows and woodlands on base-rich soils.
3. Still near Coolatrath at Coolquoy where it was recorded in 1894 (*Colgan*), PR/88.
4. Dubber Cross, DD/86. Still in St Catherine's Wood, MN/85. Furry Glen, Phoenix Park, DNFC/88. Scrub at Lucan Quarry, MN/90. East of the gateway at Luttrellstown, MN/90. Strawberry Beds, River Liffey Valley, MN/91.
5. Kinsealy, ENL/85. Hedge near Coultry Dump, DNFC/85.
6. Hedgerow, west of Athgoe Castle, JP/88. Roadside hedge, north-west of Newcastle, CB, SR/87. South bank of the River Liffey at St Edmundsbury, JS, MN/85. Path along the Grand Canal west of Clondalkin and in hedges at Gollierstown Bridge, MN/88, 89.
7. By a tributary of the River Dodder at Ballymaice, MWJ, DAW/85. Waste ground at Charlemont Bridge, PWJ/82. Woodland, hazel scrub and hedgerows, west and east of the northern reservoir in Glenasmole, DD/83 & MN/90. Hedge by Scholarstown Road, DK/c.65.
8. Still in hedges at Kilgobbin, PC/70 & PC/83. The Dingle, HOR/83. Wood at Ballycorus, SR, CB/88. Old bank in Cabinteely Park, SR/90.

AQUIFOLIACEAE

Ilex

I. aquifolium L.
Holly   Native

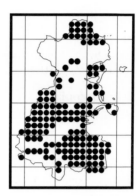

1	2	3	4	5	6	7	8

Common in woods and hedges in the uplands; rare elsewhere.
Usually occurs as single bushes in hedgerows in 1 & 2.
FID.

EUPHORBIACEAE

Mercurialis

M. perennis L.
Dog's Mercury   Possibly native in Co. Dublin

Colgan: 4. Hedgebanks near Finglas: *Wade Dubl.,* 1794. In considerable quantity in a wood near Saint Helena, Finglas, also on adjoining ditch banks, and in hedgerows and field borders, spreading for fully 100 yards, 1903: *N.C.* The above records refer to the same locality where, no doubt, the plant was introduced, though now become fully naturalised.
Suppl: 4. Still at St Helena, Finglas (1948). 5. In Santry Court near N.E. corner of garden wall (1932-1944).

(4)	5

Doubts exist as to the native status of this species in Ireland; yet it may be native in its site
in Santry Woods where it occurs with many typical woodland species. The area surrounding
St Helena, Finglas (4), where this plant was first recorded in 1794 is now built-up.
5. Santry Woods, DNFC/82 & 89.

M. annua L.
Annual Mercury   Probably introduced

1	2	3	4	5	6	7	8

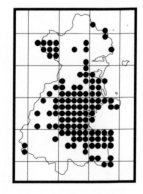

Very common as a weed of waste ground and gardens especially in
the city centre and older suburbs. Though probably an introduction,
this is one of the most characteristic members of the Dublin flora.
All plants seen in Dublin are strictly dioecious with no monoecious
material seen.
FID.

Euphorbia

E. helioscopia L.
Sun Spurge   Probably introduced

| 1 | 2 | 3 | 4 | 5 | 6 | 7 | 8 |

Very common in dry cultivated and arable land; rare in the mountains.
FID.

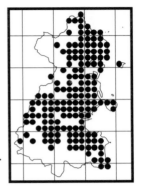

E. exigua L.
Dwarf Spurge   Probably introduced

Suppl: Occasional. 7. Left bank of Dodder above Oldbawn Bridge (1947). Apparently not as common as in Colgan's time.

| (1) | 2 | (3) | 4 | 5 | 6 | (7) | 8 |

Rare, in tilled ground. **E. exigua** was so common at the turn of the century as a cornfield weed that *Colgan* did not list localities for it. However, it had become rarer by the early 1960s, when the *Suppl* was published. Its decline is attributable to changes in cereal crop management and to the use of herbicides.
2. Cleared bulb field just east of the railway bridge at Balleally Dump, Rogerstown, DD, JRA/86.
4. Potato field, 3 km north of Lucan near Westmanstown, MN/88.
5. Waste ground, north-west of Malahide, PG/87, 88.
6. Field margin just north-east of Aderrig, JP/84.
8. Dumped soil at the south end and on a gravel car park at the west side of Leopardstown Racecourse, SR/85. Edge of an overgrown potato field, east of Shanganagh Cemetery, and in a similar field nearby, SR, HOR/84, 85, SR/91, DD/93.

E. peplus L.
Petty Spurge   Probably introduced

| 1 | 2 | 3 | 4 | 5 | 6 | 7 | 8 |

Common in dry arable land, waste places and gardens; rare in the mountains and in 1.
FID.

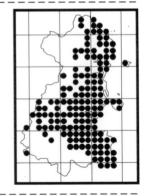

E. portlandica L.
Portland Spurge   Native

Colgan: 3. Sandhills opposite to Malahide: *Mack. Cat.,* 1825. and in 1903! 5. "On ye shore between Clantarf and ye Warren House, August, 1732": *Annot. in Threlkeld.* Shore of Dublin Bay near Howth, 1799: *Templeton MS.* On Ireland's Eye: *Wade Rar.* On the ruins of Kilbarrick Church: *Mack. Cat.,* 1825 and in 1874: *Greenwood Pim.* Sparingly on the North Bull, 1893: *N.C.* 8. At Killiney Bay, by Mr Brinkley, 1798: *Templeton MS.* abundant here on cliffs, banks, and walls from the foot of Killiney Hill to Sorrento, 1902!

| 3 | 5 | 8 |

Occasional in sand-dunes in 3, 5 and sea-cliffs in 8; frequent on the northern half of North Bull Island (5).
3. Still at the southern tip of Malahide Island and mid-way along the Island Golf-course, Donabate, DD, PR/83 & PR/83, 85.
5. Sandy soil opposite the golf-course at Malahide, MN/83. Still on Ireland's Eye above the beach, ENL/84.
8. Still near Sorrento Cottage at the north end of Killiney Bay, SR, HOR/85. On the cliffs at Whiterock, Killiney, SR/85. Seaward facing slope just north of Killiney Railway Station, SR/85.

E. paralias L.
Sea Spurge   Native

| 2 | 3 | 5 | 8 |

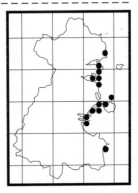

Occasional in sand-dunes in 3 & 5; rare in 2 & 8.
2. A few plants at the north end of Rush sand-hills just south of the village, DD/88.
8. Sand below Killiney Railway Station, SR/84. Sand-dunes east of the Pigeon House, SR, HOR/83.

LINACEAE

Linum

L. bienne Miller (L. angustifolium)
Pale Flax   Native

Colgan: 2. Frequent along the railway from Skerries to Balbriggan, 1894; abundant on banks by the sea north of Balbriggan, 1893-1900; 3. Banks by the sea near Seatown Castle, 1893; pastures east of Kilcrea, 1893-1902; furze brake near Knocksedan, 1894; abundant in sandy fields to the north of Portrane peninsula, 1894-1900: *N.C.* 4. Above Knockmaroon Hill: *Wade Dubl.* (as *L. usitatissimum*, corrected to *L. angustifolium* in *Wade Rar.*, 1804). Phoenix Park near Chapelizod: *Mack. Cat.*, 1825 and in 1900! Banks of the Royal Canal above Kennan Bridge, 1894: *N.C.* 5. Steep banks between Clontarf and Howth *(John White) Wade Rar.* At the Cliffs and below the Needles and Glenaveena: *Flor. Howth.* Near Shielmartin, Howth and railway banks south of Raheny and north of Portmarnock, 1894; abundant on Carrick Hill, 1900; 6. By the Grand Canal near Hazelhatch, 1893: *N.C.* 7. Banks near the Dodder opposite to the Marquis of Ely's demesne: *Mack. Rar.* Gorse brakes near Ballymount, 1892; 8. By the railway near Sydney Parade and near Booterstown, 1894; on the railway near Shankhill and on banks above Bride's glen, 1902: *N.C.* In fields between Killiney Hill and Bray: *Mack. Cat.*, 1825. At Dalkey *(Rev. S. Madden) Cyb.* Abundant on banks by the sea from the foot of Killiney Hill to Vico, and along the sides of the newly made Saval Park road above Dalkey, 1902; abundant on dry banks, Loughlinstown Commons, 1903: *N.C.*

| 2 | 3 | 4 | 5 | (6) | 7 | 8 |

Rare, in sand-dunes and calcareous grassland.
2. Grassed-over ballast pit near Skerries Railway Station, DD, EMcA/85.

3. Dump at the quarry and on sandy waste ground near the Martello Tower at Donabate DD, PR/82, PR/85. Still at the north end of Portrane Peninsula, PR/85.
4. Magazine Fort in the Phoenix Park, MN/88. Dunsink tiphead, MN/88. Just south-west of Clonsilla Railway Station, DD/82. Cardiff's Bridge, Finglas, DD/82. Grassy slope opposite the gates of the Cheshire Home in the Phoenix Park, MN/85. Grassy disturbed ground by the new airport road 1 km south of St Margaret's, CB, MN/90.
5. Baldoyle Industrial Estate, ENL/84. Along the inner sand-dunes and in the dune-slacks from just north-east of the clubhouse of the Royal Dublin Golf-course on North Bull Island, SR/88. Beside the roadway to the clubhouse at Portmarnock, DN/88. St Anne's Park, Raheny, PG/87, 88. St Doolagh's Quarry, PG, DN/89.
7. Dry banks and roadside at the 7th lock on the Grand Canal, DD/92. Dry grassy banks of the River Dodder at Oldbawn, MWJ, DAW/92.
8. Waste ground north-east of Foxrock Church, SR/85. Edge of playing fields south-east of Cabinteely, SR/85. Roches Hill, SR, HOR/83. Top of the railway embankment and in an adjoining field east of Shanganagh cemetery, SR, HOR/85. Still at Killiney by the path from the Vico Road to Killiney Hill, DNFC/83. Still at Dalkey, F. Walsh/68. Edge of a field at Rochestown Avenue, south-west of Sallynoggin, SR/90.

L. catharticum L.
Fairy Flax   Native

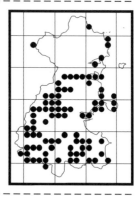

| 1 | 2 | 3 | 4 | 5 | 6 | 7 | 8 |

Occasional on walls and in thin calcareous grassland, waste places, sand-dunes and gravel quarries. Rare in 1.

POLYGALACEAE

Polygala

P. vulgaris L. (incl. *P. oxyptera*)
Common Milkwort   Native

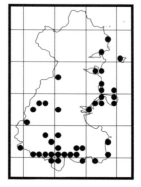

| (1) | 2 | 3 | 4 | 5 | 6 | 7 | 8 |

Occasional in unimproved grassland, on sand-hills and roadside banks. Formerly more common in lowland grassland, but nowadays most of this habitat-type has been improved or destroyed.

P. serpyllifolia Hose *(P. serpyllacea)*
Heath Milkwort   Native

| (1) | (3) | 5 | (6) | 7 | 8 |

Occasional in heathlands in 7 & 8; rare elsewhere.

Not refound in the Naul Hills (1) or Lambay Island (3).

5. Heathland, west of Casana Rock and north of the summit, Howth, PG/92. Particularly common in burnt-over peat on the Ben of Howth where white and reddish-flowered forms occur alongside the common blue-flowered plants. Absent from calcareous soils north-west of the Baily and west of the summit, Howth, CB/92.

ACERACEAE

Acer

A. pseudoplatanus L.
Sycamore   Alien

| 1 | 2 | 3 | 4 | 5 | 6 | 7 | 8 |

Widespread and extremely common in hedgerows and waste ground. Frequently planted and freely self-seeding throughout the county.
FID.

OXALIDACEAE

Oxalis

O. corniculata L.
Procumbent Yellow-sorrel   Alien

| 3 | 4 | 5 | 6 | 7 | 8 |

Occasional as a garden weed, in wasteplaces and on roadside banks.
5. Charlemont Road, Clontarf, DD/79, **NCR**.

O. acetosella L.
Wood-sorrel   Native

| 1 | 3 | 4 | 5 | 6 | 7 | 8 |

Very common in mixed woodlands and margins of conifer plantations in the uplands; rare elsewhere in shady hedges and valleys.

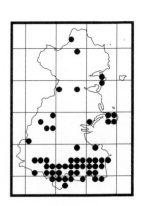

O. debilis Kunth *(O. corymbosa)*
Large-flowered Pink-sorrel   Alien

| 1 | 5 | 7 | 8 |

A persistent garden escape or discard. Frequent in the suburban parts of 7 and occasional in 8. Also recorded from Garristown, Rowlestown and Balrothery (1) and Sutton, Drumcondra, Malahide and Raheny (5). *FID.* Some of the above records may refer to **O. latifolia** Kunth with which **O. debilis** is easily confused.

GERANIACEAE

Geranium

G. rotundifolium L.
Round-leaved Crane's-bill   Probably introduced in Co. Dublin

| 5 | 6 | 8 |

Very rare, on waste ground.
5. Disturbed ground around Portmarnock Raceway, DN/88.
6. Disturbed ground in a roadside hedgerow between Newcastle and Athgoe Castle, JP/86.
8. Small patch of waste ground at Williamstown, HOR/83, gone 84. Eastern part of Ringsend Dump, SR, HOR/83, SR/87.

G. sanguineum L.
Bloody Crane's-bill   Native

Colgan: 3. On Lambay: *Ir. Flor.* On the south and west of Lambay Island and north of Ronan's Well: *Flor. Lambay.* 5. Plentifully in bushy places by the shore near the baths, Howth: *Wade Dubl.* On Ireland's Eye: *Ir. Flor.* and in 1899! Abundant round the greater part of Howth Head, but confined to the cliff tops and drift banks by the sea, 1903: *N.C.* 8. "In a Close near *Simond's Court*": *Threlkeld.* Plentifully at Killiney Bay: *Wade Dubl.*, 1794. Abundant on banks by the sea at foot of Killiney Hill and near the bathing place at Vico, 1903: *N.C.*

| 3 | 5 | 8 |

Rare; in maritime grassland and short scrub on cliffs.
3. Still on the west side of Lambay Island, DD/91. On the public golf-course on Donabate sand-hills, PR/92.
5. Below the summit, Howth, ENL/83. Near Kilrock Quarries, Howth, PG/87, 88. Cliff-top and cliff-face near the Baily lighthouse, below the Needles and at Lion's Head, Howth, MWJ/86 & DN/89, 90.
8. Coastal banks north of Killiney Railway Station and above the Vico Bathing Place, Killiney, SR, HOR/83 & SR/85.

G. columbinum L.
Long-stalked Crane's-bill   Native; introduced

Colgan: 4. On the roadside at the foot of Knockmaroon Hills, 1799: *Templeton MS.* Roadsides between Knockmaroon and Lucan and 5. On Feltrim Hill: *Ir. Flor.* abundant here in 1902! In fair quantity on Carrick Hill near Portmarnock, 1900: *Colgan 1903.*
Britten, 1905: 8. In Blackrock.
Suppl: 3. Sparingly on a bank at the Burrow, Portrane (1952-1957). 5. No longer at the site of Carrick.

(3) (4) 5 8

Extremely rare.
5. Feltrim Hill, MS/65 & DNFC/67. Not seen recently; most of the hill has been quarried away.
8. Gravel car park on the west side of Leopardstown Racecourse, SR/85, **NDR**.

G. dissectum L.
Cut-leaved Crane's-bill   Native

| 1 | 2 | 3 | 4 | 5 | 6 | 7 | 8 |

Common in waste places, on roadsides and as a weed of cultivated ground.
FID.

G. pyrenaicum Burm. f.
Hedgerow Crane's-bill   Probably introduced

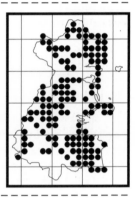

| 1 | 2 | 3 | 4 | 5 | 6 | 7 | 8 |

Occasional on dry roadsides, old walls and especially on and
near old ruins.

G. pusillum L.
Small-flowered Crane's-bill   Possibly introduced

Colgan: 3. On Lambay island in considerable quantity at the south-west corner of the large field north of the Castle: *Flor. Lambay* 1882 and in 1886: *Herb. Scully.* Sandy field bank at Portrane, 1902: *N.C.* 8. In cultivated and waste ground at Old Connaught *(Joseph Meade) Ir. Nat.,* 1900, p.285 and in 1901, spec.!

| 2 | 3 | (8) |

Very rare, in sandy fallows. Little suitable open ground now remains on Lambay Island (3)
where this species once occurred in quantity. Rogerstown (2) is the main harbour for boats
carrying limestone and produce visiting Lambay Island and this species may have been
brought to the island via this route.
2. Recently disturbed sandy ground in Rogerstown Village, SR, DD/90. Tilled ground south of
   Rush, DD/91.
3. Sandy waste ground by the Corballis Road, PR/87. Still at the north end of Portrane
   Peninsula on disturbed ground, PR/85.

G. molle L.
Dove's-foot Crane's-bill   Native

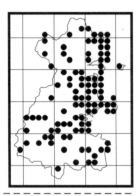

| 1 | 2 | 3 | 4 | 5 | 6 | 7 | 8 |

Common on walls, in quarries and shallow soils on dry calcareous substrates near the coast; occasional elsewhere as a weed.
FID.

G. lucidum L.
Shining Crane's-bill   Native;   introduced

Colgan: 2. At the Naul very near the Bridge: *Wade Rar.* Along a bank at the Naul: *Ir. Flor.* 5. On Feltrim Hill: *Flor. Hib.* sparingly here on limestone rocks, 1893-1904!

Suppl: 5. Only one small patch on Feltrim Hill (1928-1945). Station destroyed in 1946.

| (2) | 3 | 4 | 5 | 6 | 8 |

Rare on walls and in gravelly places. Not seen recently on Feltrim Hill (5), a major source of gravel which is mostly now quarried away. In many of its present-day locations this species has the appearance of being a short-term colonist. It was introduced to Delbrook, Dundrum (8) and "spread like wildfire" (*Ir. Nat. VII*, June 1898, p.129).
3. Gravelled path of a derelict house opposite Swords Castle, PR/85, **NDR**.
4. Plentiful on an old railway platform at Clonsilla Railway Station, MN/88, **NDR**.
5. Waste ground near Kilrock, Howth, CB/91.
6. Wall top at Badgerhill, JP, ENL/87, **NDR**.
8. Top of a wall near the east end of Corbawn Lane, Shankill; probably an introduction as the botanist, R.C. Faris lived near here, SR, HOR/83, **NDR**. Abundant on dumped soil in an old estate just south of Dundrum on the Enniskerry road, SR/84. Wall of a stone building in Dundrum, SR/89. Lanes off the west side of Wilfield Road, Sandymount, PC/88. Disturbed ground, east of Carrickmines, SR/89.

G. robertianum L.
Herb-Robert   Native

| 1 | 2 | 3 | 4 | 5 | 6 | 7 | 8 |

Widespread and abundant on walls, in waste places, open woodlands and hedgerows.
FID.

Erodium

E. maritimum (L.) L'Hér.
Sea Stork's-bill   Native

| 2 | 3 | 5 | 8 |

Rare on shallow soils over rocks near the sea.

2. Short turf by the coastal promenade at Skerries, south of the Martello Tower, PG/90, **NDR**.
3. Still abundant around the castle and in the gardens on Lambay Island, DD/91; formerly frequent throughout the island.
5. Bare ground by a path at Redrock, Howth, ENL/84 & CB/92. Ireland's Eye, PG/91. Formerly known in several places from Sutton to Howth Cliffs (Hart 1887).
8. Near the land end of the West Pier at Dun Laoghaire, SR/88. Path on the eastern side of Killiney Hill, SR/89. One large patch in short turf to the north-north-west of the church on Dalkey Island, DD, SR/91. East facing slope of Dalkey Hill, SR/91.

E. moschatum (L.) L'Hér.
Musk Stork's-bill   Probably introduced

Colgan: 2. At Rush *(Moore) Cyb.* By the shore nearly opposite Cardy Rocks, north of Balbriggan, 1900 and roadside a mile west of Skerries, 1902: *N.C.* 4. On old walls between Sarah's bridge and Chapelizod: *Wade Dubl.* 5. "On the Wayside leading to *Clantarf"*: *Threlkeld.* Along the highway at Artane and near Warren House: *Wade Dubl.* At Warren House, near the Martello Tower, and elsewhere at Sutton; roadside to Brook Lodge above Howth village; abundant by the road between Cannon Rock and the Hut: *Flor. Howth.* Banks near Brook Lodge, 1895; roadsides and waste ground near Cannon Rock and on a rocky knoll north of Red Rocks, Howth, 1902; on the new tramway track east of Raheny station, 1901; roadside near Kinsaley, 1903: *N.C.* 7. Roadside, Kilmainham to Chapelizod: *Ir. Flor.* Sparingly on wall tops and roadsides near Bluebell, 1892-1900: *N.C.* 8. Near Dunleary and at Bray Commons: *Wade Dubl.* At Bray Commons, 1902 and sparingly in a lane near Thornhill, Bray, 1897: *J. Meade.* Roadside near Vallombrosa, Bray, 1894: *Praeger.* At Donnybrook: *Flor. Hib.* Rochestown Hill, near Killiney: *Ir. Flor.* At Vico, Killiney Bay, on the roadside at the foot of a wall above the baths, and on a steep ascent to Knockachree, 1903: *N.C.*

Suppl: Rare. 1. Bog of the Ring (1948). In Skerries (J.P. Brunker, 1918). 5. Road to golf club, Portmarnock (J.P.B., 1922).

| (1) | 2 | (4) | 5 | 7 | 8 |

Rare, usually on waste ground. The Balrothery record (2) is not far from where the plant was last seen in Bog of the Ring in 1948.
2. Disturbed ground outside the car park of the Balrothery Inn, DD/82. Hedgerow at Balbriggan, RF/86.
5. Hedge-bank beside a garden in the Malahide Road at Kinsealy, ENL/85.
7. Well established and persisting in a lawn at Trinity College, JRA/81, increasing, MWJ/93. On steps in the Memorial Park at Islandbridge, DD, EMcA/83. Car park near Tara Street Railway Station, DD/88.
8. Sand, on the coast south of Killiney, SR/88.
FID.

E. cicutarium (L.) L'Hér.
Common Stork's-bill   Native

| 2 | 3 | 4 | 5 | 8 |

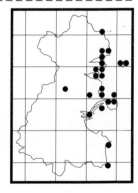

Common in sand-dunes and sandy ground near the sea; rare in 8.
4. Disturbed ground by roadside c. 1 km to south-west of St Margaret's, MN/90, **NDR**.
8. Grassy bank at Cork Abbey, north of Bray, SR, HOR/85. Short grass south of the obelisk on Killiney Hill, SR/85.

BALSAMINACEAE

Impatiens

I. glandulifera Royle
Indian Balsam   Alien

| 2 | 4 | 5 | 6 | 7 | 8 |

Occasional on river and canal banks and urban waste ground. Abundant along the banks of the River Liffey from Chapelizod to Lucan.
FID.

ARALIACEAE

Hedera

H. helix L.
Ivy   Native

| 1 | 2 | 3 | 4 | 5 | 6 | 7 | 8 |

Widespread and abundant on walls, trees, hedges and cliffs. Some of the plants in Dublin appear to have all their leaf hairs prostrate and correspond in this respect to **Hedera helix** subsp. **hibernica** (Kirchner) D. McClint. However, some of these plants differ in the other major characteristic of this subspecies in that they are strongly climbing.
FID.

APIACEAE (*UMBELLIFERAE*)

Hydrocotyle

H. vulgaris L.
Marsh Pennywort   Native

| (1) | (2) | 3 | 4 | 5 | 6 | 7 | 8 |

Frequent in marshes and other wet habitats in the mountainous parts of 7 and 8; rare elsewhere.
3. Dune-slack at the south end of Malahide Island, PR/85.
4. By ditch at Dunsoghly, MN/84.
5. Wet fields at Kilrock, Howth, PG/87, 88. Pond on the eastern side of Portmarnock Golf-course, DN, RF/88. Abundant in the Alder Marsh dune-slack on North Bull Island, ENL, MN/84.
6. Western slope of Saggart Hill, HOR/85. North end of Brittas Ponds, DNFC/83.

Sanicula

S. europaea L.
Sanicle   Native

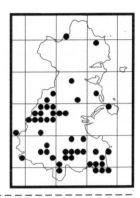

| 1 | 2 | 3 | 4 | 5 | 6 | 7 | 8 |

Occasional in base-rich deciduous woodlands and hedgerows.
Extremely rare in 1 and 2.
1. Naul, GS/83, 88.
2. Milverton Estate, RF/87.

Eryngium

E. maritimum L.
Sea-holly   Native

| 2 | 3 | 5 | 8 |

Rare, in sand-dunes and on shingle seashores. It is a conspicuous and therefore easily
recorded species and the number of plants in the county is now known to be small outside
of the Donabate/Portrane area due to public recreational pressure and disturbance of its
coastal habitat.
2. Sand-dunes to the south-east of Rush Golf-course, RF/90 & PG/90.
3. South end of Malahide Island, PR/85. Stony beach at Corballis, PR/83. Gravel beach and in
   sand-hills at the north end of the Portrane Peninsula, PR/85.
5. North-eastern tip of North Bull Island, ENL, MN/84 & ENL, CB/85. North-east of the
   Causeway on North Bull Island, PG/87, 88. South end of North Bull Island, DN/92. The
   Cosh, Sutton, ENL/82 & PG, PR/90.
8. One plant near the Martello Tower, south of Killiney, SR/83.

Chaerophyllum

C. temulum L. (*C. temulentum*)
Rough Chervil   Probably introduced

Colgan: 1. Between Garristown and Ashtown: *Flor. Howth.* 2. Roadside banks between Ballough and Lusk, 1903: *N.C.* 3. Near
Kilsallaghan: *Flor. Howth.* Abundant, and in places luxuriant, in hedgebanks by the Malahide creek from near Lissen Hall to
Prospect Point, stretching for about half a mile, 1902: *(Scully & N.C.) Colgan 1903.* 4. Fields between Glasnevin and Finglas:
Mack. Cat. Old ditches beyond Glasnevin: *Ir. Flor.* In fair quantity on a roadside bank between Lucan and the Royal Canal,
1895-1903: *N.C.* 5. Between Raheny and the shore: *Ir. Flor.* Hedgebanks near Coolock (Moore); about Kinsaley churchyard (J.
White) *Cyb.* 8. About Windy Harbour: *Ir. Flor.* Hedge near Old Connaught, 1868 *(Barrington) Rec. Add. & Herb.* Near
Dundrum: *Hart MS.* Roadside bank at Ballybrack, 1903: *N.C.*
Suppl: 2. Abundant on N. shore of Rogerstown Creek between viaduct and pier (A.W. Stelfox, 1923). Still there (1942).
Still near Rush railway station (1948).

| (1) | (2) | 3 | (4) | (5) | (8) |

Extremely rare. *Colgan* considered this species to be an introduction in most of its Dublin sites. This opinion appears to be supported by the manner of its decline and disappearance from many roadside and ruderal locations with no obvious cause.
3. Still at Prospect Point, in very small quantity in a roadside bank, DD/83 & PR/89.

Anthriscus

A. sylvestris (L.) Hoffm.
Cow Parsley   Native

| 1 | 2 | 3 | 4 | 5 | 6 | 7 | 8 |

Widespread and abundant on roadside verges and in hedgerows.
FID.

A. caucalis M. Bieb. *(A. vulgaris, A. neglecta)*
Bur Chervil   Native

Colgan: 2, 3 and 5. Abundant in sandy ground and on roadsides about Rush, Skerries, Portrane, Portmarnock, Sutton &c., and sparingly inland on Feltrim Hill, 1902; 4. Roadside near Glasnevin cemetery, 1894; 6. Roadside near Lucan, 1896; at Newcastle, 1897; near Esker, 1900; 7. Roadsides at Green Hills, 1894; between Blue Bell and the Grand Canal, 1900; at Ballyfermott, 1903: *N.C.* 8. "In an old Mudd Wall at the ruined Church of *Mirian*": *Threlkeld.* Between Foster's Avenue and Stillorgan: *Wade Dubl.* By the Dodder below London Bridge, 1900: *N.C.* Sparingly by the Cabinteely road near Johnstown, 1904: *Miss L. Colgan.*

| 2 | 3 | (4) | 5 | (6) | (7) | 8 |

Occasional in sandy fallows near the sea and in gull colonies.
2. St Patrick's Island, Skerries, DD/83. Sandy roadside banks at Rogerstown Boat Club, DD/83. Sandy places by the road on the south beach at Rush, DD/83.
3. Sandy roadsides and disturbed ground south of Donabate, DD/82. Waste ground in the Island Golf-course, PR, HOR, DD/85. Roadside banks and sandy ground on the Portrane Peninsula, PR, ENL/85. Hedge on Portrane beach and at Burrow, Portrane, PR, ENL/85. Seabird colonies on the south and east sides of Lambay Island, DD, SR/91.
5. Abundant on Ireland's Eye, MS/70 & ENL/84. South end of the Portmarnock Golf-course, DN, RF/88. Sutton Strand, DN, RF/88 & DD/87. Howth Harbour, ENL/85.
8. Beside a derelict building at the land end of South Wall, SR, HOR/83.

Scandix

S. pecten-veneris L.
Shepherd's-needle   Probably introduced

Colgan: 2. Abundant in a cornfield north of Lusk, 1893: *N.C.* 4. In waste ground and on roadsides between Chapelizod and Luttrell's town: *Wade Dubl.* Broken fields about Glasnevin, Finglas and Courtduff: *Ir. Flor.* 5. Abundant in fields around Raheny and Baldoyle: *Wade Dubl.* At Clontarf, 1843 *(Dr Litton)*; at Kilbarrick, 1868 *(Rev. H.G. Carroll) Herb. S. & A. Mus.* About Drumleck and the Needles: *Flor. Howth.*

Suppl: 5. Alexandra Road waste ground (1935). Railway sidings at North Wall (1948). 7. Rubbish dumps at Kimmage (1948). Only a casual in all stations.

| (2) | (4) | (5) | (7) |

Not refound at any of its former sites in the county.

Smyrnium

S. olusatrum L.
Alexanders   Probably introduced

| 1 | 2 | 3 | 4 | 5 | 6 | 7 | 8 |

Common on roadsides and amongst ruins. Commonest near the sea where it occurs in a variety of roadside and ruderal habitats. *FID.*

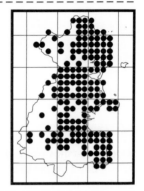

Conopodium

C. majus (Gouan) Loret *(C. denudatum)*
Pignut   Native

| 1 | 3 | 4 | 5 | 6 | 7 | 8 |

Occasional in woodlands, hedgebanks and unimproved grassland especially under bracken.
1. Roadside, 1.5 km north-east of Naul, GS/86, **NDR**.

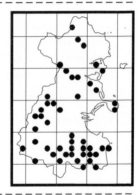

Pimpinella

P. saxifraga L.
Burnet-saxifrage   Native

| 1 | 2 | 3 | 4 | 5 | 6 | 7 | 8 |

Occasional in coastal grassland and sandy and gravelly ground inland.

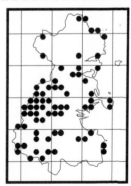

Aegopodium

A. podagraria L.
Ground-elder, Bishop's-weed   Alien

| 1 | 2 | 3 | 4 | 5 | 6 | 7 | 8 |

Widespread and common on roadsides, in abandoned or poorly tended gardens and amongst ruins where it often forms almost pure stands. Nearly always associated with habitation, which it may outlast.
FID.

Berula

B. erecta (Hudson) Cov. *(Sium angustifolium, S. erectum)*
Lesser Water-parsnip   Native

| 1 | 2 | (3) | 4 | (5) | 6 | 7 |

Rare, in marshes and canal banks.
1. In a pond beside Broad Meadow River just west of Lispopple Bridge, DN/91.
2. Marshy field at the Corn Mill south of Balbriggan, DD/87.
4. Pools in the Tolka River Valley at Blanchardstown, MN, GS, DD/83 & MN/88.
6. Banks of the River Liffey at Lucan Demesne, HOR, PR, MN/85. Banks of the Grand Canal west of Gollierstown Bridge and west of the 12th Lock and at Clondalkin DNFC/83 & MN/89.
7. Palmerston Marsh, DD/82. Stream from the Grand Canal above 7th Lock, DN/90. Drains at the 8th Lock on the Grand Canal at Gallanstown, DD/92.

Crithmum

C. maritimum L.
Rock Samphire   Native

Colgan: 2. Abundant on the rocky shore between Loughshinny and Rush, and 3. Abundant on cliffs near the Martello Tower, Portrane, 1903: N.C. 5. On sea cliffs near the Light House, Howth, and on Ireland's Eye: Wade Dubl., 1794. On Ireland's Eye 1899; frequent on cliffs on the south and east sides of Howth Head, 1901 and on rock reefs south of Rob's Walls, Malahide, 1902: N.C. 8. Near the Lead Mines, Dalkey: Wade Dubl., 1794 and in 1904! On the east side of Dalkey island, 1901; rocks near Vico and at Sorrento, 1902: N.C. By the railway near Blackrock, 1872: Greenwood Pim and in 1904!

| 2 | 3 | 5 | 8 |

Common on sea-cliffs and rocks near the sea. Commonest in 5 (all around Howth and Ireland's Eye) and 8 (on the cliffs at Killiney Bay); rare elsewhere.
2. Pier at Rush, RF/86. Still abundant on the sea-cliff between Loughshinny and Rush, DD/88.
3. Rocks by the sea on the cliff walk south-east of Portrane, PR/84.
8. On the sea-railway wall along Merrion Strand, DN/94.

Oenanthe

O. fistulosa L.
Tubular Water-dropwort   Native

Colgan: 1. In Garristown Bog, 1893-1902; and 3. Pools by the Ward river above Knocksedan, 1903: N.C. 4. Near Dunsink (Mr Brinkley) Templeton MS. Abundant along the Royal canal from Liffey Junction to Lucan, 1893-1903; and 5. In Baldoyle Pits, and in drains near Baldoyle village, 1903: N.C.
Suppl: 4. Confirmed only from the Royal Canal where it is still abundant (1957).

268

Extremely rare. Its former site at Garristown Bog (1) has been drained, whilst that at Dunsink (4) is now filled-in and that at Baldoyle (5) is now built on. The pools by the Ward River at Knocksedan (3) may now be the site of a reservoir. It has not been refound on the Royal Canal (4) following recent dredging.

4. Royal Canal, north of Beech Park, Clonsilla, JS/73; site destroyed in 1988.

O. lachenalii C. Gmelin
Parsley Water-dropwort   Native

Colgan: 2. Near the coast between Balbriggan and Skerries: *Wade Rar.* Abundant in a marsh by the shore south of Balbriggan 1893 no doubt Wade's station: *N.C.* 3. On the west side of Lambay *(Mr Underwood) Mack. Rar. & Flor. Lambay.* By the Malahide creek at Lissen Hall, 1893-1902; by the Rogerstown creek at Turvey, 1893, and at Raheen Point, 1902: *N.C.* 5. In a marsh between Baldoyle and Howth: *Mack. Rar.* Frequent round the Baldoyle creek, 1902; in a marsh near Baldoyle Pits, 1892: *N.C.* (8. In ditches and marshes about Sandymount and Merrion: *Wade Dubl.* now extinct.) Wade's and Mackay's records for 2, 3 and 5 are given under (*O. peucedanifolia* and Wade's record for Sandymount under *O. pimpinelloides,* but in all cases the plant observed was no doubt *O. lachenalii).*

2   3   5   (8)

Very rare, in salt-marshes.

2. Still in several places on the rocky shore at Hampton, south of Balbriggan, DD/89. Shore at Loughshinny, DD/90.
3. Still by Malahide creek on banks of the estuary of the Broad Meadow River, PR/83. Seashore south of Kilcrea House, PR/84. Path near the estuary at Raheen Point, PR/83. In the salt-marsh on the Portrane Peninsula, PR/85.
5. Salt-marsh, east of Portmarnock Bridge, DN/88.

O. crocata L.
Hemlock Water-dropwort   Native

Colgan: 3. By the Broad Meadow Water at Rowlestown and above Fieldstown, 1894: *N.C.* 4. "It grows below *Finglass Bridge* upon the River Side": *Threlkeld.* Abundantly on the river banks at Cardiff's Bridge, Ashtown and Scribblestown: *Wade Dubl.* and in 1903! By the Royal Canal from Cross Guns to Ashtown 1903; 7. In the Slade of Ballymaice near Bohernabreena, 1894; in Kelly's glen and along the stream thence from Kilmashogue to near Willbrook, 1903; 8. By the riverside at Bray Commons, 1903; and sparingly by the stream above Glencullen bridge, 1893: *N.C.*

Suppl: 1 and 3. Along both banks of Broad Meadow Water (1948). 3. Between Lissenhall and Prospect Point (1946-1956). 8. Still at Glencullen Bridge (1952).

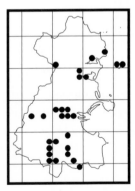

(1)   2   3   4   5   7   8

Occasional; locally frequent on river and canal banks. Apparently commoner now than it was at the end of the 19th century when it was sufficiently rare to warrant Colgan giving a list of localities.

2. Edge of a stream on Rush beach, RF/88, **NDR**, DD/91.

FID.

O. fluviatilis (Bab.) Coleman (*O. phellandrium* var. *fluviatilis*)
River Water-dropwort   Native

Colgan: 4. In the Royal Canal near Dublin and Lucan, 1890 (*Scully*) *Cyb. II.*

(4)	6

Extremely rare, in the Grand Canal.
6. Grand Canal at Gollierstown and near the 12th lock, DN/90.

O. aquatica (L.) Poiret *(O. phellandrium)*
Fine-leaved Water-dropwort   Native

Colgan: 3. Pool by the Ward river above Knocksedan, 1903: *N.C.* 4. By the verge of the large pond at Woodlands *(Mr Underwood) Mack. Cat.* Abundant all along the Royal Canal, 1903; in a quarry hole near Dunsoghly, 1900; 6. In the Grand Canal at Hazelhatch, 1893, and 7. At Ballyfermot, 1904: *N.C.*
Suppl: Confirmed from Royal and Grand Canals (1957).

(3)	4	6	7

Occasional along the Grand Canal throughout 6; very rare elsewhere. Its former site in pools by the Ward River above Knocksedan (3) may now be a reservoir.
4. Still at Luttrellstown, at the southern end of the main lake, MN/85.
7. Grand Canal opposite the Lyons Tea Factory, DN/89.

Aethusa

A. cynapium L.
Fool's Parsley   Probably introduced

1	2	3	4	5	6	7	8

Occasional in dry waste ground, neglected gardens and roadside verges.
FID.

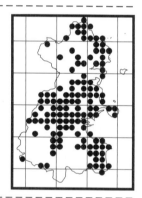

Foeniculum

F. vulgare Miller *(F. officinale)*
Fennel   Probably introduced

Colgan: 3. Abundant on banks above the Ward river near the church at Swords, 1893-1903: *N.C.* 4. Near Chapelizod: *Wade Dubl.* At Knockmaroon: *Ir. Flor.* At Chapelizod, 1902; abundant at Knockmaroon, in Phoenix Park near Chapelizod, and on roadsides between Island Bridge and Chapelizod, 1901: *N.C.* 5. Near Howth station, about Howth village, and at Balscaddan: *Flor. Howth.* 7. Roadside banks near Blue Bell, 1892-1900; near Templeogue Bridge, 1892-1902; banks near Balrothery and Fir House, 1902: *N.C.* 8. On rough banks by the Bray river about a mile above the town: *Templeton MS.* circa 1820. Roadside and banks south-west of Bray Common, abundant, 1903 (no doubt Templeton's station); by the railway near Killiney station, 1894-1904; by the river in Bride's Glen, 1902: *N.C.*
Suppl: 2. Rogerstown (1956). 5. Sutton (J.P. Brunker, 1922). Still there (1941). 8. Near Clonskea Bridge (1941-1957). Recently confirmed in most of Colgan's stations.

| 2 | 3 | 4 | 5 | 7 | 8 |

Occasional on waste ground. Commonest near the sea.

2. Still at Rogerstown, DD/84.
3. The Slips and still on waste ground at Swords, PR/83, 85.
4. Roadside at the Strawberry Beds, near the Guinness Metal Bridge, JS, MN/83. Still at Knockmaroon on a calcareous grassy slope, MN/83. Still near Chapelizod at the Gates of the Phoenix Park, MN/85. Still near Islandbridge at Conyngham Road, MN/86. Royal Canal and railway about 0.75 km north of its Canal mouth, MN, DN/87.
5. Still at Balscadden, Howth, CB/90. Still behind Sutton Railway Station, DD/91. Hole in the Wall beach, ENL/85.
7. Waste ground at Ballyfermot, PWJ/86. 250 m west of Clonskeagh Bridge, HOR/85.
8. Ringsend Dump and environs, PWJ/82, JP/90. Abundant on waste ground south of Pigeon House Road, SR, HOR/84. Still on railway banks north and south of Killiney Railway Station, SR/84.

FID.

Conium

C. maculatum L.
Hemlock   Possibly introduced in Co. Dublin

Colgan: I. Sparingly near Walshestown, Naul Hills, 1903: *N.C.* 2, 3 and 5. Abundant in many stations along the coast north of the Liffey mouth, as at Sutton, Baldoyle, Howth, Portrane, Rush, Skerries, &c., and occasional inland, as at Balrothery, Lusk and Man of War, 1902: *N.C.* 4. Very sparingly near Cardiff's Bridge, 1903: *N.C.* 7. Near Harold's Cross, 1901: *H.W.D. Dunlop.* At Ballyfermott, 1902: *N.C.* 8. Sparingly about Old Connaught, 1902: *J. Meade.* At Bray harbour, 1903: *N.C.*

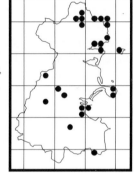

| I | 2 | 3 | 4 | 5 | 7 | 8 |

Occasional on waste ground. Commonest near the sea.
FID.

Apium

A. graveolens L.
Wild Celery   Native

Colgan: 2, 3, 5, 8. Frequent in salt marshes as at Rush and Balbriggan, and by the mouth of Delvin river, 1900; at Portrane, at Lissen Hall, at Portmarnock, and by the shore near Raheny, 1902; in drains by the railway at Booterstown, 1894: *N.C.* I. Sparingly near Baldwinstown, Wyanstown, and Bog of the Ring, 1893; at Westpalstown, 1902; 3. West of Swords, 1903; 6. In the main street, Newcastle, 1892; 7. Near Tallaght, and near Inchicore, 1902: *N.C.*

| (I) | 2 | 3 | 5 | (6) | (7) | 8 |

Rare, in salt-marshes. Now gone from all its inland sites where, at the turn of the century, it was a fairly obvious relic of cultivation. In its surviving sites it is clearly a native.

2. Still near the mouth of the River Delvin north-west of Balbriggan, RF/88.

3. North end of the beach, south of the hospital at Portrane, PR/88. Drains, south of the river near Newport House, DN/90.
5. Banks of the Sluice River and nearby in flooded areas beside tidal drains, Portmarnock, DN/89.
8. Still by drains in Booterstown Marsh, DD/82 & SR, HOR/85.
FID.

A. nodiflorum (L). Lag.
Fool's Water-cress   Native

| 1 | 2 | 3 | 4 | 5 | 6 | 7 | 8 |

Widespread and common in ditches and open drains and slow streams in lowland Dublin; rare elsewhere.
FID.

A. nodiflorum x **A. inundatum** (**A.** x **moorei** (Syme) Druce)

| (4) |

Not refound at its former site in the Royal Canal at Lucan and from Glasnevin to Drumcondra (Praeger 1934b).

A. inundatum (L.) H.G. Reichenb.
Lesser Marshwort   Native

Colgan: 1. Abundant in pools at Bog of the Ring, 1902; 2. Abundant at Balrothery pond, 1893, and at Lusk ponds, 1902: *N.C.* 4. Ditches above Cardiff's Bridge: *Ir. Flor.* By the Tolka above Mulhuddart, 1893: *N.C.* 5. Marsh near the summit of Howth abundantly: *Mack. Cat.* not seen recently. At Baldoyle: *Ir. Flor.* Raheny quarries, 1894: *N.C.* 8. In pools at Foxrock, 1903: *Scully.*
Suppl: 4. Royal Canal below Kennan Bridge (1947). 7. Head of Upper Reservoir, Glenasmole (1941) and in Lower Reservoir (1946).

| (1) | (2) | (4) | 5 | 7 | (8) |

Extremely rare, in marshes. The former sites at Lusk Quarries (2) and Raheny Quarries (5) are now filled in.
5. Abundant in marshes to the west of Portmarnock, DD/86; possibly the record for Baldoyle given in *Ir. Flor.*
7. Still in the southern reservoir in Glenasmole, DD/83.

Petroselinum

P. crispum (Miller) Nyman ex A.W. Hill *(P. sativum)*
Garden Parsley   Alien

Colgan: 1. On the walls of the ruined church of Ballyboghil, 1894 *(N.C.) Cyb. II.* 2. In considerable quantity on a bank by the sea near the Martello Tower, Skerries, 1902: *Colgan 1903.* 4. Dunsoghly, 1895 *(Praeger) Top. Bot.* A relic of ancient cultivation, apparently naturalised at Skerries.
Suppl: 1. Wall near the old church at Garristown (1948). No longer at Ballyboghil Church (1955). 2. Still at Skerries (1946). 3. By road from Swords to Lissenhall (1931). 8. Loughlinstown Common (1953).

| (1) | 2 | (3) | (4) | (8) |

Very rare, by the sea.
2. Still on old ruins and walls on the foreshore at Red Island and at Holmpatrick, Skerries Village, DD/82, 83.

Angelica

A. sylvestris L.
Wild Angelica   Native

1	2	3	4	5	6	7	8

Widespread and common in hedgerows, drains, streams, rivers, canals and dune-slacks.
FID.

Pastinaca

P. sativa L. subsp. **sativa** *(Peucedanum sativum)*
Wild Parsnip   Probably introduced

Colgan: 2. Fields at Baldrummond near the Man of War: *Mack. Cat.* Frequent as a relic of cultivation about Rush, 1902: *N.C.* 4. Plentifully about the quarry near Finglas Bridge: *Wade Dubl.*, 1794 in profusion all round the quarries here in 1903! 7. Abundant and evidently long established on quarry spoil-banks near the 3rd Lock, Grand Canal, 1902: *Colgan 1903.*
Suppl: 4. Abundant about Glasnevin (1932). 5. By the R. Tolka near Drumcondra Bridge (1932). Decreasing at all stations except Rush, due to the reclamation of waste ground.

1	2	3	4	5	7	8

Occasional on waste ground. The survival of the colony of this species at Finglas Bridge (4), where it was recorded by Wade before 1794 and confirmed by Colgan in 1903, is of note. Until recent building operations, several hundred plants appeared every year, growing in closed grassland. The colony is now much reduced but a few plants persist on part of the hill that is believed to be a remnant of the Greenhills esker.
1. Roadside ditch at Naul, almost certainly a garden escape, GS/83. Beside the Belfast to Dublin road, 2 km south of Balrothery, GS/84.
2. Waste ground near the railway line at Ballealy Dump, DD/84. Rogerstown Dump, DD/82. North of Ballykea, RF/86.
4. Still plentiful on the esker ridge behind the Royal Oak pub at Finglas Bridge and occasional on waste ground 1 km to the west, DD/68-92 & MN, JS/83, 84.
5. St Doolagh's Quarry, HJH/83. Waste ground opposite Sutton Railway Station, ENL/83.
7. In a waste ground near St Patrick's Cathedral, MSS, PWJ/80.
8. Near the coal dump at Ringsend Dump, HOR/86.
FID.

Heracleum

H. sphondylium L.
Hogweed   Native

| 1 | 2 | 3 | 4 | 5 | 6 | 7 | 8 |

Widespread and abundant in neglected pastures, hedgebanks and roadsides.
FID.

H. sphondylium × H. mantegazzianum
Native

| 4 | 5 | (6) | 8 |

Very rare. This hybrid was first described and recorded by Praeger, from near Lucan (6) in 1950 and 1951 but not refound there during this survey.
4. A single plant in the National Botanic Gardens, Glasnevin, DS/87.
5. Portmarnock Bridge, DD/92.
8. Along the lower reaches of the Shanganagh River, Loughlinstown, SR/88, 89.

H. mantegazzianum Sommier & Levier *(H. villosum)*
Giant Hogweed   Alien

| 4 | 5 | 6 | 7 | 8 |

Locally abundant on riverbanks and roadsides and now common near Howth Castle, following its spread from the garden. This species, an introduction from the Caucasus, is spreading widely in the county, especially on riverbanks, such as those of the Rivers Tolka and Dodder. To some extent it poses a health hazard, particularly to young children who have been known to use its stems as pea-shooters. When handled, the juice released may initiate a photosensitive reaction causing a blister or burn to appear on the skin when it is exposed to sunlight. Wyse Jackson (1989) and Reilly (1993) have reported an undated specimen in **TCD**, annotated by W. Harvey who died in 1866. This is the earliest known Irish record. Full details of its spread in Ireland are given in Wyse Jackson (1989).
FID.

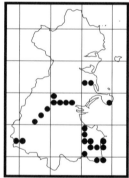

Torilis

T. japonica (Houtt.) DC. *(Caucalis anthriscus)*
Upright Hedge-parsley   Native

| 1 | 2 | 3 | 4 | 5 | 6 | 7 | 8 |

Common by roadsides and on banks especially in dry sandy ground.

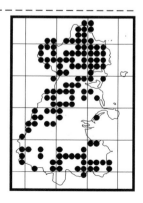

T. nodosa (L.) Gaertner *(Caucalis nodosa)*
Knotted Hedge-parsley   Native

Colgan: 1. Near the Bog of the Ring and 2. At Skerries, 1902; on Colt island and abundant on St Patrick's island, 1893:
N.C. 3. On Lambay island: *Flor. Lambay.* Near Donabate, 1895; abundant in sandy banks and fallows, Portrane peninsula,
1900; frequent along the Malahide creek from Lissen Hall to Corballis, 1902; 4. Sparingly at Lucan bridge, Royal Canal,
1893: *N.C.* 5. Sandy banks on the Burrow: *Flor. Howth.* At Baldoyle, 1892; 6. South of Clondalkin, 1893; near Lucan
railway station, 1900; 7. Roadside banks near Drimnagh, 1894; near Whitehall quarries, 1895; near Ballynamanagh, 1900;
and at Ballyfermot, 1902: *N.C.* 8. "In dry Banks below *Ring's-end* lying upon the Ground near the Sea": *Threlkeld.*
Abundant on roadside banks and at the foot of walls near Crinken, 1894: *N.C.*
Suppl: Occasional. 5. Cloghran (J.P. Brunker, 1920). Kilbarrack (J.P.B., 1920). 7. St Joseph's Clondalkin (1953). 8. Opposite
Sandyford National Schools (R.W. Scully, 1920).

(1)	(2)	(3)	(4)	**5**	(6)	(7)	(8)

Very rare, in dry ground near the sea. Very much rarer now than at the turn of the century.
One of its former habitats, dry sandy ground at the base of walls, has been much reduced
through local authority cleansing operations.

5. A single plant by the bridge on the cliff path above Whitewater Brook, Howth, DD/88. Sea
    wall by the Marine Hotel at Sutton, PG/87. Still at Baldoyle where a few plants grow on a dry
    bank near the north end of the former Racecourse, west of Mayne River bridge, DN/91.

Daucus

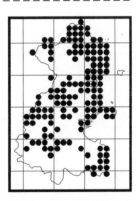

D. carota L.
Wild Carrot   Native

1	2	3	4	5	6	7	8

Dry sandy soils especially near the sea. Locally frequent inland
on gravel banks and ridges and sandy places. Forms similar in
morphology to subsp. **carota** and subsp. **gummifer** Hook. fil.
occur in the county. However, the distinction between them
does not appear particularly clear in Co. Dublin or in Ireland.

GENTIANACEAE

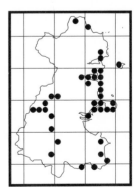

Centaurium

C. erythraea Rafn *(Erythraea centaurium, Centaurium minus)*
Common Centaury   Native

(1)	2	3	4	5	6	7	8

Common on the coast in mature dune grassland and occasional
on sandy ground and banks inland.

C. pulchellum (Sw.) Druce *(Erythraea pulchella)*
Lesser Centaury   Native

Colgan: 5. On the North Bull in tolerable plenty, 1867 *(D. Orr) Rec. Add.* By the edges of damp hollows near the Club-
house at the southern end of the North Bull, and again abundantly in the salt marsh towards the northern end in
association with *Statice occidentalis* and *Sagina maritima,* 1903: *N.C.*

5

Very rare, on bare sandy ground subject to occasional inundation by the sea where it may be
locally abundant. It has apparently become more common in recent years on North Bull Island
(5). Legally protected under the Wildlife Act of 1976 as an endangered species in Ireland.
5. Salt-marsh on Portmarnock Golf-course, DN/91. Upper part of the salt-marsh near the
    northern tip of North Bull Island and to the south, ENL, CB/86 & DN, W. Bradley/89, 91.
    Frequent in the large salt-pan at the south end of North Bull Island and north from there
    along a dune-slack to just south-east of the Farm, DN, PG/91.

Blackstonia

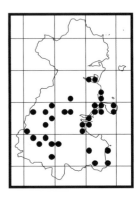

B. perfoliata (L.) Hudson *(Chlora perfoliata)*
Yellow-wort   Native

Colgan: Frequent and locally abundant. Abundant and often luxuriant along the
coasts of the county.

(2)	3	4	5	6	7	8

Common in dune-slacks and sand-hills in 3 & 5. Occasional on
sandy ground and banks inland. Much less common now in inland
sites in north Co. Dublin than at the end of the 19th century.
FID.

Gentianella

G. campestris (L.) Boerner *(Gentiana campestris)*
Field Gentian   Native

Colgan: 2. Sandy fields and banks about Rush: *Ir. Flor.* 5. Near Warren House: *Wade Dubl.* Plentiful on the hill of Howth
near the Light house: *Mack. Rar.* Between Howth and Baldoyle: *Ir. Flor.* Fields by the Baily Light-house; near the Needles:
Flor. Howth. Ireland's Eye, 1897 *(Praeger) Top. Bot.* Abundant in a field from Earlscliff to the Baily Light-house, Howth,
1903: *Miss R. Mahaffy.* 7. Near the summit of Mount Seskin, 1892, and abundant in hill pastures at Augh Farrell, 1894; 8.
Sparingly above the bridge at Glencullen, 1893: *N.C.*
Suppl: 5. Still on Howth Head near Baily (1937). 7. Glenasmole (1920-1942). Not confirmed in other stations.

(2)	5	(7)	(8)

Some of the early records for this species may refer to **G. amarella**.
5. Alder Marsh on North Bull Island, with **G. amarella**, JP/92.

G. amarella (L.) Boerner (incl. subsp. **hibernica** N. Pritch.; *Gentiana amarella*)
Autumn Gentian   Native

Colgan: 3. Abundant in the Portrane sandhills, 1902; 4. Quarries near Dunsoghly, and abundant by the Ward river above
Chapelmidway, 1894: by the Tolka near Blanchardstown, 1895; by the Royal Canal, Clonsilla, 1903: *N.C.* 5. On the Cosh,

Howth, 1883: *Herb. Vowell*. On Shielmartin, Howth *(Miss R. Mahaffy) Praeger 1895*. Frequent on the south side of Howth Head, and abundant in sandhills and sandy fallows at Portmarnock, 1902; 6. Roadside at the top of Mount Seskin, 1892; abundant along the Grand Canal for about 2 miles east from Hazelhatch, 1900, quarry banks at Colganstown, 1894; &c; 7. Grand Canal below Clondalkin, 1893; abundant in hill pastures at Augh Farrell, 1896; by the Dodder from Old Bawn to Bohernabreena, 1903: *N.C.* 8. In upland pastures at Barnikeula near Kilgobbin: *Wade Dubl.* Hilly pastures at Ballyman, 1894: *N.C.* This species is specially luxuriant in hollows of the Portmarnock sandhills, where it attains to a height of 13 inches. A white-flowered variety occurs in marshy ground above Saggard: *N.C.*

DNFC Annual Report for 1953: 7. Old Bawn, J.P. Brunker.

Suppl: 5. Abundant on the North Bull.

| (3) | (4) | 5 | 6 | (7) | (8) |

Rare, in sand-dunes and limestone grassland. The former site at Dunsoghly Quarries (4) is now filled in. Plants on North Bull Island are all a very dark blue-purple in colour and are therefore similar in colour to and occur intermixed with plants of the previous species.

5. Scattered in dune-slacks and adjoining sand-hills near the Alder Marsh and on west side of Royal Dublin Golf-course and just west of tip of North Bull Island, MS/70, ENL, MN/84, ENL, CB/86 & DN/89. Still at Portmarnock dunes, DD/86-94.
6. Still by the Grand Canal on spoil heaps at Gollierstown Bridge, MN/88, 89.

APOCYNACEAE

Vinca

V. minor L.
Lesser Periwinkle   Alien

| 1 | 2 | 3 | 4 | 5 | 7 | 8 |

An occasional garden escape; mainly in hedgerows.

V. major L.
Greater Periwinkle   Alien

| 1 | 2 | 3 | 4 | 5 | 6 | 7 | 8 |

An occasional garden escape, mainly in hedgerows. Often associated with dwellings and persisting long after they have been abandoned.

SOLANACEAE

Lycium

L. barbarum L./L. chinense Miller *(L. halimifolium)*
Duke of Argyll's Teaplant/Chinese Teaplant   Alien

Colgan: 5. Coast near Baldoyle, 1868: *Herb. R.M. Barrington.* Thoroughly established in sandy ground and by the roadside between Greenfields and Sutton: *Flor. Howth.* In considerable quantity in this last station, stretching along the shore for

100 yards, and apparently reproducing itself from seed, also covering fully 600 square yards of a rough sandy pasture near Sutton school-house, 1903: sparingly by the shore near Malahide, 1902: *N.C.* A single well-grown plant near the northern end of the North Bull more than a mile distant from the nearest house or garden and growing amongst *Artemisia Stelleriana*, 1901-03: *Colgan 1903.* 8. A few small plants on the East Pier, Kingstown, near Victoria Beach, 1902, and well-established on steep drift banks near the gas-works, Kingstown, 1903: *N.C.* A native of Southern Europe much grown in cottage gardens and appearing as an introduced plant on sandy shores so far north as Stockholm. Derived from cultivation in all of its Dublin stations, but fully naturalised about Sutton.

Suppl: 1. Near Bog of the Ring (1947-1957). 2. Rogerstown (1952). Rush (1955).

(1)	2	3	4	5	6	7	8

Rare, on roadsides and sandy ground by the sea. The distinction between these species is far from clear in Co. Dublin and records here are grouped together.

2. Shore north of Skerries, DD/87. Frequent just east of Rogerstown Coastguard Station, DD/87.
3. Hedge along the western side of the Island Golf-course, PR/88, **NDR**.
4. Royal Canal at Cross Guns Bridge, MN, DN/87, **NDR**.
5. Hedge, near Kinsealy, ENL/85. Eastern side of St Anne's Park, Raheny, DN/88. Drumcondra, DN/88. Drumleck, Howth Head, DN/89. Hole-in-the-wall Beach, Sutton, PG/88.
6. Hedgerow, 1.5 km west of Rathcoole, JP/86. By the Grand Canal, 3 km north of Newcastle, JP, DAS/84. Roadside, 2 km east of Fortunestown, JP/84.
7. Waste ground at Crumlin, PWJ/84.
8. Sea front at the land end of East Pier at Dun Laoghaire, SR, HOR/84.

- -

Atropa

A. belladonna L.
Deadly Nightshade   Alien

4	5	7	(8)

Rare, on waste ground.

4. Abbotstown grounds, DNFC/c.89
5. Waste ground at Holy Cross College grounds, Drumcondra, DN/88. By the Railway Station at Killester, BB, DD/76, **NDR**.
7. Bank of the River Dodder at Delaford, JP, DK/83. Weed on the wall outside T.C.D. Botanic Garden, Palmerston Park, PWJ/87. Garden weed at Pembroke Road, Ballsbridge, MWJ/81 (probably an escape from the former T.C.D. Botanic Garden on Lansdowne Road), **NDR**.

- -

Hyoscyamus

H. niger L.
Henbane   Native;   probably introduced

Colgan: 2. Sparingly by the shore at Loughshinny and 3. near Corballis, 1893; by the shore near Newport House, 1902: *N.C.* On the south-east side of Lambay island: *Flor. Lambay* abundant here in 1896: *Ir. Nat.*, 1896. 4. Waste ground at Tyrrellstown, Mulhuddart, 1893: *N.C.* 5. "In a ditch at Portmaddock (Portmarnock), 1732, and frequent on ye sea shore beyond Clantarff, 1736": *Annot in Threlkeld.* Clontarf and Howth: *Wade Dubl.* Portmarnock sandhills, 1882: *Herb. Vowell.* Ireland's Eye, 1872

(Greenwood Pim) Cyb. II. and in 1899! A garden weed at Fairview, Clontarf, 1890-92 *(Miss A.G. Kinahan) Cyb. II.* Near the Martello tower, Sutton, 1895; near the Old Baily, Howth, 1900; in some quantity on banks by the sea between Glenaveena and the Baily Light-house, 1902: *N.C.* Near Greenfields, Sutton, in sandy ground and on the new tram track, also on clay banks below the Deer Park quarry: *Hart 1897.* 7. Roadsides at Kilmainham near the new gaol: *Wade Dubl.* Sparingly in a gravel pit near Newtown, Tallaght, 1895: *N.C.* 8. Sandymount and Irishtown: *Wade Dubl.* Near Sandymount railway station 1882; at Loughlinstown, 1874: *Greenwood Pim.* North side of Bray harbour, 1873: *Herb. R.M. Barrington.*

Suppl: 3. Near Portrane North Martello Tower (1920). Still on Lambay (1957). 4. Blanchardstown (J.P. Brunker, 1922). 5. Still abundant on S.E. shore of Ireland's Eye (1954). Waste ground in Baldoyle village (1954).

| (2) | 3 | (4) | 5 | (7) | 8 |

Extremely rare.
3. Still at Corballis, HJH/70, 72.
5. Still on Ireland's Eye, on a sandy beach at the west end, JP, PWJ/82 & PG/91.
8. Old walled garden at Rocklands House, east of Sandyford, PC/78, 79.

Solanum

S. nigrum L.
Black Nightshade   Probably introduced

Colgan: 5. Near Richmond: *Mack. Cat.* Occasionally as a garden weed about Raheny, as at Rose Vale, &c.: *Flor. Howth.* Furry Park, Killester, 1868: *Hart MS.* Sparingly on the North Bull, 1896: *N.C.* 7. In considerable quantity in waste ground near Clyde Road, 1902: *Miss M.C. Knowles.* 8. A very abundant garden weed at Easton Lodge, Monkstown, 1873-74, then disappearing: *Greenwood Pim.* Abundant as a garden weed at Corke Abbey, Old Connaught, 1902, and for about 15 years previously: *J. Meade.*

Suppl: Casual. 8. Garden weed at Mount Merrion (1949) and St Alban's Park, Ballsbridge (1950). Not confirmed in any of Colgan's stations.

| 2 | 5 | (7) | 8 |

Rare on waste ground, tilled fields and as a garden weed.
2. Several large plants in a neglected tilled field at Raheny, east of Lusk, DD/84, **NDR**. Rogerstown Vilage, DD/87.
5. Weedy tilled field at Malahide and in waste ground to the north-west, ENL/83 & PG/87, 88. Waste ground near the River Tolka Basin, PG/90. Dublin Port, SR/88, 91. Howth Harbour, PG/91.
8. Tilled fields near Kilgobbin and at Carrickmines, PC/75. Waste ground behind Blackrock Catholic Church, F. Richardson/80. Among planted shrubs at the north end of Sandymount Strand, SR, HOR/86.

S. dulcamara L.
Bittersweet   Native

| 1 | 2 | 3 | 4 | 5 | 6 | 7 | 8 |

Common in hedges, woodlands, drains and riverbanks in the lowlands. Frequently in damp habitats; less often on walls and waste ground.
FID.

CONVOLVULACEAE

Convolvulus

C. arvensis L.
Field Bindweed   Native

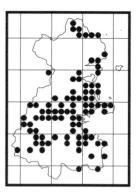

| 1 | 2 | 3 | 4 | 5 | 6 | 7 | 8 |

Common in sand-dunes and waste ground, particularly on sandy soil. Rare in 1.
FID.

Calystegia

C. soldanella (L.) R. Br.
Sea Bindweed   Native

Colgan: 2. Shore at Rogerstown, 1891: *Miss A.G. Kinahan.* 5. In the sandhills at Portmarnock: *Mack. Cat.* On the North Bull, 1866: *Hart MS.* Sparingly here in 1895 *(N.C.) Cyb. II.* Very sparingly by the shore at Greenfields *(Mrs Mahaffy) Flor. Howth.* 8. "Plentifully on ye shore behind the 3 hills beyond Bullock between Dalkey island and Bray": *Annot. in Threlkeld* not later than 1740. Sandy shores at Killiney Bay: *Wade Dubl.* (the same locality as the preceding) abundant here, occupying a space of fully 400 square yards, 1903! A decreasing maritime species, now become very rare.
Suppl: 8. Still at Killiney Bay (1918-1948).

| 2 | 5 | (8) |

Rare in sand-dunes and sand-hills. *Colgan* considered that this species was declining in frequency. Its recent rediscovery at Rogerstown where it had not been recorded for almost a century and at Portmarnock where it was last recorded in 1824 suggest that it may well also reappear at Killiney.
2. Still at Rogerstown on sand-dunes, RF/88.
5. Still at Portmarnock Peninsula on sand-hills, DN/89. Still on North Bull Island on eroding sand-dunes at the southern end and on primary dunes at the northern end, PG/87-91.

C. sepium (L.) R. Br.
Hedge Bindweed   Native

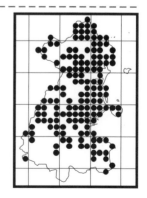

| 1 | 2 | 3 | 4 | 5 | 6 | 7 | 8 |

Common on roadsides, in hedgerows and river valleys.
FID.

C. sepium × C. silvatica (C. × lucana (Ten.) Don)

| 8 |

Very rare.

8. At the south and north ends of Booterstown Marsh, SR/88, 89. Commons Road, Loughlinstown, SR/88.

C. silvatica (Kit.) Griseb.
Large Bindweed   Alien

| 1 | 2 | 3 | 4 | 5 | 6 | 7 | 8 |

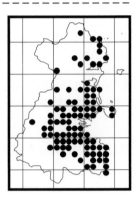

Common in dry waste ground and hedgerows, particularly in the city and suburbs. Not distinguished from **C. sepium** in *Colgan* or *Suppl.*
FID.

CUSCUTACEAE

Cuscuta

C. epithymum (L.) L. *(C. trifolii)*
Dodder   Native

Colgan: 1. Two large patches on Trifolium pratense in a field S.W. of Ballyboghil: *Colgan 1895.* 2. Abundant in Rush sandhills, especially about the coastguard station, spreading for about a quarter of a mile, chiefly on thymy and grassy banks, but also appearing in large scattered patches in fallow fields, occurring on *Anthyllis, Ononis,* Clovers and Thyme: *Colgan 1903.* 3. Abundant on *Anthyllis* and on *Trifolium pratense* in a sandy fallow to the north of Portrane peninsula: *Colgan 1895.* 5. On vetches near Sutton, 1881 *(Hart) Cyb. II.* 8. In patches for about 20 yards in a small field belonging to Clifton Lodge, between Ballybrack and Bray, 1868 *(Dr W.G. Smith) Proc. Dubl. Nat. His. Soc. V.,* p.198, 1871.

Suppl: 2. Still at Rush, and also occurring on *Galium verum.* 5. Abundant on *Ulex* near central marsh, Howth (1940). This station had disappeared in 1956 owing to quarrying.

| (1) | (2) | (3) | (5) | (8) |

Not refound at any of its former sites in the county.

MENYANTHACEAE

Menyanthes

M. trifoliata L.
Bogbean   Native

(1)	2	(3)	4	5	6	(7)	8

Scattered in the Royal Canal (4 & 5); very rare elsewhere.
2. Mill pools, south-east of Balbriggan, DD/85.
5. Wet field at Thormanby Road, Howth, DN/89.
8. In and to the south of Ballybetagh Bog, JP/83 & SR, JR/87.

BORAGINACEAE

Lithospermum

L. officinale L.
Common Gromwell   Native

Colgan: 2. Near Thomondtown, 1893; 3. Roadsides near Grace Dieu, and by the river at Knocksedan, 1894; field borders at Portrane, 1895; at Ballisk, 1902; near Swords, 1903: *N.C.* 4. Finglas Bridge: *Wade Dubl.* Cardiff's Bridge; Scribblestown; Knockmaroon: *Ir. Flor.* Near Finglas, 1894; abundant by the road through Saint Catherine's 1895; near Woodlands, by the Liffey, 1901: *N.C.* 5. Abundant on banks along the shore between Clontarf and Kilbarrick: *Ir. Flor.* Near Raheny, 1894; roadside near Malahide, 1900; bushy places on Feltrim Hill, 1904; &c.; 6. At Castle Bagot and by the Grand Canal near Gollierstown, 1903; 7. Roadside banks near Old Bawn and hedges near Drimnagh, 1893: *N.C.* "At the Foot on *Inisacore-hill* and under the Brow above *Palmerston Mills*": *Threlkeld.* 8. At Kiltiernan, 1853: *Rev. S.A. Brenan.* Abundant on roadsides and on roadside banks and hedges east of Ballycorus, 1894-1902: *N.C.* A wide-spread species in the county, but seldom occurring in abundance. *Suppl:* 4. By Royal Canal near Kirkpatrick Bridge (1932). Furry Glen (1943-1957). Between Ballymun and Dubber Cross (1943). 5. Between Cloghran and Feltrim (1932). Site of Carrickhill (1956). 6. Roadside between Newcastle and Rathcoole (1947). 7. Tymon Lane (1954).

(2)	(3)	4	5	6	(7)	(8)

Rare on roadsides and in hedgerows on limestone soils. Many of its former sites in 5 have been built-over.
4. North of Powerstown House, c. 3 km north-west of Mulhuddart, JS/87. Still in St Catherine's Woods, JS/84. Still in the Furry Glen in the Phoenix Park, DD/84. Island Pond in the Phoenix Park, JS, MN, ENL/83. Amongst scrub in sand-pits at Astagob, Strawberry Beds, MN/90.
5. Grassy verge of woodland, Howth demesne, CB/92.
6. Grassy bank at Milltown, CB/87. Hedgerow on banks of the Grand Canal at Ballymakaily Mill, CB/87 & MN/89. Still on banks of the Grand Canal, west of Gollierstown Bridge, MN/89.

L. arvense L. *(Buglossoides arvensis)*
Field Gromwell   Native

Colgan: 4. Broken fields about Glasnevin: *Ir. Flor.* A single plant near King James's Castle, Finglas, 1903: *(Miss M.C. Knowles) Colgan 1904.* 5. Broken fields about Drumcondra: *Ir. Flora.* Sparingly on steep banks above the sea near Piper's Gut, Howth

Head: *Flor. Howth.* 7. At Whitehall, 1889 *(Miss A.G. Kinahan) Cyb. II.* 8. In cornfields near Dalkey obelisk *(Mr Brinkley) Templeton MS.* Cultivated fields at foot of Three Rock mountain: *Wade Rar.* Roadside near Carrickmines, sparingly, 1903 *(Arthur D. O'Murchoe) Colgan 1904.* Appears to be now quite a rare plant in Dublin, but it is not unlikely to be overlooked.

Suppl: Casual only. 5. Garden, Hampstead, apparently ex poultry food (1956).

| (4) | (5) | (7) | (8) |

Not refound at any of its former sites in the county.

Echium

E. vulgare L.
Viper's-bugloss   Native

Colgan: 2. Between Skerries and Balbriggan *(Moore) Cyb.* On the warren south of Rush, plentifully *(More) Rec. Add.* frequent here in 1902! Dry field near Gormanstown Castle: *Praeger 1894a.* 3. Railway bank near Raheen Point, Rogerstown creek, 1894-1902: *N.C.* 4. Above an old quarry near Finglas: *Ir. Flor.* 5. At Portmarnock *(Moore) Cyb.* Roadside near Robb's walls, Malahide, and abundant in a field at Portmarnock, 1896: *J. Trumbull.* Here and there in Portmarnock sandhills, and abundant in two places on their landward margin, 1902; in sandy fallows, North Bull, 1903: *N.C.* 7. On the roadside near Mount Venus, 1802: *Templeton MS.* 8. On the railway at Foxrock, sparingly 1894: *N.C.*

Suppl: 2. Coast at Gormanstown and W.of Rush (A.W. Stelfox, 1923), S.of Rush (1956). 3. Burrow, Portrane (1953), S. of Portrane Head (1955). 5. Still at Portmarnock (1950).

Brunker MS: 3. Killeek Reservoir, '54, DNFC.

| I | 2 | 3 | 4 | 5 | 7 | (8) |

Rare, on roadsides, sandy places and former fallow land. Several of the records cited below are from beside the Dublin to Belfast Road along which the species is possibly dispersed by gravel trucks travelling from sand quarries near Gormanstown (Co. Meath) where it is common.

1. Oldtown, GS/83. Roadside of the Dublin to Belfast road, 2 km south of Balrothery, GS/84.
2. Still in quantity in former fallow land to the west of Rush Golf-course, DD/87, JP, S.Waldren/92. Hedgerow, Balscadden, RF/86.
3. In sand-hills near the sea at the north end of the Portrane Peninsula, PR/85.
4. Mountainview Graveyard, Mulhuddart, MN/82; not refound MN/83. A single plant in disturbed ground west of Finglas bridge, MN, JS/84.
5. Near the crossroads at Cloghran, on the Belfast Road, DD/69.
7. Still at Mount Venus, on the roof of ruins, where it was first recorded by Templeton in 1802, DK/85.

Symphytum

S. officinale L.
Common Comfrey   Possibly introduced

Colgan: Near Garristown, 1893; 2. Roadside near Balscaddan, 1894; 3. Near Newport House, Malahide creek, and abundant on banks and in sandy fallows near Corballis, Portrane, 1902: *N.C.* 4. By the public road at Ashtown: *Wade Dubl.* Near Blanchardstown, 1895; in several places between Knockmaroon and Woodlands, 1900: *N.C.* 5. At Portmarnock and Goose Green: *Miss A.G. Kinahan.* Banks by the railway between Clontarf and Raheny, 1893-1904; near Sutton, 1895; on field banks near Baldoyle, 1894-1900. 6. Sparingly near Raheen, Clondalkin, 1903; by the Liffey above Salmon Leap, 1904: *N.C.* 7. Near the lower end of Kelly's glen: *Mack. Cat.* Roadside near Kimmage, 1894-1900;

8. Frequent by the river near Whitechurch, 1893-1903; abundant by the Shanganagh river near its mouth, and frequent in adjacent fallows and marshy ground, 1894-1904: *N.C.*

| I | (2) | 3 | 4 | (5) | (6) | 7 | 8 |

Rare in river valleys. Scattered throughout the county. Some earlier records may refer to **S.** × **uplandicum** Nyman.
4. Strawberry Beds west of Knockmaroon Hill, DD/86.
7. By the River Dodder near Firhouse, DK/83 & M.B. Jones/81
8. By the Shanganagh River east of Loughlinstown, SR/85.

S. officinale × **S. asperum (S.** × **uplandicum** Nyman; *S. peregrinum*)
Russian Comfrey   Alien

| I | 2 | 3 | 4 | 5 | 6 | 7 | 8 |

Occasional on waste ground and roadsides.

S. asperum Lepechin
Rough Comfrey   Alien

| 8 |

Extremely rare.
8. By the Shanganagh River, east of Loughlinstown, SR/85.

S. tuberosum L.
Tuberous Comfrey   Alien

| I | 5 | 8 |

Very rare on roadsides. A persistent garden escape or outcast.
1. Walshestown, DD/84.
5. Baily Post Office, Howth, S. Clark, F. Perring/68. Roadside at Feltrim Hill, S. Dickinson/67.
8. Roadside west of Shankill, HOR/85.

Anchusa

A. arvensis (L.) M. Bieb. *(Lycopsis arvensis)*
Bugloss   Native

Colgan: 2. Frequent at Skerries, 1900, and in profusion at Rush, 1902; *N.C.* 3. On the south-east side of Lambay: *Flor. Lambay.* Very abundant in sandy fields in the Portrane peninsula, 1902: *N.C.* 5. Sandy fields near Kilbarrick church and about Baldoyle: *Mack. Cat.* Very abundant here and at Portmarnock in sandy cornfields, 1903; abundant on clay banks on the south-east side of Howth Head, 1900: *N.C.* On Ireland's Eye: *Flor. Howth.* (8. Killiney: *Ir. Flor.* not seen recently).

| 2 | 3 | 5 | (8) |

Frequent in fallows along the coast between Portmarnock and Rush. Also as a garden weed, on sandy ground at Rush, Skerries and Donabate; very rare elsewhere.
5. Common around the Martello Tower at Howth Harbour, PG/92.

Pentaglottis

P. sempervirens (L.) Tausch ex L. Bailey *(Anchusa sempervirens)*
Green Alkanet   Alien

| 4 | 5 | 6 | 7 | 8 |

Occasional on roadsides, waste ground and in hedges. Well established in various parts of the county, especially 5 and 8. Sometimes naturalized from nearby gardens.
FID.

Borago

B. officinalis L.
Borage   Alien

Suppl: 2. Still at St Patrick's Island (1918). 5. Sutton (1935). Baldoyle (1950). 7. Still by the Dodder at Firhouse (1957). Included only in Colgan's Appendix.

| 2 | 5 | (7) | 8 |

Very rare.
2. Still on St Patrick's Island, Skerries at the ruined church, DD, N. McGough/83 & JP/83.
5. Waste ground at Portmarnock Raceway, DN/88.
8. Coast near the Martello Tower, south of Killiney, SR/85. Roadside north-east of Carrickgollogan, SR/90.

Mertensia

M. maritima (L.) Gray
Oysterplant   Native

| (2) |

Almost certainly extinct in Dublin. A very rare and endangered plant in Ireland. Legally protected under the Wildlife Act of 1976. Farrell and Randall (1992) review the past and present distribution of this species in Ireland, up to the last Dublin record in 1858. It was formerly recorded at Portmarnock, Loughshinny and Skerries-Balbriggan.

Amsinckia

A. micrantha Suksd. *(A. calycina)*
Common Fiddleneck   Alien

| 2 |

Very rare. There are specimens of this species and/or of **A. lycopsoides** (Lehm.) Lehm. in **DBN** collected from other sites in the county prior to the present survey.
2. Weedy field just north of Baldongan cross roads, RF/85. Sandy fallow north-west of Rush Golf-course, DD/89.

Myosotis

M. scorpioides L. *(M. palustris)*
Water Forget-me-not   Native

| 1 | (2) | 3 | 4 | 5 | (6) | 7 | 8 |

Common in ditches streams and marshes; rare in 8.
8. The Dingle, HOR, ENL, J.Doyle/84.

M. secunda A. Murray *(M. repens)*
Creeping Forget-me-not   Native

| (1) | (5) | 6 | 7 | 8 |

Occasional to common on acid and marshy ground in 6, 7 and 8.

M. laxa Lehm. subsp. **caespitosa** (Schultz) Hyl. ex Nordh. *(M. caespitosa)*
Tufted Forget-me-not   Native

| (1) | 2 | (3) | 4 | 5 | 6 | 7 | 8 |

Rare to occasional in marshes and muddy fields throughout the county.
2. Wet field near the Corn Mill, near Balbriggan, RF/87. Marsh, 1 km west of Loughshinny, DD/85.
4. At Dunsoghly and near Newpark House 2 km to the north of Dunsoghly, MN/83, 84.
   Near the northern border of district, west of Dublin Airport, MN/84. Dubber Cross,
   Finglas, MN/85.
5. Wet field at Portmarnock Brickfields, ENL/85 & DN/88.
6. West of the Brittas Inn, DD/82. Stream between The Killigeen and Newtown, DD/83.
7. Common in Glenasmole by the reservoirs, DD, EMcA/83 & MN/88. Marshy meadow by
   the Grand Canal at Cloverhill, Clondalkin, MWJ/87. Wet flush on heathy mountainside,
   north of Ballymaice, PWJ/84.
8. Wet meadow by a stream, south of The Scalp, HOR/86. Booterstown Marsh, SR, HOR/85.
   Ballybetagh Bog, DNFC/83. Quarry pond on the north slope of Ticknock, SR/88.

M. arvensis (L.) Hill
Field Forget-me-not   Native

| 1 | 2 | 3 | 4 | 5 | 6 | 7 | 8 |

Common in sand-hills, roadside verges and waste ground.
FID.

M. ramosissima Rochel *(M. collina, M. hispida)*
Early Forget-me-not   Native

Colgan: 2. In the sandhills at Rush, 1903: *N.C.* 3. Very abundant on Lambay and a characteristic feature in the flora of the
island: *Flor. Lambay.* Frequent in Portrane peninsula, 1904: *N.C.* 5. In a dry sandy field at Portmarnock *(F. Whitla* and *J.
Johnston) Flor. Hib.* Abundant in the Portmarnock sandhills, 1902, and on Feltrim Hill, 1904; frequent on Ireland's Eye,
1899: *N.C.* At Malahide *(Moore) Cyb.* At Kilbarrick: *Flor. Howth.*

| (2) | 3 | 5 | 8 |

Common in sand-dunes on North Bull Island (5); rare elsewhere.
3. Still in short turf, Lambay Island, DD/91.
5. Occasional in thin sand-dune grassland in Portmarnock sand-hills, DD/89.
8. Dry bank just below railway bridge at Whiterock, Killiney, HOR/85, **NDR**.

M. discolor Pers. *(M. versicolor)*
Changing Forget-me-not   Native

1	2	3	(4)	(5)	(6)	7	8

Occasional on base-poor marshy or dry ground; rarely on roadsides.
1. Weed in cultivated fields at Laurel Mount, GS/86. West and north-east of Naul, GS/84, 87. North of Ballyboghil, GS/86.
2. North-north-west of Man O'War, DD/85. Roadside just west of Collinstown Bridge, DD/85. Grassed-over ballast pit at Skerries Railway Station, DD, EMcA/85. Hedgerow at Ballykea, RF/87. Rubble by an old outhouse at Ardgillan Park, MN/90.
3. Occasional near the shore on Lambay Island, DD/91.
7. Marsh, north-west of St Ann's Chapel, Glenasmole, DNFC/88. Steep grassland bank, north of Rockbrook, CB/88. Marshy grassland on the lower slopes above the southern reservoir in Glenasmole, CB, SR/90.
8. Roadside bank in the Glencullen Valley, west of Boranaraltry Lane, HOR, SR/86. Field above the river in Ballyman Glen, DNFC/83. Cliff top at Whiterock, Killiney, SR/85. Roches Hill, SR/89. Dalkey Hill, SR/91.

Cynoglossum

C. officinale L.
Hound's-tongue   Native

Colgan: 2. Abundant in the sandhills at Rush, 1894-1903: *N.C.* 3. On the Sandy Common opposite to Malahide: *Mack. Cat.* Frequent in the southern part of Portrane peninsula, 1902: *N.C.* no doubt the same station as the preceding. On the east side of Lambay island: *Flor. Lambay.* (4. In Phoenix Park: *Wade Dubl.* not seen recently). 5. Abundant at Kilbarrick and near Warren House: *Wade Dubl.* At Kilbarrick, 1894; abundant on Ireland's Eye, 1882-1900; in great profusion in sandy fallows and amongst the sandhills at Portmarnock, 1903: *N.C.* Frequent on Howth Burrow; between Drumleck and the Baily Lighthouse; on the Cosh: *Flor. Howth.* (8. "In Mirrion churchyard": *Threlkeld.* At Merrion: *Wade Dubl.* not seen recently in this district).

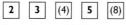

2	3	(4)	5	(8)

Rare, in sand-hills.
2. Still in sand-hills at Rogerstown, DD/87, PG/90.
3. Sandy ground on the Island Golf-course, DD, PR/83-85.
5. Sand-hills, east of Portmarnock, RF/83 & ENL/84. Abundant on trackways, blow-outs and in the lee of the main sand-dunes throughout Portmarnock sand-dunes, DD/89.

VERBENACEAE

Verbena

V. officinalis L.
Vervain   Alien

Colgan: 3. By the walls of the old church near Swords; 4. near Luttrell's town; at the foot of Knockmaroon Hill; near Finglas bridge, towards the west: *Wade Dubl.* Well established to the west of Woodlands (Luttrell's town) on a bank by the road leading from the Liffey to Clonsilla, 1893-1904, and in waste ground near Lucan bridge, 1903: *N.C.* 5. Roadside between Santry and Coolock: *Ir. Flor.* 8. At Dalkey; on the Commons near Bray: *Wade Dubl.* Abundant in waste ground near the Park, formerly the Commons, at Little Bray and several plants by the river there, 1901: *N.C.* A few plants on the lower Old Connaught road, Bray, 1900: *J. Meade.* Commons at Loughlinstown: *Ir. Flor.* Spreading for some hundreds of yards on banks and at the foot of walls along the north side of Loughlinstown Commons, 1900-03: *N.C.* A relic of cultivation which has held its ground for upwards of a century in its stations at Bray and Woodlands.
Suppl: 4. Still by road near Clonsilla (1922) and near Lucan Bridge, 8. Still by Old Connaught Road (1933) and Loughlinstown (1918).

(3)	4	(5)	(8)

4. Still near Lucan, just west of the bridge, JS, MN/85.

LAMIACEAE (*LABIATAE*)

Stachys

S. sylvatica L.
Hedge Woundwort   Native

1	2	3	4	5	6	7	8

Common in shady hedgerows and woods.
FID.

S. sylvatica x S. palustris (S. x ambigua Smith)
Hybrid Woundwort   Native

Colgan: 2. North of Balscaddan: *Praeger 1894 a.* 3. In Brackenstown wood; and 4. St Catherine's wood, 1894: *N.C.* Fields near Glasnevin *(Mr. Underwood) Mack. Cat.* 5. In a potato field near Howth chapel: *Praeger 1895.* 7. About Ballinascorney: *Ir. Flor.* Glenasmole: *(Greenwood Pim) Cyb. II.* By the Grand Canal near Ballyfermot, 1903: *N.C.* 8. Field between the Black Rock and Cabinteely *(Captain Pratt) Mack.Cat.* Glendruid, 1858: *Herb. R. Barrington.* Hedgebanks near Killiney, 1894-1903; in a copse by the Shanganagh river near Loughlinstown, 1894: *N.C.* This hybrid, first recorded for the county by Mackay in 1825, approaches in the majority of the above stations more closely to *S. palustris* than to *S. sylvatica* in the form of its leaves, though it often has the deep-red flowers and rough hairs of the latter species. The Balscaddan and Ballyfermot plants are closer to *S. sylvatica* than to *S. palustris.*
Suppl: 1. Decoy Bridge, Bog of the Ring (1934). 3. Still at Knocksedan.

(1)	2	(3)	4	(5)	6	7	8

Occasional on stream, river and canal banks.

2. Forming an extensive stand along a lane just south of Lusk, DD/87-92.
4. Occasional, but in large stands along the banks of the River Liffey; near Lucan, near the Guinness Metal Bridge and west of Chapelizod, JS, DD, ENL/84 & MN/88. Several plants by the Royal Canal tow-path at Collins Bridge, MN/87.
6. Lucan Demesne, JS/85, **NDR**.
7. Several plants at the west of Palmerston Marsh, MN, ENL, CB/85.
8. Wet field, south-west of Kiltiernan, SR, MN/87. Shanganagh River near Loughlinstown, SR/85.

S. palustris L.
Marsh Woundwort   Native

| 1 | 2 | 3 | 4 | 5 | 6 | 7 | 8 |

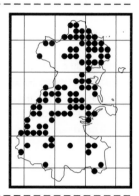

Common in drains, canal and river banks. A weed of cultivation on moist soils.
FID.

S. arvensis (L.) L.
Field Woundwort   Probably introduced

Colgan: 1. Sparingly in a cornfield near Garristown, 1894; and 2. Abundantly in a potato field at Rush, 1894-1903: *N.C.* 5. By the Martello tower, Howth village, and in potato gardens and waste ground opposite the Abbey gate: *Flor. Howth.* Needles field, Howth *(Miss R. Mahaffy) Praeger 1895.* 8. About the railway at Foxrock: *Praeger 1894 a.* In turnip fields at Ballyedmonduff, Three Rock, 1894, and at Ballybrack, 1903: *N.C.*
Suppl: 2. Still about Rush (1956). 4. On Navan branch railway track near Clonsilla (1953-1956). 5. Howth golf links (1956).

| (1) | 2 | (4) | 5 | 8 |

Formerly a weed associated with root crops such as potato and turnip, and also with corn.
2. Weed in gardens on the seafront at the north end of Skerries village, DD/87. On the slipway of the boatclub at Rogerstown Harbour, DD/88.
5. Waste ground near the railway at Malahide, PG/87, 88.
8. Edge of overgrown potato fields, east of Shanganagh Cemetery, north of Bray, SR, HOR/84, 85 & SR/92. Wheat field, east of Ballycorus, SR/91.

Ballota

B. nigra L. subsp. **foetida** (Vis.) Hayek
Black Horehound   Alien

Colgan: 1. Near Garristown, 1893; 2. Fully established in hedges near the old wind mill at Skerries, 1893-1902; near Balscaddan, 1893; near Balbriggan, 1894; &c.; 3. Banks by the sea and sparingly in field borders near Corballis, 1902; walls near the old Church of Killossory, 1893; banks north of Swords, 1902: *N.C.* 4. "Under the Hedges about *Glasnevan*": *Threlkeld.* Near Blanchardstown, 1900; near Island Bridge, 1902; abundant near Lucan, 1903; &c.: *N.C.* 5. At Howth: *Wade Dubl.* Abbey grounds and elsewhere about Howth: *Flor. Howth.* Frequent between Feltrim Hill and Swords, 1893: *N.C.* At Goose Green, 1894: *Miss A.G. Kinahan.* 6. Sparingly near Milltown, 1900: *N.C.* 7. "It grows in the Church-yard at Crumlin": *Threlkeld.* Roadside banks near Crumlin, 1892; near Tallaght, 1894; near Blue Bell, 1900; & c.: *N.C.* 8. Near Kilgobbin and Bullock: *Wade Dubl.* By the old Church at Kilgobbin and by the river below Loughlinstown, 1900: *N.C.* Near Carrickmines, 1887 *(Dr McWeeney) Cyb. II.*
Suppl: Frequent. Now generally established throughout the county.

Brunker MS: 2. Rogerstown, '32, '41. 3. Prospect Pt Swords, '54. 4. Blanchardstown, '51. 6. Milltown, '47. 7. S. bank of Dodder above Firhouse Weir, '42. Abundant, ruined cottages above Clonskeagh Bge, '54. 8. Pigeon House Rd, '50.

| (1) | 2 | 3 | 4 | 5 | 6 | 7 | 8 |

Occasional on roadsides near old buildings and on waste ground.

2. Hedgerow, 2 km north-west of Balbriggan, RF/86. Rogerstown Village, DD/83. Wasteground at Skerries, DD/82 & RF/87.
3. Near farm gates at Turvey Bridge, PR/85. Burrow, Portrane, PR/85.
4. Royal Canal banks, inner city stretch, HJH/80. West of the Islandbridge Gates of the Phoenix Park in Conyngham Road, MN/87. Dump and laneside hedge at Cardiff's Bridge, Finglas, DD/82. Waste ground and roadside west of Finglas Bridge, MN, JS/84. Finglas Industrial Estate, DN/90. Cross Guns Bridge, Phibsborough, MN, DN/87.
5. Beside a ruined house at Kinsealy, ENL/85. Martello Tower, Howth Village, ENL/83.
6. Roadside verge just south of Esker, ENL, JP/87. Manure heap by the Grand Canal across from Ballymakaily Mill, DN/90.
7. Still on the bank of the River Dodder at Clonskeagh Bridge, MWJ/85, 93. Hedgerow in Tymon Lane, CB/90. Waste ground by a roadside between Tallaght and Walkinstown, DK/86.
8. Corner of Eden Terrace and Eden Road, south of Sandycove Railway Station, SR, HOR/85. Hedge just north of Bray Harbour, HOR/86. One plant at Ballyogan tiphead, east of Stepaside, SR, JR/94.

FID.

‒ ‒

Lamiastrum

L. galeobdolon (L.) Ehrend. & Polatschek subsp. **montanum** (Pers.) Ehrend. & Polatschek
(Lamium galeobdolon, Galeobdolon luteum)
Yellow Archangel   Native

Colgan: 4. In Luttrell's-town wood (Woodlands) and amongst bushes between Ballyboghil Bridge and Ashtown, and near Cardiff's Bridge: *Wade. Dubl.* Abundant between Woodlands and Lucan 1904: *N.C.* Abundant in Woodlands, 1867: *Hart MS.* At Finglas *(Rev. H.G. Carroll) Cyb.* Near St Helena, Finglas, and very abundant in St Catherine's wood, 1904: *N.C.* 5. Near the Old Church at Artane, 1892 *(Miss A.G. Kinahan) Cyb. II.* By the Santry river, 1895: *N.C.* 6. Near the Salmon Leap, Leixlip *(Moore) Cyb.* and in 1904! In profusion in Crooksling glen above the Embankment, 1896-1903; abundant in Vesey's demesne, Lucan, 1894-1904: *N.C.* "Among Bushes beyond *Roper's-rest": Threlkeld.* Near Tymon Castle, 1890 *(Miss A.G. Kinahan) Cyb. II.* and in 1900! In Kelly's Glen on the upper Dodder *(W. Archer) Rec. Add.* At Bohernabreena, 1893; near Drimnagh, 1900; abundant in Lugmore Glen, 1903: *N.C.* On steep banks by the boat-club walk above Island Bridge, 1903: *F.W. Burbidge & N.C.* 8. Near Rathfarnham *(Dr A. Smyth) Cyb.* In Glencullen, 1853: *Rev. S.A. Brenan.*
One of the most characteristic species of the Dublin flora, nowhere abundant in Ireland outside the limits of the county, save in the adjoining parts of Wicklow and, so far, recorded for only four of the Irish counties.
Suppl: 4. Still abundant in St. Catherine's (1956). 5. Fields below Santry Court (1935). By Coolock Avenue near Larch Hill (1933). 6. Still in Crooksling Glen (1956) and Lucan Demesne (1954). 7. L. bank of stream below Edmondstown (1948). Abundant in Friarstown (1948) and in Slade of Ballymaice (1955). Still in Lugmore Glen (1956), Glassamucky (1948), and Tymon Lane, Balrothery (1956).

| 4 | (5) | 6 | 7 | 8 |

Rare, in damps woods and shaded roadsides. Sometimes locally abundant and forming extensive stands. The following records relate to the native form of this species and not to the occasionally naturalized, often cultivated, usually variegated and larger-leaved form (subsp. **argentatum** (Smejkal) Stace).

4. St Catherine's Woods, JS/84. Occurring from Luttrellstown to verge of Lucan Quarry, MN/85, 90 & JS/87.
6. Road bank and in a ditch south of Rathcoole near Redgap, HOR/86. Lucan Demesne, JP/85.
7. Roadside opposite the Embankment, Tallaght, JP/91. Abundant in Lugmore Glen, just east of Tallaght Hill, JP/83, MN/90. South bank of the River Liffey west of the Wren's Nest Weir, MN, JS/85. Edge of the River Liffey below King's Hospital School and by the River Liffey Millrace, east of Palmerston Marsh, MN, RF/85. Abundant under hazel scrub on the eastern slopes of the Glenasmole Reservoirs, DK/86, MWJ, JP/88 & MN/90. Memorial Park, Islandbridge, PR/86.
8. Edges of fields north and east of Kilgobbin Church, PC/76 & PC, DNFC/83.

Lamium

L. album L.
White Dead-nettle   Alien

| 1 | 2 | 3 | 4 | 5 | 6 | 7 | 8 |

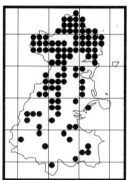

Common in waste places and on roadsides and ruins. Locally abundant in some parts of the north of the county and occasional in the southern half. In gardens it can be a very persistent weed.

L. purpureum L.
Red Dead-nettle   Native

| 1 | 2 | 3 | 4 | 5 | 6 | 7 | 8 |

Widespread. Very common on waste ground, arable land and as a garden weed.
FID.

L. hybridum Villars
Cut-leaved Dead-nettle   Possibly introduced

Colgan: 2. At Balbriggan, 1894 *(Praeger) Top. Bot.* Rush bulb farm, frequent, 1904:
Miss M.C. Knowles. 3. Near the Coastguard station and east of the Castle, Lambay:
Flor. Lambay. 5. Cornfields at Howth: *Ir. Flor.* Potato fields at Howth, 1894: *N.C.*
At Saint Doulough's 1865: *Hart MS.* 8. Plentiful by the sides of the footway between
Simmon's Court and Donnybrook: *Mack. Cat.*

| 1 | 2 | (3) | 4 | 5 | 6 | 7 | 8 |

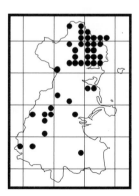

Common in 2, infrequent or rare elsewhere. A weed of gardens and arable land.
1. Oldtown, GS/86.
4. Potato field, 3km north of Lucan near Westmanstown, MN/87, **NDR**.
6. Near Saggart, JP/86, **NDR**. Field, east of Athgoe Castle, JP/86.
7. Waste ground at Oldbawn Bridge, 85/DD, **NDR**.
8. Frequent in tilled fields just north of Kilgobbin, PC/72-77.

L. confertum Fries *(L. intermedium, L. molucellifolium)*
Northern Dead-nettle   Possibly introduced

Colgan: 2. Abundant in sandy potato fields near Rush harbour, 1894: *Colgan 1895* and in 1903! 8. Fields at Little Bray, 1900: *Praeger.*

2	3	6	(8)

Occasional to common in tilled rootcrop fields in 2; very rare elsewhere.

2. Just south of Corduff House, DD/87. Below Bettyville House, DD/85. Five Roads junction, RF/85. Rathmooney, DD/85. West of Collinstown Bridge, DD/84. North of Rush Railway Station, DD/84. North-east of Tyrrelstown, DD/85. South-west of Ballykea, DD/85. East of Baldongan Castle, DD/83, 84.
3. In an untilled field, Donabate, DD/94, **NDR**.
6. Tilled field near Badgerhill, JP, ENL/87, **NDR**.

- -

L. amplexicaule L.
Henbit Dead-nettle   Possibly introduced

Colgan: 2. By the railway near Skerries, and north of Balbriggan, 1894; at Skerries and frequent in sandy lanes and fallows at Rush, 1902: *N.C.* 3. In cultivated ground, Lambay island: *Flor. Lambay.* Abundant on banks and in sandy fallows, Portrane peninsula, 1900; and 4. Sparingly on roadsides near Finglas wood, 1902: *N.C.* 5. Frequent round Howth village, 1894; abundant in potato fields, Baldoyle, 1900; frequent at Sutton, and sparingly near Malahide, 1902; 6. Near Gollierstown, Grand Canal, 1894; 7. Sparingly near Tymon Castle, 1894, and at Kimmage, 1900; at Island Bridge, 1902; at Mount Argus, 1903: *N.C.* 8. On Bray Common, 1865: *Herb. R.M. Barrington;* frequent along the railway from Sidney Parade to Kingstown, 1894-1901; in cultivated land near Ballybrack, 1903: *N.C.*

Suppl: 8. By miners' cottages at Ballycorus (1945).

2	(3)	4	5	(6)	7	8

Common in tilled fields and fallows in 2; rare elsewhere. It is also a rare garden weed.

4. Cultivated runnerbean field in the River Liffey Valley, MN, HOR/86. Cross Guns Bridge, DD/87. Weed in the National Botanic Gardens, Glasnevin, MN/88.
5. Shore behind Sutton Station, DD/83. Between the entrance to St Anne's Golf-course and the Causeway on North Bull Island, PG/87.
7. Flower beds at T.C.D., DD/85, 90.
8. Dumped soil at the top of the shore, near the Martello Tower south of Killiney, SR/88. Ringsend Dump, SR/93. Roadside flower-beds, Whitethorn Road, Clonskeagh, DK/94.

- -

Galeopsis

G. angustifolia Ehrh. ex Hoffm.
Red Hemp-nettle   Possibly introduced

Colgan: 2. At Skerries (Dr McWeeney) *Cyb. II.* and in 1903! On the railway north of Balbriggan and 3. In a cornfield near Raheen point, Portrane, 1894; on the railway near Donabate, 1902: *N.C.* 4. By the roadside and in hedgebanks between Chapelizod and Luttrell's-town: *Wade Dubl.* Foot of Knockmaroon Hill, 1866: *Hart MS.* Near Cardiff's Bridge: *Flor. Hib.* At Clonsilla, 1884 *(Vowell) Cyb. II.* 5. Abundantly among crops near the shore at Malahide: *Wade Dubl.* Howth; Feltrim Hill; and lands of Peatown: *Ir. Flor.* In several stations at Howth, as above Drumleck; between St Fintan's and Sutton, &c., 1869-1884 *(Hart) Flor. Howth & MS.* 7. Gravelly margin of the Dodder near Old Bawn, 1882: *(Rev. W. Colgan) Cyb. II.* In profusion among river shingle by the Dodder for fully half a mile below the bridge at Old Bawn, also about half a mile above the bridge, 1903: *N.C.* 8. At Dundrum *(Moore) Cyb.* Glendruid, Cabinteely, 1856: *Herb. R. Barrington.*

Suppl: 7. Frequent by the lane from Bohernabreena to Ballymaice (1941). 8. Roadside at Ballycorus (1943).

(2) (3) (4) (5) (7) **8**

Extremely rare, on trackside gravel. An endangered species that is legally protected under the Wildlife Act of 1976. Formerly one of the most characteristic species of the county, where it occurred as both a native on river gravel exposures and as a colonist of corn fields and, to a lesser extent, of waste ground. Present-day cornfield management makes it difficult for weed species to survive. The site of the main native population of the species on the River Dodder gravels at Old Bawn has apparently been destroyed by the construction of Dodder Valley Park. 8. Forestry road between Three Rock road and Two Rock Mountain, MS/67.

G. tetrahit L.
Common Hemp-nettle   Possibly introduced

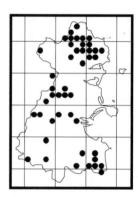

1 **2** **3** **4** **5** **6** **7** **8**

Occasional in base-poor arable soils; rare elsewhere. It is much less common now than in Colgan's time. Plants intermediate in morphology between **G. tetrahit** and **G. bifida** Boenn. with small pale flowers, a lower lip somewhat emarginate, the lateral nectary lobes moderately well developed and variable nutlet development have been found in 7 at the junction of Ballycullen and Daletree roads, SR/92.

FID.

Scutellaria

S. galericulata L.
Skullcap   Native

Colgan: 4. Sparingly by the Royal Canal below Lucan, 1886: Scully Herb. & Colgan 1893. First record in 1893: Ir.Nat.Il., p.283; first found in 1886 by R.W. Scully. Wade's earlier record for District 5: "In the marshes of Howth" (Wade Rar.) has never been confirmed and is no doubt referable to the next species.

(4)

Not refound at its former site on the Royal Canal at Lucan (4).

S. minor Hudson
Lesser Skullcap   Native

Colgan: 5. On Howth Head, in a marshy place near Cabeena's and in several places along Whitewater brook: Flor. Howth. By the Whitewater brook. 1903: N.C. Marsh on the south side of Howth Head, 1897 (Miss S. Colgan); on Ireland's Eye (Miss A.G. Kinahan) Cyb. II. First record in 1818: Warburton. This, no doubt, was the plant observed by Wade at Howth so early as 1804 and erroneously recorded by him as S. galericulata. The Howth stations mark the northern limit, so far as it is at present known, of S. minor in east Ireland.

Suppl: 5. A few plants still survived in a small marsh above the cliff path between Howth and Baily (Miss F. Davis and H.J. Hudson, 1930), but the station has not been located since.

(5)

Not refound at its former sites on Howth Head and Ireland's Eye (5).

Teucrium

T. scorodonia L.
Wood Sage   Native

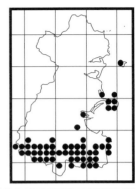

| 3 | (4) | 5 | 6 | 7 | 8 |

Common on dry acid mineral soils on roadside banks, forest
margins and rocky places in the mountains; rare elsewhere.
Not refound on a wall at Luttrellstown Woodlands (4) where
its original site recorded in 1893 (*Colgan*) has been cleaned-up.
3. Still on Lambay Island, DD/91.

Ajuga

A. reptans L.
Bugle   Native

| 4 | 5 | 6 | 7 | 8 |

Common in woodlands in 7 and in the River Liffey Valley; occasional elsewhere.
4. St Catherine's Woods, MN, JS/84. Luttrellstown and nearby, JS/83. Between Abbotstown
   and Blanchardstown Hospital, MN, J. Earley/84.
5. Edge of a wood in Howth Demesne, PG, DN/91.
6. Sparingly, along the east bank of the River Liffey at Lucan Demesne, JP/85 & HOR, MN/85.
8. By the stream below the cromlech west of Kiltiernan SR, HOR/86. Ballyman Glen,
   DNFC/83. Along the Bride's Glen River south-west of Loughlinstown, SR, HOR/87.
   Druid's Glen, east of Carrickmines, SR/89 & MN/90.

Glechoma

G. hederacea L. *(Nepeta glechoma)*
Ground-ivy   Native

| 1 | 2 | 3 | 4 | 5 | 6 | 7 | 8 |

Widespread and very common in woods and hedgerows.
FID.

Prunella

P. vulgaris L.
Selfheal   Native

| 1 | 2 | 3 | 4 | 5 | 6 | 7 | 8 |

Widespread and very common in damp grassland, hedgerows, lawns and roadsides.
FID.

Clinopodium

C. ascendens (Jordan) Samp. *(Calamintha officinalis, C. ascendens, C. sylvatica* subsp. *ascendens)*
Common Calamint   Probably introduced

Colgan: 4. "Under the Deer Park Wall, A.D. 1730, also plentiful between Chapelizod and Lucan, on ye N. side of ye River": *Annot in Threlkeld.* In the hedgebanks near Luttrell's-town and plentifully in waste ground and by hedges and roadsides near the foot of Knockmaroon hills: *Wade Dubl.* Frequent on banks and by roadsides at Knockmaroon, in many places close to dwellings, in others sufficiently remote from them, 1901; abundant on a field bank west of Lucan, 1903, and sparingly to the east of it near Woodlands, 1904: *N.C.* (5. Along the shore from Clontarf to Howth: *Ir. Flor.* 7. "In ye road in a Hedge S.E. of Rathfarnham going to ye Mountains, August, 1732": *Annot. in Threlkeld,* not seen recently in Districts 5 or 7). 8. Roadside between the village of Monkstown and Glenageary: *Mack. Cat.* Roadside near Vallombrosa, Bray, 1894 *(More) Cyb. II.*

Suppl: 3. North bank of Ward River a little below Knocksedan Bridge (1936). 4. Still plentiful about Knockmaroon and Luttrellstown (1956). 8. Roadside between Brenanstown House and Old Tully, and on Loughlinstown Common (1953). Confirmed from Vallombrosa Bray (1935).

Very rare.
3. Still by the Ward River, in a sand-pit east of Knocksedan Bridge, RF, DD/84.
4. Still at Luttrellstown, on the wall of Luttrellstown Estate opposite Shackleton's Mills, MN/88.

C. acinos (L.) Kuntze *(Calamintha acinos, Acinos arvensis)*
Basil Thyme   Probably introduced

Colgan: 3. At Portrane, 1869 *(Hart) Rec. Add.* Scattered along the edge of a barley field to the south of Portrane peninsula, 1902: *N.C.* 4. Sparingly in a cornfield at Clonsilla: *Colgan 1895.* 5. "Found in July, 1840, in a sandy field at Portmarnock by several of my botanical friends and myself": *Mackay 1859.* Abundant over a large area of sandy fallows at Portmarnock 1903: *N.C.* 8. A few plants near Tulla churchyard, Carrickmines: *Guide.*
Suppl: Never refound.

An endangered species that is legally protected under the Wildlife Act of 1976, not refound at any of its former sites in the county. As far as can be ascertained this species grew in cornfields and fallow ground. Weedkillers and the reduction or grassing over of fallow land would seem to account for its disappearance in the county. It still occurs in neighbouring Co. Kildare in disused sand/gravel pits.

Origanum

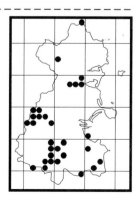

O. vulgare L.
Wild Marjoram   Native

Colgan: 1. Sparingly between Ballyboghil and the Wren's Nest, and near Grallagh, 1894; 2. Sparingly on roadside banks west of Rush railway station, and about a mile S.W. of Skerries, 1902; 3. Abundant on banks and roadsides by the Ward river from Swords to Knocksedan, 1903: *N.C.* 4. "Between the Mill-dam and the River above *Chapple-izod-bridge": Threlkeld.* Frequent and locally abundant in this district, as on

Knockmaroon Hills, 1901; along the Royal Canal and the Tolka river, 1903:&c.; 5. North-west of Feltrim Hill, 1893, and sparingly at Cloghran quarry, 1903: *N.C.* At Killester: *Flor. Howth.* 6. By the Liffey above Lucan and at Leixlip, 1894; near Aderrig, 1897; 7. Abundant all along the Dodder valley from Rathgar to near Castle Kelly, ceasing with the limestone drift, also on the basalt in Ballinascorney glen to above the gap, 1882-1903; 8. Abundant on drift banks near Glencullen bridge, 1893; at Rathmichael and near Shankill, 1902: *N.C.*

| 1 | 2 | 3 | 4 | (5) | (6) | 7 | 8 |

Occasional on calcareous banks, grassland and sand-pits.
FID.

Thymus

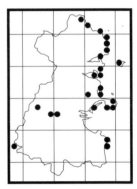

T. polytrichus A. Kerner ex Borbas subsp. **britannicus** (Ronn.) Kerguelen *(T. serpyllum, T. drucei, T. praecox)*
Wild Thyme   Native

| 2 | 3 | 4 | 5 | 6 | (7) | 8 |

Common in stable sand-dunes; now very rare inland on sandy soil.
6. Roadside banks leading to Athgoe Castle, JP/87, **NDR**.
8. Killiney Hill, DNFC/82. Banks below Vico Road, SR, HOR/83. Wall around the tower on Dalkey Hill, SR/85.

Lycopus

L. europaeus L.
Gipsywort   Native

Colgan: 2. Sparingly in marshy ground by the shore near Rogerstown, 1902: *N.C.* 4. "In a Ditch of the *Deer Park*" (Phoenix Park): *Threlkeld.* In the Phoenix Park, by the pond in the Zoological garden, 1904, and in the Furry Glen, 1900; by the Royal Canal, at intervals from Cross Guns to Blanchardstown, 1903: *N.C.* 5. Howth and Baldoyle: *Ir. Flor.* Auburn, near Malahide: *Flor. Howth.* 6. Abundant at intervals along the Grand Canal from Hazelhatch to Clondalkin, and 7. From Clondalkin down to Ringsend basin, 1903; in Landsdown valley, Blue Bell, 1892: *N.C.* 8. At Cabinteely, 1866: *Hart MS.* At Donnybrook, 1867 *(Rev. H.G. Carroll) Herb. S. & A. Mus.*
Suppl: 4. Island Pond, Phoenix Park (1956). 5. Alder marsh on North Bull (1953).

| (2) | 4 | 5 | 6 | 7 | (8) |

Occasional on stream, river and canal banks; especially near lock gates in 4.
5. Edge of Howth Reservoir, DN/88. Bank of the Royal Canal at Drumcondra, DN/89.
6. Banks of the Grand Canal, north-east of Hazelhatch and at Gollierstown Bridge and Ballymakaily Mill, JP/84, MN/89 & DNFC/89. South bank of the River Liffey by the Hermitage Golf-course, JS, MN/85.
7. Palmerston Marsh, MN, ENL/85. Grand Canal at Charlemont Bridge, PG/91. Along the Grand Canal at Suir Road, DN/90. Marsh beside the Grand Canal at Gallanstown, DD/92.
FID.

Mentha

It is not possible to equate some old records and names in *Colgan* and *Suppl* with current usage.

M. arvensis L.
Corn Mint   Native

Colgan: 2. Abundant in cornfields at Skerries and along the shore southward to Rush and to Whitestown, also in potato fields near Balrothery, 1902; 3. Cornfields near the Martello tower, Portrane, 1894; and near Donabate, 1901: *N.C.* 5. Common on the north side of Howth: *Flor. Howth.* Abundant in cornfields at Baldoyle, 1900; and 8. Near Loughlinstown, 1903: *N.C.*

| 1 | (2) | (3) | (5) | (8) |

Extremely rare. Much rarer now than at the turn of the century.
1. Banks of Hynestown Reservoir and fields nearby, GS/84, **NDR**.

M. arvensis × M. aquatica (M. × verticillata L.; *M. sativa*)
Whorled Mint   Native

Colgan: 1. Wet roadsides north of Cockle's bridge, Garristown, 1894: *N.C.* 5. Field between Woodside and Balscaddan: *Flor. Howth.* 7. Watery places by the Dodder near Newtown, Tallaght, 1894-1900: *N.C.*

| 1 | (5) | (7) |

Extremely rare but perhaps under-recorded.
1. Along the upper water limit of Hynestown Reservoir, GS/84.

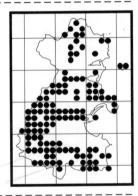

M. aquatica L. (*M. hirsuta*)
Water Mint   Native

| 1 | 2 | 3 | 4 | 5 | 6 | 7 | 8 |

Common on canal and river banks and in marshes.
FID.

M. aquatica × M. spicata (M. × piperita L.)
Peppermint   Alien

Colgan (Appendix): 8. Waste ground by Dodder.

| 6 | (8) |

Extremely rare.
6. Wet flush at Badgerhill, JP, ENL/87. Banks of the Grand Canal just north-east of Hazelhatch bridge, DNFC/89.

M. spicata L.
Spear Mint   Alien

| 2 | 3 | 4 | 5 | 8 |

2. Cul-de-sac south of Lusk, DD, ENL/84.
3. Sand-pit by the Ward River east of Knocksedan Bridge, RF, DD/84.
4. Field near Hartstown, north of Clonsilla, JS/86.
5. Kilrock, Howth, PG/87, 88. Portmarnock Raceway, DN/88.
8. Ballyogan tiphead, east of Stepaside, SR/94.

M. suaveolens Ehrh. *(M. rotundifolia)*
Round-leaved Mint   Alien

Colgan: 1. Roadside north of Cockle's bridge, Garristown, 1894; and 2. At Balscaddan, 1893: *N.C.* 7. Between Ballinascorney gap and Castle Kelly *(D.Orr) Cyb.* Near Castle Kelly: *Guide.* Dodder banks between Milltown and Rathfarnham, 1867: *Flor. Howth.* By the Dodder at Newtown, Tallaght, 1900; and frequent in large patches along the same river from the Waterworks, Glenasmole, to Old Bawn bridge, 1903: *N.C.* 8. At Dalkey, 1883: *Greenwood Pim.* By the river below Loughlinstown, 1894-1903: *N.C.* A relic of cultivation fully naturalised along the course of the Dodder river.

Suppl: 6. Newcastle, outside the church (1944-1948). Lane from Peamount to canal near the old churchyard (1955). 7. Still by River Dodder and spreading down towards Firhouse (1957). 8. Still at Loughlinstown (1918-1954).

| (1) | (2) | 4 | (6) | 7 | 8 |

Very rare.
4. Old garden, south of Gallanstown, MN/84.
7. Grand Canal banks, MSS/81. In grass on the south side of the Grand Canal near Leeson Street, MWJ/84. Waste ground at Oldbawn, DNFC/83. By a pond at Delaford, JP, DK/83. Banks of the River Dodder, west of Firhouse, SR/89.
8. Still on the banks of the Shanganagh River along Commons Road, Loughlinstown, SR/89.
FID.

Salvia

S. verbenaca L. *(S. horminoides)*
Wild Clary   Native

Colgan: 2. On the coast below Skerries, 1882: *Flor. Lambay.* Sparingly by roadsides in the town of Skerries, 1893: *N.C.* 4. Near old walls between Long Meadows and Chapelizod: *Wade Dubl.,* 1794. Sparingly along the roadside by the wall of the Phoenix Park opposite Long Meadows, and in considerable quantity on the inside of the field bank at the opposite side of the road, 1904: *N.C.* Common at Glasnevin and Cardiff's Bridge; Knockmaroon Hill; Phoenix Park; and 5. Along the shore from Clontarf to Howth: *Ir. Flor.* In the Abbey grounds, Howth: *Flor. Howth.* On the seaward face of the sea wall and on banks below it at Kilbarrick, 1902; abundant on roadsides and on roadside banks between Kilbarrick and Sutton, spreading for about 100 yards into adjacent pastures, also on drift banks above Balscaddan, Howth, 1903; a few dozens of plants on a rocky roadside bank at Cloghran church, 1893-1903: *N.C.* (7. "Upon the Brow below the Hospital near the Road, and in such sandy Places about the City": *Threlkeld.* In gravelly places between Rathmines and Milltown: *Wade Dubl.* not seen recently in this district).

Suppl: 5. On the Cosh, Sutton (1922). North Bull near the Royal Dublin club-house (1939-1944). A few plants still survive at the site of Cloghran Church (1952) and a few on the remnants of roadside banks between Kilbarrack and Baldoyle Road (1955). Otherwise this species continues to decrease.

(2)	4	5	(7)

Common in sand-dunes at the south end of North Bull Island; very rare elsewhere. Now gone from Kilbarrack due to building works, DD/70.

4. As a weed in the National Botanic Gardens, Glasnevin, DS/91.

5. Roadside at Cloghran, DD, HJH/65-87; not refound in 1988. North Bull Island, KF/62. Frequent at the south end of North Bull Island, DD/83-92.

HIPPURIDACEAE

Hippurus

H. vulgaris L.
Mare's-tail   Native

1	2	3	4	5	6	7	8

Common in canals and reservoirs; very rare elsewhere.

8. Booterstown Marsh, RG/70, **NDR**; but not refound in recent years.

FID.

CALLITRICHACEAE

In many instances **Callitriche** plants are found with neither flowers or fruits and are not possible to identify to species.

Callitriche

C. hermaphroditica L.
Autumnal Water-starwort   Native

(1)	(4)	(5)	(7)

Recorded in *Suppl* (as *C. autumnalis* L.) in Bog of the Ring (1) and in the Central Marsh in Howth (5) but not refound during this survey. Also noted in *Colgan* as being recorded in error from the Grand and Royal canals (4 & 7).

C. stagnalis Scop.
Common Water-starwort   Native

1	2	3	4	5	6	7	8

Common in wet mud, ditches, drains and by rivers and canals.

C. platycarpa Kuetz.
Various-leaved Water-starwort   Native

| 1 | 3 | 4 | 5 | 6 | 7 | 8 |

Probably common but under-recorded; in reservoirs, ponds, wet ditches, rivers and streams. Many of the records for *C. verna* agg. in *Colgan* probably refer to this species.
1. Delvin River at Cockles Bridge, NS/92.
3. Knocksedan Reservoir, MN/88.
4. Pond, south of Dubber Cross, Finglas, MN/85. River Tolka between Clonee and Glasnevin, JS/88, MN/88, 89 & PR/88. Eastern part of Clonsilla, JS/88.
5. Pool in Santry Woods, DN/88. Pond on the Royal Dublin Golf-course on North Bull Island, DN/88.
6. Wet hollows in a field east of Colganstown House, JP/87. Edge of a ditch east of Casement Aerodrome, MN/90.
7. South end of the northern reservoir in Glenasmole, SR/89.
8. Ballybetagh Bog and just south of it, SR/84, 87. West of Kiltiernan, SR/85. Top of the Ticknock road, SR/87. Stream at Cabinteely Park, SR/89.

C. obtusangula Le Gall
Blunt-fruited Water-starwort   Native

Colgan: 1. Ditches at Garristown Bog, 1894: *Colgan 1903.* At Bog of the Ring, 1903: N.C. 2. In Lusk Ponds, 1902: *Colgan 1903.* 4. In bog ditches at Dunsoghly, 1903: *N.C.*

| (1) | (2) | 4 | 6 |

Rare, in ponds and canals.
4. Shallow, muddy pond east of Clonee, MN, JS/87. Still at Dunsoghly, now in drainage ditches, MN/88.
6. Grand Canal at Ballymakaily Mill, CB/87.

C. hamulata Kuetz. ex Koch (*C. intermedia* subsp. *hamulata*)
Intermediate Water-starwort   Native

Colgan: 1. Quarry pool at Hollywood, 1894: *Colgan 1895.* 3. Pools by the Ward river above Swords, 1903; 4. Royal Canal near Lucan, 1900; 5. Pool near the signal station, Howth, 1902; 6. Grand Canal above Clondalkin, and 7. Below Clondalkin, 1900; abundant in the upper Dodder near Castle Kelly and in bog pools above Piperstown, 1902: *N.C.* 8. Pools at Loughlinstown Commons, 1894: *Colgan 1895.* Pools near Killiney, 1902: *N.C.*
Suppl: 1. Knockboy Bridge, Bog of the Ring (1956).

| (1) | (3) | (4) | (5) | (6) | 7 | 8 |

Very rare, in ponds and reservoirs.
7. South-east corner of the southern reservoir in Glenasmole, near *Colgan's* site in the upper Dodder, SR/89. Concrete ponds at Edmondstown Road beside the Owendoher River, DN/90.
8. Lake at the Roadstone Works at Ballycorus, SR, JR/88.

PLANTAGINACEAE

Plantago

P. coronopus L.
Buck's-horn Plantain   Native

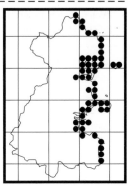

| 2 | 3 | 5 | 8 |

Abundant in the upper parts of salt-marshes and common on coastal cliffs, rocks and walls near the sea.

P. maritima L.
Sea Plantain   Native

| 2 | 3 | 5 | 8 |

Very common in salt-marshes and on coastal cliffs and rocks.

P. major L.
Greater Plantain   Native

| 1 | 2 | 3 | 4 | 5 | 6 | 7 | 8 |

Intermediates between the two following subspecies occasionally occur.

---

subsp. **major**

| 1 | 2 | 3 | 4 | 5 | 6 | 7 | 8 |

Widespread and abundant on waste ground, roadsides and in pastures.
FID.

---

subsp. **intermedia** (Gilib.) Lange *(P. major* var. *intermedia)*

| 2 | (3) | 5 |

Rare in dune-slacks and flooded ground near the sea. Not refound in its former sites on the Portrane Peninsula and at Malahide (5).
2. Rush, JRA, DD/86. Muddy grassland of the upper salt-marsh at Balleally, DD/87.
5. South of the roundabout at the end of the causeway on North Bull Island, JRA, DD/86.

P. media L.

Hoary Plantain   Alien

Praeger, 1939 and 1946b: Spreading, 1930-36 at Dublin Zoo.

Brunker MS: 5. At Malahide Hotel, '47.

| (2) | 3 | 4 | 5 | 8 |

Occasional as a lawn weed and in fallow ground. This species may increase in frequency as it is often included in commercially imported "wild flower" mixes.

3. Portrane Peninsula, DD, PR, ENL/83, **NDR**.
4. Lawn weed at Beech Park, Clonsilla, L.K. Shackleton/75, JS/88.
5. Lawn at Marino Institute of Education, DD/80-84.
8. Grounds of the Church of Ireland church on Whitechurch Road, east of Edmondstown, HOR, SR/84, **NDR**. Near Avoca Avenue entrance of Carysfort College, Blackrock, HOR/84.

P. lanceolata L.

Ribwort Plantain   Native

| 1 | 2 | 3 | 4 | 5 | 6 | 7 | 8 |

Widespread and abundant on waste ground, roadsides, in pastures and gardens.
FID.

Littorella

L. uniflora (L.) Asch.

Shoreweed   Native

Suppl: 2. Balrothery Lough (1949). 6. Lower pond at Brittas (1933-1957). 7. Upper reservoir in Glenasmole (A.W. Stelfox 1922) – still there (1957). Included in Colgan's Appendix on the strength of a record for Howth, with the note "no doubt an error".

| (2) | 6 | 7 |

Rare, on reservoir margins. Often abundantly found after periods of extensive drought when water levels are low along the shores of reservoirs. Little suitable ground now remains at its former site at Balrothery Lough (2) due to the stabilisation of the water level.

6. Common along the shores of Brittas Ponds, ENL/83 & DN/88 and covering the exposed mud floor of the northern reservoir, JP, S. Waldren/94.
7. Along the edge of the north end of the southern reservoir in Glenasmole, and at its southern tip, JP, DD/83, MN/88 & DN/90.

BUDDLEJACEAE

Buddleja

B. davidii Franchet
Butterfly-bush   Alien

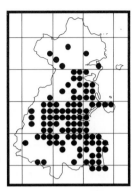

| I | 2 | 3 | 4 | 5 | 6 | 7 | 8 |

Abundant as an urban weed of waste ground and derelict buildings. One of the commonest weeds of the inner city where it may form dense large stands, becoming less frequent in the suburbs. Though not included in the *Suppl* this species has become widely established and in places dominant. See *FID* for further details.
FID.

OLEACEAE

Fraxinus

F. excelsior L.
Ash   Native

| I | 2 | 3 | 4 | 5 | 6 | 7 | 8 |

Widespread and abundant in hedgerows, woodlands and waste ground.
FID.

Ligustrum

L. vulgare L.
Wild Privet   Native; planted

| I | 2 | 3 | 4 | 5 | 6 | 7 | 8 |

Common in hedges; occasional in woodland margins.

SCROPHULARIACEAE

Verbascum

V. thapsus L.
Great Mullein   Native

| (1) | 3 | 4 | 5 | (6) | 7 | 8 |

Occasional on sandy and waste ground and in quarries and gravel pits.
FID.

Scrophularia

S. nodosa L.
Common Figwort   Native

| 1 | 2 | 3 | 4 | 5 | 6 | 7 | 8 |

Common on waste ground, in damp woodland, river valleys and ditches.
FID.

S. auriculata L. *(S. aquatica)*
Water Figwort   Native

| 2 | 3 | 4 | 5 | 6 | 7 | 8 |

Occasional in damp woodland, river valleys and ditches.

S. auriculata x **S. umbrosa** (**S. x hurstii** Druce)
Native
Recorded from Co. Dublin by the River Liffey at Lucan by Praeger (1939) and (1951) but
not encountered during the present survey.

S. umbrosa Dumort.
Green Figwort   Native

Colgan: 4. In considerable quantity by the northern bank of the Liffey between Knockmaroon and Woodlands, 1895 N.C. Ir. Nat., 1896, p.182. Along the Liffey banks at Saint Catherine's, 1901-04: N.C. 6. On the southern Liffey bank opposite Woodlands, 1895, also by the river in Lucan demesne, 1894 N.C. Ir. Nat. l.c. In damp woods, Lucan demesne, about 20 yards from the river bank, and in woods by the river near Salmon leap, 1904: N.C. 7. Frequent by the Liffey banks and by the adjoining mill race near Palmerston and Cursis Stream, 1895: N.C. A somewhat critical species, yet well distinguished in the field from its congener, S. aquatica, with which it is associated on the Liffey banks, by the form of its inflorescence, the lighter green of its foliage, especially in the early stages, and by its later flowering. Observations made at Woodlands, at Lucan and at St Catherine's in 1901 showed that the flower-buds of this species had only begun to make their appearance while S. aquatica was in full flower. In Ireland the plant seems to be altogether confined to the Liffey banks.

| 4 | 6 | 7 |

Rare, on river banks. A very rare plant in Ireland and in greatest abundance in the River Liffey catchment. In Co. Dublin it is confined to the River Liffey Valley where it is commonest on the northern bank.
4. Banks of the River Liffey at each of the following sites: midway between Lucan and Leixlip, wood near St Catherine's weir, and opposite Lucan Demesne, at Lucan by the base of Oonavarra Hill, at Luttrellstown and by a stream on the estate, at Broomfield Estate, opposite the Hermitage Golf-course, at the Wren's Nest, at Somerton House, near the Guinness Metal Bridge, at Chapelizod and at Knockmaroon, MN/85, 88, 90 & JS, ENL/84.
6. Banks of the River Liffey at Lucan Demesne and the Hermitage Golf-course, JS, MN/85.
7. River Liffey millrace at Fonthill, MN/90.

Mimulus

M. guttatus DC.
Monkeyflower   Alien

Colgan: 5. Established in a wild locality by a rivulet, between Shielmartin and Saint Fintan's: *Flor. Howth.* 7. Planted in Kelly's glen (Glenasmole) *(Prof. Harvey) Cyb.* By the Dodder at Bohernabreena, 1873: *Greenwood Pim.* By the Dodder near Templeogue, 1883, and near Newtown, 1894; abundant in ditches by the upper Dodder below Cobb's Lodge, 1895; abundant in the shingly river bed and in adjacent swampy ground at the head of Glenasmole, 1895-1902; frequent in the walls of the artificial channel of the Rathmines Waterworks at the head of Glenasmole, 1900-02; below Bohernabreena bridge, 1903: *N.C.* 8. By a stream near Ticknock road, 1902: *Praeger.* A garden plant from western North America now thoroughly naturalised in Co. Dublin as in many other parts of Ireland. Introduced into the upper Dodder valley about 40 years ago, it has become fully established along a considerable part of the course of that river.

Suppl: 5. By rivulet below Stella Maris, Baily (1945), but no longer there in 1955. 7. Still by River Dodder at Glenasmole (1957). Aghfarrell (1956). Rathfarnham (1912). Islet under Templeogue Bridge (1957). Milltown Bridge (1942-1957). 8. Rathfarnham Weir and opposite Castle gate (1957). Weir below Clonskea (1948). Ballsbridge (1951-1956). Evidently spreading down the entire Dodder valley from its original station as Glenasmole.

| 4 | 5 | 6 | 7 | 8 |

Occasional on stream and river banks. Some of the records included for this species may be hybrids with **M. luteus** L. which have also escaped from garden cultivation. Further work is needed to confirm how widespread these are in nature.

4/6. Scattered along the banks of the River Liffey from St Catherine's through Lucan, the Hermitage Golf-course and past the Guinness Metal Bridge to near the T.C.D. Boathouse at Island Bridge, MN/84, **NDR**, 88, HOR/85, MN, JS/85 & MN, PR/88.

5. Still near the Baily at Whitewater Brook, Howth, DD/88.

7. Palmerston Marsh, DD/82. Still by the River Dodder in Glenasmole on the southern and western sides of the southern reservoir, KF/63, DD/83 & PWJ, MWJ, SR/86. Stream in the sand-hills to the east of Aghfarrel, JP/83. One plant by the edge of the River Dodder, Herbert Park, SR/91.

8. By the River Dodder east of Rathfarnham Road Bridge, south-west of Milltown and east of Lansdowne Road Railway Station, SR/87.

Chaenorhinum

C. minus (L.) Lange *(Linaria minor)*
Small Toadflax   Alien

Colgan: 4. Along the Midland Great Western Railway near Dublin: *Guide.* On the same railway near Lucan, 1891: *D. McArdle* near Clonsilla, 1899-1901: *N.C.* and near Blanchardstown, 1903: *Scully.* 5. Occasionally, and sometimes abundantly, as a garden weed about Howth, as at Hillside: *Flor. Howth.* 7. Great Southern and Western Railway near Ballyfermot, 1895, and at Clondalkin, 1903: *N.C.* 8. At Stillorgan, 1865 *(Simon Foot) Cyb. & Herb. Glasnevin.* Near Sidney Parade railway station, 1867 *(V.A. Smith) Rec.Add.* and in 1903! At Glenageary station, 1874: *Greenwood Pim* and in 1894! On the railway at Foxrock, 1893: *Praeger.* Abundant along the railway from Killiney to Bray, 1894-1903, from Milltown to Foxrock, 1894, at Carrickmines, 1899, and at Shankill, 1902 *N.C.* Fully established on all the Dublin railway lines save the Great Northern, though rendered uncertain in its appearances by the frequent cleaning of the permanent way.

Suppl: 3. G.N. Railway between Corballis viaduct and Donabate (1942-1945). 5. Near Sutton Railway Station (1946).

| (3) | 4 | 5 | 7 | 8 |

Rare, on railway ballast, gravel and in waste places.

4. Cross Guns Bridge, DD/87. Potato field, 3 km north of Lucan at Westmanstown, MN/88. Railway line and Royal Canal west of Clonsilla, L.K.Shackleton/77. Towpath of the Royal Canal south-west of Pakenham Bridge, MN/89. Weed in the National Botanic Gardens, Glasnevin, DS/80, 91.

5. Railway viaduct at Malahide, PG/87, 88. Many plants on gravel near the level crossing, Sutton, ENL, MN/83 & CB/91. Dublin Port, SR/93.

7. Garden weed in St Columba's College, DK/c.65. Base of a wall in Grosvenor Road, Rathmines, MWJ/85.

8. Abandoned railway line at Sandyford Industrial Estate, SR/86. Gravel car park on the western side of Leopardstown Racecourse, SR/85. Abandoned railway line near Foxrock Railway Station, SR/84.

Cymbalaria

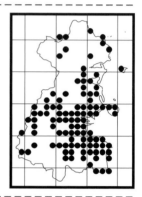

C. muralis P. Gaertner, B. Meyer & Scherb. *(Linaria cymbalaria)*
Ivy-leaved Toadflax   Alien

| 1 | 2 | 3 | 4 | 5 | 6 | 7 | 8 |

Common on old walls and waste ground. Widespread in southern districts and urban Dublin. A long-established and well naturalized garden escape.
FID.

Kickxia

K. elatine (L.) Dumort.
Sharp-leaved Fluellen   Probably introduced

| 4 | 8 |

Extremely rare. Legally protected under the Wildlife Act of 1976 as an endangered species.

4. As a common weed in the National Botanic Gardens, Glasnevin, DS/91.

8. On the edge of a potato field east of Shanganagh Cemetery, SR, HOR/84, **NCR** & SR/91.

Linaria

L. vulgaris Miller
Common Toadflax   Introduced in Co. Dublin
Brunker MS: 8. Abundant in fallow field E. of Carrickmines Stn, '47.

| (2) | (4) | (5) | 8 |

Extremely rare. Recorded by Colgan from waste ground probably as a garden outcast, but also from the railway near Dalkey (8).

8. Many plants on the abandoned railway line at Sandyford Industrial Estate, HOR/83.

L. purpurea (L.) Miller
Purple Toadflax   Alien

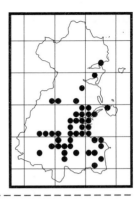

| 3 | 4 | 5 | 6 | 7 | 8 |

Occasional on urban and suburban waste ground and walls in
5, 6 & 7 as a garden escape; rare elsewhere.
3. Quarry at Donabate Village, PR/85, **NDR**.
4. Quarries near Cloghran House, MN/83, 84.
FID.

L. repens (L.) Miller
Pale Toadflax   Probably introduced

| 5 | (7) | 8 |

Rare, on waste ground.
5. Reclaimed waste ground at Dublin Port, DN/88, **NDR**.
8. Wall south of the Martello Tower at Sandymount, SR, HOR/84, **NDR**. Bank at Ringsend
    Dump, SR/86. Wall on Military Road just east of Ballybrack, and nearby at the Martello
    Tower, Ballybrack, SR/84, 85. Railway bank near Merrion Gates, DN/94.

Digitalis

D. purpurea L.
Foxglove   Native

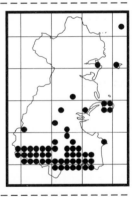

| 3 | 5 | 6 | 7 | 8 |

Very common on dry acid mineral soils, on walls, roadside banks and
quarries; on Howth Head and the mountains. A garden escape in 3.
FID.

Erinus

E. alpinus L.
Fairy Foxglove   Alien

| 4 | 5 | 7 | 8 |

Occasional on walls.
4. Garden escape colonising a wall at Broomfield in the River Liffey Valley, MN/88. Walls at
    Coolmine House, MN/87. Wall at Glasnevin Cemetery and in the National Botanic
    Gardens, Glasnevin, MN/83, **NDR**. Conyngham Road, MN/87.
5. Bank at the edge of Feltrim Hill Quarry, DN/88, **NDR**.
7. Path at the north end of Mount Jerome Cemetery, PWJ/87, **NDR**.
8. Wall-top at Blackrock College, HOR/85.

Veronica

V. serpyllifolia L.
Thyme-leaved Speedwell   Native

| 1 | 2 | 3 | 4 | 5 | 6 | 7 | 8 |

Common in grassland, hedges, gardens, lawns and tilled fields.
FID.

V. officinalis L.
Heath Speedwell   Native

| (1) | 2 | 3 | 4 | 5 | 6 | 7 | 8 |

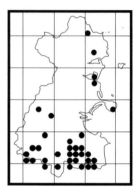

Common in the upland parts of 6, 7 & 8, on dry acid soils; rare in
the lowlands. Formerly recorded by Colgan as frequent in the
Naul Hills (1).

2. Deciduous woodland at Ardgillan Park, MN/90. Still near
   Lusk by a lane north of Lusk Common, DD/88.
3. Mature sand-hills, south of Donabate, DD, PR/87.
4. Furry Glen, DD/85. Scattered in and near Luttrellstown, MN/88.
6. Forming a sward on a rock outcrop in River Liffey Valley near
   St Edmundsbury, JS, MN/85.
7. Several clumps at the bases of trees at Fonthill, west of King's
   Hospital School, MN/90.

V. chamaedrys L.
Germander Speedwell   Native

| 1 | 2 | 3 | 4 | 5 | 6 | 7 | 8 |

Widespread and very common in woodlands, hedgerows, roadsides and grassland.

V. montana L.
Wood Speedwell   Native

Colgan: 1. Hedgebank near Westpalstown, 1902; 3. Abundant in Brackenstown Wood, 1903:
N.C. 4. In Luttrellstown wood, by the wall of the road leading to Lucan: *Wade Dubl.* 1794
abundant here in the wood and along the roadside, 1901! Near St Helena, Finglas, 1894;
in Abbotstown woods, 1895; by the pond in the Zoological Gardens, Phoenix Park, 1903;
in Saint Catherine's wood, and by the Liffey below Lucan, 1904: *N.C.* 5. In Killester Park,
1903: *Miss M.C. Knowles.* 6. Very abundant in Lucan demesne, 1904; in Crooksling glen,
above Saggard, 1903: *N.C.* 8. Old Connaught, 1871: *Herb. R.M. Barrington.* Roadside north
of the Scalp, 1893; by the Dodder near Ely's gate, Rathfarnham, 1897; by the Bride river
above Loughlinstown, 1902; in Kilbogget wood, 1903: *N.C.* A truly woodland and lowland
species in Co. Dublin especially abundant along the Liffey valley and reaching its highest
point above sea-level in Crooksling glen, near the Embankment, Saggard, at 550 feet.
Suppl: 3. Still at Brackenstown (1953). 4. St Catherine's (1956). 5. Feltrim Hill

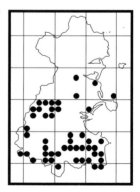

(A.W. Stelfox, 1921). 6. Lucan Demesne and Crooksling Glen (1956). 7. E. side of lane about half a mile W. of Jobstown
(R.W. Scully, 1919). Abundant in Lugmore Glen and Slade of Ballymaice (1956). 8. Marley Grange (A.W. Stelfox, 1943).

$\boxed{(1)}$ $\boxed{3}$ $\boxed{4}$ $\boxed{5}$ $\boxed{6}$ $\boxed{7}$ $\boxed{8}$

Common in base-rich deciduous woodlands and hedgebanks in the south of the county; rare elsewhere.

3. Still common in Brackenstown Woods, DD/84.
5. St Anne's Park, Raheny, PG/88-92. Santry Woods, DD/82.

V. scutellata L.
Marsh Speedwell Native

Colgan: 1. Bog of the Ring, 1903; Garristown Bog, 1894; 2. Balrothery Pond, 1893; Lusk Ponds, 1902; near Whitestown, 1903: *N.C.* 5. Plentiful on the Hill of Howth: *Mack. Cat.* Marshy spot near Cabeena's Howth: *Flor. Howth.* Marsh in the centre of Howth Head, 1895; 6. Abundant in a marsh on Saggard Hill, 1892; 7. On Seecawn and Kippure mountains, 1892; abundant in bogs above Piperstown, 1902, and in the Brakes of Ballinascorney, 1903; 8. On Kilmashogue mountain, and on Three Rock mountain, 1894; on Two Rock mountain, 1899: *N.C.*

Suppl: 1. Still at Bog of the Ring (1955). 2. Still at Balrothery Lough (1955). 7. Still at Piperstown (1955). 8. Still on Three Rock (1950) and Kilmashogue (1956). Ballybetagh (1923-1955). Not confirmed in Howth or Saggart stations.

$\boxed{(1)}$ $\boxed{2}$ $\boxed{4}$ $\boxed{5}$ $\boxed{6}$ $\boxed{7}$ $\boxed{8}$

Common in marshes in the mountains of 8; very rare elsewhere.
2. Muddy area in a marsh near the Corn Mill, near Balbriggan, DD/87.
4. Drainage ditches of the former marsh at Dunsoghly, MN/83, **NDR**.
5. Still in Greenhollows and in marshy patches, Howth, DN/89 & CB/91.
6. South end of Brittas Ponds, DD/83, 90.
7. Near Castlekelly, Glenasmole, DD, EMcA/83.

V. beccabunga L.
Brooklime Native

$\boxed{1}$ $\boxed{2}$ $\boxed{3}$ $\boxed{4}$ $\boxed{5}$ $\boxed{6}$ $\boxed{7}$ $\boxed{8}$

Widespread. Very common in marshes, ditches and on streambanks.
FID.

V. anagallis-aquatica L. *(V. anagallis)*
Blue Water-speedwell Native

$\boxed{1}$ $\boxed{2}$ $\boxed{3}$ $\boxed{4}$ $\boxed{5}$ $\boxed{6}$ $\boxed{7}$ $\boxed{8}$

Common in marshes and on stream, canal and riverbanks.
FID.

V. anagallis-aquatica × V. catenata (V. × lackschewitzii J. Keller)
Native

$\boxed{4}$

River banks.
4. River Tolka, east of Clonee, MN/87; also collected from this river in 1905 from Finglas by N. McArdle (**DBN**).

_ _

V. catenata Pennell
Pink Water-speedwell   Native
Suppl: 4. Botanic Gardens, Glasnevin (Miss E. Malone, 1882); 5. Sutton (R.W. Scully, 1893).

| 3 | 4 | 5 | 6 | 7 |

Rare, on riverbanks and by pools and canals. Common along the River Tolka Valley (4). This species was not distinguished by _Colgan_ who probably included it in **V. anagallis-aquatica**.
3. Marshy ground by a stream at Swords, PR, DD/83, **NDR**. Knocksedan Reservoir, PR, MN/85.
4. St Catherine's, MN/85. Lake margin at Luttrellstown, MN, RF/85.
5. Wet area in farmland at Malahide, DN/88. Portmarnock and nearby at the Brickfields and Raceway, DN/88 & ENL/85. Wet depression on Ireland's Eye, ENL/84.
6. Wet field-side ditch, south of Brittas, JP/86. Shallow pool, south of Esker, JP, ENL/87. Banks of the Grand Canal at Clondalkin, JP/83, **NDR**.
7. Edge of the River Liffey around King's Hospital School and near the River Liffey millrace, MN, ENL/85, **NDR**. Drains and pools north of the Grand Canal at Gallanstown, DD/92.

_ _

V. arvensis L.
Wall Speedwell   Native

| 1 | 2 | 3 | 4 | 5 | 6 | 7 | 8 |

Common on walls, arable ground and sand-hills.

_ _

V. agrestis L.
Green Field-speedwell   Possibly introduced

| (1) | 2 | (3) | 4 | 5 | 6 | 7 | 8 |

Rare as a garden weed and in disturbed ground. Formerly so common that _Colgan_ did not list individual sites; now much rarer and often in transitory sites.
2. Cabbage field south of Nevitt Cross, DD/84.
4. Rubble of a crumbled wall at White's Gate, Phoenix Park, MN/84. Finglas, F.H.Perring/62. Pathway by the Royal Canal, 1 km west of Lucan Bridge, MN/89. Vegetable garden at the National Botanic Gardens, Glasnevin, DD, MS/87.
5. Shore behind Sutton Railway Station, ENL/83. Disturbed ground in St Anne's Park, Raheny, DN/88.
6. Car park by the weir in Lucan village, MN/87.
7. East of Piperstown, PWJ/84. Gravel pathway in Raglan Road, Ballsbridge, MS/69.
8. Seafront, south-east of Dun Laoghaire swimming baths, SR, JR/84. Park between the road and the sea south of Coliemore Harbour, SR, HOR/83. Tilled fields east of Shanganagh Cemetery, south of Shankill, SR/88, still here 1994.

V. polita Fries
Grey Field-speedwell   Possibly introduced

| (1) | (2) | (3) | 4 | (5) | 6 | (7) | 8 |

Very rare, on disturbed ground and ruins.
4. One plant in Beech Park, Clonsilla, L.K. Shackleton/76.
6. Ruins near Hazelhatch, JP/84. Old ruins at Hazelhatch, JP, DAS/84.
8. Disturbed ground by Murphystown Road, south-east of Sandyford, SR/88.

V. persica Poiret *(V. tournefortii)*
Common Field-speedwell   Alien

| 1 | 2 | 3 | 4 | 5 | 6 | 7 | 8 |

Very common as a garden weed and in disturbed ground. Now well established and much more common than **V. agrestis** - the reverse of the situation in Colgan's time.
FID.

V. filiformis Smith
Slender Speedwell   Alien

| 1 | 2 | 3 | 4 | 5 | 6 | 7 | 8 |

Now common as a weed of lawns and flower-beds. Not recorded in *Suppl* in the following districts: 1, 2, 3, 4 & 6. An early Dublin record is included in *The Irish Times*, 5 May 1952 and another from a golf-course on Howth Head (5) (Bangerter and Kent 1957).
FID

V. hederifolia L. *(V. hederaefolia)*
Ivy-leaved Speedwell   Possibly introduced

| 1 | 2 | 3 | 4 | 5 | 6 | 7 | 8 |

----

subsp. **hederifolia**

| 1 | 2 | 3 | 4 | 5 | 6 | 7 | 8 |

Common on roadsides and in flowerbeds and open waste places. First recognised in a collection made by the Rev. H.G. Carroll in 1867 from Glasnevin (4) (**DBN**).

----

subsp. **lucorum** (Klett & Richter) Hartl.

| 1 | 2 | 3 | 4 | 5 | 6 | 7 | 8 |

Common in shady habitats. First recognised from a collection made by R.W. Scully in 1893 from Portmarnock (5) (**DBN**).

Melampyrum

M. pratense L.
Common Cow-wheat   Native

Colgan: 4. In woods at Luttrel's town and Phoenix Park; and 5. At Santry: *Wade Dubl.* Woods on the side of the bushy mountains above the Long Lane, near Sutton House, Howth, *Ir. Flor.* At Carrickbrack: *Flor. Howth.* Under Dung Hill, Howth, 1903: *Miss R. Mahaffy.* 7. Frequent in Glenasmole, 1894-1900; sparingly by the upper Killakee river, 1894; on Seecawn, 1903: *N.C.* 8. At Shankill, 1858: *Herb. R. Barrington.* Mountain ridge west of Three Rock, 1894: *Praeger.* Sparingly on the Three Rock above Barnacullia, and on Ballycorus Hill, 1902; on the north slope of the Two Rock and abundant in Glencullen, 1903: *N.C. Suppl:* 7. Corrig Mountain (1942). Confirmed from Glenasmole (1957), Killakee (1956), and Seecawn (1956). 8. N. slopes of Kilmashogue (1956). Mount Merrion woods (1949).

| (4) | (5) | 7 | 8 |

Rare, in heath and moorland.
7. Still in Glenasmole by the Cot Brook above Castlekelly and by the Slade Brook, HOR/85. Eastern slopes above the River Dodder near the northern reservoir in Glenasmole, MN/90.
8. Several sites in the Glencullen Valley south-east of Boranaraltry Bridge, SR, HOR/85. East and south-east slopes of Glendoo Mountain, HOR, CB/86. Ballyedmonduff, HOR, CB/86.

Euphrasia

E. officinalis L. agg.
Eyebright   Native

| (1) | 2 | 3 | 4 | 5 | 6 | 7 | 8 |

Some **Euphrasia** records made in the county were not determined beyond the aggregate species level. The records identified to species are given below and to a large extent are the work of DN who took a particular interest in the group. Many of the determinations were made by Dr A.J. Silverside. As little prior critical work has been done on this genus in Co. Dublin (but see Bobear 1964, 1969) virtually all of the district records are new to the county. However we have not so indicated them in the text, confining ourselves to highlighting new county or Irish records.

E. rostkoviana Hayne subsp. rostkoviana
Native

| (6) | 7 | 8 |

Rare, in heathland and forest margins. Specimens of this species in the county are very difficult to separate from those of the next species which was not recognised in Colgan's time.
7. Piperstown Hill at 395 m and on a grazed roadside to the south-east, HOR/85 & DN/88. Clearing at the edge of the forestry plantation to the east of Mount Seskin, nearby in an ungrazed grassy field and by a lane, PWJ, MWJ/86 & DN/88. Wet slope above the southern reservoir at Glenasmole, DN/88. Wet slope above Ballymorefinn, DN/88.
8. Grazed field at Ticknock, DN/88. St Columba's College, Rathfarnham, JB/62, (**DBN**). Recorded as formerly abundant in Glencullen (Colgan 1903) but not refound.

E. anglica Pugsley
Native

| 5 | 6 | 7 | 8 |

Scattered in and around Brittas, Saggart, Verschoyles Hill, Stone Cross, Ballinascorney, Seahan and in upland Ballymorefinn grassland; rare.
5. Rough on the edge of the fairway north-east of the Royal Dublin club-house, DN/88.
6. Grassland at Brittas, JP/83.
8. Kilmashogue Mountain, DK/c.65. Roadside and at various points near the transmitter on Three Rock Mountain, HOR, CB/86, SR/87, DD/87 & DN/88. Steep bank in Kelly's Glen, SR/87, DN/88. Edge of a field at Ticknock, DN/88.

- -

E. anglica × **E. rostkoviana**

| 6 |

6. Long grass on the roadside verge on Verschoyles Hill, DN/88, **NCR**.

- -

E. arctica Lange ex Rostrup subsp. **borealis** (F. Towns.) Yeo *(E. borealis, E. brevipila)*
Native

| 3 | 5 | 6 | 7 | 8 |

Occasional in lime-rich grassland in 6, 7 & 8; rare elsewhere.
3. Sandpit at the edge of the Island Golf-course, Malahide, DN/88. Knocksedan Reservoir, MN/88.
5. Royal Dublin Golf-course, DN/88, 89. Broken-down wall at Whitewater Brook, Howth, DN/88. Bank at Balscadden, Howth, DN/88. Track leading to the Ben of Howth, DN/88. Feltrim Hill quarry, DN/88.
6. East of the southern runway, Casement Aerodrome and by the nearby road, JP/86 & DN/88. Still by the Grand Canal, west of Gollierstown, JP, DAS/87, MN/89. Ungrazed pasture east of Saggart and at the side of the road leading to forest south-east of Saggart Hill, DN/88. Banks of the Grand Canal at Gollierstown, Hazelhatch and the 12th lock, DN/88, 89.
7. Roadside, west of Ballinascorney House, MWJ/87, & DN/88. At various sites around Mount Seskin, PWJ, MWJ/86 & DN/88. Just west of Ballymaice at 345 m, PWJ, MWJ/86. Forest road leading to the summit of Seahan, DN/88. Abandoned quarry near Piperstown School, DN/88.
8. Dry field with short grass at the top of Ticknock Road and on the pathside at the Rifle Range, SR/87 & DN/88. Along a track in the forestry plantation in the Glencullen Valley east of Boranaraltry Bridge and on the roadside nearby, SR, HOR/84 & DN/88. Calcareous drift above Glencullen Bridge, SR/88. Hill near Stepaside, SR/84.

- -

E. arctica subsp. **borealis** × **E. rostkoviana**

| 7 |

7. Gravelled road leading into Knockannavea Wood from the east side, DN/88, **NCR**.

E. arctica subsp. **borealis** x **E. scottica**

| 7 |

7. Roadside bank in wet upland area east of Piperstown Hill, DN/88, **NIR**.

E. arctica subsp. **borealis** x **E. nemorosa**

| 4 | 5 | 8 |

4. Limestone Hill above the River Tolka at Blanchardstown, DN/88, **NCR**. Disused quarry west of Cloghran House, MN/88.
5. Edge of a path near the Royal Dublin Golf-course, North Bull Island, DN/88. Beside Feltrim Hill quarry, DN/89.
8. Granite quarry below Three Rock Mountain, DN/88.

E. arctica subsp. **borealis** x **E. confusa**

| 5 | 7 | 8 |

5. Royal Dublin Golf-course, DN/88. In the rough on Howth Golf-course, DN/88.
7. Upland heath north of Ballinascorney, MN/88.
8. Edge of a field at Kilmashogue, SR/87, **NCR**. Ticknock, DN/89.

E. tetraquetra (Bréb.) Arrond. *(E. occidentalis)*
Native

| 3 | 5 | 7 |

Occasional on the coast, extremely rare inland.
3. Malahide Island peninsula, E. Ni Lamhna/82.
5. Plentiful on old sand-dunes with short grass at Portmarnock, DN/88. Grazed field north of The Summit, Howth, DN/89. In short grass near the sea between Redrock and Drumleck, DN/89. Alder Marsh on North Bull Island, ENL, DD/87 & DN/92.
7. Roadside west of Killakee Forest, DN/88.

E. tetraquetra x **E. nemorosa**

| 5 |

5. Old sand-dunes at Portmarnock with **Salix repens**, DN/88. South end of North Bull Island, DN/88, **NIR**.

E. nemorosa (Pers.) Wallr.
Native

| 3 | 4 | 5 | 7 | 8 |

Rare to occasional in sand-dunes.
3. Sand-dune at Portrane, DN/88. At Island Golf-course clubhouse, Malahide and in sand-dunes nearby, DN/88.
4. Limestone hill beside the bypass at Blanchardstown, DN/89.
5. Alder Marsh, in nearby sand-dunes and in St Anne's Golf-course on North Bull Island, ENL, MN/84 & DN/88. Gravel on reclaimed land near the Calor Gas installation, Dublin

Port area, DN/88. Near the northern tip of North Bull Island, ENL, CB/85. Sands-hills at Portmarnock, JB/62, (**DBN**), ENL/84 & DN/88. Feltrim Hill quarry, DN/88.

7. Roadside near the quarry at Ballinascorney, DN/88. Roadside at Mount Seskin, DN/88. Near Ballinascorney House, MN/88.

8. Abandoned granite quarry below Three Rock Mountain, DN/88. Ticknock Rifle Range, DN/88.

E. confusa Pugsley
Native

| 3 | 5 | 6 | 7 | 8 |

Rare, in sand-hills and grassland.

3. Malahide Golf-course, JB/63, (**DBN**). Sand-hills at Burrow, Portrane, DD, PR/87.

5. Broken-down wall near Whitewater Brook, Howth, DD, DN/88. Royal Dublin Golf-course, DN/89.

6. Grassland beside the Grand Canal south of Ballymakaily Mill, JP/89.

7. Forest path leading to Seahan Mountain, DN/89.

8. Three Rock Mountain, SR/87.

E. confusa x **E. nemorosa**

| 3 | 6 | 8 |

3. Landward side of the Island Golf-course, Malahide, DN/88.

6. Verschoyles Hill, MN/88.

8. Roadside bank at Glencullen, SR/87, **NIR**. Beside the road on Three Rock Mountain, SR/87.

E. micrantha Reichb.
Native
Recorded from the county in *CC2* but not re-confirmed during the present survey.

E. scottica Wettst.
Native

| 7 | 8 |

7. Wet mountain flush east of Ballymorefinn, DN/88.

8. Wet flush on south-west slope of Two Rock Mountain in Glencullen, SR/87, DN/88.

Odontites

O. vernus (Bellardi) Dumort. *(O. rubra, Bartsia odontites)*
Red Bartsia   Native

Colgan: A pure white flowered variety occurs in abundance at Raheny quarries (1902) and at Loughlinstown Commons (1894-1903). This apparently comes true from seed, as it has been observed in precisely the same spot at Loughlinstown after a lapse of nine years: *N.C.*

| 1 | 2 | 3 | 4 | 5 | 6 | 7 | 8 |

A white-flowered variant still occurs by the Bray Road at Loughlinstown (8). Plants from North Bull Island (5) are unusual in morphology and require further investigation.

subsp. **vernus**
Native

| I | 2 | 3 | 4 | 5 | 6 | 7 | 8 |

Common in poor pasture and roadsides.
FID.

---

subsp. **serotinus** (Syme) Corbiere
Native

| 5 |

Extremely rare.
5. In sandy areas subject to inundation by the sea on North Bull Island, DD/91.

Rhinanthus

R. minor L. *(R. crista-galli, R. stenophyllus)*
Yellow-rattle   Native
Suppl: [**R. stenophyllus**] 6. By Grand Canal near Hazelhatch (1956).

| I | 2 | 3 | 4 | 5 | 6 | 7 | 8 |

Occasional on roadside banks, meadows and sand-dunes. The predominant form in Dublin is
subsp. **minor**. Subsp. **stenophyllus**, recorded in *Suppl*, is still there.

Pedicularis

P. palustris L.
Marsh Lousewort   Native

| (1) | (3) | (4) | (5) | 6 | 7 | (8) |

Rare, in wet calcareous ground; very rare in 6 & 7.
6. Slade Valley north-west of Verschoyles Hill, JP/86.
7. Runnels at the bottom of the slope west of the River Dodder to the south-west of the
   southern reservoir in Glenasmole, SR/91.

P. sylvatica L.
Lousewort   Native

| (2) | (3) | 5 | 6 | 7 | 8 |

Occasional in moorland and on peat or mineral
soil in the mountains and on Howth; common in 8.

OROBANCHACEAE

Lathraea

L. squamaria L.
Toothwort   Native

Colgan: 4. "In St Katharine's Wood, May, 1739": *Annot. in Threlkeld.* In a very shady part of the wood of St Catherine's: *Wade Rar.* still there in 1896! In the wood of Luttrell's town (Woodlands): *Mack Rar.,* 1806 frequent here towards the Liffey road in 1900! 6. Sparingly in one spot by the river walk in the woods of Vesey's demesne near Leixlip, 1896-1904, and in thickets below the Salmon Leap, 1904: *N.C.* In a second station in Vesey's demesne, 1904: *Miss L. Colgan.* 8. "Found upon a moist Acclivity as we came up the Sea Shore from *Dunlary to Newton": Threlkeld.*

Suppl: 6. Still in Lucan Demesne on *Prunus laurocerasus,* by river path just below the Oratory and on hazel about 100 yards W. of the boundary fence opposite St Catherine's (1952). 7. Mouth of Friarstown glen, Glenasmole (J.A.J. Palmer, *I.N.,* XXIV, 1915 and J.P. Brunker, *I.N.,* XXVII, 1918). Still there in 1947.

4	(6)	7	8

Rare, in deciduous woodland.

4. Very common in St Catherine's Woods, JS/84. At Luttrellstown and nearby, MN/83, 86. Beech Park, Clonsilla, JS/84, 89. Dubber Cross, Finglas, DD/67, 88. National Botanic Gardens, Glasnevin, J. O'Shea/74, MS/75, 77, DS/81 & MN/90.
7. South bank of the River Liffey, south of the club-house and to the east of Hermitage Golf-course, J.S. Jackson/67 & JS/84. Edge of the River Liffey below King's Hospital School and near the millrace, PWJ/86.
8. Lawless's Wood, Kilgobbin, PC/72-79.

Orobanche

O. hederae Duby
Ivy Broomrape   Native

Colgan: 2. Banks by the sea north of Loughshinny, spreading for about 200 yards, 1893-1903: *N.C.* 4. "On the side of the road going to Lucan about a mile from it among the elm and other bushes in the hedge, August, 1799": *Templeton MS (as O. minor).* Between Luttrell's-town and Lucan: *Wade Rar. (as O. major).* Abundant in and about Woodlands, on wall-tops in thickets, and by the roadside, also frequent along the Liffey banks to Lucan and by Saint Catherine's, 1895-1904: *N.C.* 5. Hill of Howth, south side, on steep banks near the sea: *Mack. Cat. (as O. minor).* Very sparingly on banks above the sea, both north and south of Piper's Gut: *Flor. Howth.* 6. In Vesey's demesne, Lucan, 1892: *Miss A.G. Kinahan* very abundant here, 1902! 7. Plentiful in Palmerstown woods: *Flor. Hib.* Wall top at Palmerstown, 1901: *N.C.* By the Dodder above Rathgar Bridge *(Praeger) Ir. Nat.,* 1902, p. 322. 8. In Mr Semple's garden near the harbour of Dunleary: *Mack. Cat. (as O.minor).* On a wall near Kingstown railway station, up to about 1890, when the ivy was removed; in a garden at Alma road, Monkstown, 1893: *Greenwood Pim.* In the grounds of Blackrock House, 1893: *Scully.* Wall by the railway between Seapoint and Blackrock, 1903; drift bank by the sea below Killiney Hill, 1893-1902: *N.C.*

Suppl: 2. Still at Loughshinny (1955). 3. N. shore of Malahide estuary near Prospect Point (1937-1956). 4. Glenmaroon Hill (1942). Still between Luttrellsown and Lucan (1957). 6. Still in Lucan Demesne (1952).

2	3	4	(5)	6	7	8

Widespread and locally common in woodlands and shady sites in the River Liffey Valley in 4, 6 and 7; very rare elsewhere though sometimes locally abundant. Not seen recently on Howth Head (5).
2. Still at Loughshinny, on top of a low cliff, PG/90.
3. Hedgerow at Balheary, PR/84. Still on shady banks, wall-tops and roadsides on the north side of the Malahide estuary near Prospect Point, PR/83-89.
4. Banks of the River Tolka in the National Botanic Gardens, Glasnevin, DK/c.65 & MN/86.
8. By the railway near the Seapoint Martello Tower, MWJ/95.

- -

O. minor Smith
Common Broomrape   Alien

Colgan: 2. Abundant on Shennicks's island, Skerries *(Rev. W. Colgan) Colgan 1893.* Between Skerries and Loughshinny, 1895; by the shore north of Balbriggan, 1900; near Skerries railway station, 1902: *N.C.* 3. Very abundant in sandy fields to the north of Portrane peninsula, 1894: *Colgan 1895* and in 1900! 4. Sparingly near the old church of Mulhuddart, 1900: *N.C.* 5. Abundant in a field above Malahide hotel, 1894: *Colgan 1895.* On a bank at Tansy, Howth *(Miss R. Mahaffy);* abundant near Sutton station *(Praeger) Praeger 1895* abundant in the latter station, 1903! In Portmarnock sandhills: *Hart 1897.* 6. On the eastern slope of Slieve Thoul, 1902: *N.C.*

Suppl: 2. Still about Skerries and Loughshinny (1957). 3. Still at Portrane (1954). 5. North Bull near the Coastguard cottages (J.P. Brunker, 1922). 7. By Naas Road quarter of a mile E. of Newlands cross-roads (1944). Not confirmed elsewhere.

Rare, in sand-dunes and flower-beds.
2. Coastal grassland at Red Island, Skerries, DD, NMcG/83 & RF/87. North of Ballykea, RF/86.
4. Cross Guns Bridge, DNFC/80 and DD/87. Calcareous bank north of Cappagh Hospital, MN/83. National Botanic Gardens, Glasnevin, D.P. Murphy/72.
5. On the southern half of the North Bull Island, east of The Farm, in short dune turf and at the edge of the road and near the Causeway, HJH/85, MWJ/86, DN, MN/88, KF/62 & PG/87, 88. Hole-in-the-Wall beach, Sutton, DN/88. A few plants on gravelly ground at the Sports Club, Balscadden, Howth, PG/88 & CB/91.
7. Flower-bed in College Park, T.C.D., JRA/88. Disused road, Allenton, CB/90.
FID.

- -

LENTIBULARIACEAE

Pinguicula

P. lusitanica L.
Pale Butterwort   Native

Colgan: 7. Frequent in upper Glenasmole, 1901: *N.C.* 8. Near the Three Rock mountain above Dundrum: *Ir. Flor.* Frequent on the eastern slope of the Two Rock mountain, 1899, abundant on the southern slopes above Glencullen chapel, 1894, and abundant on Glencullen mountain, 1901: *N.C.*

Suppl: 7. Still at Glenasmole (1957). 8. N.E. slopes of Kilmashogue (J.P. Brunker, 1922).

7	8

Rare, in bogs and moorland flushes.
7. Flush above the stream east of Ballymorefinn Hill, HJH, SR/87. 0.5 km west of Castlekelly,

DD/83. By the River Dodder south-east of Glenasmole Lodge, SR, C. Breen/86. Mountain bog by the roadside 0.5 km south of Glassamucky, DD/82.

8. Wet places on both sides of Glencullen Valley, SR, HOR, JR/84-87. Ballyedmonduff, on the south-east slope of Three Rock Mountain, JR/92.

P. vulgaris L.
Common Butterwort   Native

Colgan: 2. Frequent on wet banks and in swampy ground by the shore from Skerries to Balbriggan, 1895: *N.C.* 4. In the glen in the Phoenix Park: *Ir. Flor.* frequent here in the Furry Glen, 1900! By the Tolka above Blanchardstown, 1895; and 5. Howth Head, 1903: *N.C.* In the sandhills, North Bull, 1902: *Scully.* 6. By the Grand Canal near Hazelhatch, 1893, and above Clondalkin, 1900; on Slieve Thoul, Brittas, 1895: *N.C.* 7 and 8. Common in the mountain bogs, and frequent along the lower Dodder, as at Old Bawn and Templeogue: *N.C.*

| 2 | (4) | 5 | (6) | 7 | 8 |

Occasional in bogs and moorland flushes in the southern parts of 7 & 8 (Glenasmole, Corrig Mountain, Kippure, the Featherbed, Glendoo Mountain, Glencullen Valley, Two Rock, north slopes of Three Rock, Ballyedmonduff and south of Ballybetagh Bog); very rare elsewhere. Most of the wet coastal banks on the coast in District 2, where this species was once frequent, are now either dried-out or overgrown.

2. Marsh on the coast between Loughshinny and Skerries, DD/83.
5. Still in the Central Marsh, Howth, PG/90.

Utricularia

U. vulgaris L.
Greater Bladderwort   Native

Colgan: 1. Abundant in pools at Bog of the Ring, and in drains at Garristown Bog, 1902: *N.C.* 4. Phoenix Park: *Ir. Flor.* Frequent in the Royal Canal from Lucan to Ashtown, 1901: *N.C.* 5. In marshy ditches at Howth: *Wade Rar.* Plentiful in boggy places near the summit of Howth: *Mack. Cat.* not seen recently at Howth. At Raheny quarries, 1866: *Herb. Hart* and in 1902!
Suppl: 1. Either this species or *U. neglecta* is present in Bog of the Ring (1948) but has not been seen flowering. 5. Raheny Quarries (1951).

| (1) | (4) | 5 | 7 |

Extremely rare.
5. Still at Raheny Quarries, DD/66, which were filled in shortly after.
7. Palmerston Marsh, MN, ENL, CB/85, **NDR**.

U. australis R.Br. *(U. neglecta)*
Bladderwort   Native

Colgan: 1. Pools in the Bog of the Ring and 3. In a quarry hole by the Ward river below Chapelmidway, 1893: *Colgan 1893.* 5. Abundant and luxuriant at Raheny quarries, 1902: *Colgan 1903.*
Suppl: 5. Confirmed only from Raheny Quarries (1951).

| (1) | (3) | (5) |

Not refound at any of its former sites in the county. Its former stations at Raheny Quarries (5) are now filled-in and there are few suitable habitats left in the Bog of the Ring (1).

CAMPANULACEAE

Campanula

C. rapunculoides L.
Creeping Bellflower   Alien

Colgan: 2. Well established for about 100 yards along a sandy bank by the roadside south-west of Rush village, 1893-1904; frequent in a sandy fallow near the old wind-mill at Rush, 1904: *N.C.* Abundant over a considerable area in a sandy potato field and on adjoining banks west of the coast-guard station at Rogerstown, 1900-03: *Colgan 1903.* 8. Walls near Bray Harbour *(More) Rec. Add.* In a pasture above the sea below Vico Road, Killiney, spreading over a space of 30 paces by 15 paces, 1899-1902; well established on the permanent way at the north side of Kingstown railway terminus, 1899-1903: *Colgan 1903.* An obvious introduction in all of its stations, but fully entitled by its standing in District 2 to a permanent place in the county flora. In cultivated land in many parts of Germany the plant is a noxious weed, and well nigh ineradicable by reason of its deep-seated and widely creeping roots.

Suppl: 2. Still at Rush (1923-1941) and Rogerstown (1956). 8. Still at Vico (1947) and Dun Laoghaire Railway Station (1947).

(2) (8)

Not refound at any of its sites in the county.

C. rotundifolia L.
Harebell   Native

Colgan: 2. Frequent and in some spots abundant, in Rush sandhills, 1900-02: *N.C.* 3. Frequent in Lambay island: *Flor. Lambay.* Frequent on the Portrane sandhills, 1903: *N.C.* 5. "On a highish place near the sea side beyond Clontarf, August 31, 1732": *Annot in Threlkeld.* About Warren House: *Wade Dubl.* Portmarnock sandhills: *Ir. Flor.* frequent here in 1902! On the Cosh and on Ireland's Eye: *Flor. Howth.* Near the Martello tower, Malahide, 1897-1902: *N.C.* This species is quite absent from the mountain districts of Co. Dublin, though a frequent alpine plant from north to south in Ireland.

2 3 5

Occasional in sand-dunes where it may be locally common. Confined to sand-dunes in Co. Dublin, though found in the uplands elsewhere in Ireland.
2. Still common in sand-hills between Rush and Rogerstown, DD/88.
3. Sand-hills near Malahide Point, PR/85. Sandy banks, north of Burrow, Portrane, PR/84.
5. Around the Alder Marsh and in adjacent sand-dunes on North Bull Island, ENL, MN/84. Abundant in sand-hills on Portmarnock Golf-course, and in sand-dunes to the north of the Country-club, Portmarnock, DN, RF/88 & HJH/83.

Wahlenbergia

W. hederacea (L.) Reichb.
Ivy-leaved Bellflower   Native

Colgan: 7. Sparingly in grassy places near the summit of Feather Bed road, Killakee mountain, 1902: *Colgan 1903.* 8. In Glencullen, near the bridge *(Greenwood Pim) Rec. Add.* In considerable quantity along the Glencullen river at intervals for about half a mile above the bridge, 1893-1901; in wet grassy ground by a rill on the mountain side south-west of Glencullen bridge, 1894; frequent in moist pastures and in *Sphagnum* swamps on the mountain west of Glencullen quarries, 1901: *N.C.* Ascends to 1, 150 feet on Glencullen mountain, and to 1, 600 feet on Killakee, mountain. This most delicate and elegant species reaches in Co. Dublin its northern limit and its highest vertical range for Ireland.

Suppl: 8. Still at Glencullen Bridge (1947), but most of the station as recorded in Colgan's *Flora* is in Co. Wicklow.

(7)　**8**

Extremely rare.

8. One plant in **Sphagnum** on the south side of the Glencullen Valley, south-west of Glencullen Bridge, between 250 and 300 m, SR/86. This site has since been drained for forestry.

Jasione

J. montana L.
Sheep's-bit　　Native

(3)　**5**　**6**　**7**　**8**

Common in coastal acid heaths on Howth (5), rarer on base-poor mineral soil in the mountains. In these areas it is now often confined to roadside banks or steep rocky bluffs where there is minimal competition. Plants of var. **latifolia** Pugs. with very large inflorescences often containing more than 60 flowers, thickened peduncles and relatively broad leaves and involucral bracts, are occasionally found on Howth.

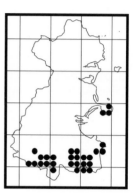

RUBIACEAE

Sherardia

S. arvensis L.
Field Madder　　Native

1　**2**　**3**　**4**　**5**　**6**　**7**　**8**

Occasional in sandy ground and as a lawn weed.

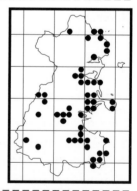

Galium

G. odoratum (L.) Scop. *(Asperula odorata)*
Woodruff　　Native

1　**2**　**4**　**5**　**6**　**7**　**8**

Common in deciduous woodlands in the River Liffey Valley; rare elsewhere.
FID.

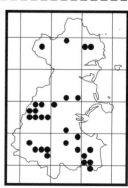

G. uliginosum L.
Fen Bedstraw   Native

Colgan: 8. In considerable quantity amongst *Sphagnum* in a marsh on the flank of Kilmashogue mountain above Stackstown, 1903: *Colgan 1904*.

Suppl: 7. E. side of Upper Reservoir, Glenasmole (R.W. Scully, 1919), still there in 1957. Glen above Embankment near Crooksling (A.W. Stelfox, 1922), probably Lugmore where it was confirmed in 1956. Abundant by Seecawn Brook (1949). *Brunker MS:* 8. Ticknock, '58.

| 7 | (8) |

G. uliginosum is a plant of fens and base-rich marshes.
7. West side of southern reservoir in Glenasmole, BM/97.

G. palustre L.
Common Marsh-bedstraw   Native

| 1 | 2 | 3 | 4 | 5 | 6 | 7 | 8 |

Occasional in marshy places and drains. Frequent by ponds, streams, canals and ditches, and in the River Liffey Valley; rarer elsewhere. *FID.*

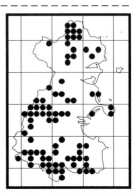

G. verum L.
Lady's Bedstraw   Native

| 1 | 2 | 3 | 4 | 5 | 6 | 7 | 8 |

Very widespread. Abundant in sand-dunes; very common on dry calcareous banks, gravel quarries and other exposures on the drift. *FID.*

G. mollugo L. (incl. *G. erectum*)
Hedge Bedstraw   Probably introduced

Colgan: G. erectum - 4. In a meadow by the Tolka adjoining the Botanic Gardens *(Moore & More) Cyb.* Violet Hill, Glasnevin: *Guide.* 5. Roadside banks at Saint Fintan's: *Flor. Howth.* At Sutton 1896 *(Praeger) Top. Bot.* 8. On the north side of Killiney Hill, 1834, *(Miss Green) Flor. Hib.* In a field at Stagstown, south of Rathfarnham *(S. Foot) Cyb.*

Suppl: G. erectum - 2. On lawn in rose garden at Kenure Park, Rush (A.W. Stelfox, 1923).

Colgan: G. mollugo - 2 and 3. Between Swords and Skerries, plentiful in hedges and field borders *(Moore) Cyb.* 2. Roadside bank at Ballough, sparingly, 1903: N.C. 3. Lands about Knocksedan *(J. White) Cyb.* A few plants near Lissen Hall, 1902; abundant in a field border at Portrane, 1904: N.C. 4. Fields and roadsides between Finglas quarries and Glasnevin: *Ir. Flor.* Finglas quarries, 1894 *(N.C.) Cyb II.* 5. Common on the lands of Abbeville and Ballymun: *Ir. Flor.* Plentiful on an embankment by the new road, Howth, 1883: *Flor. Howth* and in 1902! Railway bank near Killester, 1894; 6. Between Lucan and Esker, 1900; near Hazelhatch, 1904; 7. Near Crumlin cross-roads, 1900: N.C. 8. Near the Martello Tower, Sandymount: *Mack. Cat.* Near Old Connaught and Rathmichael, 1902: *J. Meade.* Sparingly near Dalkey, 1902: N.C.

Suppl: G. mollugo - 3. Still in hedge, Lissenhall Lane (1950). 5. Bank at St Anne's, Clontarf (1946). 6. Roadside at Castlebagot (1956). 7. Waste ground by R. Liffey above Islandbridge (R.W. Scully, 1922).

DNFC Annual Report for 1962: G. mollugo - Howth village/Ben of Howth, M. Hallinan.

Rare on banks by roadsides in calcareous areas.

5. Still at Sutton, on a roadside bank opposite St Fintan's Church, DD/82.
6. Hedge west of Newcastle House, JP/84. One clump at Milltown bridge and nearby at Milltown House, CB/87 & MN/90.
8. Grassy bank on the south side of the Stillorgan Reservoirs, SR, HOR/85. Field just north of Stillorgan Reservoirs, SR/92.

G. saxatile L.
Heath Bedstraw   Native

Suppl: North of the R. Liffey it has been confirmed only from Naul Hills, Lambay and Howth Head.

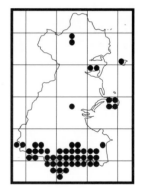

Common in dry acid grassland and heathland in the mountains, Howth Head and Lambay; very rare elsewhere. Occasionally spreading into gardens from garden centre pot plants.

1. Roadside banks at and south of Murphy's Quarry, Nag's Head, GS/82, 86, 88.
3. Grounds of Newbridge House, Donabate, PR/91.
4. Weed in heather beds at the National Botanic Gardens, Glasnevin, where no doubt it is an introduction, MN/88, **NDR**.

G. aparine L.
Cleavers, Goosegrass, Robin-run-the-hedge   Native

Widespread and abundant on roadside verges, waste ground and in hedges.
FID.

Rubia

R. peregrina L.
Wild Madder   Native

Colgan: 5. On the Hill of Howth, but not in quantity: *Wade Rar.,* 1804. Casana's Rock and elsewhere along the steep cliffs on the east side of Howth; Drumleek, Ceanchor, Earlscliff and the Needles, on the south side: *Flor. Howth,* 1887. Drumleck, Earlscliff, and the Needles, also on tramway bank below Roxborough, 1903: *Miss R. Mahaffy.* Cliffs under the old Baily, east side of Howth, 1900 *(N.C.) Top. Bot.* 8. Sparingly near the Lead Mines, Killiney Bay, towards Dalkey: *Wade Dubl.,* 1794 - in fair quantity here in 1902, on both sides of the Lead Mines, but chiefly on the south-west!

Suppl: 3. Lambay (A.W. Stelfox, 1923). 5 and 8. Still found in all Colgan's ststions on Hill of Howth (1955) and at Dalkey (1957).

(3) | 5 | 8

Rare in low scrub on coastal cliffs.

5. Still scattered on the south and east sides of Howth, DD/85. Common on Broad Strand, Doldrum Bay, CB/91.
8. Just below the railway bridge at Whiterock, Killiney, SR/83, 85.

CAPRIFOLIACEAE

Sambucus

S. nigra L.
Elder   Native

| 1 | 2 | 3 | 4 | 5 | 6 | 7 | 8 |

Extremely widespread. Very common in hedgerows, scrub woodland and on waste ground. *FID.*

S. ebulus L.
Dwarf Elder   Alien

Colgan: 3. On the island of Lambay it occurs in great profusion: *Wade Rar.* Sparingly on a roadside bank near a cottage below Forest, 1894: *N.C.* 4. Fully established at intervals for about 130 paces on railway banks east of Liffey Junction, 1903 *(F.C. Crawford & N.C.) Colgan* 1903. 5. Waste ground near Sutton Station, 1893-1903: *N.C.* 8. Roadsides near Bray, 1863: *R.M. Barrington.* In all cases an outcast from cultivation. It is occasionally grown as a medicinal herb in cottage gardens.
Suppl: 4. Liffey Junction (1957). 5. Still at Sutton Railway Station (1957). 6. Rathcoole (R.W. Scully, 1923, still there 1956). Opposite the main gate of Baldonnel Aerodrome (1943).

| 3 | 4 | 5 | 6 | (8) |

Rare, on waste ground.

3. Still at Forrest Great, PR/85.
4. Still at Liffey Junction on waste ground between the railway and canal, DN/87.
5. Still at Sutton Station, DD/67-90.
6. Just west of Jobstown, JP/83.

Viburnum

V. opulus L.
Guelder-rose   Native

Colgan: 1. In a glen below Clonany Bridge, Naul Hills, 1895; 3. Near Rathbeal and between Killeek and Little Forest, 1903: *N.C.* 4. Cardiff's Bridge: *Wade Dubl.* Frequent in hedgerows near Santry School and between Ballymun and Coultry, 1894; in Saint Catherine's wood and frequent between Westmanstown and Clonsilla, 1895; sparingly near Dunsoughly, and near Hollywoodrath, 1900; near Damastown, 1903; 5. At Kilmore, 1895; frequent in hedges near Drinan, 1892-1902; 6. Near

Aderrig 1894; in Crooksling glen above the Embankment, Saggard, and near Milltown, 1903; in Lucan demesne, and in woods by the Liffey above Leixlip bridge 1901; 7. At Drimnagh eskers, 1900; near Ballinascorney, 1902; and frequent in Glenasmole and Lugmore, 1903: *N.C.* 8. Sparingly in a glen near Carriggollagher, 1902; *J. Meade.*

Suppl: 3. Abundant at Coolatrath (1953). 4. Between Barberstown Bridge and Shackleton's Mill, Lucan (1923). By Royal Canal above Clonsilla (1956). 6. Castlebagot (1923).

| (1) | 3 | 4 | 5 | 6 | 7 | 8 |

Occasional in hedgerows; increases in frequency towards the west of the county. Relatively common in 4, 6 & 7; rare elsewhere.

3. Balcarrick, Donabate, PR/92.
5. Roadside hedge, 1 km north of Ballymun, HJH/85. Field beside Turnapin Lane, north of Santry, ENL/85.
8. Opposite Kilgobbin Church and in a hedge north of Kilgobbin, PC/83. Frequent between Lamb's Cross, Sandyford and Kilgobbin, PC/71.

Symphoricarpos

S. albus (L.) S.F. Blake *(S. racemosus, S. rivularis)*
Snowberry   Alien

| 1 | 2 | 3 | 4 | 5 | 6 | 7 | 8 |

Widespread and common in hedgerows, perhaps having grown from bird-distributed seeds and certainly spreading from nearby gardens.
FID.

Leycesteria

L. formosa Wallich
Himalayan Honeysuckle   Alien

| 2 | 4 | 5 | 6 | 7 | 8 |

Rare, in hedgerows, ditches and drains adjoining woodland; often in old estates. Not reported in *Colgan* or *Suppl* and therefore new to the above districts.

Lonicera

L. periclymenum L.
Honeysuckle   Native

| 1 | 2 | 3 | 4 | 5 | 6 | 7 | 8 |

Common in hedgerows, woodlands and scrub on sea-cliffs.

ADOXACEAE

Adoxa

A. moschatellina L.
Moschatel   Alien

8

Extremely rare. Not recorded in *Colgan* or *Suppl.*
8. Woods in an old estate near Leopardstown Park Hospital, SR, HOR/85, **NCR**.

VALERIANACEAE

Valerianella

V. locusta (L.) Laterr. *(V. olitoria)*
Common Cornsalad   Native

1	2	3	4	5	6	7	8

Common in sand-hills by the coast; rare inland.
1. Open sandy ground in Garristown village, GS/86, **NDR**.
4. Near Clonsilla Railway station DNFC/82. Near Ashtown Railway Station, MN/86.
6. Railway line south of St Helen's, JP/84, **NDR**.

V. carinata Lois.
Keeled-fruited Cornsalad   Alien
Praeger, 1939: A good colony in a rough lane-way among gardens on N. side of "Greenfield", Dalkey.

4	5	7	8

Common in sandy and waste places in 8; rare and possibly under-recorded elsewhere.
4. Bank, east of Kennan Bridge, DNFC/90, **NDR**.
5. St Anne's Park, Raheny, PG/87, 88, **NDR**. Roadside south of the summit on Howth Head, DD/87. Kilbarrack Graveyard, PG/91. Malahide Railway Station, DD/97.
7. Weed in the T.C.D. Botanic Garden, DD/87, **NDR**. Back of House 38, T.C.D., PG/90.

V. rimosa Bast. *(V. auricula)*
Broad-fruited Cornsalad   Alien
Colgan: 3. In sandy fallows, Portrane, 1900: a few plants on the railway north of Donabate, 1902: Colgan 1903. 5. Oatfield above Ceanchor: Flor. Howth. Sandy fields at Portmarnock, 1894, and roadside near Sutton station: Praeger 1895.

(3)	(5)

Never refound at any of its sites in the county.

V. dentata (L.) Pollich
Narrow-fruited Cornsalad   Alien

Colgan: 2. Sparingly at Balbriggan, 1893; frequent in cornfields north of Lusk, 1893-1902; 3. Abundant in a cornfield by the shore at Kilcrea, 1893-1902; in cultivated land near Chapelmidway and roadside at Newbridge, 1893; abundant in sandy fallows, Portrane, 1900-02; 4. Sparingly in cornfields near Kennan Bridge, Royal Canal, 1894, and north of Lucan, 1903; abundantly near Westmanstown, 1895: *N.C.* 5. Cornfields, Feltrim Hill: *Ir. Flor.* Baldoyle, 1840 *(Moore) Herb. Glasnevin.* Frequent in sandy fields, Portmarnock, 1902; 6. Sparingly at Hazelhatch and abundantly in a cornfield near Esker, 1893; cornfield above the Embankment, 1895: *N.C.*

Brunker MS: 3. Seen in 1942 at Colgan's Kilcrea station.

| (2) | (3) | 4 | (5) | (6) |

Extremely rare.
4. Still near Westmanstown, in a potato field, MN/87.

Valeriana

V. officinalis L.
Common Valerian   Native

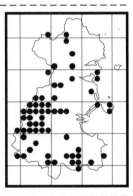

| I | (2) | 3 | 4 | 5 | 6 | 7 | 8 |

Occasional in wet marshy ground by rivers, woods and reservoirs.
1. North-east of Garristown, GS/86.
FID.

Centranthus

C. ruber (L.) DC.
Red Valerian   Alien

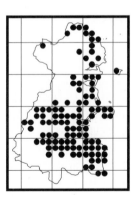

| I | 2 | 3 | 4 | 5 | 6 | 7 | 8 |

Originally introduced as a garden plant that has now become a weed. In Colgan's time at the beginning of the 20th century, it was still rare but becoming well established at many sites. Now common on old walls and railway sidings in most districts.
1. Naul, GS/90, **NDR**.
FID.

DIPSACACEAE

Dipsacus

D. fullonum L. *(D. sylvestris)*
Wild Teasel   Native

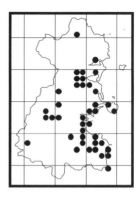

1	2	3	4	5	6	7	8

Occasional in waste places, dry banks, ditches and quarries; commonest near the coast and in the Liffey Valley.
FID.

Knautia

K. arvensis (L.) Coulter *(Scabiosa arvensis)*
Field Scabious   Native

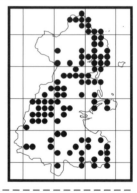

1	2	3	4	5	6	7	8

Common on roadsides in base-rich areas and waste ground.

Succisa

S. pratensis Moench *(Scabiosa succisa)*
Devil's-bit Scabious   Native

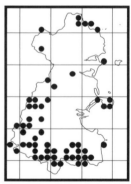

1	2	3	4	5	6	7	8

Common in damp grassland, marshes and canal banks; very common in the upland areas of 7 & 8.

ASTERACEAE (*COMPOSITAE*)

Carlina

C. vulgaris L.
Carline Thistle   Native

Colgan: Frequent in 3, 4, 5, 6, 7 and 8, and especially abundant on the sandhills at Portrane and Portmarnock; apparently quite rare in 2, where it has been observed only at Rogerstown.

| (2) | 3 | 4 | 5 | 6 | 7 | 8 |

Occasional in sand-dunes and rare on sandy ground inland.

3. Sand-hills at Malahide Island, PR/83, 85.
4. Disused part of Lucan Quarry, MN, PR/85. On esker ridge at Finglas Bridge, MN, GS/83. Cross Guns Bridge, DD/87.
5. Just west of Feltrim, DD/84. The Baily, Howth, DD/83. Lion's Bay, Howth Head, DN/90. Common in sand-hills all along the southern half of Portmarnock Peninsula, PR, DD/83, 91.
6. Dry steeply sloping grassland on the eastern side of Crooksling Glen, Brittas, JP/84.
7. Gravel banks of the Dodder River 1 km above Oldbawn, CB/90.
8. Dry slope above Glencullen Bridge, SR, JR/86. Steep bank above the Vico Bathing Place, Killiney, SR/85.

FID.

Arctium

A. lappa L. *(A. majus)*
Greater Burdock   Native

Colgan: 5. Roadside near Saint Doulough's *(Praeger) Ir. Nat.,* 1897, p. 94.

Suppl: Very rare. 5. Not re-found at St Doolagh's. 7. Bushy Park, Terenure (1955).

| (5) | (7) |

Not recently recorded from the county.

A. minus (Hill) Bernh. *(A. nemorosum)*
Lesser Burdock   Native

| 1 | 2 | 3 | 4 | 5 | 6 | 7 | 8 |

Widespread and common on waste ground, roadside verges, poor pastures and disturbed areas in sand-dunes in the lowlands. Most Dublin plants belong to subsp. **nemorosum** (Lej.) Syme, though plants with small heads approaching subsp. **minus** have been seen at Gollierstown (6), DD, JP/89 and by the bridge 0.5 km south of Richardstown (3), SR, JR/89.
FID.

Carduus

C. tenuiflorus Curtis *(C. pycnocephalus)*
Slender Thistle   Native

| (1) | 2 | 3 | 4 | 5 | (6) | 7 | 8 |

Common on waste ground, cliffs near the sea and in sea-bird colonies; rare inland.

4. Waste ground close to the Royal Canal at Cross Guns Bridge, DD/80 & MN/88.
5. Behind Artane Castle shopping centre, ENL/85. Waste ground at Kinsealy, ENL/85. Darndale housing estate, Malahide Road, ENL/85. St Doolagh's Quarries, DNFC/83. Many plants in a disused quarry at Corr Castle, Howth, CB/92.

7. Roadside, 1 km south of Firhouse, PWJ, Diane Wyse Jackson/87. Garden weed off St Mary's Road, Crumlin, PWJ/87. Waste ground 300 m east-north-east of the church north of Drimnagh, PWJ, MWJ/87. Tymon Lane, DK/83 & CB/90. Banks of the 7th lock of the Grand Canal at Gallanstown, DD/92.
8. On waste ground at the south-east corner of the Stillorgan Reservoirs, SR, HOR/83.

- -

C. crispus L. subsp. **multiflorus** (Gaudin) Gremli *(C. acanthoides)*
Welted Thistle   Native

Colgan: 2. At Balbriggan and in the grounds of Gormanstown Castle: *Praeger 1894.* Railway banks near Skerries, 1895, and roadsides near Balrothery, 1900-02; 3. Roadside east of Roganstown, 1893, and west of Balheary, 1902; in a quarry near Killeek, 1894; *N.C.* 4. Waste ground about Finglas, Glasnevin, & c. *Ir. Flor.* Near the Model Farm, Glasnevin: *Miss E. Malone.* Quarry banks near Kilshane, 1894, and near Dunsoghly, 1900; near Knockmaroon and near Blanchardstown, 1895; near Mulhuddart, 1900: *N.C.* 5. By the Martello tower, Howth village: *Flor. Howth.* Abundant by the quarry above Saint Fintan's, Howth, 1895; and 6. Sparingly by the Grand Canal above Clondalkin, 1902: *N.C.* 7. Near Tymon Castle, 1891: *More MS.* At Inchicore, 1900: *R.A. Phillips.* At Bohernabreena, 1903: *N.C.* 8. Neglected fields near Ball's Bridge: *Mack. Cat.*
Suppl: 3. Fieldstown (1953). Roadside N. of Swords (1954). 7. Near Tymon Castle (1954). 8. By path to Vico bathing-place, Dalkey (1955).

| 2 | 3 | 4 | 5 | (6) | 7 | (8) |

Very rare, in sandy ground.
2. Headland near the railway line at Balleally Dump, DD/87.
3. Ground recently disturbed by building operations at Swords Village, DD/92.
4. West of Finglas Bridge, MN, JS/84. Roadside 4 km north of Mulhuddart, MN/86. 1 km west of Mulhuddart, MN/88. Roadside leading to St Margaret's, MN/84. Abbotstown House, A. Mangan/90.
5. Sutton Strand, DNFC/88. On Howth Head at Howth Golf-course, Howth Harbour and the Martello Tower, ENL/83, 84 & PG/90. South-east part of Portmarnock Golf-course, DN/89. North Bull Island Causeway, PG/90. Ireland's Eye, PG/91.
7. Dry bank on waste ground in the western half of Ballyfermot, PWJ/86. Gravel pit at Tymon Lane, CB/90.

- -

C. nutans L.
Musk Thistle   Probably introduced

| 5 | 8 |

A species included in the Irish Red Data Book recorded at two sites in the county.
5. Malahide, TC/75.
8. Dun Laoghaire, TC/77.

- -

Cirsium

C. vulgare (Savi) Ten. *(Cnicus lanceolatus)*
Spear Thistle   Native

| 1 | 2 | 3 | 4 | 5 | 6 | 7 | 8 |

Widespread and abundant on waste ground, roadsides and pastures.
FID.

C. dissectum (L.) Hill *(Cnicus pratensis)*
Meadow Thistle, Bog Thistle   Native

Colgan: 8. On a bog near Killiney Bay, 1814: *Templeton MS.* Above Marlay: *Ir. Flor.* Although this species is rare in the counties adjacent to Dublin, and has not been recently seen in the latter county, it occurs just over its borders in Glencree, Co. Wicklow. There is no reason to doubt the accuracy of the above records, and further search in the county is likely to show that it is not yet extinct there, if very rare.

Suppl: 7. St Anne's, Glenasmole (*I.N.* XIX, 1921, W.B. Bruce). In abundance in fields from Piperstown school to Castlekelly (1957).

| 6 | 7 | (8) |

Extremely rare, in damp pastures.
6. Wet field south-south-west of Rathcoole, 2.25 km east of Kilteel, HOR/85, **NDR**.
7. Still in a damp pasture near St Ann's Chapel, Glenasmole, KF/63, ENL/83 & CB, SR/90.

C. dissectum x C. palustre (C. x forsteri (Smith) Loudon)
Native

| 7 |

Extremely rare, in damp pastures.
7. St Anne's fields, Glenasmole, DD/87.

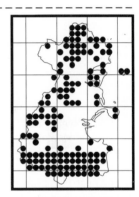

C. palustre (L.) Scop. *(Cnicus palustris)*
Marsh Thistle   Native

| 1 | 2 | 3 | 4 | 5 | 6 | 7 | 8 |

Common in marshes and damp pastures.
FID.

C. arvense (L.) Scop. *(Cnicus arvensis)*
Creeping Thistle   Native

| 1 | 2 | 3 | 4 | 5 | 6 | 7 | 8 |

Widespread and abundant in waste ground, pastures and on roadsides.
FID.

Silybum

S. marianum (L.) Gaertner
Milk Thistle   Alien

Colgan: 2. Sandy fields at Rush: *Ir. Flor.* 3. In considerable quantity, more than 100 plants, by the shore road near Corballis, Portrane, 1892-1903; also spreading for some distance into adjacent tilled land, 1903: *N.C.* 5. Near Warren House, *Wade*

Dubl. It grows in great luxuriance in Kilbarrick churchyard: *Warburton 1818.* Still about the churchyard, but in small quantity, and several plants on sandy ditch banks in its vicinity, 1903: *N.C.* About Baldoyle and Howth: *Ir. Flor.* Sparingly at Baldoyle, 1900: *N.C.* Near the Martello tower, Howth; by the shore along the old Sutton road: *Flor. Howth.* Waste ground near the Cliffs, Howth, 1904: *N.C.* 7. Donnybrook, 1894 *(Moore) Cyb. II.* 8. Whitechurch, above Roebuck: *Ir. Flor.* Always an obvious introduction, occurring in the neighbourhood of ruins or dwellings, but long established in some of its stations.
Suppl: 2. Still at Rush (1941). 3. Still at Corballis (1955). 5. St Nessan's Bay, Ireland's Eye (1955). Still on Howth cliffs (1957). 7. Near Tallaght Road, Templeogue (R.W. Scully, 1918). 8. Kiltiernan (R.W.S., 1918). Path to Vico bathing-place, Dalkey (1947).

(2) **3** (5) (7) (8)

Extremely rare.
3. Still at Corballis on the stony seashore at Corballis House, and to the east at the top of the embankment at Corballis Road, PR/83, 84.

Centaurea

C. scabiosa L.
Greater Knapweed   Native
Colgan: 2. Sparingly at Rogerstown, 1894; abundant by the railway between Skerries and Hampton Hall, 1902; and 3. Sparingly in sandy fields near Corballis, 1900: *N.C.* 4. Near Glasnevin Bridge and bewtween Chapelizod and Lucan: *Wade Dubl.* Banks in Phoenix Park near Chapelizod, 1904; by the Tolka above Finglas bridge and pastures by the Ward river above Chapelmidway, 1894: *N.C.* 5. By Warren House on the Burrow: *Flor. Howth.* Railway banks at Killester, 1894; at Raheny quarries, 1902; and 6. Roadside at Ballydowd, east of Lucan, 1901: *N.C.* 7. Near Clondalkin, 1894: *Praeger.* Near Ballyfermot, 1895; by Cromwell's Fort road, and abundant on the Green Hills, 1900: *N.C.* 8. On the shore near Blackrock and Bullock, 1798: *Templeton MS.* At Monkstown 1872: *Greenwood Pim.* Railway banks south of Stillorgan, 1899; roadside east of Rathmichael, 1900; abundant on banks near Shankill railway station, 1902: *N.C.*
Suppl: Frequent. 2. Railway above Balbriggan (1933). 7. Tymon Lane and Greenhills Road (1956).
DNFC Annual Report for 1962: 8. Stillorgan to Dundrum along the old disused railway line, M. Scannell.

2 **3** **4** **5** (6) **7** **8**

Rare, in sandy ground and on dry banks.
2. Still near Hampton Hall on a roadside bank, beside the railway line, RF/90.
3. On disturbed ground on the Portrane Peninsula, PR/85.
4. Still near Chapelizod on roadsides and sandy ground at Knockmaroon Hill, DD/74, MN/83.
5. Raheny Quarries (now in-filled), DD/66.
7. Still near Greenhills in abandoned fields and on waste ground by the Greenhills Industrial Estate, PWJ, HOR, SR/84. Grassy bank at the south end of Tymon Lane, CB/90. Gravel banks of the River Dodder 1 km above Oldbawn, CB/92.
8. Still near Stillorgan on the bank of the disused railway line north-west of Sandyford Industrial Estate, SR/84. Still near Shankill, on a roadside bank, SR/87.

C. cyanus L.
Cornflower   Alien
Brunker MS: 2. Cornfield N. of Balbriggan. '46. 5. Near Warren House, '18.

(2) **4** **5** **8**

Extremely rare. Formerly a weed of cultivated fields and crops.

4. Three plants on a disturbed roadside arising from dormant seed, c. 1 km south-west of St Margaret's, MN/89, 90, **NDR**.
5. Near the entrance to Sutton Golf-course, on disturbed ground, CB/91.
8. By a sliproad to the M11, near Bray, NS/92, **(DBN)**.

C. nigra L.
Common Knapweed   Native

1	2	3	4	5	6	7	8

Widespread. Very common on roadsides, pastures and dry banks. Radiate forms, *i.e.* plants with large ray florets, occur occasionally near Five Roads (2).
FID.

Cichorium

C. intybus L.
Chicory   Alien

Colgan: 2. Fields near Balbriggan *(Dr Scott): Mack. Rar.* Plentiful near Balbriggan: *Flor. Hib.* Sparingly in sandy fields at Rush 1902; and 3. Near Corballis, 1900-02: *N.C.* 4. Plentifully in fields at Scribblestown: *Wade Dubl. & Ir. Flor.* 5. Banks near the shore a little south of Malahide *(Moore): Cyb.* Potato field at Baldoyle, 1881: *N.C.* Plentiful in a cornfield near Maine Bridge, Baldoyle, 1903, and in a field at Feltrim, 1901: *Miss R. Mahaffy.* Near the Needles, Howth *(Mrs Mahaffy),* and about Warren House: *Flor. Howth.* Potato field at Howth, 1896 *(Miss S. Colgan) Cyb. II.* Cornfield at Portmarnock, 1866: *Hart MS.* sparingly here in 1902! 7. "Found near *Kilmainham* Hospital": *Threlkeld.* Near the new gaol at Kilmainham: *Wade Dubl.* Pastures at Old Bawn, 1893: *Praeger.* 8. Sparingly in a cornfield near Old Connaught, 1902: *J. Meade.* This species occurs in but small quantity in all of its recent Co. Dublin stations, but seems to be fully established in District 5.

Suppl: 2. Still at Rush (1941). 4. Liffey Junction (1947). 5. Hampstead, Glasnevin (1954). 6. Roadside near Corkagh (R.W. Scully, 1918). 8. Near Carrickmines Railway Station (H.J. Hudson, 1938).

(2)	3	4	(5)	(6)	7	8

Rare, on roadsides and waste ground.
3. Field near Corballis, Donabate, DK/60.
4. One plant at Dunsink tiphead, SR, JR/93. North Wall Quay, SR/94.
7. Ballycullen, DK/60.
8. Beside a patch of woodland at Greygates, Mount Merrion, HOR/84. Waste ground at the Pigeon House, Ringsend, R.L.C. Rohu/79. Ringsend Dump, PWJ/83. One plant on a dry roadside bank at the junction of the Bray road and Wyattville Road, SR/86. Meadow at Ballybrack, J.S. Jackson/61. Grass verges in Stillorgan and Sandyford Industrial Estate, SR/94-97.

Lapsana

L. communis L.
Nipplewort   Native

1	2	3	4	5	6	7	8

Widespread and very common on waste ground and in hedgebanks.
FID.

Hypochaeris

H. radicata L.
Cat's-ear   Native

| 1 | 2 | 3 | 4 | 5 | 6 | 7 | 8 |

Widespread and very common on roadsides, banks, in pastures and sand-dunes.
FID.

- -

Leontodon

L. autumnalis L.
Autumn Hawkbit   Native

| 1 | 2 | 3 | 4 | 5 | 6 | 7 | 8 |

Very common on waste ground and dry banks, and in sand-dunes and pastures. Plants approaching var. **salina** (Aspegren) Lange in morphology, with almost entire leaves, occur occasionally in salt-sprayed areas of the north Dublin coast.
FID.

- -

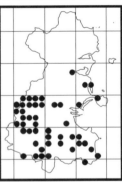

L. hispidus L.
Rough Hawkbit   Native

| (2) | 3 | 4 | 5 | 6 | 7 | 8 |

Occasional in calcareous grasslands and banks in the lowlands of the southern half of the county; much rarer elsewhere.

- -

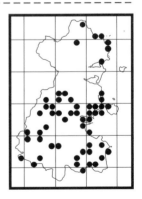

L. saxatilis Lam. *(L. hirtus, L. leysseri, L. taraxacoides)*
Lesser Hawkbit   Native

| 1 | 2 | 3 | 4 | 5 | 6 | 7 | 8 |

Common in stable sand-dunes, calcareous grasslands, dry banks and gravel workings.

Picris

P. echioides L.
Bristly Oxtongue   Native

Colgan: 2. Roadside banks between Swords and Balbriggan (Moore) *Cyb.* At Lusk, 1872: *Herb. Carroll.* Roadside between Balbriggan and the Delvin river, 1900: *N.C.* 3. Railway bank north of Malahide, 1866: *Hart MS.* and in 1903, in considerable quantity! In a potato field near Donabate, 1901 and on a roadside bank near Corballis, 1902: *N.C.* In considerable quantity on banks near the Martello tower, Portrane, 1902: *Scully.* 4. "It is frequent under Hedges and above the Barracks in a Brow to the Westward": *Threlkeld.* Knockmaroon Hill and Cardiff's bridge: *Ir. Flor.* Knockmaroon, 1866: *Hart MS* 5. Howth, Raheny, and Kilbarrick: *Ir. Flor.* By the quarry near Byron House, Sutton, and on ditch banks by a field above it, plentifully: *Flor. Howth.* Near Portmarnock church, sparingly, 1894: *Praeger.* Steep banks at the Needles, Howth: *Praeger 1895.* 7. Between Beggar's Bush and Sandymount: *Wade Dubl.* Abundant by the side of the mill stream a little way above Donnybrook: *Mack. Cat.* 8. Windy Harbour, Roebuck and Whitechurch: *Ir. Flor.* Casual at Killiney, 1902: *N.C.* Occurs but sparingly in most of its Co. Dublin stations and is apparently extinct in many of those recorded by the earlier authorities.

Suppl: Rare. Still at several of Colgan's stations along the coast, but almost absent inland.

2	(3)	(4)	5	(7)	8

Rare, on cliffs and in ruderal habitats near the sea.
2. Waste ground between Balscadden and Tobertown, RF/87. Dump east of the railway bridge at Balleally, DD/84.
5. Disturbed ground at Portmarnock Railway Station, ENL/84, 85.
8. Cliff top below the railway bridge at Whiterock, Killiney, SR/85.

Tragopogon

T. pratensis L.
Goat's-beard   Native

Colgan: Frequent in Districts 2, 3, 5, 7, and 8, on railway embankments along the Great Northern, the Great Southern and Western and the Wicklow and Wexford lines; rare in distinctly inland stations, but occurs in 3, by the Ward river, at Knocksedan, in 4, at Blanchardstown and on Knockmaroon Hills, in 6, in pastures above the Embankment, Saggard, and in 7, at Templeogue: *N.C. Var. minor (Fries)* 2. Railway embankment at Skerries, 1893; and 5. Banks by the sea near the Martello tower, Sutton, 1900: *N.C.*

1	2	3	4	5	6	7	8

Occasional in waste places and on roadside banks, particularly near the coast and on sandy ground inland.
FID.

Sonchus

S. arvensis L.
Perennial Sow-thistle   Native

1	2	3	4	5	6	7	8

Very widespread. Abundant in ruderal habitats and on drift lines on estuaries.
FID.

S. oleraceus L.
Smooth Sow-thistle   Native

| 1 | 2 | 3 | 4 | 5 | 6 | 7 | 8 |

Widespread and abundant in ruderal habitats.
FID.

S. asper (L.) Hill
Prickly Sow-thistle   Native

| 1 | 2 | 3 | 4 | 5 | 6 | 7 | 8 |

Very common in ruderal habitats.
FID.

Cicerbita

C. macrophylla (Willd.) Wallr. subsp. **uralensis** (Rouy) Sell
Common Blue-sow-thistle   Alien

| 5 | 8 |

Very rare, on roadsides. Not in *Colgan* or *Suppl,* but noted in *CC2* from the county.
5. Roadside at Kinsealy, ENL/84, .
8. One plant on the edge of an old vegetable plot, west of the church in St John's Road, Sandymount, SR, HOR, EMcA/84; gone 1987. Roadside at Kiltiernan, DD/83. Roadside, north-east of Rockbrook, S. Waldren/86. Roadside just west of Loughlinstown, SR/87. Dalkey Hill, F.E.R. Walsh/68.

Mycelis

M. muralis (L.) Dumort. *(Lactuca muralis)*
Wall Lettuce   Alien

Suppl: 5. Wall of St. Marnock's, Portmarnock, near steps to the strand (1945-1955). 7. Walltop between foot of Temple Road and Milltown Railway Station (1934). 8. Road from Killiney Railway Station to Vico (1948).

| 4 | 5 | 6 | (7) | 8 |

Occasional on shaded walls and pavements. Clabby and Osborne (1994) list twenty records from Dublin.
6. Just south of Ballymakaily Mill, JP/89.
FID.

Taraxacum

The arrangement of sections in this critical genus follows Dudman and Richards (1995). Although **T. officinale** agg. has been recorded from almost all of the 1 km squares surveyed, critical determinations have only been obtained for a limited number of specimens, including some collected before 1961. Determinations were largely made by A.J. Richards and the late

C. Haworth. All of the district records for individual species of dandelion are new. In most cases we have been unable to make comments on their frequency or distribution. Voucher specimens are deposited in **TCD. T. officinale** s.s. is now believed to be a rare Scandinavian montane species.

T. officinale agg.
Dandelion   Native

| 1 | 2 | 3 | 4 | 5 | 6 | 7 | 8 |

Widespread and common throughout the county. It is especially common by roadsides and on waste ground.

- -

Section ERYTHROSPERMA

T. lacistophyllum (Dahlstedt) Raunkiaer

| 3 | 5 |

Sandy ground near the sea.
3. Sandy turf at Portrane Peninsula, DD/86. Inland-side of sand-dunes at Donabate Golf-course, DD, JP/89.
5. Drift above the beach on Ireland's Eye, MSS/79, (**TCD**), (Webb, 1984). Sand-dunes on North Bull Island, JP/84, (**TCD**). Sand-dunes at Portmarnock, DD/87, CH, DD/86, 89 & DN/88.

- -

T. brachyglossum (Dahlstedt) Raunkiaer

| 5 | 8 |

5. Tarmacadam at the Howth Golf-course, ENL/85, **NCR**. Sand-dunes at Portmarnock, CH, DD/86, 89.
8. Bray Road at Loughlinstown, CH, SR/89.

- -

T. argutum Dahlstedt

| 2 |

2. Roadsides at Balrothery Lough, AJR/90, **NCR**.

- -

T. arenastrum A.J. Richards

| 3 | 8 |

Sandy ground by the sea.
3. Grass-covered sand midway between the beach and the road, and near the foreshore on Malahide Island, PR/88, **NCR**.
8. Sandy ground at the South Wall, DD/88.

- -

T. laetum (Dahlstedt) Raunkiaer

| 5 |

5. Sand-dunes at Baldoyle, RLP/1894, (**DBN**). Sandy pastures on Howth where it was collected by Colgan in 1894, (**DBN**).

T. haworthianum Dudman & Richards (*T. oxoniense*)

| 2 | 3 | 4 | 5 |

2. Coastal grassland north of Loughshinny, DD/88. Sandy ground west of Rush Golf-course, DD/88.
3. Thinly grassed knolls near the Island Golf-course, Corballis, PR/88. Grass over sand midway between the beach and the road at Corballis, PR/88.
4. Roadside at Finglas, M.C. Knowles/04, (**DBN**).
5. Sandy ground in the Alder Marsh on North Bull Island, DD/88. Sand-dunes at Portmarnock, DN/88.

- -

T. fulviforme Dahlstedt

| 2 |

2. Sandy soil between Balbriggan and Gormanstown, MS/62, (**DBN**).

- -

T. degelii Haglund

| 3 |

3. Seaward-side of the sand-dunes at Donabate Golf-course, DD, JP/89, **NCR**.

- -

Section OBLIQUA

T. obliquum (Fries) Dahlstedt

| 3 | 5 |

Sand-dunes.
3. Halfway between the beach and the road at Corballis, PR/85.
5. Baldoyle, RLP/1894, (**DBN**). Sand-dunes at Portmarnock, DD/87.

- -

Section SPECTABILIA

T. faeroense (Dahlstedt) Dahlstedt (*T. spectabile*)

| 2 | 3 | 4 | 6 | 8 |

Dune grassland.
2. Grasslands overlooking the Delvin River, RF/88.
3. Malahide Island, PR/88.
4. Damp grassland at St Margaret's, MN/88.
6. Marshy ground at the top of the Ballinascorney Gap, DD, JP/89.
8. Marsh at the head of the Little Dargle River, at 305 m where is was collected by Colgan in 1894, (**DBN**). In damp grassland at Boranaraltry, DD/86. Wet flush at Ballyedmonduff, DD/87. Wet flush in Ballyman Glen, HOR/87 & SR/87.

Section NAEVOSA

T. naevosiforme Dahlstedt

7

7. Palmerston Marsh, DD/85, 86, **NCR**.

- -

T. euryphyllum (Dahlstedt) Hjelt

7

7. Roadside near Castlekelly, Glenasmole, DD, JP/89, **NIR**.

- -

T. maculosum A.J. Richards

2

2. Roadside verge of a cul-de-sac 1 km north of Lusk Village, DD/88, **NCR**.

- -

T. drucei Dahlstedt

3	5	6	8

3. Woodland above the river above Swords Castle, DD, JP/89.
5. Sand-dunes at Portmarnock, CH, DD/89.
6. Flush opposite Knockandinny Golf-course, DD, JP, MWJ/88, **NCR**.
8. Roches Hill, CH, SR/89. Garden at Stillorgan, CH, SR/89.

- -

Section CELTICA

T. gelertii Raunkiaer (*T. adamii*)

1	2	3	4	6	7	8

1. Nag's Head, AJR/90.
2. Field between Balbriggan and Gormanstown, M.P. O'Sullivan/62, (**DBN**), **NIR**. Roadsides at Balrothery Lough, AJR/90.
3. Seaward-side of sand-dunes at Donabate Golf-course, DD, JP/89.
4. Roadside verge at Cardiff's Bridge, Finglas, DD, ENL, JP/88.
6. Marsh at the top of Slade Valley, DD, JP, MWJ/88. Roadside, by Brittas Ponds, DD, JP, MWJ/88. Roadside verge at Knockandinny, DD, JP, MWJ/88. Roadside south of Brittas, DD, JP, MWJ/88.
7. Beech woodland beside the River Dodder at Tallaght, JP/84.
8. Grassy edge of old woodland at Stillorgan, SR/87. Bank of disused railway line near Sandyford Industrial Estate, SR/88. Ballycorus Road, east of Kiltiernan, CH, SR/89. Ballyman Glen, CH, SR/89.

T. bracteatum Dahlstedt

| 5 | 8 |

5. Sand-dunes south of the Country Club at Portmarnock, CH, DD/89.
8. Clinker dump at the old Ballycorus Lead Mines, HOR, SR/85, **NCR**. Roadstone works at Ballycorus, SR/86.

T. britannicum Dahlstedt

| 1 | 2 | 6 | 8 |

1. At Oldtown Village and on roadsides 1 km to the north, AJR/90. Nag's Head, AJR/90.
2. Wet cliff slope south of Loughshinny, DD/88. Coastal flush north of Loughshinny, DD/88. Damp ground in the Delvin River Valley, RF/88. Roadsides at Balrothery Lough, AJR/90.
6. Grassland beside the stream at Crooksling Glen, JP/84, **NCR**.
8. Slope above Killiney Bay, SR/87. Roches Hill, CH, SR/89. Ballycorus Road, east of Kiltiernan, CH, SR/89.

T. oellgaardii C.C. Haworth

| 1 |

1. Oldtown village and on roadsides 1 km to the north, AJR/90, **NIR**.

T. duplidentifrons Dahlstedt

| 1 | 2 | 6 | 8 |

1. At Oldtown Village and on roadsides 1 km to the north, AJR/90. Nag's Head, AJR/90.
2. Roadsides at Balrothery Lough, AJR/90.
6. Roadside at Knockandinny, DD, JP, MWJ/88. Quarry at the top of the Ballinascorney Gap, DD, JP, /89.
8. Sand at the top of the shore south of Killiney, SR/87, **NIR**. Roches Hill, CH, SR/89. Ballycorus Road, east of Kiltiernan, CH, SR/89.

T. excellens Dahlstedt

| 4 | 6 |

4. Waste ground at the Broadstone, DD/88.
6. Roadside verge at Knockandinny, DD, JP, MWJ/88.

T. haematicum Haglund ex H. Olleg. & Witzell.

| 5 |

5. Roadside verge on the inland-side of the sand-dunes at Portmarnock Peninsula, DD/81, **NIR**.

T. nordstedtii Dahlstedt

| 1 | 4 | 5 | 8 |

1. Oldtown Village, AJR/90.

4. Damp grassland at St Margaret's, MN/88, **NCR**.
5. Thinly covered grassy knolls by the green path to the sea and sand-dunes near the Portmarnock Golf-course, PR/88. Dune-slacks south-east of the Country Club at Portmarnock, CH, DD/89.
8. Rough pasture beside Ballybetagh Bog, CB, SR/88. Sandy ground at the South Wall, AJR/90.

T. cambricum A.J. Richards

| 2 | (8) |

First noted in a collection by Colgan from the head of the Little Dargle River (8) in 1894 (**DBN**).
2. Roadsides at Balrothery Lough, DD/88, **NDR**, DD, AJR/90.

T. fulvicarpum Dahlstedt

| 2 | 5 | 8 |

2. Sandy ground west of Rush Golf-course, DD/86.
5. Sand-dunes south of the Country Club at Portmarnock, DD/86. Grassy bank above Howth Golf-Club, ENL/85. Greenhollows, Howth, DD/86.
8. Roadside ditch at Kilmashogue Mountain, HOR/85. Roadstone Works at Ballycorus, HOR, SR/85.

T. unguilobum Dahlstedt

| 7 | 8 |

7. Roadside at the southern end of southern reservoir in Glenasmole, DD, JP/89.
8. Roadside at Glencullen, DD/86, **NCR**. Bank on the north facing slope of Glencullen Mountain at 275 m, HOR/87. Roches Hill, CH, SR/89.

T. luteum C.C. Haworth & A.J. Richards

| 6 |

6. Marsh, near the top of Crooksling Glen, DD, JP/89, **NCR**.

Section HAMATA

T. hamatum Raunkiaer

| 1 | 2 | 3 | 5 | 6 | 8 |

1. Nag's Head, AJR/90.
2. Roadside at Balrothery Lough, AJR/90.
3. Inland-side of sand-dunes of Donabate Golf-course, DD, JP/89.
5. Roadside at St Fintan's church, Sutton, DD/88. Greenhollows, Howth, DN/88. Waste ground at Baldoyle, DD, JP, MWJ/88. Sandy ground near the west harbour wall at Howth, DD, JP, MWJ/88.
6. Field margin at Tallaght, DD, ENL, JP/88. Flush below Knockandinny Golf-course, DD, JP, MWJ/88, **NCR**.
8. Ballycorus Road, east of Kiltiernan, CH, SR/89.

T. subhamatum M.P. Christiansen

| I | 8 |

1. At Oldtown Village and on roadsides I km to the north, AJR/90.
8. Bank above the Ballyman River, CH, SR/89, **NCR**. Garden at Stillorgan, CH, SR/89.

T. hamiferum Dahlstedt

| 2 | 8 |

2. Waste ground at Rogerstown Harbour, DD/88, **NIR**.
8. Sandy ground at South Wall, AJR/90.

T. quadrans H. Oellgaard

| I | 6 | 8 |

1. Roadsides, I km north of Oldtown, AJR/90.
6. Roadside verge at Clondalkin, JP/82, (**TCD**), (Webb 1984).
8. Roadside at Glencullen, DD/86. Ballycorus Road, east of Kiltiernan, CH, SR/89.

T. pseudohamatum Dahlstedt

| I | 2 | 4 | 5 | 6 | 7 | 8 |

1. At Oldtown Village and on roadsides I km to the north, AJR/90. Nag's Head, AJR/90.
2. Roadsides at Balrothery Lough, AJR/90.
4. Cross Guns Bridge, DD, ENL, JP/88. Trampled ground at Cardiff's Bridge, DD, ENL, JP/88. Waste ground at Summerhill, DD, ENL, JP/88.
5. Waste ground at Coolock, at Kilbarrack and at Techrete, Howth, DD, ENL, JP/88.
6. Roadside at the top of the Slade Valley, near Knockandinny and near Brittas, DD, JP, MWJ/88.
7. Garden at Terenure, JRA/79, (**TCD**).
8. Roadside at Ballycorus, SR/85. Roches Hill, CH, SR/89. Sandy ground at the South Wall, AJR/90. Disturbed earth dumped at the roadside at the Pigeon House, AJR/90.

T. boekmanii Borgvall

| 4 | 8 |

4. Waste ground near Harristown House, MN/87, **NCR**. Roadsides at Dunsoghly Castle, AJR/90.
8. Sandy ground at the South Wall, Ringsend, and nearby HOR/87, DD/88 & SR/88. Boranaraltry Bridge, SR/88. Ballycorus Road, east of Kiltiernan, CH, SR/89.

T. atactum C.I. Sahlin & Von Soest

| 4 |

4. Near the bridge by the Grand Canal at Lucan, MN/88. Waste ground at Mulhuddart, DAW/79, (**TCD**), (Webb, 1984).

T. hamatiforme Dahlstedt

| 4 | | 8 |

4. Roadsides at Dunsoghly Castle, AJR/90.
8. Commons Road at Loughlinstown, CH, SR/89, **NCR**. Ballycorus Road, east of Kiltiernan, CH, SR/89.

T. lamprophyllum M.P. Christiansen

| 2 | | 6 |

2. Roadsides at Balrothery Lough, AJR/90.
6. Causeway dividing Brittas Ponds, DD, JP, MWJ/88, **NCR**.

Section RUDERALIA

T. laeticolor Dahlstedt

| 5 |

5. Beside the footpath along the cliff at Howth, ENL/85, **NCR**.

T. subexpallidum Dahlstedt (*T. linguatum*)

| 2 | | 8 |

2. Sandy shore at Loughshinny, RF/88, **NIR**.
8. Coarse sand at the top of the seashore at Killiney, SR/88.

T. undulatum H. Lindberg & Marklund

| 8 |

8. Roches Hill, CH, SR/89, **NIR**. Commons Road at Loughlinstown, CH, SR/89.

T. alatum H. Lindberg fil.

| 2 | | 8 |

2. Roadsides at Balrothery Lough, AJR/90, **NCR**.
8. Sandy ground at South Wall, AJR/90.

T. pannulatiforme Dahlstedt

| 7 | | 8 |

7. Waste ground at the J.F. Kennedy Industrial Estate near the Naas Road, DD, ENL, JP/88, **NIR**.
8. Garden at Stillorgan, CH, DD/89.

T. laticordatum Marklund

| 2 | 3 | 8 |

2. Pier at Balbriggan Harbour, DD/86, **NIR**.
3. Hedgerows at Swords, DD, JP/89.
8. Ballycorus Road at Kiltiernan, CH, SR/89. Garden at Stillorgan, CH, SR/89.

T. expallidiforme Dahlstedt. / **T. subcyanolepis** M.P. Chr.

| I | 2 | 3 | 4 | 5 | 6 | 8 |

1. At Oldtown Village and on roadsides 1 km to the north, AJR/90.
2. Roadsides, Balrothery Lough, AJR/90.
3. Seaward-side of the sand-dunes at Donabate Golf-course, DD, JP/89.
4. Roadsides, Dunsoghly Castle, AJR/90.
5. Howth golf-course, S.W.M.Locket-Foster/49, **OXF**.
6. Roadside verge at the top of the Slade Valley, DD, JP, MWJ/88.
8. Garden at Stillorgan, CH, SR/89. Beside the Bray road and nearby beside the Shanganagh River, Loughlinstown, CH, SR/89.

T. pallidipes Marklund

| 2 |

2. Roadsides at Balrothery Lough, AJR/90, **NIR**.

T. croceiflorum Dahlstedt

| 8 |

8. Disturbed earth dumped at roadside at the Pigeon House, AJR/90, **NCR**.

T. lacerifolium Haglund

| 4 |

4. Roadsides at Dunsoghly Castle, AJR/90, **NIR**.

T. leucopodum Haglund

| 8 |

8. Beside the Shanganagh River at Loughlinstown, CH, SR/89, **NIR**.

T. undulatiflorum M.P. Christiansen

| I | 4 | 5 | 6 | 7 | 8 |

Common in waste places.
1. Oldtown Village, AJR/90.
4. Cross Guns Bridge, DD, ENL, JP/88. Waste ground at Summerhill, DD, ENL, JP/88, **NIR**.
5. Waste ground at Techrete, Howth, DD, ENL, JP/88.
6. Cookstown Industrial Estate near the Naas Road, DD, ENL, JP/88.

7. Waste ground in the J.F. Kennedy Industrial Estate, DD, ENL, JP/88.
8. Ballycorus Road, east of Kiltiernan, CH, SR/89. Garden at Stillorgan, CH, SR/89.

T. speciosum Raunkiaer

| 7 |

7. Waste ground outside the School of Botany, T.C.D., AJR/90, **NIR**.

T. cyanolepis Dahlstedt

| 8 |

8. Walls at Boranaraltry Bridge, SR/88, **NCR**. Bank of disused railway line near Sandyford Industrial Estate, SR/88. Commons Road at Loughlinstown, CH, SR/89.

T. ancistrolobum Dahlstedt

| I | 4 | 8 |

1. Roadsides, I km north of Oldtown, AJR/90.
4. Roadsides at Dunsoghly Castle, AJR/90.
8. Bray Road at Loughlinstown, CH, SR/89, **NIR**. Garden at Stillorgan, CH, SR/89. Disturbed earth dumped at the roadside at the Pigeon House, AJR/90.

T. sellandii Dahlstedt

| I | 2 | 5 | 8 |

1. At Oldtown Village and on roadsides I km to the north, AJR/90.
2. Roadsides at Balrothery Lough, AJR/90.
5. Waste ground near the Public Hall at Balgriffin, CH, DD/89. Greenhollows Quarry, Howth, DD/86, **NCR**.
8. On a boulder clay slope above Killiney Bay, SR/87. Commons Road and nearby beside the Shanganagh River at Loughlinstown, CH, SR/89. Ballycorus Road at Kiltiernan, CH, SR/89. Bank above the Ballyman River, CH, SR/89. Garden at Stillorgan, CH, SR/89.

T. angustisquameum Dahlstedt ex H. Lindberg

| 8 |

8. Tarmacadam and gravel tip at Ballinteer, HOR/85, **NIR**.

T. adiantifrons E.L. Ekman ex Dahlst.(*T. hemicyclum*)

| 8 |

8. Boulder clay slope above Killiney Bay at the Vico Bathing Place, SR/87, **NIR**.

T. aequilobum Dahlstedt

| 8 |

8. Sandy ground at South Wall, AJR/90, **NCR**.

T. acroglossum Dahlstedt

4

4. Roadsides at Dunsoghly Castle, AJR/90, **NIR**.

T. exsertum Hagendijk, Van Soest & Zevenbergen

7

7. Waste ground outside the School of Botany, T.C.D., AJR/90, **NIR**.

T. lingulatum Marklund

5   8

5. Roadside at Howth, ENL/85, **NCR**.
8. Bank of the disused railway near Sandyford Industrial Estate, SR/88. Coarse sand at top of seashore at Killiney, SR/88.

T. rhamphodes Haglund

1   2   4   8

1. Roadsides, 1 km north of Oldtown, AJR/90, **NCR**.
2. Roadsides at Balrothery Lough, AJR/90.
4. Roadsides at Dunsoghly Castle, AJR/90.
8. Sandy ground at South Wall, AJR/90.

T. procerisquameum H. Oellgaard

8

8. Ballsbridge, MS/80, (**DBN**).

T. cordatum Palmgren

1   2   5   8

1. Roadsides, 1 km north of Oldtown, AJR/90.
2. Roadside verge at Loughshinny, DD/88. Roadsides at Balrothery Lough, AJR/90.
5. St Fintan's Church, Sutton and in grassland at the edge of the playing fields at Scoil Mhuire, Marino, DD/88, **NCR**. Sand-dunes south of the Country Club at Portmarnock, CH, DD/89.
8. Roches Hill, CH, SR/89. Beside the Shanganagh River, Loughlinstown and on Ballycorus Road, east of Kiltiernan, CH, SR/89. Disturbed earth dumped at roadside at the Pigeon House, AJR/90.

T. sagittipotens Dahlstedt & R. Ohlsen

8

8. Garden at Stillorgan, CH, SR/89, **NIR.**

T. ekmanii Dahlstedt

1   8

1. Nag's Head, AJR/90.
8. Ballycorus Road, east of Kiltiernan, CH, SR/89, **NCR**. Garden at Stillorgan, CH, SR/89.

- -

T. oblongatum Dahlstedt

| 5 | 7 | 8 |

Waste ground.
5. Waste ground near the public hall at Balgriffin, CH, DD/89,
7. Waste ground at the Fox and Geese, near the Naas Road, DD, ENL, JP/88, **NIR**.
8. Bray Road at Loughlinstown, CH, SR/89. Disturbed earth dumped at roadside at the Pigeon House, AJR/90.

- -

T. pachymerum Haglund

| 8 |

8. Beside the Ballyman River, CH, SR/89, **NIR**. Base of a wall by Ballycorus Road, east of Kiltiernan, CH, SR/89.

- -

T. sinuatum Dahlstedt

| 2 | 8 |

2. Waste ground in Loughshinny Village, DD/88.
8. Stone wall/bank on south facing slope in the Glencullen Valley at 305 m, HOR/87, **NIR**. Bray Road at Loughlinstown, SR, DD/89.

- -

T. dahlstedtii H. Lindberg

| 2 | 3 | 5 |

2. Pier at Balbriggan Harbour, DD/86.
3. Roadside at the north end of the Portrane Peninsula, DD/86.
5. Shielmartin, Howth, ENL/85, **NCR**.

- -

T. fagerstroemii Saltin

| 2 |

2. Roadsides at Balrothery Lough, AJR/90, **NIR**.

- -

T. pulchrifolium Marklund

| 2 | 4 | 5 | 7 | 8 |

Very common in waste places.
2. Waste ground at Rogerstown Village, DD/88. Roadsides at Balrothery Lough, AJR/90.
4. Waste ground at Summerhill, DD, ENL, JP/88, **NIR**. Finglas Industrial Estate near Cross Guns Bridge, DD, ENL, JP/88. Lagan Road, Finglas, DD/88. Glasilawn Road, Glasnevin, CH, DD/89. Waste ground at the Broadstone, DD, JP/89. Royal Canal Terrace, DD/89.
5. Roadside banks at St Fintan's Church, Sutton, DD/88. Waste ground at Coolock Industrial Estate, Kilbarrack, DD, ENL, JP/88. Techrete, Howth, DD, ENL, JP/88. Waste ground near the public hall at Balgriffin, CH, DD/89.

7. Waste ground in the J.F. Kennedy Industrial Estate, DD, ENL, JP/88. Fox and Geese, near the Naas Road, DD, ENL, JP/88. Emmet Road, Kilmainham, DD/88.
8. Gravel at Killiney, HOR/87. Waste ground near Ringsend Park, SR/87. Roches Hill, CH, SR/89. Commons Road at Loughlinstown, CH, SR/89. Bray Road at Loughlinstown, CH, SR/89. Beside the Shanganagh River at Loughlinstown, CH, SR/89. Ballycorus Road, east of Kiltiernan, CH, SR/89. Stillorgan, CH, SR/89. Sandy ground at South Wall, AJR/90. Disturbed earth dumped at the roadside at the Pigeon House, AJR/90.

T. polyodon Dahlstedt

| 1 | 2 | 4 | 5 | 8 |

1. Oldtown Village, AJR/90.
2. Waste ground at Loughshinny Village, DD/88. Roadsides at Balrothery Lough, AJR/90.
4. Roadside verge above Cardiff's Bridge, DD, ENL, JP/88. St Margaret's, DD, ENL, JP/88.
5. Waste ground near the public hall at Balgriffin, CH, DD/89.
8. Sandy turf beside shingle at Killiney, JRA/79, (**TCD**). Gravel at Killiney, HOR/87. Roadside at Old Conna Hill, HOR/85. Commons Road at Loughlinstown, CH, SR/89. Sandy ground at South Wall, AJR/90.

T. xanthostigma H. Lindberg fil.

| 4 | 7 | 8 |

4. Royal Canal Terrace, DD/89. Waste ground at the Broadstone, DD, JP/89.
7. South Circular Road, (Portobello), G. Pasley/80, (**DBN**).
8. Sandy ground at the South Wall, AJR/90. On disturbed earth dumped on the roadside at the Pigeon House, AJR/90.

T. longisquameum H. Lindberg

| 1 | 8 |

1. Oldtown Village, AJR/90, **NCR**.
8. Disturbed earth dumped on roadside at the Pigeon House, AJR/90.

T. fasciatum Dahlstedt

| 2 | 4 | 5 | 8 |

2. Roadsides at Balrothery Lough, AJR/90.
4. Waste ground at Summerhill, DD, ENL, JP/88, **NCR**. The Broadstone, DD, ENL, JP/88. Royal Canal Terrace, DD/89.
5. Sand-dunes at Portmarnock, DN/88.
8. Sandy ground at the South Wall, AJR/90. Disturbed earth dumped on roadside at the Pigeon House, AJR/90.

Crepis

C. paludosa (L.) Moench
Marsh Hawk's-beard   Native

Colgan: 2. Sparingly in a marsh at Whitestown, Rush, 1903; 3. By the Ward river below Chapelmidway, 1894: *N.C.* 4. At Scribblestown: *Ir. Flor.* By the Tolka in Abbotstown woods, 1895, and above Blanchardstown, 1903; by the Liffey at Saint

Catherine's, 1904: *N.C.* 5. Moist fields about Santry: *Ir. Flor.* 6. Marshes at Athgoe, 1892; abundant in glens on Mount Seskin, 1895, and in woods by the Liffey at Leixlip and Lucan, 1904; above Johnstown, 1904; 7 and 8. Abundant in the mountains, 1903: *N.C.*

| (2) | (3) | 4 | (5) | 6 | 7 | 8 |

Occasional in marshes in the River Liffey Valley (4, 6 & 7) and the upland part of 8; rare elsewhere. The marsh at Whitestown (2) has been drained and is now tilled.
4. Still in the River Tolka Valley around Blanchardstown and near Ashtown, PR, MN/85 & DD/88.
6. Riverbank, south of Badgerhill, JP/86.
7. Woods between Ballymaice and Fort Bridge, MN/90. Lugmore Glen, MN/90. By a stream about 700 m south-south-west of Ballinascorney House, MWJ/87.
8. Ballyman Glen, SR, HOR, CB/86, 87.

C. biennis L.
Rough Hawk's-beard   Native

Colgan: 6. Abundant in several grass fields beyond the Embankment station, 1904 *(Praeger) Ir. Nat. XIII.,* p.156; 8. Abundant in a meadow south of Killiney railway station and by the railway and on adjoining banks, 1902 *(N.C.) Ir. Nat.,* 1902 spreading rapidly here, northward to near the station and southward almost to the Shanganagh river, 1904! *Suppl:* 6. Still abundant beyond Embankment and spreading along the main Blessington Road for nearly a mile (1956). 8. Never re-found at Killiney.

| I | 3 | 4 | 6 | 7 | 8 |

Occasional on sandy roadsides, especially in 4, 6 & 7. Now increasing rapidly especially on roadsides in sandy/gravelly areas and new to districts 1, 3, 4 & 7. The original colony at the Embankment is still present (6) where it was first found by Praeger in 1904, and recorded at intervals since then.

C. capillaris (L.) Wallr. *(C. virens)*
Smooth Hawk's-beard   Native

| I | 2 | 3 | 4 | 5 | 6 | 7 | 8 |

Widespread. Very common on banks, waste ground and roadsides.
FID.

C. vesicaria L. subsp. taraxacifolia (Thuill.) Thell. ex Schinz & R. Keller *(C. taraxacifolia)*
Beaked Hawk's-beard   Alien

| I | 2 | 3 | 4 | 5 | 6 | 7 | 8 |

Abundant on dry banks, waste ground and roadsides, usually in urban and suburban situations.
FID.

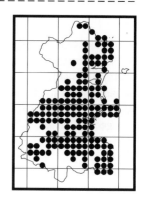

Pilosella

P. officinarum F.W. Schultz & Schultz Bip. *(Hieracium pilosella)*
Mouse-ear-hawkweed   Native

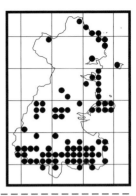

| 1 | 2 | 3 | 4 | 5 | 6 | 7 | 8 |

Common on shallow soils and in sand-dunes and calcareous grassland along the coast; rare elsewhere.

Hieracium Hawkweed

We are grateful to David McCosh for identifying some of our **Hieracium** material. Except where indicated, the comments expressed are those of the editors.

H. angustisquamum (Pugsl.) Pugsl. *(H. vulgatum)*
Native

Colgan: **H. vulgatum** - 4. Occasional in bushy places on the Liffey banks at Saint Catherine's, 1895-1904: N.C. 6. Banks of the Liffey above Leixlip *(More) Cyb.* and in 1904: N.C.

| 4 | (6) |

It is not clear what was meant in *Colgan* by **H. vulgatum** as there are no extant specimens of this taxon which have been annotated by him in **DBN**. In *Suppl* the species is "not confirmed". However, **H. angustisquamum** has been recorded from wall tops at Anna Liffey Mills (Shackleton's Mills) at Lucan (4) by J.P. Brunker in 1957 where it still occurs and which is very close to the site at St Catherine's for **H. vulgatum** in *Colgan*.

4. Still on a wall adjoining the River Liffey opposite Luttrellstown, near Shackleton's Mills, MN, PR/85, DD/92. Wall, west of the bridge at Lucan, MN, GS/85, DD/92.

H. exotericum Jordan ex Boreau
Native

| 8 |

8. Wall on Military Road, east of Ballybrack, SR/84. This may be var. **grandidens** Dahlst. *(fide D. McCosh).*

H. gougetianum Gren. & Godron *(H. murorum L. var. maculosum)*
Alien

Colgan: 4. Abundant on railway banks and adjacent spoil mounds near Liffey Junction, 1903 *(F.C. Crawford & N.C.) Ir.Nat.,* 1903, p.247. The above is the only Co. Dublin station so far known for any form of the aggregate *H. murorum.* Though fully established here, occurring in profusion over a limited area where some hundreds of plants were counted in various stages of growth, this Hawkweed has nevertheless the appearance of an introduction. The leaves are conspicuously marbled with deep red brown blotches, which remain quite constant under cultivation and the general facies of the plant agrees fairly well with the *var. Maculosum* of Dahlstedt, at one time ranked by that author as a distinct species.

Suppl: 4. Still at Liffey Junction (1956). 5. Railway sidings at North Wall, where it evidently was carried from Liffey Junction (1953-1957).

4	5

The *Crit. Suppl* records **H. gougetianum** as naturalized on the banks of the River Liffey near Dublin. *Crit. Suppl* also equates **H. gougetianum** with **H. maculosum**. This latter taxon was recorded in *Colgan* from Liffey Junction. There appears therefore to have been a confusion in *Crit. Suppl* between the River Liffey Valley and Liffey Junction. However, plants of this taxon do occur near the River Liffey at Astagob. **H. gougetianum** is very close to **H. scotisticum** Hyl. and forms part of the **H. glaucinum** group. The material from Astagob (4) differs from that occurring elsewhere in Dublin (for example, it has much paler spotting on its leaves) and appears to approach **H. zygophorum** Hyl. in aspects of its indumentum.
4. Whitworth Road, DD/72. Wall at Glasnevin Cemetery, MN/83. Liffey Junction, DD/86. Astagob sand-pits, DD/92. Between Liffey Junction and Cabra, DD/86-92.
5. Walls between the Royal Canal and the railway at Drumcondra, DN/89.
FID.

H. diaphanum Fries *(H. sciaphilum)*
Native

Colgan: 7. Abundant on the bank and retaining wall of a deep cutting of the Great Southern and Western Railway between Island Bridge and Inchicore, completely clothing the face of the wall for fully 100 yards, and spreading along the opposite bank for about a quarter of a mile, 1903 *(N.C.) Ir. Nat.,* 1903, p.247. First observed by Dr Scully about 1886, and first recorded in 1903: *Ir. Nat.* This plant was previously recorded by Mr Praeger in 1901 *(Top. Bot.)* for a station on the same railway, but in Co. Kildare, and has perhaps been introduced into Co. Dublin by means of the railway.
Suppl: Recorded as *H. lachenalii* Gmel (**H. sciapilum**)- 7. Still abundant by railway between Islandbridge and Inchicore (1956).

4	7

Material from Inchicore and elsewhere in Dublin have considerable variability in the density of glandular hairs on their involucral bracts and pedicels.
4. Walls of the Phoenix Park near Cabra, PR/86. Cabra Road, DD/87-92, **NDR**.
7. Still on walls of the railway at Kingsbridge, Islandbridge and Inchicore, DD/84-90.

H. sabaudum L. *(H. boreale, H. perpropinquum)*
Native

Colgan: 7. Banks of the Dodder above Old Bawn, 1896 *(N.C.) Cyb. II.* and in 1903! At intervals along the west bank of the Dodder from Old Bawn almost up to Bohernabreena, and sparingly on the opposite bank, 1896: *N.C.* Wall on the north bank of the Dodder opposite Rathfarnham, 1903: *Praeger 1904.*
Suppl: Recorded as *H. bladonii* Pugsl. *(H. boreale)* - 7. Now frequent along the River Dodder from Castlekelly to Oldbawn (1956).

7

Colgan gives the name of **H. boreale** to Praeger's specimen collected from Rathfarnham. Pugsley (1948) calls it **H. bladonii** var. **brunkerii** and *Crit. Suppl* calls it **H. perpropinquum** because it lacks the glandular hairs in the involucral bracts of **H. bladonii**. All of *Colgan's* **H. boreale** records appear to belong here.
7. Still by the River Dodder between Oldbawn and Fort Bridge, under gorse, DD/72 & CB/92.

H. umbellatum L.
Native

Colgan: 7. Abundant along both sides of the Dodder from above Old Bawn to near Bohernabreena, in gravelly banks and flats and amongst furze brakes, 1896-1901; abundant in furze brakes by the river above Bohernabreena, 1901, and near Castle Kelly, 1902; on field banks in the Slade of Augh Farrell, 1896: *N.C.* 8. Banks of the Glencullen river: *Colgan 1893.* Field banks above the Glencullen river, 1899: *N.C.*

Suppl: 7. Still abundant in this district (1957) although not found elsewhere in the county.

---

subsp. **umbellatum**
Native

Never refound in Glencullen (8).

7. Still at Oldbawn, DD/89 & CB/92. Bridge over the River Dodder at Glenasmole, PWJ, MWJ, SR/86. Still occasional in Glenasmole Waterworks by the River Dodder and by both reservoirs, DD/72 & MN/89.

Hieracium spp.
Native

Other recent **Hieracium** records from the county which have not been identified are:

2. Ballast pit at Skerries Railway Station, DD/92.
3. Sand-hills, south of Donabate, ENL, PR/88.
5. Eastern part of St Anne's Park, Raheny, PG/87, 88. Inner sand-dunes at the north end of North Bull Island, PG/87.

Filago

F. vulgaris Lam. *(F. germanica)*
Common Cudweed   Native

Colgan: 3. Sparingly on the north side of Lambay: *Flor. Lambay.* Sandy banks to the north of Portrane peninsula, 1900, and on rocks at Balcarrig, 1903: *N.C.* 4. About Glasnevin and Finglas: *Ir. Flor.* 5. Between Clontarf and Howth and on Portmarnock Burrow: *Wade Dubl.* Sparingly at Light-house green; near Casana's Rocks; and below Glenaveena: *Flor. Howth.* Shielmartin, Howth, 1894: *Vowell.* Banks above the sea east side of Howth Head, and frequent on sandy banks near the coastguard station, North Bull, 1903: *N.C.* 8. Near the sea at Killiney: *Wade Dubl.* Bray Commons, 1872: *Herb. Carroll.*

Suppl: 5. Still sparingly at Lighthouse Green, near Casana Rock, and below Glenavena, Howth (1946). Not confirmed in any other station.

     [(8)]

Not refound at any of its former sites in the county.

F. minima (Sm.) Pers. *(Logfia minima)*
Small Cudweed   Native

Colgan: 8. In a granite quarry at Balalley, Three Rock mountain *(N.C.) Ir. Nat.,* 1894, p. 202. Frequent along the base of Three Rock mountain, 1900 *(Praeger) Top. Bot.* Abundant amongst old granite quarries on the slopes of the Three Rock near Barnacullia, 1902: *N.C.* Sparingly at Glencullen quarries, 1903: *Praeger 1904.*

Suppl: 5. Sheilmartin, Howth (Bradshaw, *I.N.*, XXVI, 1917). 8. Still at Balalley (1955).

[(5)]   [8]

Extremely rare. Legally protected under the Wildlife Act of 1976 as an endangered species in Ireland.
8. Still on the north side of Three Rock Mountain above Barnacullia, on bare and thinly
   vegetated granitic gravel, PC/88, DD/93.

Antennaria

A. dioica (L.) Gaertner
Mountain Everlasting   Native

Colgan: 3. Sparingly in a hollow of Portrane sandhills, 1901: *N.C.* 5. Sandy grounds at Portmarnock: *Mack. Cat.* Sparingly on the railway bank near Malahide station, 1893, and near Portmarnock station, 1893-1904: *N.C.* 8. Dublin mountains near Kilmashogue: *Wade Rar.* Above Marley: *Ir. Flor.*

Suppl: 3. Still at Portrane (1944). 5. North Bull (1945). 7. Still above Piperstown (1953). On moraines half a mile S. of St Anne's, Glenasmole (A.W. Stelfox, 1922). Still there (1955).

[3]   [(5)]   [7]   [(8)]

Extremely rare. Formerly a species of banks and heaths.
3. Still in Portrane sand-hills, in a dune-slack near Malahide Point, PR/83.
7. One clump refound on gravelly banks on the east side of the River Dodder, 1 km south of
   Oldbawn Bridge amongst **Ulex europaeus** scrub, CB/93.

Gnaphalium

G. sylvaticum L. *(Omalotheca sylvatica)*
Heath Cudweed   Native

Colgan: 5. High grounds on Howth; *Ir. Flor.* not seen recently. 6. Hills west of Saggard Slade, 1895 *(N.C.) Cyb. II.*

Suppl: 3. One plant near Trinity Well, Lambay (Praeger, 1907). No recent records.

[(3)]   [(5)]   [(6)]

An endangered species that is legally protected in Ireland under the Wildlife Act of 1976. It was not refound at any of its former sites in the county. Its former site on Slieve Thoul (6) is now wooded and that on Lambay Island (3) where a single plant was found in 1907 is now heavily sheep-grazed. The *Ir. Flora* record from Howth may refer to **F. minima** which survived in small quantity in several places on the peninsula up till 1946 (See also Bradshaw 1917).

G. uliginosum L. *(Filaginella uliginosa)*
Marsh Cudweed   Native

Colgan: 1. Quarry at Mullahow, 1893; very abundant in peaty ground at Bog of the Ring, 1900; 2. Sparingly north of Lusk, and abundant on the margin of the Lough, Balrothery, 1893: *N.C.* 5, 6, 7 and 8. Frequent in the uplands, as on Howth Head, around Brittas, in Glenasmole, Glencullen & c., In the autumn of 1902, after a very long drought, this species appeared in extraordinary profusion on the dried-up peaty bed of the upper reservoir near Castle Kelly, Glenasmole.

[1]   [2]   [5]   [6]   [7]   [8]

Occasional in damp, sparsely vegetated soils, especially in 1, 2 & 7. Commonest on mud of reservoirs, trampled ground of pathways, gateways and roads but also as a weed of damp arable fields.

1. Trampled ground at Moorepark, GS/87. Shore of Hynestown Reservoir, GS/84. Frequent in many locations in the Naul Hills, GS/85.
5. Below The Summit, Howth Head, ENL/84. Just east of Kilrock, Howth, PG/87, 88.
6. Abundant on the muddy shore of Brittas Ponds, DNFC/89, and on the muddy floor of the north pond, JP, S. Waldren/94. Trackside on the north-west side of Saggart Hill, JP/84.
7. At various sites in Glenasmole; at the south end of the northern reservoir; on the west side of the valley; by a track west of the southern reservoir; by a track over farmland and above Castlekelly, HOR/85, DNFC/87, MWJ, DAW/87 & SR/89. Above Stone Cross at Ballinascorney, DD/83. West of Ballymaice, PWJ, MWJ/86.
8. Trampled path near the cromlech west of Kiltiernan, SR, JR/88. Ballyman Glen, DNFC/83. Hill, north of Glencullen Chapel, SR/87. Field near Rathmichael House west of Shankill, SR/87. Thousands of plants in a damp depression on Dalkey Island, SR/91.

Inula

I. crithmoides L.
Golden-samphire   Native

Colgan: 3. Island of Lambay: *Ir. Flor.* Common on most of the Lambay coast, except the northern side: *Flor. Lambay.* 5. "On ye Hill of Hoath on ye rocks under ye Light House, 1740": *Annot. in Threlkeld* and in 1900! Seashore south side of Howth: *Mack. Cat.* Rocky sea coast in many places from Kilrock to Baily Light-house; on Ireland's Eye: *Flor. Howth.* Near the mouth of the Whitewater Brook, 1900; at intervals along the south side of Howth Head from the Martello tower, Sutton, to the Baily Light-house, abundant near the Baily and between Drumlock and the Needles, 1902: *N.C.* 8. South side of Killiney Hill: *Flor. Hib.* At the bathing place Vico, 1879: *Miss E. Malone.* Dalkey Island *(W. Walpole) Cyb.* Sparingly at the south-west end of Dalkey island, 1901; and frequent at intervals along the cliffs for about half a mile from near the base of Killiney Hill to Sorrento, 1902: *N.C.*

Suppl: 2. Between Rush and Loughshinny (A.W. Stelfox, 1923). Increasing (1955). 5. Still at Hill of Howth (1957). 8. Dalkey Island (1952).

2	3	5	8

Occasional on sea-cliffs.
2. Still on cliffs overlooking the beach between Loughshinny and Rush, RF/90.
3. Lambay Island, M. Jebb/96.
5. Cliffs at Redrock, ENL/83. Plentiful on cliffs around Drumleck, DN/89. Cliffs by the Whitewater Brook on Howth Head, CB/91.
8. Frequent on rocks and cliffs by the Vico Bathing Place at Killiney, SR/83. West of Sorrento Point, SR, HOR/85.

Pulicaria

P. dysenterica (L.) Bernh.
Common Fleabane   Native

1	2	3	4	5	6	7	8

Occasional on canal and river banks, in wet fields and flushed areas on sea-cliffs.

Solidago

S. virgaurea L.
Goldenrod   Native

Colgan: 5. In hilly heaths at Howth: *Wade Dubl.* At Kilrock and Drumleck Point, Howth: *Flor. Howth.* Above Howth village and at Carrickbrack, 1893; on Ireland's Eye, 1899; frequent near the Red Rock, Howth, 1902: *N.C.* 7. On Seefingan at Castle Kelly, and abundant along the Killakee river, 1894; abundant in gravelly places amongst gorse by the Dodder above Old Bawn, 1902; 8. In the Little Dargle, 1893; in Glencullen, 1901; in the Dingle, Glenamuck, and on the eastern side of the Scalp, 1902; abundant in Kelly's glen, 1903: *N.C.*

| 5 | 6 | 7 | 8 |

Occasional in heathland and on gravel banks.
5. Scattered on shallow soils by the cliff path from Kilrock to Redrock, Howth, DNFC/82, ENL/83, PG/88 & CB/91.
6. Hedgerows at Slade, JP/86, **NDR**.
7. Northern end of the southern reservoir in Glenasmole, DD/83 & MN/88. Western slopes of Kippure and the upper River Dodder Valley, SR, HOR/85. Many plants on a gravel bank, 1 km south of Oldbawn, CB/90.
8. Banks of the Glencullen River east of Boranaraltry Bridge, HOR, EMcA/83 & HOR, SR/84. Beside a forest track near the headwaters of the Little Dargle River south of Ticknock, SR, JR/83. East side of The Dingle, SR, MN/90.

Aster

A. tripolium L.
Sea Aster   Native

| 2 | 3 | 4 | 5 | 8 |

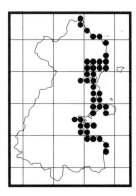

Common in salt-marshes, muddy estuaries and more rarely on maritime cliffs and rocks; very rare in 4.
4. Close to the mouth of the Royal Canal near Sheriff Street, JRA, DD, PWJ/81 and DN, MN/87.
FID.

Erigeron

E. karvinskianus DC. *(E. mucronatus)*
Mexican Fleabane   Alien

| 4 | 5 | 7 | 8 |

Rare on walls. Frequent in 8 on walls at Ballybrack, Killiney and between Shankill and Bray; rare elsewhere. Not distinguished in *Colgan* or *Suppl,* but noted in *CC2.*
4. Wall by the River Liffey at Conyngham Road, MN/87, **NDR**. Garden wall just east of Shackleton's Mills at Lucan, JS/88.
5. Wall of the Capuchin Friary, Raheny Road, Raheny, PG/89, **NDR**. Walls of outhouses, Howth Demesne, CB/92.
7. Wall by the River Liffey at Heuston Station, SR/92, **NDR**.

E. acer L. *(E. acris, E. acre)*
Blue Fleabane   Native

Colgan: 2. Ballast pits near Skerries railway station, 1903: *N.C.* 3. In the sandhills at Portrane, 1902: *Scully.* 4. Finglas quarries: *Ir. Flor.* Abundant by the canal below Clonsilla, 1894; *N.C.* 5. Between the Rabbit Warren and Howth: *Ir. Flor.* and in 1892, on walls by the railway! Railway banks at Raheny *(More) Cyb.* and in 1902! On the North Bull, 1893; quarry at Killester and on the railway near Portmarnock, 1894; 6. Frequent on the south bank of the Grand Canal below Hazelhatch, 1893, and on the north bank at Gollierstown, 1900: *N.C.* 7. Dodder above Templeogue: *Flor. Hib.,* 1836 and in 1893; In lower Ballinascorney glen and on the eskers at Green Hills, 1892; wall tops and quarry banks at Robinhood, 1893; abundant along the Dodder from Balrothery to Bohernabreena, 1903: *N.C.* 8. "Upon a dry hilly Pasture to the Eastward facing the Hutts at the *Blackrock*": *Threlkeld.* Near Rathfarnham and between Sandymount and Merrion: *Wade Dubl.* Frequent on Loughlinstown Commons, 1903: *N.C.*
DNFC Annual Report for 1953: 7. Old Bawn, J.P. Brunker.

(2) (3) **4** **5** (6) (7) (8)

Extremely rare, on walls. This species has declined sharply in frequency since the end of the 19th century, at least in part due to the grassing-over or filling-in of suitable habitats.
4. Wall-top by the Finglas/ Blanchardstown road, 1.25 km east of Blanchardstown, DD/82, near to its former sites by the Royal Canal at Clonsilla and in Finglas Quarries.
5. Wall by the railway behind Hole-in-the-Wall beach (Claremont Strand), Sutton, close to the Howth Railway line record of 1892, ENL/84. North Bull Island, R.Baldwin/85.

- -

Conyza

C. canadensis (L.) Cronq.
Canadian Fleabane   Alien

4 **5** **7** **8**

Rare but spreading, on waste ground and roadsides. Not in *Colgan, Suppl* or *CC2*. Some of the records given below for (4) and (7) may have been *C. bilbaoana,* a taxon not recognised in the British Isles before 1996 (Reynolds 1997).
4. By pond in the People's Gardens in the Phoenix Park, MN/87. One plant on waste ground at King's Inns Street, DN/91. Waste ground in Parnell Street, MN/92. Several sites in the city centre, at Mary Street, Cuckoo Lane, Essex Quay and Little Strand Street, DN/94.
5. Many plants at Dublin Port, SR/88-94.
7. Lane behind Westland Row, DD/83, **NCR**. Roadside in the Bluebell Industrial Estate, MWJ/84. Edge of College Park, T.C.D. and on nearby waste ground in Nassau Street, Pearse Street and Townsend Street, MS/84, 85, MWJ/87 & DN/91. By West Link motorway at Naas Road junction, MN/92.
8. Near the toll bridge at Ringsend, SR/89. North end of Sandymount Strand, SR, Conor Reynolds/94.

- -

Bellis

B. perennis L.
Daisy   Native

1 **2** **3** **4** **5** **6** **7** **8**

Widespread and abundant in short grassy habitats, on waste ground and roadsides.
FID.

Tanacetum

T. parthenium (L.) Schultz Bip. *(Chrysanthemum parthenium)*
Feverfew   Alien

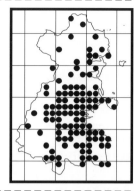

| I | 2 | 3 | 4 | 5 | 6 | 7 | 8 |

Occasional on waste ground, roadsides and ruins. A double-flowered
form is frequently cultivated in gardens and occasionally escapes.
FID.

T. vulgare L.
Tansy   Alien

| 2 | (3) | 4 | 5 | 6 | 7 | 8 |

Occasional on paths, roadsides and waste ground.
2. Roadside at Cross of the Cage, DD, EMcA/85. Roadside, south of Clonard, DD, RF/87.
   Hedgerow near Stamullin, RF/87. Roadside just west of the Corn Mill near Balbriggan,
   DD/87. Roadside, inland from Rogerstown village, DD/87.
4. Path along the Royal Canal north of where it enters the Liffey, MN, DN/87. Banks of the
   Royal Canal at Cabra, MN/88. Bank of the Royal Canal beside Pakenham Bridge, west of
   Clonsilla, L.K. Shackleton/77.
5. Summit of Howth Head, DN/89. North of the Royal Canal near Croke Park, DN/89.
6. Waste ground 3 km north of Newcastle, JP/84. Banks of the Grand Canal, north-west of
   Clondalkin, JP/83.
7. Bank behind a supermarket in Old Tallaght town centre, PWJ, MWJ/87. South bank of the
   Grand Canal near the bridge north of Fox and Geese, MWJ, PWJ/87.
8. Bank, now gone, beside the Stillorgan Road at Stillorgan, and nearby on the central
   reservation, SR/83, 89. Grassy roadside at Mount Merrion, SR/89.
FID.

Seriphidium

S. maritimum (L.) Polj. *(Artemisia maritima)*
Sea Wormwood   Native

Colgan: 2. A large patch spreading for 15 yards along a mud bank above a salt water ditch near Balleally, Rogerstown
Creek, and a few plants along the banks of the ditch, 1902: *Colgan 1903.* 3. On the coast near Portrane, plentifully: *Mack.
Cat.* Abundant over a small area on cliffs near the caves at Portrane and on grassy slopes above them, 1904: *N.C.* 5.
"Towards Baldoyle": *Annot. in Threlkeld* (not later than 1740). On the Hill of Howth, on the side of Dublin Bay, 1799:
Templeton MS. Rocks beyond the Martello tower, S.W. side of Howth: *Ir. Flor.* Rocks by the shore below the Cliffs and the
Needles: *Flor. Howth.* At Drumleck south of the Needles, 1903: *Miss R. Mahaffy.* 8. "Found between *Mirrion* and the *Black-
Rock*": *Threlkeld.* On Killiney Hill, south side *(Moore) Cyb.* In considerable quantity on Sorrento Cliffs, Killiney, 1884: still there
in 1903 towards the western end, but apparently becoming scarce and giving way to the aggressive *Cineraria maritima: N.C.*

Suppl: 2. On the shore end of Cardy Rocks, Balbriggan (*I.N.*, 1905) N. side of Red Island, Skerries (1946). 3. Still at Portrane (1957). 5. Still at Drumleck Point (1957).

| 2 | 3 | 5 | (8) |

Rare, in salt-marshes and on sea-cliffs.

2. A few clumps still at the upper end of the salt-marsh on the north side of Rogerstown estuary, south of Balleally, DD/82. Still at Red Island, Skerries, on a fragment of salt-marsh on the stony foreshore, DD/87.
3. Still abundant on cliffs between Donabate and Portrane, PR/88.
5. Still on rocks 2 or 3 m above the sea just west of Drumleck, DN/89.

Artemisia

A. vulgaris L.
Mugwort   Probably introduced

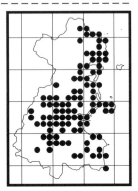

| (1) | 2 | 3 | 4 | 5 | 6 | 7 | 8 |

Common in dry waste ground and on roadside verges and disturbed ground near the coast; often near habitation.
FID.

A. absinthium L.
Wormwood   Alien

Colgan: 2. Sparingly by the shore at Skerries, 1895: *N.C.* 3. Established in the neighbourhood of cottages, Lambay island: *Flor. Lambay.* 5. Northern shores of Dublin bay, near Howth, 1799: *Templeton MS.* sparingly here in 1894! On the lands of Howth, particularly by the waysides: *Wade Rar.* By the old church at Howth: *Mack. Cat.* Plentiful about the Old Baily tavern; by Gray's Cottage, and in the village of Howth: *Flor. Howth.* 7. Well established near the hamlet of Ballymorefinn, Glenasmole, 1883; sparingly at intervals along the Water-works road, Glenasmole, from near Castle Kelly down to Bohernabreena, 1894-1903; on the old walls of St Nicholas graveyard, Nicholas Street, Dublin city, 1892-1904; abundant 1893-1904, on the *debris* of old buildings demolished in 1886 on the making of the new throughfare of Lord Edward Street, Dublin city, and spreading thence to adjacent wall-tops, 1904: *N.C.* An obvious introduction in all of its stations, though well established in some. At Lord Edward Street it is no doubt a relic of window gardening in old tenement houses now demolished.
Suppl: 7. Gravel pit near Robinhood (*I.N.*, XXVII, 1919). One plant growing from wall of Old St Audoen's, High Street, and established on old wall in chapel yard at St Nicholas of Myra, Francis Street (1948).
Brunker MS: 7. One plant still at Castlekelly, '52.

| (2) | (3) | 4 | (5) | 7 | 8 |

Extremely rare.
FID - still survived into the 1980s in the region of Christ Church Cathedral in Dublin city; Werburgh Street, wasteground off Bridge Street and at the edge of the Royal Canal at Sheriff Street, 1980 (4).
7. Tymon Lane, DK/60.
8. By Pigeon House Road, Ringsend, SR/94.

Achillea

A. ptarmica L.
Sneezewort   Native

| (1) | 2 | (3) | (4) | (5) | (6) | 7 | 8 |

Very rare, in drains and marshy ground. Very much rarer than at the turn of the century. The decline in frequency of this species is one of the most spectacular features of the recent changes that have occurred to the county flora. *Colgan* regarded it as common in damp pastures, marshy ground and as a weed of cultivated sandy or peaty soils. **A. ptarmica** is still quite common and often luxuriant in the neighbouring county of Wicklow.
2. A single plant on cleanings from an open drain 1.5 km north of Richardstown, DD/84.
7. Stream c. 700 m south-south-west of Ballinascorney House, MWJ/87.
8. Side of Three Rock Mountain, Sandyford, HJH/82.

A. millefolium L.
Yarrow   Native

| 1 | 2 | 3 | 4 | 5 | 6 | 7 | 8 |

Widespread and very common on roadsides, waste ground and in pastures.
FID.

Chamaemelum

C. nobile (L.) All. *(Anthemis nobilis)*
Chamomile   Probably introduced

Colgan: 7. Hill slopes in Glenasmole, 1882-92 *(N.C.) Cyb. II.* Abundant here close by the hamlet of Ballymorefinn, covering a space of about 20 square yards along an old roadside and on the grassy slopes above it, also again about 100 yards higher up the same roadway, 1901; apparently introduced but thoroughly established: *N.C.*

| (7) |

Not refound at Ballymorefinn (7).

Anthemis

A. arvensis L.
Corn Chamomile   Alien

Colgan: 2. Abundant in a new pasture and in adjacent fallows between Lusk and Man of War, spreading over fully half an acre, also 3. Several plants in a wheatfield at Portrane, 1902: *Colgan 1903.* 4. In the Phoenix Park near the middle: *Templeton MS.* Hibernian School, Phoenix Park: *Flor. Hib.* 5. Plentiful in sandy cultivated ground at Portmarnock, 1869 *(More) Rec. Add.* At Warren House and about Howth village: *Flor. Howth.* 6. Lyons, Co. Dublin *(T. Chandlee) Cyb. Suppl:* 4. Custom House Docks (1924). Rectory Yard, Finglas (1921). 5. Kilbarrack (1954).

| (2) | (3) | (4) | 5 | (6) | 8 |

Extremely rare.

5. Near the greens and tees at the south-eastern part of Portmarnock Golf-course, DN/89-91. Near to A.G. More's record of 1869 from Portmarnock. Also on the new I.M.G. Golf-course at Portmarnock, DD/94.
8. East side of the River Dodder between Sandymount and Irishtown, with **Agrostemma githago**, possibly of garden origin, DN/93.

A. cotula L.
Stinking Chamomile   Probably introduced

| (1) | (2) | (3) | (4) | 5 | 6 | (7) | 8 |

Very rare, on waste ground. Much rarer now than at the turn of the century. In *Suppl* no existing stations for this species in the county were known.
5. Two plants at Alexandra Basin, Dublin Port, SR/88.
6. Waste ground on the road margin 2 km east of Fortunestown, JP/86.
8. Sandyford Industrial Estate, SR, JR/93.

Chrysanthemum

C. segetum L.
Corn Marigold   Possibly introduced

| 1 | 2 | 3 | 4 | 5 | 6 | 7 | 8 |

Occasional in neutral to base-poor soils on arable land; declining in frequency.
FID.

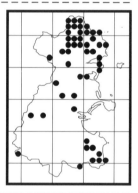

Leucanthemum

L. vulgare Lam. *(Chrysanthemum leucanthemum)*
Oxeye Daisy   Native

| 1 | 2 | 3 | 4 | 5 | 6 | 7 | 8 |

Widespread. Common in thin, ungrazed, calcareous grasslands and on waste ground and sandy ground inland.
FID.

Matricaria

M. recutita L. *(Chamomilla recutita, Matricaria chamomilla)*
Scented Mayweed   Alien

| 1 | 2 | 3 | 4 | 5 | 6 | 8 |

Occasional on waste ground and recently-sown amenity grassland. Regarded as a casual in *Colgan's* Appendix; the only reliable record was from Raheny. Not included in *Suppl*.
1. Weed in a grain field on the Dublin to Belfast road, 2 km south of Balrothery, GS/85.

2. Waste ground, south of Lusk, DD/84.
3. Waste ground at the Island Golf-course, PR, ENL, HOR/85. Sandy and waste ground at Portrane, DD, ENL/83 & ENL, PR/85.
4. Single plant by the roadside on disturbed ground at Clonsilla Railway Station and 2 km to the south-east, MN/87, 90. Disturbed ground by the farm west of Mulhuddart, MN/88. Just east of Cross Guns Bridge, MN, DN/87. Single plant on the roadside at Diswellstown House, MN/90. Roadside 1 km south of St Margaret's, MN, DN/90. Base of a cutaway wooded slope at Luttrellstown, MN/91.
5. Albert College, DD/66. Alexandra Basin, Dublin Port, SR/88, 94. On disturbed ground at Portmarnock Railway Station and nearby north of the Mayne River, ENL/85 & DN/89. South-west end of Portmarnock Golf-course, DN/91. Single plant on waste ground at the western end of St Anne's Park, Raheny, PG/88, 89.
6. Disturbed ground by the roadside at Dodsboro housing estate, MN/88. Disturbed ground at Slade, JP/86.
8. Eastern part of Ringsend Dump, SR, HOR/83. Sandyford Industrial Estate, SR/92.

- -

M. discoidea DC. *(M. matricarioides, M. occidentalis, Chamomilla suaveolens)*
Pineappleweed   Alien

| 1 | 2 | 3 | 4 | 5 | 6 | 7 | 8 |

First recorded in the county in 1894, the first Irish record; in Colgan's time it was rare but spreading. Now it is widespread and abundant on tracks, roadsides and paths, as a weed of agricultural land and in waste places.
FID.

- -

Tripleurospermum

T. maritimum (L.) Koch *(Matricaria maritima)*
Sea Mayweed   Native

| 1 | 2 | 3 | 4 | 5 | 6 | 7 | 8 |

Abundant on seashores and adjacent waste ground; rarer inland and rare on arable land in the north and in the River Liffey Valley. Material of this and the following species, especially that growing on waste ground in the city, is not always clearly distinguishable. Many populations exist in which plants with contrasting growth habit, leaf colour and oil gland characters occur. At least some of these plants may be hybrids between this and the next species. The species was first recognised from a collection made by H.C. Levinge in 1888 from Portmarnock (5) (**DBN**).
FID.

- -

T. inodorum (L.) Schultz-Bip *(T. maritimum* subsp. *inodorum, Matricaria perforata)*
Scentless Mayweed   Possibly introduced in Co. Dublin

| 1 | 2 | 3 | 4 | 5 | 6 | 7 | 8 |

Abundant on waste ground and roadsides. Replaces **T. maritimum** in much of the lowlands where it is quite common. **T. inodorum** was included with **T. maritimum** in *Colgan* and the *Suppl.* First recognised in a collection made by the Rev. H.G. Carroll from Glasnevin (4) in 1866 (**DBN**).
FID.

Senecio

S. cineraria DC. *(S. bicolor* subsp. *cineraria)*
Silver Ragwort   Alien

Colgan: 8. Abundant and luxuriant along the sea cliffs and drift banks of Killiney bay, for a quarter of a mile from Sorrento Point, Dalkey, west to Vico bathing place, also spreading to adjacent walls, roadsides, railway banks and waste places *(N.C.)* *Cyb. II.* Several plants to the northward of Sorrento Point on cliffs above Dalkey Sound and two large plants on Dalkey island near the Martello tower, 1901; one large plant on rocks below Khyber Pass, 1900-03, another on cliffs by the sea about 200 yards south of Strawberry Hill, 1902: *N.C.* The flourishing settlement of this interesting Mediterranean species now so fully naturalised on the shores of Killiney Bay originated in a packet of seed sown by Sir Francis Brady, Bart., in his garden at Sorrento Cottage about the year 1875. At that time no trace of the plant was to be seen on the cliffs which stretch east and west below the garden; today they are almost completely clothed with its dense masses of silvery grey foliage and this remarkable extension is undoubtedly due to the agency of wind-borne seeds. This alien has also established itself on sea cliffs near Torquay in Devonshire, where it appears to have been first observed in 1899.

5	8

Rare, on sea-cliffs. Locally abundant. Murphy (1981) noted that this species has not extended its range since 1902 although in the past it has been locally aggressive, probably having displaced **Seriphidium maritimum** from Killiney.
5. Cliffs at Broad Strand, Doldrum Bay, and on sand-dunes at Claremont Strand, Howth, CB/91. By the Causeway of North Bull Island, M. Forrest/74; no longer there, PG/91.
8. Still frequent at the original station at Killiney; on the cliffs at the north end of Killiney Bay, on Sorrento Point, and above and below Vico Road. Occasional in other parts of 8, Blackrock Park, near the West Pier at Dun Laoghaire, Sandycove and Coliemore Harbour, HOR, SR/82-87.

- -

S. cineraria x **S. jacobaea (S.** x **albescens** Burb. & Colgan)

8

Rare, on sea-cliffs and rough grassland but locally abundant at Killiney. This hybrid was first found in 1902 *(Colgan)*. Murphy (1981) gives a detailed account of its autoecology.
S. x **albescens** has not significantly extended its range in the county over the past three quarters of a century.
8. Coast just north of Killiney Railway Station, SR/85. Sorrento Park in Dalkey, SR, HOR/83. Dalkey Island, DNFC/83. Shore below Vico Road, MS/67. Killiney Hill, DNFC/83. Cliffs at Whiterock, Killiney, SR/85.

- -

S. jacobaea L.
Common Ragwort   Native

1	2	3	4	5	6	7	8

Widespread and abundant on waste ground, roadsides and in pastures.
FID.

- -

S. jacobaea x **S. aquaticus (S.** x **ostenfeldii** Druce)
Native

Brunker MS: 3. Ward R. above Swords.

| 1 | 2 | (3) | 4 | 5 | 8 |

Rare, in damp grassland.

1. Damp grassland on the south side of Hynestown reservoir, GS/86.
2. Marsh north-east of the Corn Mill, south of Balbriggan, DD/87.
4. Grassland by the River Tolka at Blanchardstown, DD/88.
5. Near a pond at Portmarnock Raceway, DD, ENL/83.
8. Field near Rathmichael House, west of Shankill, SR/89.

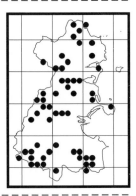

S. aquaticus Hill
Marsh Ragwort   Native

| 1 | 2 | 3 | 4 | 5 | 6 | 7 | 8 |

Occasional in moist pastures near streams and rivers and in marshes.
FID.

S. erucifolius L.
Hoary Ragwort   Native

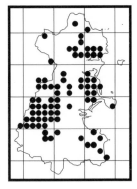

Colgan: Quite a common plant over the greater part of Districts 3, 4, 5 and in the lowlands of 6 and 7, spreading from the coast to the extreme west of the county; frequent in 2 and 8, but extremely rare in 1, where it has been observed in one station only, and but sparingly, near Bog of the Ring, 1902: *N.C.* Frequent in poor pastures. This is one of the most characteristic species of County Dublin, apparently rare outside its borders, and save for one locality in Louth, confined to the adjoining counties of Meath, Kildare and Wicklow.

| 1 | 2 | 3 | 4 | 5 | 6 | 7 | 8 |

Occasional on roadside and railway embankments by the coast and sandy ground inland; rare elsewhere.

S. squalidus L.
Oxford Ragwort   Alien

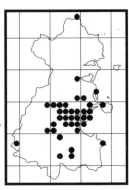

Colgan: 4. A few plants on the park wall, near Riverside, Island Bridge, 1902-03: *Colgan 1903.* 7. At Inchicore, on walls by the railway, also on other walls and by pathways in the vicinity, in profusion in an enclosure in which old railway and building material was stored, and in disused garden plots and other waste places, 1900 *(R.A. Phillips) Ir. Nat.,* 1900, p.245. Abundant and fully established here on walls, waysides, waste ground, and neglected garden plots, 1904; also a single plant by the roadside near Ballyfermot, a mile distant from Inchicore, in the same year: *N.C.* Observed on and about the railway at Inchicore, *circa 1890: Scully.* First observed in the county about 1890. A native of Southern Italy, obviously introduced into the county by railway traffic along the Great Southern and Western line from Cork city, where the plant has been fully naturalised for more than half a century.

Suppl: Rare. 5. Wall of Watson's Nurseries, Clontarf (R.W. Scully, 1913). Railway sidings at North Wall (1954 and 1957). Lane between Baldoyle and Baldoyle pits (1956). 7. Wall of Grosvenor Park, Rathmines (1952). Old walls in Donore Avenue and Dolphin's Barn Street (1933). Taylor's Lane, St John's Road and Kingsbridge (1935). Now rapidly spreading.

| 2 | 4 | 5 | 6 | 7 | 8 |

Common as an urban weed of waste ground and walls. Plants which appear to be intermediate between this species and **S. vulgaris** and which are referable to **S. x baxteri** Druce are occasionally encountered in the city. Praeger (1934b) recorded this hybrid at Islandbridge with both parents.

2. Railway line at Lowtherstone, DD/82, **NDR**.
6. Athgoe Castle, JP/86, **NDR**.
8. Sorrento Park, Dalkey, HOR, SR/83, **NDR**.
FID.

S. vulgaris L.
Groundsel   Native

Colgan: Var. radiatus Koch. 7. About a dozen plants on the towing path of Dublin University Boat Club grounds, Island Bridge, 1899: *F.W. Burbidge.* In profusion, associated with the type and with *S. squalidus,* in waste ground near Inchicore Railway works, 1902 *(F.W. Burbidge & N.C.) Colgan 1903.* This well marked variety, which comes quite true from seed, is abundant about Cork city, where it was first observed some 40 years ago, and there can be little doubt that it has been introduced thence to its Dublin stations by railway traffic.
Brunker MS: 8. Dump at "Waxey's Dargle" Irishtown, '52.

| I | 2 | 3 | 4 | 5 | 6 | 7 | 8 |

Widespread and common on disturbed ground, in gardens and in many ruderal habitats. **S. vulgaris** subsp. **vulgaris** forma **radiatus** (also called **S. vulgaris** var. **hibernicus** Syme in some works) is believed to be a result of introgression of **S. x baxteri** with **S. vulgaris**. Therefore all records of forma **radiatus** have been included here.

4. Aughrim Street, MS/81. The Haymarket, Stoneybatter, DD/92. By the railway at Liffey Junction, DD/81.
7. Car park at Parliament Street below Christchurch Cathedral, MWJ/84. Waste ground at City Hall, PWJ/86.
8. Central reservation of the Stillorgan Road, just south of Donnybrook Church, SR/85. Irishtown, SR, HOR/87.
FID.

S. sylvaticus L.
Heath Groundsel   Native

Colgan: 5. On Howth: *Ir. Flor.* Abundant in many parts of Howth Head, especially where gorse has been recently fired, 1903: *N.C.* Ireland's Eye: *Flor. Howth.* 7. Sparingly in granite "freestone" tracks at Castle Kelly, Glenasmole, 1894; 8. Heathy ground on granite near Barnacullia, Three Rock mountain, frequent above the Dingle, Glenamuck, and luxuriant on Killiney Hill, 1902: *N.C.*

| 5 | (7) | 8 |

Common in heaths on Howth and on the North Bull Island (5), and in heathland on Roches, Killiney and Dalkey Hills (8); rare elsewhere.
5. Portmarnock Golf-course, DN/91.

S. viscosus L.

Sticky Groundsel   Probably introduced

Colgan: 5. Sandy places by the sea, especially between Clontarf and Howth: *Wade Dubl.* Sandy fields near Kilbarrick Church and Howth: *Mack. Cat.* Seashore at Kilbarrick Church, 1858: *Herb. R. Barrington.* Banks by the roadside between the Baily Light-house and Sutton *(Moore) Cyb.* - and in 1900 (Miss R. Mahaffy): Colgan 1904. Waste places by the shore between Greenfields and Sutton: *Flor. Howth.* In small quantity on the beach near Sutton, *1896 (Miss S. Colgan) Cyb. II.* Several plants here in 1903 *(Miss R. Mahaffy) Colgan 1904.* Between the Baily and the Drumleck, Howth: *Herb. Hart.* Now become extremely rare, though apparently well established along the northern shore of Dublin Bay towards the beginning of last century. As an Irish plant, it appears to be at present confined to Co. Dublin where it seems doomed to early extinction, though at Howth it has persisted for upwards of a century.

Suppl: Apparently extinct.

| 4 | 5 | 7 | 8 |

Rare, on waste ground. This species had not been seen for many years prior to 1961. In recent years it has spread at several sites in the county, where it occurs in the form of scattered individuals or groups of plants; occasionally forming very large populations. **S. viscosus** appears to have become commoner during the last two decades throughout Ireland, occurring on railway sidings and urban waste ground. Akeroyd (1982) gives further details and Nash (1995) includes an up-to-date comprehensive review of the species in Ireland.

4. Gravel car park at the Customs House, MN, DN/87. At Cabra level crossing, MN/88. One plant in Glasilawn Road, Glasnevin, DD/88. People's Garden in the Phoenix Park, PR/88. Glasnevin Cemetery, D. Wyse Jackson/87, still there, SR/94. Grounds of the Incorporated Law Society at Blackhall Place, Smithfield, DN/87. Car park on Little Strand Street, DN/87. Weed in the National Botanic Gardens, Glasnevin, A. Hart, MS/81, **NDR**, DS/84, 91. Aughrim Street, PWJ/81. At Liffey Junction, DN/92. Botanic Road, Glasnevin, PG/92. Canal bridge at Clonsilla Railway Station, DN/97.

5. By factory railings in Santry, ENL/84. Waste ground and at the rail junction at the North Wall and Sheriff Street, DN/88. Dublin Port, SR/89-93. On the edge off a pathway east of the Summit, Howth, C. Breen/94. At Kilbarrack, PG/92.

7. Abundant in Mount Jerome Cemetery where it probably formed the largest population ever recorded in Ireland, PWJ/86, 87, **NDR**. Base of a wall in the car park at the north-east corner of T.C.D., MWJ, DAW/87. One plant on the pavement at the Belgrave Square end of Upper Mountpleasant Avenue, MWJ/86. Curb beside old Johnston, Mooney and O'Brien bakery works at Ballsbridge, SR/91. One plant on Lower Leeson Street, MWJ/92. Car park at Royal Hospital, Kilmainham; Fishamble St; Sidings at Pearse Station, DN/92-95. Near Dr Steeven's Hospital and Heuston Station, SR/94. One plant at Bass Place, off Fenian St, MWJ/94. Several plants on gravel, Castlewood Terrace, Rathmines, MWJ/94. Wasteground at Essex Quay, DN/94. At Heuston Station on ballast and pavement cracks, N. Lockhart, DN, MWJ/93. Pavement on Northumberland Road, DN/92.

8. Scattered plants on Ballyogan tiphead, east of Stepaside, SR/93, **NDR**.

FID.

Tussilago

T. farfara L.

Colt's-foot   Native

| 1 | 2 | 3 | 4 | 5 | 6 | 7 | 8 |

Widespread and abundant on roadsides, sandy places and seepage areas inland and by the sea.

Petasites

P. hybridus (L.) P. Gaertner, Meyer & Scherb.
Butterbur   Native

1	2	3	4	5	6	7	8

Common in waste places and on damp river banks and roadsides.

P. fragrans (Villars) C. Presl
Winter Heliotrope   Alien

1	2	3	4	5	6	7	8

Widespread and very common on road and track sides in the lowlands. Often locally abundant and clearly associated with former habitation. This species became widely naturalized from the middle of the 19th century onwards having been planted in gardens and woodlands.
FID.

Galinsoga

G. quadriradiata Ruiz Lopez & Paton (*G. ciliata*)
Shaggy-soldier   Alien

6	7	8

Rare on waste ground and in flower-beds.
6. Farmyard, 1.25 km west of Rathcoole, JP/86.
7. Weed in a tub in Nassau Street, PC, PWJ/80 & MS/82.
8. Abundant in a weedy garden off Ailesbury Road, Ballsbridge, SR/83. Garden weed at Dun Laoghaire, M. Ramming/87. Ballyogan tiphead, east of Stepaside, SR/93. By entrance to Leopardstown Hospital, SR/93.
FID.

Bidens

B. cernua L. *(B. cernuus)*
Nodding Bur-marigold   Native

Colgan: 1. In considerable abundance at the western end of the Bog of the Ring, 1893-1900, and about the middle, 1902: *N.C.* 4. Occasionally with *Bidens tripartita* on the river banks between Knockmaroon and Lucan: *Wade Dubl.* Island in the Liffey at Island Bridge, 1866: *Hart MS.*

Suppl: 1. Naul Reservoir (1939). Plentiful in Bog of the Ring (1939-1956). 2. Balrothery Lough (1934-1955). 4. North bank of the Royal Canal at Lucan (1922-1945). 7. Several plants by the Grand Canal at Portobello Bridge (A.W. Stelfox, 1922).

(1)	(2)	(4)	7

Extremely rare. Most of the open muddy areas in Bog of the Ring and at Balrothery Lough are now overgrown.
7. Still between Knockmaroon and Lucan in Palmerston Marsh, DD/82.

B. tripartita L. *(B. tripartitus)*
Trifid Bur-marigold   Native

Colgan: I. Sparingly in ditches to the south of the Bog of the Ring, 1895 *(N.C.) Top. Bot.* 2. In considerable quantity by the margin of the Lough, Balrothery, 1893-1902: *N.C.* (4. River banks between Knockmaroon and Lucan: *Wade Dubl.* 7. "In moist Rills as under *Inisacore Hill* near the Liffey banks": *Threlkeld* - not seen recently in these districts.)

Suppl: I Still at one place in the Bog of the Ring (1955). 2. Still at Balrothery Lough (1934) when it covered the entire area of the dried-up lough.

| I | (2) | (4) | (7) |

Extremely rare. The former station at Balrothery Lough (2) now has no bare mud.
I. Exposed mud at Hynestown Reservoir, GS/84.

Eupatorium

E. cannabinum L.
Hemp-agrimony   Native

| I | 2 | 3 | 4 | 5 | 6 | 7 | 8 |

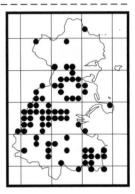

Occasional in ditches, river and canal banks, and seepage areas on cliffs in 2 & 5. Much more common in the south than the north of the county.
FID.

LILIIDAE (Monocotyledons)

BUTOMACEAE

Butomus

B. umbellatus L.
Flowering-rush   Native

Colgan (Appendix): 5. In the Tolka below Glasnevin bridge, possibly introduced *(Moore) Cyb.* Old quarry below the Garden beside the Tolka, 1873: *Spec. in Herb. Glasnevin.* Planted or an escape from the Botanic Garden.

Suppl: 5. Not confirmed from River Tolka. 8. Foundry pond by River Dodder at Clonskea (1932-1957).

| 4 | (5) | 6 | 7 | (8) |

Common in the River Liffey and rare in the Grand Canal. Not refound in the River Tolka (5) or by the River Dodder at Clonskeagh (8), where the foundry pond has been filled in. Not recorded by *Colgan* for the River Liffey, though it is now common there. Individuals appear to flower there quite infrequently.
4. Banks of the River Liffey at the U.C.D. Boat Club in Conyngham Road, MN/87, **NDR**. River Liffey at the Strawberry Beds and upstream from Islandbridge, DN/90.
6. By the 12th lock on the Grand Canal, MN/87. Lucan Demesne, JS/85, **NDR**. South bank of the River Liffey at St Edmundsbury and nearby at Weston Aerodrome, and near Cooldrinagh House, HOR/85, JP/89.
7. Along the length of the River Liffey millrace, DD/82, **NDR**, MN, CB, ENL/85 & DN/90. River Liffey from the weir near the T.C.D Boathouse at Islandbridge to Chapelizod Bridge, DN/90.

ALISMATACEAE

Sagittaria

S. sagittifolia L.
Arrowhead   Native

Colgan: 4. Quarry hole by the Tolka near Liffey Junction, 1894; abundant all along the Royal Canal from Lucan to Cross Guns, 1903: *N.C.* (5. Watery holes in the waste ground between Drumcondra and Glasnevin: *Ir. Flor.* probably extinct here.). 6 and 7. Abundant all along the Grand Canal from Hazelhatch by Clondalkin to James's Street Harbour, and along the branch canal to near Ringsend, 1903: *N.C.*

Suppl: Common in both canals only. 4, 5. Now extends down Royal Canal to Newcomen Bridge (1957).

| 4 | (5) | 6 | 7 |

Occasional in the River Liffey (4) and the Grand Canal (6 & 7). Not seen recently on the Royal Canal (4) where it was recorded in 1894 and 1905 by Praeger and McArdle, (**DBN**).

Baldellia

B. ranunculoides (L.) Parl. *(Alisma ranunculoides)*
Lesser Water-plantain   Native

Colgan: 1. Abundant in pools and in marshy ground at the Bog of the Ring, 1903; 2. Frequent in drains at Balrothery and in pools on Lusk Commons, 1902; 3. Sparingly in drains east of Donabate, 1901; 4. Frequent along the Royal Canal, 1903: *N.C.* 5. On the Howth: *Mack. Cat.* Marsh in the centre of Howth, 1895; abundant in Raheny quarries, 1902; 6 and 7. Frequent along the Grand Canal, 1903: *N.C.* 8. In marshes near Bullock: *Wade Dubl.*

Suppl: Common in both canals, occasional elsewhere. 1. Still in Bog of the Ring (1948). 4. Island Pond, Phoenix Park (J.P. Brunker, 1922). 8. Pond-holes on Foxrock golf course (R.W. Scully, 1918). Ballybetagh Bog (J.P. Brunker, 1923).

| (1) | (2) | (3) | (4) | 5 | 6 | (7) | (8) |

Extremely rare, in marshes and pools. Most of its former pool and drain-side sites are now overgrown, drained or filled-in.
5. Frequent in a marsh west of Portmarnock, DD/86.
6. Margin of a pool on the north side of the Grand Canal at Gollierstown, JP, DD/89 & MN/89.

Alisma

A. plantago-aquatica L. *(A. plantago)*
Water-plantain   Native

| 1 | 2 | 3 | 4 | 5 | 6 | 7 | 8 |

Common in canals, slow-moving rivers and streams; occasionally occurring on pond margins and artificial lakes; rare in 8.
8. Booterstown Marsh, RG/70; but not refound during the present survey. Pond at Rathfarnham Castle, DD, EMcA/83. Pond at Woodbrook House, SR, HOR/84. Ditches on both sides of the railway at Cork Abbey, SR, HOR/85.
FID.

A. lanceolatum With.
Narrow-leaved Water-plantain
Recorded in the *BSBI Atlas* from Co. Dublin but not noted during the present survey.

HYDROCHARITACEAE

Hydrocharis

H. morsus-ranae L.
Frogbit   Native

Colgan: 1. Common in the Bog of Curragha: *Wade Rar.* Abundant in one bog hole at the bog of Curragha and in a couple of adjacent ditches: *Colgan 1893.* Abundant in pools and drains at the Bog of the Ring, 1895-1903: *N.C.* In the bog of Garristown: *Guide.* Still at Garristown, spreading along a drain for about 500 yards, 1902: *N.C.* 2. In bog-pits near Balruddery *(Dr Scott) Mack. Rar.* Abundant in deep bog drains near the high road south-west of Balrothery, 1902: *N.C.* 3. Sparingly in a still pool of the Broad Meadow Water below Rowlestown: *Colgan 1893.*

Suppl: 1. Still at Curragha (1953) and in Bog of the Ring (1956). Not confirmed elsewhere.

| (1) | (2) | (3) |

Not refound in the county since 1956. Its former sites at Curragha and Garristown Bogs (1) have been drained.

Elodea

E. canadensis Michaux
Canadian Waterweed, Canadian Pondweed   Alien

| 1 | 2 | 3 | 4 | 5 | 6 | 7 | 8 |

Occasional in streams, rivers, ponds and canals.
FID.

E. nuttallii (Planchon) H. St. John
Nuttall's Waterweed   Alien

| 4 | 7/8 | 8 |

Rare in ponds, streams and rivers.
4. Lake, National Botanic Gardens, Glasnevin, MS/74, (Scannell 1977).
7/8. River Dodder at Ballsbridge, RG/90.
8. Stream, east of Cabinteely, SR, HOR/85, and in the same stream at Loughlinstown, and from Wyatville Road to where it enters the sea south of Killiney, SR, HOR, DAS/85 (Reynolds and O'Reilly 1986). Millpond near Dundrum, RG/94.

JUNCAGINACEAE

Triglochin

T. palustre L.
Marsh Arrowgrass   Native

(1)	2	(3)	4	5	6	7	8

Occasional in marshes in 7 & 8; rare elsewhere. This species has declined as its habitats have been drained in most areas.
2. Corn Mill south of Balbriggan, DD/87.
4. Marsh at Luttrellstown, MN/83. River Tolka Valley at Blanchardstown, DD/82. Marsh by Royal Canal near Ashtown, MN/83. Drainage ditch at Dunsoghly, MN/88. Marsh behind St Margaret's Church, MN/83.
5. Baldoyle Racecourse, near the Mayne River, DD/84-92. Portmarnock Peninsula, DN, RF/88. Kilrock, Howth, PG/87, 88. Marsh beside Thormanby Road, Howth, DN/89.
6. Marshland, east of Athgoe Castle, JP/86. Marshy ground west of Brittas, DD/82, Slade, JP/86.

T. maritimum L.
Sea Arrowgrass   Native

2	3	5	8

Common in salt-marshes and on muddy shores on the north coast; very rare elsewhere.
8. Occasional in Booterstown Marsh, DD/82, **NDR**.

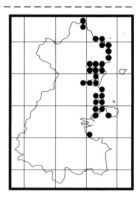

POTAMOGETONACEAE

Potamogeton

Chris Preston determined many of the specimens collected from sites given below.

P. natans L.
Broad-leaved Pondweed   Native

1	2	3	4	5	(6)	7	8

Occasional in pools, canals, rivers and reservoirs.
1. Old quarry hole north-west of Oldtown, GS/87.
2. Small pool in Raheny townland, DD/84.
3. Knocksedan Reservoir, PR, MN/85. Brackenstown House, RF/85.
4. Royal Canal west from Pakenham Bridge at Barberstown, Clonsilla, JS, MN/84. Small Pond in the Phoenix Park, JS/83. Farmyard pond west of Cappagh Hospital at Ballycoolin road,

MN, JS/86. Drain on the disused railway line at Barnhill Bridge, MN/88. Royal Canal at Collins Bridge, MN/90. Quarry pond 0.75 km east of Dunsoghly Castle, MN/88.
5. Water trough just south of Gay Brook, ENL/85.
7. River Liffey millrace, DD/85. Pond at Delaford, JP, DK/83. River Liffey at the Memorial Park, JP, DD, EMcA/83. Southern end of the southern reservoir in Glenasmole, MN/88.
8. Artificial pond west of Kiltiernan, SR, HOR/85. Artificial pond at the southern end of Leopardstown Racecourse, SR, HOR/85. Artificial pond at Carysfort College, Blackrock, HOR/84.

- -

P. polygonifolius Pourret
Bog Pondweed   Native

Colgan: 1. In pools in the Bog of the Ring, 1893; and 5. In the marsh in the centre of Howth Head, 1895: *N.C.* 6, 7, 8. Frequent in the water runnels and bog holes throughout the mountains, as on the hills around Brittas, on Seecawn, on Three Rock, on Glencullen mountain, &c., 1900-03: *N.C.* This alone of all the County Dublin pond-weeds is distinctly montane in its distribution.

Suppl: 1. Still in Bog of the Ring (1948). 5. Not seen recently in Howth.

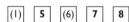

Common in wet acid habitats in the uplands (7 & 8); not refound in 6 where many of its former sites are now forested.
5. Pond at Greenhollows, Howth, ENL/82 & DN/90.

- -

P. coloratus Hornem. *(P. plantagineus)*
Fen Pondweed   Native

Colgan: 4. Occasional in the Royal Canal from Lucan to Clonsilla, 1901: *Colgan 1904.* No doubt introduced into the county from central Ireland by means of the canal. The record in *Cybele*, 1866. "Common in ditches on the bogs among the Dublin mountains, " has never been confirmed and should perhaps be referred to the preceding species.

4

4. In a drainage ditch, formerly marsh, near Dunsoghly Castle, MN/83.

- -

P. lucens L.
Shining Pondweed   Native

Colgan: 4. In lakes in the Phoenix Park: *Wade Dubl.* In the river Tolkay and the Royal Canal: *Ir. Flor.* Canal near Glasnevin: *Guide.* Abundant in the Tolka river at Mulhuddart and at Blanchardstown, 1893-1903; and 6. In the Liffey above Leixlip Bridge, 1894: *N.C.*

Suppl: 4. Still in ponds in Furry Glen, Phoenix Park (1956). By the Liffey below Lucan (1956). Not confirmed elsewhere.

(4)   (6)

Not refound at any of its sites in the county.

- -

P. lucens x P. gramineus (P. x zizii Koch ex Roth)
Long-leaved Pondweed   Native

(6)

There is a single authentic specimen from the county, from the Liffey river near Salmon Leap (6), H.C. Hart, 1866, **DBN**, conf. J.E. Dandy and subsequently by C.D. Preston. Other records are probably in error for **P. x salicifolius**.

P. lucens × P. perfoliatus (P. × salicifolius Wolfg.; *P. decipiens*)
Willow-leaved Pondweed   Native

Colgan: 4. In the Royal Canal near Clonsilla, 1889 (Scully) *Cyb. II.* Abundant in the Canal from above Lucan to below
Clonsilla, 1901: *N.C.* 6. River Liffey near Leixlip, 1894 *(Praeger) Top. Bot.* and in 1904!

4	(6)	7

Extremely rare, in the River Liffey only. Plants recorded as **P.** × **zizii** from the River Liffey in
recent years belong to this taxon.
4. Edge of the River Liffey at the U.C.D. Boat Club in Conyngham Road, MN/87. Edge of the River
    Liffey at the base of Oonavarra Hill, MN/87. River Liffey at the Strawberry Beds, DN/91.
7. River Liffey millrace at Palmerston Marsh and nearby in the River at Waterstown Dump,
    MN, ENL, CB/85 & DK/91. River Liffey at the T.C.D boathouse at Islandbridge, DN/90.

- -

P. gramineus L. *(P. heterophyllus)*
Various-leaved Pondweed   Native

Colgan: 4. In the Liffey above and below Lucan, 1893-1901: *N.C.* 6. River Liffey above the Salmon Leap: *Flor. Hib.*
Between the Salmon Leap and Leixlip, 1894-95 *(N.C.) Cyb II.* and in 1904!
Suppl: 4. Still in Liffey above and below Lucan (1956).

(4)	(6)

Not refound at any of its sites in the county, which were all on the River Liffey. Its decline
may be attributed to changes in the trophic status of the river.

- -

P. perfoliatus L.
Perfoliate Pondweed   Native

Colgan: 4. In the Liffey above Chapelizod: *Guide.* Abundant in the Royal Canal from Lucan to Clonsilla, 1895-1901: *N.C.*
6. In the Liffey between the Salmon Leap and Leixlip, 1882: *Hart MS.* 7. In the upper reservoir, Glenasmole, 1903: *N.C.*
Suppl: 7. Grand Canal, James's Street Harbour (1944).

(4)	(6)	7

Extremely rare.
7. Still in the southern reservoir in Glenasmole, at both ends, RMcM/85 & MN/87.

- -

P. friesii Rupr.
Flat-stalked Pondweed
Not seen this century in Dublin. There is a single record for this species: Canal, Dublin, W.
Wilson, 1829, **BM & MANCH**, det. J.E. Dandy.

- -

P. friesii × P. crispus (P. × lintonii Fryer)
Native

7

A specimen collected from the Grand Canal near Baggot Street Bridge in 1972 by L. Farrell
(**DBN**) was previously identified as **P. obtusifolius** and included in *FID* as such. C.D.
Preston redetermined it to be this hybrid (Preston and Wolfe-Murphy 1992)).

P. pusillus L.
Lesser Pondweed   Native

| (1) | 2 | (3) | 4 | 5 | 6 | 7 | 8 |

Rare, in rivers and ponds.
2. Balrothery Lough, DN/90.
4. Edge of the River Liffey at the U.C.D. Boat Club in Conyngham Road, MN/87. Quarry lake, Phoenix Park, NS/91. People's Pond, MN/88. Citadel Pond in the Phoenix Park, MN/87 & NS/91.
5. Pond on Portmarnock Raceway, DN/89.
6. North pond at Brittas, DN/89.
7. River Liffey at the T.C.D. Boathouse, DN/90.
7/8. River Dodder along Lower Dodder Road, DN/90.

P. berchtoldii Fieber
Small Pondweed   Native

| 3 | 4 | 5 | 6 | 7 | 8 |

Occasional in ponds. Included in **P. pusillus** in *Colgan*. Not distinguished in *Suppl*. Early collections were made by Colgan in 1893 from near Mulhuddart (4) (**BM**), from Lissen Hall, Broad Meadow Water (3) (**BM**), and by R.Ll. Praeger in 1894 from Rathfarnham (8) (**DBN**).
3. Pond at Brackenstown, Swords, JK/88. Knocksedan Reservoir, PR, MN/85 & DN/90. Tonelagee Reservoir, west of Swords, DN/90. Drain near Kilcrea Home, DN/93.
4. River Tolka south-west of Abbotstown and in Abbotstown Pond, MN/84-89. Lake in a quarry east of Huntstown, Finglas, DN/89.
5. St Doolagh's Quarries, MS/60, (**DBN**). Royal Dublin Golf-course, North Bull Island and in a nearby pond, DN/88, 89. Ponds at Thormanby Road, Howth, DN/89. Pond on Portmarnock Raceway, DN/89. Near Malahide Castle, C.D. Preston/95.
6. South pond at Brittas, DNFC/89.
7. Herbert Park, Ballsbridge, MS/62. Pond in quarries near Aghfarrel, HOR/86. Pond in Tymon Park near Wellington Road, DN/90.
8. Pond at the south end of Leopardstown Racecourse, SR, HOR/85.

P. crispus L.
Curled Pondweed   Native

| 1 | 2 | 3 | 4 | 5 | 6 | 7 | 8 |

Occasional in ponds, ditches, canals and rivers; most frequent in 8 and rare in 5.
5. Pond in Howth Demesne, DN, PG/91.
FID.

P. pectinatus L.
Fennel Pondweed   Native

Colgan: 2. Muddy ditches near Balleally, Rogerstown creek, 1902; 4. Abundant in the Liffey from Lucan to Chapelizod, 1893-1904; 5. Ditches between Coolock and Baldoyle, 1899; 6. Abundant in the Grand Canal and in adjacent watercourses from Hazelhatch to Clondalkin, and 7. From Clondalkin at intervals down to Ringsend basin, 1903; mill-race between Chapelizod and Cursis Stream, and abundant in a watercourse by the Grand Canal at Inchicore, 1895; in the Liffey above Island Bridge, 1902: *N.C.* 8. Ditches near Sandymount *Mack. Cat.*

Suppl: 4, 6 and 7. Confirmed from River Liffey (1956) and Grand Canal (1956).

2	4	(5)	6	7	(8)

Occasional in ponds. Commonest in the River Liffey (4 & 6) where exceptionally large plants are locally dominant replacing clean-water species e.g. **Ranunculus penicillatus.** It is the most pollution tolerant pondweed. The record in *FID* for the Grand Canal is for this species not **P. filiformis**.

2. Heavily polluted pool below Clonard Cross, DD/87.
4. Island Pond in the Phoenix Park, JS/83. Abbotstown Pond, MN/90.
6. Under the bridge over the Grand Canal at Ballymakaily Mill, CB/87. Stream leading to the Grand Canal at the 12th lock, Lucan, M. Kennedy/65.
7. Grand Canal at Baggot Street Bridge, DN/89. Grand Canal, at the 7th lock, DN/89.

Groenlandia

G. densa (L.) Fourr. *(Potamogeton densus)*
Opposite-leaved Pondweed   Native

Colgan: 6. Frequent in the canal between Clondalkin and Hazelhatch, 1893-1903, becoming rare here through cleansing of the waterway in the latter year: N.C. 7. In the canal at Portobello *(Moore)* Cyb. In profusion at intervals from Clondalkin all along the canal to James's Street Harbour and along the branch canal to Ringsend Harbour, 1903; quarry holes by the Grand Canal at the 3rd lock, Inchicore, 1902: N.C.

4	(6)	7

Rare, in canals and streams. Common in the Grand Canal. Legally protected under the Wildlife Act of 1976 as an endangered species.

4. Between the 3rd and 4th locks on the Royal Canal east of Cross Guns Bridge and east of Drumcondra (Binn's Bridge) Bridge, MD/90, **NDR**, & NS/92.
7. Grand Canal, inner city stretch, MS/67, JS, DD/81. In a swiftly flowing stream in the Robin Hood Industrial Estate off the Long Mile Road, PWJ/87. Scattered along the Grand Canal at Dolphin's Barn from Portobello to Charlemont Bridge, and between Drimnagh and Kilmainham, PWJ/87 & MWJ/87, 89.

FID.

RUPPIACEAE

Ruppia

R. maritima L. *(R. rostellata)*
Beaked Tasselweed   Native

Colgan: 2. Abundant on mud flats near Rogerstown, and 3. Near Turvey, 1893; abundant near Mullan, Malahide creek, 1900: N.C. 5. At Portmarnock: *Flor. Howth.* Pool by the shore near Warren Cottage, Howth, 1892; abundant in pools by the shore between Saint Anne's and Watermill Bridge, Raheny, 1902: N.C.

Suppl: 5. Drains on North Bull opposite St Anne's (1943).

2	3	5

Rare, in brackish drains and on estuarine mud.

2/3. Outer part of the Rogerstown Estuary, BM/91.

3.   Dense growths in one channel near the mouth of the Broad Meadow River, BM/91.

3/5. Dominant in the outer estuary at Malahide, BM, EJ/91.

5.   Plentiful in a drain on the western boundary of the Royal Dublin Golf-course and around the north lagoon on North Bull Island, DN/89 & BM/90.

- -

R. cirrhosa (Petagna) Grande *(R. spiralis)*
Spiral Tasselweed   Native

Colgan: 3. Abundantly in two stations on the Malahide creek, near Lissen Hall at the mouth of the Broad Meadow Water, and about a mile eastward near Newport House, 1893: *Colgan 1893.* Abundant in pools by the sea near Mullan, north side of Malahide creek, 1902: *N.C.*

Suppl: Not confirmed from Swords Estuary [3].

(3)

Not refound at Malahide (3) during this survey.

- -

ZANNICHELLIACEAE

Zannichellia

Z. palustris L.
Horned Pondweed   Native

Colgan: 2. By the shore north of Balbriggan and again south of Loughshinny, 1900; pond near Rogerstown and ditches near Balrothery, 1902; &c.; 3. By the Ward river below Chapelmidway and by the sea near Raheen Point, 1894; pools near Lissen Hall, 1902; 4. By the Tolka below Mulhuddart, 1903; 5. Drains at Baldoyle, 1903; &c.; 6. Abundant in the Grand Canal from Lucan to Hazelhatch, and 7. From Clondalkin to James's Street Harbour and Ringsend Harbour, 1903: *N.C.* 8. Ditches at Sandymount: *Mack. Cat.* Pools on Loughlinstown Commons, 1894; &c.: *N.C.*

Suppl: 1. Pools in Bog of the Ring (1934-1956). 5. St Doolagh's Quarries (1953). 7. River Dodder above Firhouse Weir (1935-1955).

(1) 2 3 4 5 6 7 8

Occasional in ponds, rivers, ditches and canals; sometimes locally abundant.
FID.

- -

ZOSTERACEAE

Zostera

Z. marina L.
Eelgrass   Native

(2) (3) (5)

Colgan noted that this species was abundant north of the Liffey mouth, but absent in the south; in muddy estuaries. It was not refound during this survey.

Z. angustifolia (Hornem.) Reichb. *(Z. marina var. angustifolia, Z. hornemanniana)*
Narrow-leaved Eelgrass   Native

Colgan: Var. ANGUSTIFOLIA *Fries* 5. Malahide inlet, 1899: *Praeger 1902.* Muddy shore at Portmarnock, 1901, and below
Raheny, 1902: *N.C.*

Suppl: 5. Still at Malahide Inlet (1921) and Portmarnock (1922).

3	5

Rare, in mudflats. First noted from a collection made by the Rev. H.G. Carroll in 1867 from
Baldoyle (5) (**DBN**).
3/5. Dominant species in the **Zostera** beds in the Malahide estuary, BM, EJ/91.
5. Lagoon on North Bull Island at the Howth end, PC/73. Small (100 m^2) but dense stand in
   the north lagoon on North Bull Island, BM/91. Covering a large area in both the inner and
   outer Baldoyle estuary, BM/91.

- -

Z. noltii Hornem. *(Z. nana)*
Dwarf Eelgrass   Native

Colgan: 5. On mud in the creek close to the railway station at Baldoyle *(More) Cyb.* Abundant on the mud below the
Club house at Portmarnock golf links: *Hart 1897.* and in 1901!

Suppl: 2. and 3. Sparingly on mud-flats near centre of Rogerstown Creek below railway bridge (Miss H.M. Parkes, 1951).
5. Still at Portmarnock (1950). 8. Strand outside Merrion Gates (M. Kennedy, 1954).

(2)	(3)	5	8

Rare, in mudflats.
5. Sandy mud flats on North Bull Island at the Howth end, C.H. Dickenson/67. Lagoon on
   North Bull Island, PC/73. Patchily distributed over about 2 ha at the north-east corner of
   the estuary close to the road leading to the Island Golf-course, Portmarnock, EJ/90. One
   small 100 m^2 patch at Sutton Creek opposite North Bull Island, EJ/90. Several small
   patches in the Baldoyle Estuary off the southern and eastern sides of the grassy
   promontory which backs onto the railway embankment, BM, EJ/91.
8. Still at Merrion covering large areas of wet sand on Merrion and Sandymount Strands,
   SR/85 & BM, EJ/89, 90.

- -

ARACEAE

Arum

A. maculatum L.
Lords-and-Ladies, Cuckoo-pint   Native

1	2	3	4	5	6	7	8

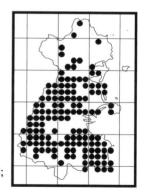

Common in base-rich shaded hedgerows and woodlands;
very rare in the north of the county in 1 & 2.
2. Still near Gormanstown where it was recorded by Colgan in 1893;
   in a lane leading to the quarry south of Gormanstown College,
   DD/83, 88; not refound at the *Colgan* Balscaddan site (2).

A. italicum Miller
Italian Lords-and-Ladies   Alien

2	6	8

Rare. Not recognised in *Colgan* or *Suppl.*
2. Lane at Balrothery Churchyard, DD/84.
6. Grand Canal at Ballymakaily Mill, JP/84.
8. Roadside, north-west of Old Connaught Crossroads, DNFC/84.

LEMNACEAE

Spirodela

S. polyrhiza (L.) Schleiden *(Lemna polyrhiza)*
Greater Duckweed   Native

Colgan: 4. Pond in the Phoenix Park *(More) Cyb.* 8. Brackish ditch near Irishtown *(Moore) Cyb.*
Suppl: 4. Still in the Island Pond, Phoenix Park (1950), now the only Dublin station.

2	(4)	7	(8)

Very rare.
2. Abundant on wet mud at the south end of Balrothery Lough, DD/84, **NDR**.
7. Pools by a disused railway line at Cabra, PR, PWJ/81, **NDR**.
FID.

Lemna

L. gibba L.
Fat Duckweed   Native

Colgan: 2. Abundant in a mill pond at Balbriggan: *Colgan 1895.* 3. Abundant in a pond near Ballisk, Donabate: *Colgan 1893.* Roadside drains near Portrane House, 1895: *N.C.* 4. Pond near Glasnevin *(Moore) Cyb.*
Suppl: 7. Pond S.E. of Limekiln Farm Lane, Crumlin (J.P. Brunker, 1932) - now filled in. Pond at Rathfarnham Castle (R.A. Phillips, 1920). 8. Mill-dam at Clonskea (1937-1956). Pond at S. end of Woodbrook golf course between the railway and the sea (1939).
Praeger, 1939: In the Dodder above Ballsbridge, J. Doyle. Ponds at Rathfarnham Castle, A.W. Stelfox.

(2)	3	(4)	(7)	(8)

Extremely rare.
3. Still in a pond at Ballisk, Donabate, DD, PR/83.

L. minor L.
Common Duckweed   Native

1	2	3	4	5	6	7	8

Very common in pools, canals, drains and streams.
FID.

L. trisulca L.
Ivy-leaved Duckweed   Native

(1)	2	(3)	4	5	6	7

Common in canals; rare in ponds and marshes elsewhere.
FID.

JUNCACEAE

Juncus

J. squarrosus L.
Heath Rush   Native

Colgan: 1. One large patch in a remnant of peat bog a few yards square near
Streamstown, Naul Hills, 1900; 6 Sparingly in a swamp on the northern slope
of Slieve Thoul, 1904: *N.C.*

Suppl: 1. There is now no sign of peat at Streamstown and the station must be
considered lost. 6. Not confirmed from Slieve Thoul.

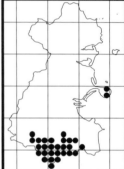

(1)	5	(6)	7	8

Common in moorland on peat or mineral soil in 7 & 8; very
rare elsewhere. Slieve Thoul (6) has been largely planted with conifers.
5. Sparingly at Greenhollows, Howth, DN/89, **NDR**.

J. gerardii Loisel
Saltmarsh Rush   Native

Colgan: 8. Sparingly by the salt ditch between Booterstown and Blackrock, 1901, and in moist rock-hollows near Bullock
harbour, 1902: *N.C.*

2	3	5	8

Common in salt-marshes and rocky shores in the north;
rare in the south.
8. South of Merrion Gates, HOR/84. Booterstown Marsh, DD/82. Seepage areas at the
   north end of Killiney Bay, SR, HOR/85. South end of Dalkey Island, SR/91.

J. foliosus Desf.
Leafy Rush   Native
Not distinguished from **J. bufonius** in *Colgan* and *Suppl.*

5	6	7	8

Rare, in wet acid grassland.
5. Grassy track in wet grassland at Redrock, Howth, DD/87, **NDR**. Abundant in wet ground
   at Portmarnock, DD/94.
6. Valley between Brittas and Saggart Hill, south of Glenaraneen, DNFC/90, **NDR**.
7. Very large plants on wet ground by the old gasworks at Sir John Rogerson's Quay, DD/90, **NDR**.
8. Damp field margin on the lower slopes of Two Rock Mountain near Ballybrack, Glencullen
   Valley, SR/87. North-north-east slope of Three Rock Mountain, MS/62. This was the first
   record for the county (Scannell 1965).

J. bufonius L.
Toad Rush   Native

| 1 | 2 | 3 | 4 | 5 | 6 | 7 | 8 |

Common in muddy ground.

J. ambiguus Guss. (*J. ranarius*)
Frog Rush   Native
Not distinguished from **J. bufonius** in *Colgan* and *Suppl.*

| 2 | 3 | 5 | 8 |

Occasional in salt-marshes and on sea-sprayed rocks.
2. Rocks by the sea north of Skerries Village, DD/87. Dry mud of the upper salt-marsh in Balleally Dump, DD/87. Shore at Loughshinny, DD/90.
3. Salt-marsh at Donabate, H. Lahert, G. Pasley & N. McLaughlin/79.
5. Sandy ground by the bridge on North Bull Island, MS/72. Salt-marsh at Portmarnock and nearby in the Brickfields, DN/88 & DN/90. Common in the salt-pan at the south end of North Bull Island, PG/90.
8. Booterstown Marsh, SR/88.

J. subnodulosus Schrank (*J. obtusiflorus*)
Blunt-flowered Rush   Native

Colgan: 1. In a drain at Garristown Bog, 1894: *Colgan 1895* and in 1902! 3. Abundant in a marsh by the northern shore of Portrane peninsula, spreading for fully a quarter of a mile, 1894: *Colgan 1895* and in 1904! Frequent in ditches in the Portrane peninsula, east of Donabate, 1901: *N.C.* 5. Boggy margin of the shore a little east of Dollymount: *Guide* and in 1903! 6. Abundant in a marsh above Saggard, 1894: *Colgan 1895.*
Suppl: 6. By Grand Canal at Hazelhatch (1956).

| (1) | 3 | (5) | (6) |

Extremely rare. The former site at Garristown Bog (1) is now drained.
3. Still frequent on a large dune-slack on the Portrane Peninsula, DD, PR/87. Noted by Praeger (1922) from Lambay Island but not refound recently there.

J. articulatus L.(*J. lamprocarpus*)
Jointed Rush   Native

| 1 | 2 | 3 | 4 | 5 | 6 | 7 | 8 |

Common in moorland, poorly drained pastures, canal banks and drains.
FID.

J. articulatus × J. acutiflorus (J. × surrejanus Druce ex Stace & Lambinon)

| 6 | 7 | 8 |

Rare, in poorly drained pastures.
6. Field, east of Athgoe Castle, JP/86. Grand Canal, west of Golierstown Bridge, MN/89.
7. Fields by the River Dodder at Oldbawn, JP/83.
8. Wet meadow at Ballycorus, SR/88. Wet area below the cromlech, west of Kiltiernan, SR/88. South end of Ballybetagh Bog, SR/88.

J. acutiflorus Ehrh. ex Hoffm.
Sharp-flowered Rush   Native

| (1) | (2) | (3) | (4) | 5 | 6 | 7 | 8 |

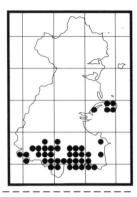

Many of its lowland marshy habitats have been drained and in much of the county this species is no longer as common as it was in Colgan's time. Common in moorland and poorly drained pasture in the uplands; very rare elsewhere.

J. bulbosus L. (J. supinus, J. kochii)
Bulbous Rush   Native

Colgan: 1. Abundant in the Bog of the Ring and 5. On Howth Head, 1903: N.C.

| (1) | 5 | 6 | 7 | 8 |

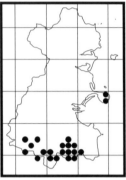

Common in upland pools, streams and flushes, and moorland. Var. **fluitans** has been recorded during the present survey.

J. maritimus Lam.
Sea Rush   Native

| 2 | 3 | 5 |

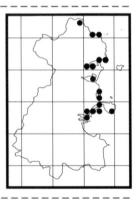

Common in upper parts of salt-marshes and dune-slacks.

J. acutus L.
Sharp Rush   Native

Suppl: 5. Two large clumps on the North Bull about 300 yards N.E. of "The Farm" (H.J. Hudson, 1936). Still there and increasing (1957). Included in Colgan's Appendix from a record by Wade which Colgan considered an error. However, in Wade's *Flora, J. acutus, J. maritimus, J. gerardi and J. obtusiflorus* are bracketed together for this station. Before the formation of the North Bull the delta of the Naniken and Santry Rivers was probably more extensive and the present station may be derived from there.

| 5 |

Praeger (1939) regarded this as a recent immigrant to Co. Dublin, apparently by natural means. Refound north of The Farm on Royal Dublin Golf-course (ten plants), North Bull Island, CB, PG, DN/93.

J. inflexus L. *(J. glaucus)*
Hard Rush   Native

| 1 | 2 | 3 | 4 | 5 | 6 | 7 | 8 |

Very common in marshes, canal sides, pastures, usually on calcareous soils.
FID.

J. inflexus x **J. effusus (J. x diffusus** Hoppe)
Native

Colgan: 7. In a wet bog on Killakee mountain: *Colgan 1895.*

| (7) |

Not refound at its site on Killakee Mountain (7).

J. effusus L.
Soft-rush   Native

| 1 | 2 | 3 | 4 | 5 | 6 | 7 | 8 |

Widespread and very common in damp pastures, canal banks, marshes and waste ground.
FID.

J. conglomeratus L.
Compact Rush   Native

Colgan: Var. conglomeratus (L.) [of **J. effusus**]. Apparently quite rare, at least in forms clearly distinguishable from the type, but occurs in 1. In the Naul Hills; 3. Near Brackenstown; 5. At Portmarnock; 7. In Glenasmole; 8. At Ballycorus and Kilgobbin.

| 1 | 2 | (3) | 4 | 5 | 6 | 7 | 8 |

Common in damp pastures and marshes in the uplands; rare in the lowlands.
4. Marsh by the Royal Canal just west of Ashtown, MN/83, **NDR**. Roadside at Dublin
   Airport, MN/85. Royal Canal just west of Clonsilla, below Beech Park House, MN/88.
FID.

Luzula

L. pilosa (L.) Willd. *(L. vernalis)*
Hairy Wood-rush   Native

Colgan: 4. In woods, Luttrel's-town; and 5. At Santry: *Wade Dubl.* Sparingly in Howth demesne: *Flor. Howth.* 7. Near the head of Glenasmole, 1894; in Glendhu and on Tibradden mountain, 1895: *N.C.* 8. On Kilgobbin mountain; *Wade Dubl.* Above Marley: *Ir. Flor.* In the Little Dargle and on the east slope of Two Rock, 1903: *N.C.*
Suppl: 7. Still at Glendhu (1950). 8. Dingle, Glenamuck (A.A. Lisney, 1928).

| (4) | (5) | 7 | 8 |

Very rare, in woodland. Not refound at Luttrellstown (4) despite repeated searches.
7. Wood, north of Glenasmole, DK/86. Eastern slope above the northern reservoir in
   Glenasmole, DK/c.65 & MN/90.

8. On the south-west slope of Two Rock Mountain in the Glencullen Valley, on either side of the Wicklow Way, SR, HOR/87. Ballybetagh Wood, SR/83. Woodland at the north end of The Scalp, SR/84. Still in The Dingle, HOR/83. Glencullen mountain, south-west of Boranaraltry Bridge, SR, DNFC/94.

L. sylvatica (Hudson) Gaudin *(L. maxima)*
Great Wood-rush   Native

| 5 | 6 | 7 | 8 |

Common in upland woodlands and streamsides in moorland. North of the Liffey only on Howth Head.

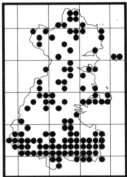

L. campestris (L.) DC.
Field Wood-rush   Native

| I | 2 | 3 | 4 | 5 | 6 | 7 | 8 |

Common in sand-dunes, calcareous grassland and on roadside banks.

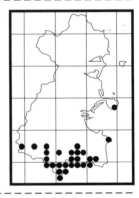

L. multiflora (Ehrh.) Lej.
Heath Wood-Rush   Native

| 5 | 6 | 7 | 8 |

---

subsp. **multiflora**

| 5 | 6 | 7 | 8 |

Common on wet acid mineral soil or peat in 6, 7 & 8; rare elsewhere.
5. In a marshy area on the Ben of Howth, DN/89.

---

subsp. **congesta** (Thuill.) Arcang.

| 8 |

Extremely rare but probably under-recorded.
8. In a wet area below the cromlech, west of Kiltiernan, SR/88.

CYPERACEAE

Eriophorum

E. angustifolium Honck.
Common Cottongrass, Bogcotton   Native

Suppl: 1. Bog of the Ring (1955).

(1)	2	(3)	4	5	(6)	7	8

Common in moorland and bogs, and on Howth Head (5); rare elsewhere. Not refound on Bog of the Ring (1) which has been drained.

4. In a marsh immediately north of the 'Rabbit Warren' in Luttrellstown, JS/83. The site has since been significantly altered and is now an artificial lake.
5. Small boggy area on the edge of Howth Golf-course, DN/89. Central marsh on Howth Head, DN/90. Marsh at Kilrock, Howth, DN/90. Wet area in Royal Dublin Golf-course on the North Bull Island, PG, DN/93.

E. latifolium Hoppe
Broad-leaved Cottongrass   Native

Suppl: 7. In several places along E. side of upper reservoir at Glenasmole, mixed with *E. angustifolium* (R.W. Scully and J.P. Brunker, 1919). 8. In Ballyman Glen (R.M. Barrington, 1909). Still in both stations (1956).

DNFC Annual Report for 1968: ?7. Report of discovery "near Tallaght" of a new station. No further details, but known to be Whitestown, Tallaght (fide DD).

7	(8)

7. Whitestown, Tallaght, DNFC/68.

E. vaginatum L.
Hare's-tail Cottongrass   Native

Colgan: 5. Common on moors and bogs on Howth Head: *Flor. Howth.* - the only lowland station.

(5)	7	8

Common in moorland and bogs.

Trichophorum

T. cespitosum (L.) Hartman *(Scirpus cespitosus)*
Deergrass   Native

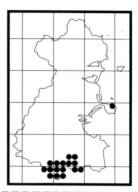

| 5 | 7 | 8 |

Abundant in moorland.

Eleocharis

E. palustris (L.) Roemer & Schultes subsp. **vulgaris** Walters
Common Spike-rush   Native

| I | 2 | 3 | 4 | 5 | 6 | 7 | 8 |

Common in canals and marshes; rare in 8.
8. South of Ballybetagh Bog, SR, JR/87. South of Killiney near the mouth of the Shanganagh River, SR, HOR/83. Abandoned railway line, north-west of the Sandyford Industrial Estate, HOR/83.

E. uniglumis (Link) Schultes
Slender Spike-rush   Native

Colgan: 5. On the shore east of Dollymount opposite the North Bull (M. Dowd) Rec. Add. sparingly here in 1903!

| 5 |

Extremely rare, in damp grassland near the sea.
5. Portmarnock Brickfields and Raceway, DN/90.

E. quinqueflora (F. Hartmann) O. Schwarz *(Scirpus pauciflorus)*
Few-flowered Spike-rush   Native

| 2 | (3) | (4) | 5 | (6) | 7 | 8 |

Rare; flushes in the uplands. Now very much rarer than in Colgan's time due to drainage operations.
2. Still in the marsh between Loughshinny and Skerries, DD/91.
5. North Bull Island, on the Royal Dublin Golf-course, north of The Farm and at the south end, PG, DN/93.
7. West side of the Glenasmole Valley, SR, DD/87. West side of the River Dodder south-east of Glenasmole Lodge, SR, HOR/85.
8. Wet slope above the Glencullen River south-east of Ballybrack, SR, JR/86. North facing slope above Boranaraltry, HOR, CB/86. Just south-east of Ballyman Glen Bridge on the county boundary, SR, HOR/86.

E. acicularis (L.) Roemer & Schultes
Needle Spike-rush   Native

6	7

Locally abundant in the Grand Canal from where it has been known since 1893 when it was discovered by Colgan; unknown elsewhere.
6. Still in the Grand Canal at Gollierstown, DN/90.
7. Still in mud in shallow water in the Grand Canal along a 300 m stretch at Davitt Road, Drimnagh, DN/89.

Bolboschoenus

B. maritimus (L.) Palla *(Scirpus maritimus)*
Sea Club-rush   Native
Suppl: 2. In Balrothery Lough (1955).

2	3	4	5	8

Common in muddy shores and brackish drains along the coast in the north of the county; very rare elsewhere.
4. Pond in the People's Garden at Phoenix Park, probably introduced, MN/87, **NDR**.
8. Booterstown Marsh, DD/82, SR/96.

Schoenoplectus

S. lacustris (L.) Palla *(Scirpus lacustris)*
Common Club-rush   Native
Colgan: 3 and 4 Abundant along the Broad Meadow Water, the Ward River, and the Tolka, and frequent along the Liffey and the Royal Canal, 1900-03; 5. In Killester Quarries, 1893; and 6. Sparingly in the Grand Canal near Gollierstown, 1903: *N.C.*

1	3	4	5	6	8

Common in Rivers Tolka and Liffey, and the Grand and Royal Canals; rare elsewhere.
1. Pond beside Broad Meadow River upstream from Lispopple Bridge, DN/91, **NDR**.
3. Broad Meadow River north of Swords, SR/89.
8. South of the Stillorgan Reservoirs near the disused railway, HOR/83, **NDR**.

S. tabernaemontani (C. Gmelin) Palla *(Scirpus tabernaemontani,*
S. lacustris subsp. *tabernaemontani)*
Grey Club-rush   Native
Colgan: 3. In the salt marsh near Turvey House, 1893; by the estuary near Lissen Hall, 1902: *N.C.* 5. Marsh between Clontarf and Kilbarrick church: *Mack. Cat.* Salt water ditches between Howth and Baldoyle: *Ir. Flor.* In a quarry pond on the Quarry, Howth: *Flor. Howth.* In the Sluice river, in Portmarnock Pits, near the old mill, Portmarnock, at Baldoyle, and by the shore below Raheny, 1903: *N.C.*

3	5	8

Occasional in salt-marshes and drains near the sea where it may be locally abundant.
3. Still in a salt-marsh on the estuary at the Broad Meadow River, PR/90.
5. Portmarnock Brickfields, DN/90. Pond on Portmarnock Raceway, DN/90. Water hazards on Portmarnock Golf-course, DN/91. Yacht-club, 0.5 km west of Malahide, DN/90.
8. Booterstown Marsh, RG/70, **NDR**, DD/82, SR/96.

Isolepis

I. setacea (L.) R. Br. *(Scirpus setaceus)*
Bristle Club-rush   Native

| (1) | 2 | 3 | 4 | 5 | 6 | 7 | 8 |

Frequent in bare muddy ground in the upland parts of 6, 7 and 8; rare elsewhere.
2. Flush close to the sea at Barnageeragh, north of Skerries, DD, ENL/84.
3. Disused quarry near Donabate Railway Station, DD/82.
4. Wet flush by the River Tolka at Blanchardstown, DD/88. Marshy field at St Margaret's, MN/83. Ditch adjacent to the Royal Canal at Coldblow, JS, MN/84. Damp ground by the Hole-in-the-wall, Phoenix Park, DD/88.
5. In and near Kilrock Quarries, Howth, DN/89.
6. Just south-west of Badgerhill, JP/86. North end of Brittas Ponds, ENL/83.

I. cernua (Vahl) Roemer & Schultes (*Scirpus cernuus, S. savii*)
Slender Club-rush   Native

Colgan: 2. By the coast near Balbriggan, 1904; near Skerries, 1893; between Skerries and Loughshinny, 1903: *N.C.* 3. On Lambay island: *Flor. Lambay.* Sparingly east of Raheen Point, Portrane, 1894, and near Corballis, 1902: *N.C.* 5. Pointed out to me on the Hill of Howth in August, 1835, ...by Mr Babington of St John's College, Cambridge" *(Mackay) Flor. Hib.* Between St Fintan's and Shielmartin, Howth: *Flor. Howth* and in 1902! Abundant in the marsh in the centre of Howth Head, 1893; frequent by the shore near Raheny, 1903: *N.C.*

| 2 | 3 | 5 |

Rare, in damp coastal grassland.
2. Still near Skerries in flushed grassland, near the shore, towards Barnageeragh, DD, ENL/84.
3. Damp patches on Malahide Island, DD/84-90.
5. Marsh at Kilrock, Howth, PG/90.

Eleogiton

E. fluitans (L.) Link *(Scirpus fluitans)*
Floating Club-rush   Native

Colgan: 1. Pools at Bog of the Ring, 1903: *Colgan 1904.* 4. In the marshy ground at Cardiff's Bridge; and 5. At Howth: *Wade Rar.* In a large marsh at the summit of Howth: *Mack. Cat.* and in 1904! By Ballsaggart stream, Howth: *Flor. Howth.* *Suppl:* 8. Dried-up pool, Ticknock (J.P. Brunker, 1922-1935).

| (1) | (4) | 5 | (8) |

Very rare.
5. Ponds at Greenhollows, Howth, ENL, DD/82, ENL/84 & DN/90.

Blysmus

B. rufus (Hudson) Link *(Scirpus rufus)*
Saltmarsh Flat-sedge   Native

Colgan: 2. In a salt marsh between Balbriggan and Hampton, 1803: *Mack. Rar.* Abundant here, 1904, in smaller quantity by the shore between Skerries and Loughshinny, 1895: *N.C.* 3. Carnoon Bay, Lambay island *(Barrington) Flor. Lambay.* Marsh by the shore north of Portrane peninsula, 1893-1903: *N.C.* 5. Salt marsh between Baldoyle and Howth: *Mack. Rar.* Abundant in the marsh between Baldoyle and Portmarnock, 1904; margin of a pool near Warren Cottage, Howth, 1892-1904: *N.C.* Abundant on the North Bull *(More) Rec. Add.* and in 1904! This species is a prominent feature in the autumn flora of the North Bull, where large areas of the sandy and peaty flats towards the southern end are tinged a dark brown by the close-set fruiting spikes.

2	(3)	5

Rare in dune-slacks and salt-marshes on the northern part of the coast.
2. Scattered along the coast between Skerries and Loughshinny, DD/83, 90. Still between Balbriggan and Hampton, in a coastal marsh at Fancourt, DD/88.
5. Still on North Bull Island, in dune-slacks east of The Farm and abundant in dune-slacks nearby, MS/74, J.E. Fitzharris/74, HJH/85 & DD/86. On the Royal Dublin Golf-course, PG, DN/93.

Schoenus

S. nigricans L.
Black Bog-rush   Native

Colgan: 2. Plentiful on wet banks, seaside between Balbriggan and Skerries: *Mack. Rar.*, 1806. Abundant here, 1904, spreading along moist drift banks for about a mile and a half from Hampton Hall to near Balbriggan, also rather sparingly between Skerries and Loughshinny, 1903: *N.C.* 3. Talbot's Bay and Carnoon Bay: *Flor. Lambay.* In several of the moist hollows of Portrane sandhills, 1904: *N.C.* 5. Plentiful at Portmarnock sands and between Baldoyle and Howth: *Mack. Cat.* Sparingly in two or three places near the southern end of Portmarnock sandhills, 1903; at Bellingham's Harbour and frequent on the east side of Howth Head, 1900; 6. In a marsh by the Grand Canal at Hazelhatch, 1902: *N.C.* 8. At the foot of the Dublin mountains, especially near Stagstown, *Wade Dubl.*

Suppl: Not confirmed from either of its inland stations at Hazelhatch or Stagstown.

DNFC Annual Report for 1968: 7. Report of discovery "near Tallaght" of a new station. No further details, but known to be Whitestown, Tallaght (fide DD).

2	3	5	(6)	7	(8)

Rare, in coastal marshes, dune-slacks and other habitats near the coast where the ground water percolates through drift deposits.
2. Still by the shore between Skerries and Loughshinny, DD/83. Still on a sloping bank near the shore at Hampton Hall, RF/90.
3. Dune-slacks on the southern part of Malahide Island Peninsula and nearby east of Corballis Road at Donabate, DD/82 & PR/85.
5. Still in dune-slacks midway along western side of Portmarnock Peninsula, DN, RF/88. One clump by the Whitewater Brook, Howth, PG/90.
7. Whitestown, Tallaght, DNFC/68.

Carex

C. paniculata L.
Greater Tussock-sedge   Native

Colgan: 7. Abundant by the main stream of the Dodder above Cobb's Lodge, 1895: *Praeger.* In two places on the right bank of the Cot Brook, Upper Dodder, 1901: *N.C.* 8. Abundant in a marsh on Glencullen mountain, 1902 *(N.C.)*; abundant by the steam draining the marsh near Ballybetagh House, 1902 *(Praeger) Colgan 1903.* Also recorded in *Wade Rar.*, 1804, for Curragha Bog, and in *Irish Flora*, 1833, for marshes at Howth, in both of which stations, the first being doubtfully in Co. Dublin, the plant has become extinct.

Suppl: 7. Still at Upper Dodder (1939). 8. Still in marsh near Ballybetagh House (1955). Not confirmed from Glencullen Mountain.

4	6	7	8

Rare in bogs, canals and marshes.
4. Edge of the Royal Canal west of Collins Bridge, MN/88, **NDR**.
6. By a stream, east of Athgoe Castle, JP/86, **NDR**.
7. River Dodder, east of Glenasmole Lodge, DNFC/86.
8. Ballybetagh Bog and along the stream draining the bog, DNFC/83 & SR, JR/87. Still in the Glencullen Valley south of the Glencullen River at over 300 m, SR, JR/84.

C. diandra Schrank *(C. teretiuscula)*
Lesser Tussock-sedge   Native

Colgan: 4. Sparingly by the Royal Canal above Clonsilla, 1893; *Colgan 1893.* In considerable quantity by the Royal Canal below Lucan station, and frequent thence down the canal by Clonsilla to Blanchardstown, 1903: *N.C.* An abundant species in Westmeath, and no doubt introduced thence by the canal into Co. Dublin.

(4)	(5)

Not recently refound at any of its stations in the county. The former site at Raheny Quarries (5) *(Suppl)* has been filled in.

C. otrubae Popd. *(C. vulpina)*
False Fox-sedge   Native

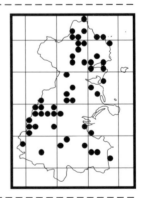

I	2	3	4	5	6	7	8

Occasional in ditches and marshes, especially near the sea.
FID.

C. otrubae × C. remota (C. × pseudoaxillaris K. Richter; *C. axillaris*)

Colgan: 5. A few tufts in marshy ground by the railway near Malahide in association with *Carex vulpina, C. remota* and *C. divulsa*, 1894 *(N.C.) Ir. Nat.*, 1894, p. 202. 6. At Castle Bagot, Milltown, 1903: *Colgan 1904.* This plant is considered by some authors to be a hybrid between *C. muricata* and *C. remota*, but it is more probably due to the crossing of *C. remota* and *C. vulpina.* The two last named species are frequent throughout County Dublin, where *C. muricata* is extremely rare. Variable, like all hybrids, the Malahide plant having much branched female spikelets while those of the Castle Bagot plant are almost simple.

Suppl: 5. Confirmed from station near Malahide railway sidings (1928). 6. Not confirmed from Castlebagot.

(6)

Very rare.
5. Many plants in a roadside drain south of Malahide Castle, DD/89 & DD, M. Ward/90. This site is near the railway at Malahide where it was first found by Colgan, though it has not been seen there recently, despite a careful search in 1989.

- -

C. spicata Hudson
Spiked Sedge   Native

7

Extremely rare, in damp grassland.
7. Field by the River Dodder near the bridge at Oldbawn, JP, DD/83, **NCR**.

- -

C. muricata L. subsp. **lamprocarpa** Celak *(C. pairaei)*
Prickly Sedge   Native

Colgan: 8. Near Stepaside on the way to Holly Park *(Moore) Cyb.* Also recorded for 1. "Curragha, Co. Dublin": but the habitat given for both stations renders the records dubious, so that the claim of this species to a place in the county flora rests mainly on Dr Moore's record. Mr R.M. Barrington has observed the plant growing in 1902, and for many years previously, at Fassaroe, Co. Wicklow just outside the Dublin boundary.
Suppl: 8. Still at Moore's station near Stepaside (1956), although Colgan does not appear to have seen it there. By Scalp road about a quarter of a mile S. of Stepaside (J.P. Brunker, 1936). Large tuft on Old Connaught-Ballyman road near county boundary (R.W. Scully, 1916).

8

Extremely rare.
8. Roadside bank on the Kilgobbin Road just south-east of Sandyford Cross Roads, PC/73-79, 88. This is very close to and may be identical to D. Moore's *(Cybele)* record from "Near Stepaside on the way to Holly Park."

- -

C. divulsa Stokes
Grey Sedge   Native

Colgan: 1. At Westpalstown, at Brown's Cross, and at Mullahow, 1902; near Rowlestown, 1893; &c. 2. Near Balbriggan, 1900; at Man of War, 1902; &c. 3. At Roganstown, at Chapelmidway, &c., 1893: *N.C.* 4. At Castleknock *(More) Rec Add.* At St Catherine's, 1894, and near Lucan, 1895: *N.C.* 5. Near Feltrim Hill *(More) Rec. Add.* Near Kinsaley, &c., 1893: *N.C.* 8. Found in grassy hedges going from Dublin to Killiney Bay, 1814: *Templeton MS.* Grassy hedges near Killiney Bay: *Flor. Hib.* Abundant in hedgebanks in Caubawn Lane, near Killiney Bay, 1893: *N.C.*

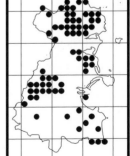

| 1 | 2 | 3 | 4 | 5 | 6 | 7 | 8 |

Occasional on dry sandy roadsides and hedgebanks in the lowlands.

C. arenaria L.
Sand Sedge   Native

| 2 | 3 | 5 | 8 |

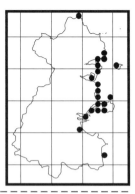

Very common on semi-consolidated sand-dunes in 2, 3 & 5; rare in 8.
8. Coast, south of Killiney, SR/86. Near Merrion Gates, on a wall,
    DN/92.

C. disticha Hudson
Brown Sedge   Native

| I | 2 | 3 | 4 | 5 | (6) | 7 | 8 |

Occasional in damp grassland and marshes in the lowlands; rare elsewhere.
5. Damp field near Portmarnock Brickfields, DN/88.
8. Three Rock Mountain above Barnacullia, HOR/83. By Burrow Road at Ballyedmonduff,
    HOR/85. Booterstown Marsh, SR, HOR/85. Small marsh near the Roadstone Works at
    Ballycorus, SR, JR/84.

C. divisa Hudson
Divided Sedge   Native

*Colgan: 5. Along the side of a ditch in the marshes of the North Strand; still growing there in some plenty in 1866
(Moore) Cyb. Nearly extinct in the preceding station but two large and flourishing patches were found in 1871 in a
damp meadow close to the glass works on the north bank of the Liffey (More) Rec. Add. A large patch about 5 yards
square near the south end of the East Wall, 1894, the same station as the preceding: (N.C.) Cyb. II. & MS. The East Wall
station has been much changed since 1894 by the building of sheds and storage of timber, and it is to be feared that
this rare species may have become extinct. A search made for it in 1903 was unsuccessful, but as some likely ground in
the vicinity could not then be fully examined the plant may possibly survive in small quantity: N.C.*

| (5) |

Not recorded for many years from the county and probably extinct.

C. remota L.
Remote Sedge   Native

| I | 2 | 3 | 4 | 5 | 6 | 7 | 8 |

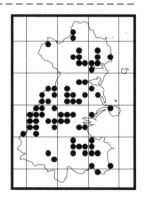

Occasional in hedgerows, drains, deciduous woodland
and damp grassland.

C. ovalis Gooden.
Oval Sedge   Native

| 1 | (2) | 4 | (5) | 6 | 7 | 8 |

Common in damp grassland in the uplands; rare elsewhere.
4. Damp bank behind the church on Ballygall Road, Finglas, DD/67. Damp grassland in the
   Phoenix Park, JS, MN/86. Roadside verge near Huntstown, MN/86.
FID.

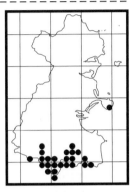

C. echinata Murray
Star Sedge   Native

Colgan: 3. In a marsh to the north of Portrane peninsula, 1895; 4. Sparingly by the
Tolka above Blanchardstown, and 5. Frequent on Howth Head, 1904: *N.C.*

| (3) | (4) | 5 | 6 | 7 | 8 |

Common in acid moorland pools and other wet areas on peat
or mineral soil in the uplands.

C. dioica L.
Dioecious Sedge   Native

Colgan: 5. In a marsh on the east end of the Hill of Howth; *Mack. Rar.* not seen here recently and perhaps extinct. 6.
Abundant in a marsh by the Grand Canal at Hazelhatch, 1893; 8. Sparingly in a wet bog on the south-east slope of the
Two Rock, 1895; on Kilmashogue mountain, 1903: *N.C.*
Suppl: 7. Foot of Seecawn, Glenasmole (J.P. Brunker, 1920-1955), and above Killakee (A.W. Stelfox, 1923). Bog on
Featherbed Mountain near corner of Military Road at 1, 300 ft. (A.W. Stelfox, 1923).
DNFC Annual Report for 1968: 7. Report of discovery "near Tallaght" of a new station. No further details, but known to
be Whitestown, Tallaght (fide DD).

| (5) | (6) | 7 | 8 |

Extremely rare.
7. Whitestown, Tallaght, DNFC/68. Wet flush on the south-east slope of Ballymorefinn Hill,
   DN/90. Marsh in the Ballinascorney Gap, CB/92.
8. Wet area east of the road and south of the stream at Ballyedmonduff, HOR, SR/86. By the
   Ballyman Glen Bridge, on the county boundary, SR, HOR/86.

C. curta Gooden.
White Sedge   Native

Colgan: 1. Curragha Bog, County Dublin: *Wade Rar.* 8. Foot of the Three Rock mountain above Marley: *Ir. Flor.* Though
this species has not been recently recorded for County Dublin there is no reason to doubt the accuracy of the above
records. Curragha Bog is now drained away, but further search in the mountain bogs is not unlikely to corroborate the
Irish Flora record.

| (1) | (8) |

C. hirta L.
Hairy Sedge   Native

| (1) | 2 | 3 | 4 | 5 | 6 | 7 | 8 |

Common in damp grassland and rarely on waste ground.
FID.

C. acutiformis Ehrh. *(C. paludosa)*
Lesser Pond-sedge   Native

Colgan: 3. By the Ward river near Chapelmidway, 1895, and at intervals from Knockesdan to near Swords, 1903; 4. Abundant at intervals by the Tolka river from Damastown to Blanchardstown, and sparingly by the Royal Canal near Blanchardstown, 1903; 5. Abundant in marshy ground near Raheny quarries 1894; and 6. Abundant in a swamp beyond Lucan Crescent 1897: *N.C.* 7. Banks of the Grand Canal *(Moore) Cyb.* By a mill-race near Old Bawn, 1895, and in ditches near Drimnagh, 1900: *N.C.*

Suppl: 3. By Broadmeadow Water S.E. of Fieldstown Bridge (1947). 6. Grand Canal near Gollierstown (J.P. Brunker, 1924). Near Hazelhatch (1956). 7. Swampy slope on W. side of Glenasmole (A.W. Stelfox, 1929). Grand Canal above Clondalkin (1941) and below Clondalkin (A.W. Stelfox, 1946).

| 2 | 3 | 4 | 5 | 6 | (7) |

Occasional in marshes, ponds, canals and rivers, and on their banks.
2. Marsh, 1 km west of Loughshinny, DD/87, **NDR**.
3. Knocksedan Reservoir, PR, MN/85. Brackenstown House, RF/86.
4. Kilmartin House 3.5 km north of Mulhuddart, MN/83.
5. Pond in the grounds of Malahide Castle, DN/90.
6. South of Badgerhill, JP/86. 3 km north of Newcastle, JP, DAS/84. West of the 12th lock, Grand Canal, SR/89.

C. riparia Curtis
Greater Pond-sedge   Native

Colgan: 2. Abundant in ditches near Balrothery, 1900, and near New Haggard, 1902: *N.C.* 3. Ditches near the shore at Donabate *(Moore) Cyb.* abundant here in 1893 in roadside ditches between Donabate and Portrane, but much reduced by drainage in 1901! Abundant around Donabate and Turvey, 1902; in ditches by the Ward river near Coolatrath, 1894; and 4. Abundant in ditches near Dunsoghly castle, 1903: *N.C.* 5. At Santry near Dublin *(Dr Scott)* Templeton *MS.* Abundant in Baldoyle Pits, and in ditches near Kilbarrick, &c., 1903; pools by the railway near Killester quarries, 1904; and 8. Sparingly near the mouth of the Shanganagh river, 1904: *N.C.*

Suppl: 6. Marsh by S. side of Grand Canal at Hazelhatch (1956). 7. Bushy Park (1945).

| (2) | 3 | 4 | (5) | (6) | (7) | (8) |

Rare, in drains near the sea.
3. Still around Donabate in a drain, 1 km east of Corballis House, PR/83. Drain, 1 km west of Portrane, PR/85.
4. Still in a ditch, west of Dunsoghly Castle, DD/76 & MN/83.

C. rostrata Stokes *(C. ampullacea)*
Bottle Sedge   Native

Suppl: 8. Ballybetagh Bog (A.W. Stelfox, 1920) - still there (1956).

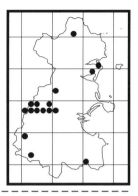

| (1) | 2 | 3 | 4 | (5) | 6 | (7) | 8 |

Occasional; Royal Canal, pools, reservoirs and bogs; rare in 7 & 8.
8. Still at the north end of Ballybetagh Bog, DNFC/83.

C. pendula Hudson
Pendulous Sedge   Native; introduced

Colgan: 3. In the moist part of Brackenstown wood: *Wade Rar.* 4. Woods by the Liffey near Lucan *(More) Cyb.*
Occasional by the Liffey from Lucan to below Woodlands, in Saint Catherine's wood, and frequent by the Liffey
alongside it, 1904: *N.C.* In Woodlands, 1900: *Miss Hunter.* 5. In Santry wood: *Wade Rar.* Abundant by the Santry river
below the wood, 1894; 6. Frequent by the Liffey from below the Salmon Leap to near Lucan, 1894-1904: *N.C.* 7. In a
ditch by the pathway from Dublin to Milltown, 1799: *Templeton MS.* Ditches near Drimnagh, 1882-1901; by the stream
in Lansdown Valley and sparingly by the canal near Leeson Street Bridge, 1893; along the mill-race by the Liffey above
Palmerstown, 1895; sparingly by the river below Chapelizod, 1902; abundant by the old City Water course at Tongue
Fields near Mount Argus, 1893-1903: *N.C.* By the Dodder above Rathgar, 1894: *Praeger.* 8. Frequent along the stream
near Glendruid, 1893, and above Carrickmines, 1899: *N.C.*

Suppl: 2. Milverton near Skerries (J.P. Brunker, 1912). Still at most of Colgan's stations in other districts.

| 1 | (2) | 3 | 4 | 5 | 6 | 7 | 8 |

Occasional in damp ground and hedgerows; often by streams.

C. sylvatica Hudson
Wood-sedge   Native

| 1 | (2) | 3 | 4 | 5 | 6 | 7 | 8 |

Occasional in base-rich deciduous woodlands and
shaded hedgerows.

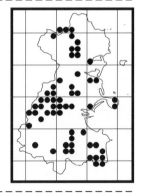

C. strigosa Hudson
Thin-spiked Wood-sedge   Native

Colgan: 3. Shady ditch banks by the Oldtown road about a mile north of Kilsallaghan, 1893 *(N.C.) Cyb. II. & MS.* 4.
Luttrell's town wood (Woodlands), rather common: *Wade Rar.* 5. At Marino near Dublin *(Dawson Turner) Mack. Rar.* -
there is a specimen from this locality in the Admiral Jones Herb., *S. & A Museum, Dublin.* 7. Hedgerows near Drimnagh,
1893: *Colgan 1893.* and in 1900!

Suppl: 3. Still N. of Kilsallaghan(A.W. Stelfox, 1923). 4. Still at Luttrellstown (1957). 7. Glenasmole, E. end of upper dam
(A.W. Stelfox, 1926). No longer there (A.W. Stelfox, 1946). By the road from Mount Venus to Rockbrook. Bushy Park,
Terenure (1956).

(3)	4	(5)	(7)

Extremely rare, in wooded valleys.
4. A single tussock by a streamside in the Tolka River Valley at Cardiff's Bridge, MN/83. Abundant by a stream on Luttrellstown Estate, MN/85, 86.

C. flacca Schreber *(C. glauca)*
Glaucous Sedge   Native

I	2	3	4	5	6	7	8

Widespread and common in grassland, on banks and by the canals.
FID.

C. panicea L.
Carnation Sedge   Native

(1)	2	(3)	4	5	6	7	8

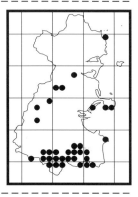

Occasional in marshes and by canals in the lowlands; commoner on higher ground.
2. Marsh on the coast north of Loughshinny, RF/90.

- -

C. laevigata Smith
Smooth-stalked Sedge   Native

Colgan: 7. Kelly's glen *(Moore) Cyb.* By the Slade in Glenasmole (Kelly's glen), 1903: *(W.H. Bloomer & N.C.) Colgan 1904.*
8. In a marsh on the south-east slope of Kilmashogue mountain, 1894: *Colgan 1895.* Abundant here in alder swamps along the course of the Peacock stream, 1903: *N.C.*
Suppl: 7. Still in Glenasmole by the stream between Corrig and Ballymorefinn (1942). Swamp in valley S.W. of Jobstown (Lugmore Glen). 8. Still on Kilmashogue (1957).

7	8

Rare, by streamsides in the uplands; frequent by three streams in Glenasmole (7).
7. Northern sections of the Cot and Slade Brooks on Kippure, HOR/85. Side of a stream flowing down between Corrig Mountain and Ballymorefinn on the west side of the Glenasmole Valley, DD, HJH, SR, DN/87. North facing lower slopes of Kippure on sides of the River Dodder gorge at 300m, SR, HOR/85.
8. Streamside on the south-east slope of Glendoo, HOR, CB/86. Stream south-east of Boranaraltry Bridge, SR, HOR/85. Stream below the Cromlech, west of Kiltiernan, SR, HOR/86. Marsh east of and below Barnacullia, SR/88.

C. binervis Smith
Green-ribbed Sedge   Native

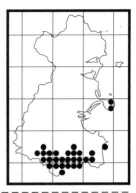

| 5 | (6) | 7 | 8 |

Common in wet peat or acid mineral soils (moorland); rare
on Howth Head (5).
5. Kilrock Quarries, Howth Head, PG/87, 88. Ben of Howth,
   DN/89. Drumleck, DN, PG/90.

C. distans L.
Distant Sedge   Native

Colgan: 8. Sparingly on wet rocks near the foot of Killiney Hill, 1902, perhaps the only station in this district: *N.C.*

| 2 | 3 | 5 | 8 |

Common in upper parts of rocky shores in seepage areas and salt-marshes. Frequent in 2, 3
and 5; rare in 8.
8. Still at Whiterock, Killiney, SR/85. Booterstown Marsh, DD/82. Dalkey Island, DN, SR/90.

C. distans x **C. hostiana (C.** x **muelleriana** F. Schultz)
Native
In Stace (1975, 1991) with no details of its locality. Not refound during the present survey.

C. extensa Gooden.
Long-bracted Sedge   Native

| 2 | (3) | 5 |

Occasional in salt-marshes and rocky sea shores north of the River Liffey.

C. hostiana DC. *(C. hornschuchiana)*
Tawny Sedge   Native

Colgan: 3. Abundant in a marsh by the shore north of Portrane peninsula, 1895; and 4. In marshy pastures at Dunsoghly,
1903: *N.C.* 5. At Portmarnock: *Guide.* Marsh near the Summit of Howth: *Flor. Howth* and in 1893! 6. In swampy ground
north of Slieve Thoul, 1895; by the Grand Canal above Clondalkin, 1903; 7. Marsh above Killakee, 1893; abundant in wet
pasture below St Anne's, Glenasmole, 1895; 8. Abundant on Kilmashogue mountain, 1903: *N.C.*

| (3) | (4) | (5) | (6) | 7 | 8 |

Rare, in marshes and flushes in the uplands.
7. Still in Glenasmole, KF/63. Marshy meadow 400 m north-west of St Ann's Chapel,
   Glenasmole, SR, DD/88.
8. Wet slope, south-east of Boranaraltry Bridge, SR, HOR/84. South of Ballybetagh Bog on
   the county boundary, SR, CB/89.

C. hostiana x C. viridula (C. x fulva Gooden.)
Native

Suppl: ...frequent between roadside and Lower Brittas pond (A.W. Stelfox, in I.N. XXXII, 1923). Still there (1956).

| (6) | 8 |

Extremely rare, in damp grassland. Not refound, despite careful search at Brittas Ponds (6).
8. Damp meadow, south of Ballybetagh Bog on the county boundary, SR/89.

C. viridula Michaux (C. flava)
Yellow-sedge   Native

| (1) | 2 | (3) | 4 | 5 | 6 | 7 | 8 |

----

subsp. brachyrrhyncha (Celak.) B. Schmid (C. lepidocarpa)
Native

| (1) | 2 | (3) | 4 | 5 | (6) | 7 | 8 |

Rare in marshes.
2. Marsh on the shore south of Skerries, DD/83.
4. Marsh immediately north of the 'Rabbit Warren' at Luttrellstown, JS/83. River Tolka Valley at and west of Blanchardstown, MN, GS/83 & DD/88.
5. Marsh at Kilrock, Howth, PG/87, 88.
7. Marsh at St Ann's Chapel, Glenasmole, DNFC/88. Wood in Glenasmole, DK/86.
8. South of Ballybetagh Bog on the county boundary, SR, DD, CB/87. Field between Ballycorus and Barnaslingan Lane, SR, HOR/84. Ballyman Glen Bridge, SR, HOR/86.

----

subsp. oedocarpa (Andersson) B. Schmid (C. demissa)
Native

| 6 | 7 | 8 |

Frequent in wet flushes and boggy ground.

----

subsp. viridula (C. serotina)
Native
Listed in CC2 from Co. Dublin but not seen during the present survey.

C. pallescens L.
Pale Sedge   Native

Colgan: 5. In moist meadows at Howth: Ir. Flor. not seen here recently. 7. Kelly's glen: Mack. Cat. Moist grassy places by the upper reservoir near Ballymorefinn, Glenasmole (Kelly's glen), 1903: (W.H. Bloomer & N.C.) Colgan 1904. The record in Wade Rar., 1804, for Curragha Bog has never been confirmed and the locality is doubtfully in Co. Dublin.
Suppl: 7. Very common in Colgan's station on slope E. of upper reservoir Glenasmole (J.P. Brunker, 1921-1956).

| (5) | 7 |

Extremely rare, in marshes.
7. Still in Glenasmole, in a marsh 300 m north-west of St Ann's Chapel, Glenasmole, SR/88.

C. caryophyllea Latour. *(C. praecox)*
Spring Sedge   Native

| 2 | (3) | 4 | 5 | 6 | 7 | 8 |

Frequent in heathland and unimproved pastures in the uplands; rare elsewhere.
2. Occasional in coastal grassland between Skerries and Loughshinny, DD/91.
4. Embankment of a roadside in the Phoenix Park, and near the Magazine Fort, DD/82 & MN/86.
5. Heathland south of Casana Rock and west of Fox Hole, Howth, CB/92.
8. Rear of Burton Hall near Sandyford Industrial Estate, HOR/84.

- -

C. pilulifera L.
Pill Sedge   Native

Suppl: 3. Freshwater Bay, Lambay (Praeger, 1907).

| (3) | 5 | (6) | 7 | 8 |

Occasional in heathland and moorland; sometimes locally frequent and probably under-recorded. Rare in the lowlands.
5. Still on Howth amongst bracken, north-west of The Summit, CB/92.

- -

C. aquatilis Wahlenb.
Water Sedge   Native

Colgan: 7. Sparingly by the shore of the Rathmines Waterworks reservoir in Glenasmole, 1896-1900 *(N.C.) Ir. Nat.*, 1901, p. 49 still there in 1904, one large patch covering a couple of square yards! So far, this species has not been found in any station in the mountains about Glenasmole whence it might have spread to the reservoir or large artifical lake formed in 1888 by the damming of the Dodder river for the Rathmines Waterworks. Yet it seems more reasonable to suppose that the plant does exist somewhere in these mountains than to assume its accidental introduction in the course of planting the slopes adjoining the reservoir.

Suppl: 7. One large patch still at Colgan's station in Glenasmole, and a second patch covering about 10 x 5 yards some fifty yards further north (J.P. Brunker, 1919-1957).

| 7 |

Extremely rare.
7. Still in Glenasmole at the south end of the northern reservoir, SR/89.

- -

C. acuta L.
Slender Tufted-sedge   Native

| 4 | (5) |

Occasional in damp grassland and marshes in the River Tolka Valley (4). The record from Howth (5) derives from an unconfirmed 19th century record of Mr Underwood from marshes at Howth (*Colgan*). Vegetative material, which may well be this species, has been seen recently in Bog of the Ring (1) and needs confirmation.
4. In River Tolka Valley: at and west of Blanchardstown, MN/83, **NDR**; at and 1 km west of Mulhuddart, MN/83, 88.

C. nigra (L.) Reichard (*C. vulgaris*)
Common Sedge　　Native

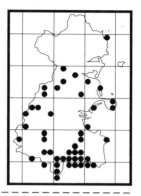

(1)	2	3	4	5	6	7	8

Occasional in marshes and by canals; frequent in 8.

C. pulicaris L.
Flea Sedge　　Native

(3)	(4)	5	6	7	8

Common in moorland and marshes in the uplands. Not seen recently at any of its lowland sites in the county.
5. Marsh at Kilrock, Howth, PG/87, 88.

POACEAE (*GRAMINEAE*)

Nardus

N. stricta L.
Mat-grass　　Native

Colgan: 3. Lambay island: *Flor. Lambay.* 5. On Ireland's Eye and frequent on Howth Head: *Flor. Howth.*

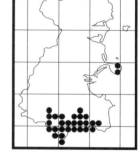

(3)	5	(6)	7	8

Common in heathland and moorland in the mountains.
Not seen recently on Lambay Island (3) or Ireland's Eye (5).

Milium

M. effusum L.
Wood Millet　　Native

Suppl: 5. Santry Court (1946). 7. Still in Bushy Park (1955). 8. Mount Merrion woods (1945-1957). Included only in Colgan's Appendix.

4	5	(7)	(8)

Very rare, in woodlands. Sometimes possibly planted. Not refound in Bushy Park, Terenure (7) or Mount Merrion Woods (8).
4. Occasional and localised in Luttrellstown, MN/85, **NDR**, 88. This site has since been partially cleared, MN/89. Shaded slopes near the River Tolka in the National Botanic Gardens, Glasnevin, MN/86, 88.
5. Still in Santry Woods, DD/80 & MN/88. Eastern side of St Anne's Park, Raheny, PG/87, 88.

Festuca

F. pratensis Hudson *(F. elatior)*
Meadow Fescue   Native

1	2	3	4	5	6	7	8

Common in damp pastures and on roadsides; occasional in 8.
FID.

F. arundinacea Schreber
Tall Fescue   Native

1	2	3	4	5	6	7	8

Occasional on roadside banks and neglected pastures. New to 1, 2 & 3. Widely sown in
north Co. Dublin and persists on roadsides.

F. gigantea (L.) Villars *(Bromus giganteus)*
Giant Fescue   Native

Colgan: 4. Between Glasnevin and Finglass Bridge: *Wade Dubl.* In Woodlands: *Mack. Cat.*, 1806 and in 1893! In Abbotstown
woods, 1895: *N.C.* 5. Santry and Kilmere (Kilmore) woods: *Ir. Flor.* Howth demesne: *Flor. Howth.* In Killester Park, 1903; and 6.
Abundant in Vesey's demesne, Lucan, 1904: *N.C.* 7. By the Dodder above Rathgar bridge, 1902 *(Praeger) Ir. Nat.*, 1902, p. 322.
8. At Ballinclea, 1903: *N.C.*

3	4	5	6	7	8

Occasional in woodlands and scrub in 4, 6, 7 & 8; especially frequent in the River Liffey Valley,
rare elsewhere.
3. Brackenstown Woods, RF, DD/84, **NDR**.
5. Woodland at the gate to Clontarf Castle, ENL/85. St Doolagh's Quarries, HJH/83. Still at
   Santry Woods, MN/90.

F. altissima All.
Wood Fescue   Native

7

Extremely rare.
7. Two clumps on a dark wooded slope on the south bank of the River Liffey, c. 1 km east of
   the Hermitage Golf-course, MN, JS/85, **NCR**.

F. arenaria Osbeck *(F. rubra subsp. arenaria)*
Rush-leaved Fescue   Native

5

5. North Bull Island, MAF/c.70.

F. rubra L.
Red Fescue   Native

1	2	3	4	5	6	7	8

Widespread and very common.
FID.

---

subsp. **rubra**

| 1 | 2 | 3 | 4 | 5 | 6 | 7 | 8 |

Very common on roadside banks and sandy soil inland, and in a variety of coastal habitats.

---

subsp. **juncea** (Hackel) K. Richter (*F. rubra* subsp. *pruinosa*)

| 2 | 5 | 8 |

Occasional on rocky soils on the coast in the maritime spray zone.
2. Rocks in the spray zone at Cardy Point, DD/87. Barnageeragh, DD/90.
5. Just west of the Nose of Howth, CB/90.
8. Land end of the West Pier at Dun Laoghaire, HOR/86. Cliffs north of Sorrento Point, opposite Dalkey Island, SR/90. Dalkey Island, SR, DD/91. Cliffs and rocks at Killiney Bay, SR/87, 89.

---

subsp. **megastachys** Gaudin (*F. rubra* subsp. *multiflora*)

| 6 |

6. Roadsides near Colganstown House, JP, MWJ/87.

F. ovina L.
Sheep's-fescue   Native

| (1) | (2) | 3 | (4) | 5 | 6 | 7 | 8 |

Common in dry upland grassland, heathland and on leached sand-dunes.

F. vivipara (L.) Smith
Viviparous Sheep's-fescue   Native
This species has been recorded from Dublin by MAF/64-69 (Farragher 1973), as **F. ovina** subsp. **ovina** var **vivipara**, but was not noted in the present survey.

F. pratensis x **Lolium perenne** (x **Festulolium loliaceum** (Hudson) P. Fourn.)
Native

| 1 | 3 | 4 | 5 | 6 | 7 | 8 |

Occasional in damp grassland, especially in river valleys; rare on waste ground.

F. pratensis x **Lolium multiflorum** (x **Festulolium braunii** (K. Richter) A. Camus)
Native

| 6 |

Extremely rare, in disturbed ground.
6. Waste ground at Clondalkin, MAF/69. Path, by the Grand Canal at Clondalkin, MS/72.

Lolium

L. perenne L.
Perennial Rye-grass   Native; planted

| 1 | 2 | 3 | 4 | 5 | 6 | 7 | 8 |

Widespread and abundant in all types of grasslands. Commonly sown for silage.
FID.

L. perenne x **L. multiflorum (L.** x **boucheanum** Kunth)
Native

| 7 | 8 |

Rare, on waste ground.
7. Bank of the Grand Canal near Grand Canal Street Bridge, PWJ, MSS/80.
8. Neglected garden at Sandymount, P. Dowding/82.
FID.

L. multiflorum Lam. *(L. italicum)*
Italian Rye-grass   Alien

| 1 | 2 | 3 | 4 | 5 | 6 | 7 | 8 |

Common in grasslands. Commonly sown.
FID.

L. temulentum L.
Darnel   Alien

Colgan: 4. Potato fields and cornfields at Glasnevin *(J. White) Mack. Cat.* 5. Wheatfields about Howth and Baldoyle: *Ir. Flor.* Plentiful in cultivated land on the south side of Howth: *Flor. Howth.* 8. Potato and cornfields at Rochestown *(J. White) Mack. Cat.* Cultivated fields between Killiney and Loughlinstown: *Ir. Flor.*

Suppl: 7. Phoenix Yard, James's Street (1942), not seen recently. Not confirmed in any of Colgan's stations, where it appears to have been only a casual.

| (4) | (5) | (7) | (8) |

Not found recently in the county and probably extinct.

Vulpia

V. fasciculata (Forsskaol) Fritsch *(Festuca uniglumis, V. membranacea)*
Dune Fescue   Native

Colgan: 2. Sandy ground near Rogerstown coast-guard station 1900: *Colgan 1903.* 3. Sandhills at Portrane *(Moore) Cyb.* Abundant in sandy fallows north of the Portrane peninsula, 1900: *N.C.* 5. Portmarnock sands, 1824: *Mack. Cat.* and in 1869: *Herb. Hart.* On Ireland's Eye *(More) Cyb.* Sandy shore at Baldoyle *(H.C. Levinge) Hart 1891.*

| 2 | 3 | 5 |

Very rare, on bare or thinly vegetated ground in sand-dunes.

2. Still at Rogerstown Coast-Guard Station, DD/88.
3. Still locally common on the Portrane Peninsula, DD/94.
5. Extreme south end of North Bull Island, DD, RF/83 & SR, CB/88. Still occasional in Portmarnock sand-hills, DD/88.

V. bromoides (L.) Gray *(Festuca sciuroides)*
Squirreltail Fescue   Native

| (1) | 2 | 3 | 4 | 5 | 6 | 7 | 8 |

Occasional on walls, rock outcrops, leached sand-dunes and gravel.
FID.

V. myuros (L.) C. Gmelin *(Festuca myuros)*
Rat's-tail Fescue   Native

Colgan: 1. A few large tufts on a wall near Lispopple, 1894: *N.C.* 3. Sparingly on the railway at Donabate, 1902: *Colgan 1903.* 4. A few plants on a wall-top near Woodlands, 1900 *(N.C) Top Bot.* At Chapelizod, 1903 *(Praeger) Colgan 1903.* 5. At Howth; and 7. Near Donnybrook: *Guide.* 8. At Bray and Golden Ball *(More) Cyb. II.*

Suppl: 3. Wall top on main road a little N. of Swords (1945-1957). 4. On Navan branch railway at Clonsilla (1953). 6. Tram track near Embankment Station (R.W. Scully, 1918).

| (1) | (3) | 4 | 5 | (6) | 7 | 8 |

Rare, in waste ground and on gravel.
4. Level-crossing at Liffey Junction, Cabra, MN/88. East of Chapelizod Village, MN/88.
5. Sandy soil at the edge of Portmarnock Golf-course, DN/90.
7. Charlotte Quay at Grand Canal Harbour, Ringsend, DN/91. On gravel in waste ground at Islandbridge, DN/94.
8. Dry track by the Glencullen River, north-west of Glencullen Bridge, SR, HOR/84. Car park on the west side of Leopardstown Racecourse, SR/83. Open ground on Ringsend Dump, west of Irishtown Park, SR/90. By the link road from the roundabout north of Bray to the Shankill/Bray bypass, MWJ/92.

Cynosurus

C. cristatus L.
Crested Dog's-tail   Native

| 1 | 2 | 3 | 4 | 5 | 6 | 7 | 8 |

Widespread. Common in pastures and on waste ground in the lowlands.
FID.

Puccinellia

P. maritima (Hudson) Parl. *(Glyceria maritima)*
Common Saltmarsh-grass   Native

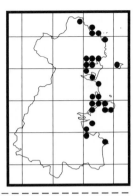

| 2 | 3 | 5 | 8 |

Common in saltmarshes and on rocks by the sea.

P. distans (Jacq.) Parl. *(Glyceria distans)*
Reflexed Saltmarsh-grass   Native

| 2 | 3 | 5 | 8 |

Occasional in muddy disturbed ground and on gravel by the sea.
2. Shore between Balleally and Rogerstown, DD/86. Head of Rogerstown Estuary, east of Daws Bridge, DN/90.
3. Occasional on the saltmarsh at the north end of the Portrane Peninsula, DD/88.
5. South end of Portmarnock Peninsula, DN/89. Near drains at Portmarnock, DN/89. Sea-front at Clontarf, DN/89. Beside Mayne River, north of Baldoyle, DN/89. Northern edge of the saltpan behind the foredunes, north of the wooden bridge on North Bull Island, PG/90.
8. Gravel at the land end of the West Pier at Dun Laoghaire, SR/88. Booterstown Marsh, SR/88. Gravel area south-east of Dun Laoghaire Swimming Baths, SR, JR/84. Seafront path, north of the Martello Tower at Sandymount, SR/87. Waste ground at Ringsend, MS/76 & SR, JR/90.

v

P. fasciculata (Torrey) E. Bickn. *(Glyceria borreri)*
Borrer's Saltmarsh-grass   Native

Colgan: 5. Plentiful in North Lotts, and –8. In the South Lotts, 1890 *(Scully) Cyb. II.* Plentiful at Sandymount and along Dublin Bay *(Moore) Cyb.* On paths in Blackrock Park, 1889: *More MS.* By the salt ditch along the railway near Booterstown, 1900-1901: *N.C.* Frequent in the clefts of the South Wall beyond the Pigeon House, 1902: *Colgan 1903.*

| 5 | 8 |

Very rare, usually in disturbed ground in salt-marshes. Legally protected in Ireland under the Wildlife Act of 1976 as an endangered species. Plants resembling **P. foucaudii** O.R. Holmberg occur on the shore west of Rogerstown (2). In some other respects they resemble **P. pseudodistans** (Crepin) Jansen & Wachter which is now included in **P. fasciculata**.
5. Plentiful in saltmarsh and along drains on either side of the Mayne River at Baldoyle, DN/89-91.
8. Locally abundant on the east side of Booterstown Marsh, C. Breen/71, SR/88-90.

Briza

B. media L.
Quaking-grass   Native

| 1 | 2 | 3 | 4 | 5 | 6 | 7 | 8 |

Common in calcareous grasslands and sand-dunes and on roadsides.
FID.

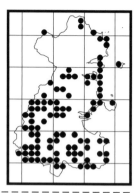

Poa

P. annua L.
Annual Meadow-grass   Native

| 1 | 2 | 3 | 4 | 5 | 6 | 7 | 8 |

Widespread and abundant on waste ground, paths and roadsides.
FID.

P. trivialis L.
Rough Meadow-grass   Native

| 1 | 2 | 3 | 4 | 5 | 6 | 7 | 8 |

Very widespread. Common on roadsides and in pastures.
FID.

P. humilis Ehrh. ex Hoffm. *(P. subcaerulea)*
Spreading Meadow-grass   Native

| 1 | 2 | 5 | 7 | 8 |

Common in sandy pastures by the sea and on wall tops. Not distinguished from **P. pratensis** in
Colgan or *Suppl.*

P. pratensis L.
Smooth Meadow-grass   Native

| 1 | 2 | 3 | 4 | 5 | 6 | 7 | 8 |

Abundant in meadows and on roadsides.
FID.

P. compressa L.
Flattened Meadow-grass   Alien

Colgan (Appendix): In *Wade Dubl.* this grass is recorded as found occasionally in the county on old walls and in dry places, and in *Cybele,* 1866, it is recorded on a much better authority, *John White's MS.,* as found in rocky ground at the foot of the Dublin mountains. This last locality is extremely vague, and as the plant does not appear to have been seen in Dublin for upwards of half a century, its claim for admission to the flora remains doubtful.

Brunker MS: 8. Wall by lane on S. side of Dodder between the bridges at Milltown, '48.

4	5	6	(7)	(8)

Very rare, on walls and roadsides. Not recorded by Colgan, and at that time it had not been seen in the county for over 50 years. First refound by A.W. Stelfox in 1920 in Rathmines (7) (Stelfox 1920, 1922a) and later in the same area by Brunker (Brunker 1948).

4. Wall of the National Botanic Gardens, Glasnevin, DS/88, **NDR.**
5. Garden wall near The Summit, Howth, ENL/84, **NDR.**
6. Roadside 1.25 km south of Brittas, JP/86, **NDR.** Roadside verge east of Colganstown House, JP/87.

- -

P. nemoralis L.
Wood Meadow-grass   Native

Colgan: 4. On the walls, &c., under the shade of the trees on the roadside near Lucan, northern road, 1799: *Templeton MS.* Between Luttrel's town and Lucan: *Wade Rar.* Common at Woodlands (Luttrel's town): *Mack. Cat.* On walls near Lucan *(More) Cyb.* and in 1904! Abundant in woods and on wall tops by the roadside at Woodlands, 1904: *N.C.* 5. Abundant in hedgerows and under trees at Ashbrook, Clontarf, 1903: *Miss C.G. O'Brien.* Abundant in St Anne's, Dollymount, 1904, N.C. 6. Frequent in Lucan demesne, 1894 *(N.C.) Cyb. II* and in 1904! 8. Sparingly in the grounds of Delbrook, Dundrum: *Tatlow 1898.*

Suppl. 4. Still at Luttrellstown (1953). In St. Catherine's (1956). 5. Still in St. Anne's (1956). 7. Wall of mill-dam at former Dartry Dye Works (1948-1957). 8. At Rockfield, Dundrum (R.W. Scully, 1918). Near Killiney railway station (1956). On Killiney Hill (1956).

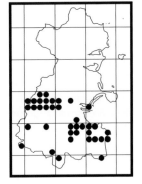

4	5	6	7	8

Common on walls, by tracks and in woods.

- -

Dactylis

D. glomerata L.
Cock's-foot   Native

1	2	3	4	5	6	7	8

Widespread and abundant on waste ground, roadsides and in neglected pastures.
FID.

Catabrosa

C. aquatica (L.) P. Beauv.
Whorl-grass   Native

(1) (2) (3) 4 5 6 (7) 8

Occasional in drains, ditches and on muddy soil. This species has declined this century through drainage of its marshy habitats particularly in the north of the county.
4. Marsh immediately north of the 'Rabbit Warren' at Luttrellstown, MN/85. Marshy field off the Ashbourne road near Cherryhound, MN/84. Drain west of Dunsoghly Castle, DD/84. Streamside leading into the River Tolka, north-west of Mulhuddart, MN/88.
5. Wet field north-west of Portmarnock, ENL/85. Streamside at Kilrock, Howth, PG/90, CB/91.
6. South end of Brittas Ponds, DD/83.
8. Field ditch by the Ticknock road, SR/87. Stream, now in a culvert, at Ballinteer Community School, SR/84. Ditch west of Kiltiernan, SR, HOR/85. Ballybetagh Bog, SR, JR/84, 87. By the bridge west of Ballyman House on the county boundary, SR/87.

Catapodium

C. rigidum (L.) C.E. Hubb. *(Festuca rigida, Desmazeria rigida)*
Fern-grass   Native

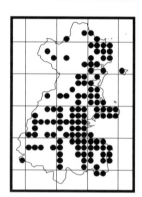

1 2 3 4 5 6 7 8

Occasional on dry sandy ground and walls. Var. **majus** (C. Presl) Laínz (subsp. **majus** (C. Presl.) F. Perring & Sell) has been recorded in several lowland localities, usually in urban sites. A complete range of intermediates between it and the type variety, var. **rigidum,** occur. FID.

C. marinum (L.) C.E. Hubb. *(Festuca rottboellioides, Desmazeria marina)*
Sea Fern-grass   Native

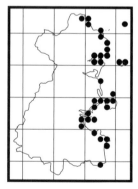

2 3 5 8

Occasional on shallow soils near the sea.
FID.

Parapholis

P. strigosa (Dumort.) C.E. Hubb. *(Lepturus filiformis)*
Hard-grass   Native

| 2 | 3 | 5 | (8) |

Occasional in salt-marshes and grassland near the sea.
2. North of Loughshinny, DD/90. Between Blake's Cross and Rush, KF/62.
3. Salt-marsh near the entrance to the Island Golf-course, Donabate and abundant over the north end of the Portrane Peninsula, PR, DD/84.
5. Salt-marsh at Malahide, R.Young/72. South end of Portmarnock Golf-course, DN, RF/88. Lawn at Clontarf Yacht Club, DN/89. Mayne River, north of Baldoyle, DN/90. Scattered in amenity grassland at the south end of Fairview Park, DD/82. Sandy ground near the Bull Wall on North Bull Island, MS/72. Abundant in moist areas at the south end of dunes, North Bull Island, DN/91.

P. incurva (L.) C.E. Hubb.
Curved Hard-grass   Native

| 5 |

Extremely rare, on shallow soils over rocks by the sea. The JRA/79 record was the first for this species in Ireland (Akeroyd 1984).
5. Martello Tower at Redrock, Sutton, JRA/79, JP/92. Steep boulder clay slope at the Baily Lighthouse, JRA/87.

Glyceria

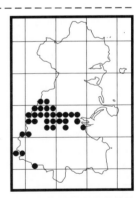

G. maxima (Hartman) O. Holmb. *(G. aquatica)*
Reed Sweet-grass   Native

| 4 | (5) | 6 | 7 | 8 |

Common in canals, lakes, reservoirs and large rivers; very rare in 8.
8. Damp area at Ringsend Dump, DNFC/83.
FID.

G. fluitans (L.) R. Br.
Floating Sweet-grass   Native

| I | 2 | 3 | 4 | 5 | 6 | 7 | 8 |

Common in drains, ditches and on stream sides and muddy ground.

G. fluitans x **G. notata** (**G.** x **pedicellata** F.Towns.)

| I | 2 | 3 | 4 | 6 | 7 | 8 |

Rare, in drains and on streamsides and muddy ground. Occasional in 4. Possibly under-recorded.
I. Broad Meadow River near Fieldstown House, SR/89.

2. Shaded drain in a cul-de-sac north of Wimbleton Lodge, DD/84.
3. Roganstown Bridge, SR/89. Wet ground by the Ward River at Knocksedan Bridge, MN/90.
6. Seepage area beside Brittas Ponds, DNFC/89.
7. Streamside at Oldcourt, Firhouse, JP, ENL/83. Marshy area, 500 m south-east of St Ann's Chapel in Glenasmole, DNFC/88. Stream-bed between Rockbrook and north of Mount Venus, DK, SR/88.
8. Marshy ground by a stream at Kilgobbin, PC/70. Damp field on the western side of Leopardstown Racecourse, SR, CB/89.

G. declinata Bréb.
Small Sweet-grass   Native

| 2 | 4 | 6 | 7 | 8 |

Rare, in muddy ground. Not recognised in *Colgan* or *Suppl.*
2. Open drain just east of Ballyboghil Village, DD/87. Bare muddy ground in a marsh west of the Corn Mill, near Balbriggan, DD/87.
4. Northern part of the Phoenix Park and nearby at the Hole-in-the-wall, DD/88. Cattle pool, near the northern border of the district west of Dublin Airport, MN/84.
6. Muddy ground about 1 km west and 1.25 km south-west of Brittas, DD/82 & JP/86.
7. Stream bank near Aghfarrel, JP/83. Muddy track at Castlekelly, DD, EMcA/83. Cot and Slade brooks at Castlekelly and Glenasmole Lodge, HOR/85. Piperstown Road east of Glenasmole Lodge, SR, HOR/85. Banks of a pond at Delaford, JP, DK/83. Muddy track at Cunard in Glenasmole, DD/89. Pools at Gallanstown, DD/92.
8. In the Glencullen Valley south-east of Ballybrack, off Walsh's Lane, SR, JR/86. Quarry pool on north facing slope of Three Rock Mountain, HOR, CB/86. Stream north of Glencullen Bridge, SR/88. Muddy sand by a stream near the bridge just east of Kilgobbin, PC/73. Field near Ballybrack in the Glencullen Valley, SR, JR/91.

G. notata Chevall. (*G. plicata*)
Plicate Sweet-grass   Native

Colgan: 1. Frequent near Bog of the Ring, near Brown's Cross, &c., 1902; 2. Abundant near Lusk, near Man of War, and 3. Near Donabate, 1902: *N.C.* 4. Near Glasnevin *(More) Cyb.* By the Royal Canal above Blanchardstown 5. Ditches near Baldoyle, and 6. Abundant by the Grand Canal from Hazelhatch to Lucan, 1902: *N.C.* 7. Near Drimnagh, 1902: *W.H. Bloomer.* Abundant near Ballyfermot, and 8. Near Carrickmines and Kilgobbin, 1902: *N.C.*

| (1) | 2 | 3 | 4 | 5 | 6 | 7 | 8 |

Common in drains, and on streamsides and muddy ground.

Melica

M. uniflora Retz.
Wood Melick   Native

Colgan: 4. In Luttrel's town wood (Woodlands): *Wade Dubl.* (as *M. nutans*). Abundant in Woodlands, and in Saint Catherine's wood, 1904; 6. Copses at Leixlip, and abundant in Lucan demesne, 1904; 7. Frequent in hedges and copses near Drimnagh, and 8. Sparingly in the Dingle, Glenamuck, 1900: *N.C.*
Suppl: 7. Drimnagh is now a built-up area and Colgan's station must be considered lost.

| 4 | 6 | 7 | 8 |

Occasional in woods in the River Liffey Valley; rare elsewhere.

4. Woods opposite Stewart's Hospital, Knockmaroon, MN, CB/85. Still at and west of Luttrellstown, DNFC/83 & JS, MN/84. St Catherine's Woods, DNFC/84. Chapelizod Gates in the Phoenix Park, MN/85.
6. Banks of the River Liffey east of Lucan demesne, JP/85.
7. East of the northern reservoir, Glenasmole, DK/c.65 & RMcM/83. South bank of River Liffey west of Wren's Nest Weir, MN, JS/85.
8. Woodland at the north end of Marley Park, ENL/84. The Dingle, HOR/83.

Helictotrichon

H. pubescens (Hudson) Pilger (*Avenula pubescens, Avena pubescens*)
Downy Oat-grass   Native

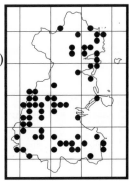

| I | 2 | 3 | 4 | 5 | 6 | 7 | 8 |

Common in sand-dunes, and inland in calcareous grassland; rare elsewhere.
FID.

Arrhenatherum

A. elatius (L.) P. Beauv. ex J. S. & C. Presl (*A. avenaceum*)
False Oat-grass   Native

| I | 2 | 3 | 4 | 5 | 6 | 7 | 8 |

Widespread and abundant on roadsides and in poorly maintained pastures and hedgerows.
FID.

---

var. **bulbosum** (Willd.) St Amans

| 2 | 8 |

The distribution and occurrence of this variety in the county is poorly known. It may be frequent.
2. Roadside and weedy tilled fields, north-east of Baldongan Cross Roads, RF/85.
8. Edge of tilled field, Laughanstown, SR/92.

Avena

A. strigosa Schreber
Bristle Oat   Alien

| 2 |

Occasional in tilled ground in 2.

A. fatua L.
Wild-oat   Alien

| 2 | 3 | 4 | 5 | 6 | 7 | 8 |

Occasional on roadsides and now becoming a troublesome weed of arable land, particularly in the north of the county. New to districts 2, 3, 5, 6, 7 & 8. First noted from a collection made by R.Ll. Praeger in 1894 from the Royal Canal near Dunsink (4) (**DBN**).
FID.

Trisetum

T. flavescens (L.) P. Beauv.
Yellow Oat-grass   Native

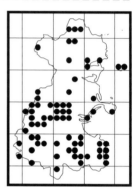

| I | 2 | 3 | 4 | 5 | 6 | 7 | 8 |

Occasional on sand-dunes and in calcareous grassland.
FID.

Koeleria

K. macrantha (Ledeb.) Schultes *(K. gracilis, K. cristata)*
Crested Hair-grass   Native

Colgan: 2. Banks by the sea south of Balbriggan, 1904; and 3. Abundant in sandy pastures and fallow fields, Portrane 1895: *N.C.* 5. On Howth: *Mack. Cat.* At Portmarnock: *Ir. Flor.* and in 1895! Frequent on Howth Head, 1903; on Feltrim Hill and on Carrick Hill, 1900; sandy pastures on the Cosh, 1901: *N.C.* 8. Near Sandymount: *Mack. Cat.* By the railway near Killiney, 1894: *N.C. Suppl:* 5. Still at Howth (1955) and Feltrim Hill (1946).

| 2 | 3 | 5 | (8) |

Rare, but locally abundant in sand-dunes and coastal grassland.
2. Cardy Point, DD/87. Grassland, 0.5 km north of Rush, DD/85. Scattered in coastal grassland between Skerries and Loughshinny, DD/83, 91.
3. Very common over sand-dunes and waste ground in the Island Golf-course, DD/82. Sand-dunes, north of Portrane, PR/85.
5. Abundant in sand-hills at Portmarnock, DD/84 & DN/89. North Bull Island, DK/c.65 & MS/66. Near the roundabout at the end of the causeway on North Bull Island, SR/89. Rocky ground just east of Kilrock, Howth, PG/90. Track, north-west of the pond at Greenhollows, Howth, DNFC/90.

Deschampsia

D. cespitosa (L.) P. Beauv.
Tufted Hair-grass   Native

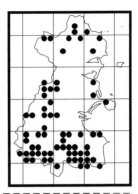

| 1 | 2 | 3 | 4 | 5 | 6 | 7 | 8 |

Occasional in neglected pastures, roadsides, damp grasslands and woodlands.

D. flexuosa (L.) Trin.
Wavy Hair-grass   Native

Suppl: Lambay, Howth and common on mountains.

| (3) | 5 | 6 | 7 | 8 |

Common on dry mineral or peaty soils (heathlands).
Not rediscovered on Lambay Island (3).

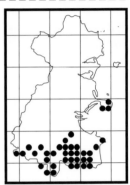

Holcus

H. lanatus L.
Yorkshire-fog   Native

| 1 | 2 | 3 | 4 | 5 | 6 | 7 | 8 |

Widespread and common in pastures, on roadsides and waste ground.
FID.

H. lanatus × **H. mollis** (**H. × hybridus** Wein)

| 8 |

Rare.

8. Still on a south facing slope of Two Rock Mountain where it was first found by MAF/c.70, SR, HOR/85. High ground above the east side of The Scalp, HOR/86. By the Bray Road south-west of Crinken, HOR/86. Roches Hill, SR/89.

H. mollis L.
Creeping Soft-grass   Native

| 1 | 2 | 3 | 4 | 5 | 6 | 7 | 8 |

Occasional on heathy ground, in woods and hedgerows, mainly on acidic soils.
4. Luttrellstown Woods, MN/86, **NDR**.
FID.

Aira

A. caryophyllea L.
Silver Hair-grass   Native

$\boxed{(1)}$ $\boxed{2}$ $\boxed{3}$ $\boxed{5}$ $\boxed{6}$ $\boxed{7}$ $\boxed{8}$

Occasional on dry sandy, usually base-poor, shallow soils.

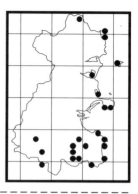

A. praecox L.
Early Hair-grass   Native

$\boxed{(1)}$ $\boxed{(2)}$ $\boxed{3}$ $\boxed{5}$ $\boxed{6}$ $\boxed{7}$ $\boxed{8}$

Occasional on dry sandy, usually base-poor, shallow soils.

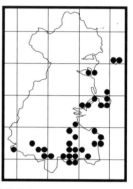

Anthoxanthum

A. odoratum L.
Sweet Vernal-grass   Native

$\boxed{1}$ $\boxed{2}$ $\boxed{3}$ $\boxed{4}$ $\boxed{5}$ $\boxed{6}$ $\boxed{7}$ $\boxed{8}$

Widespread and very common in pastures and on roadsides.
FID.

Phalaris

P. arundinacea L.
Reed Canary-grass   Native

$\boxed{1}$ $\boxed{2}$ $\boxed{3}$ $\boxed{4}$ $\boxed{5}$ $\boxed{6}$ $\boxed{7}$ $\boxed{8}$

Common in and by canals, rivers and drains. A variegated form (cv. Picta) is commonly cultivated in gardens and occasionally becomes established in the wild as a garden discard.
FID.

P. canariensis L.

Canary-grass   Alien

| 2 | 4 | 5 | 7 | 8 |

Occasional on waste ground, disturbed ground, roadsides and footpath cracks; a casual which seldom persists. It is a common constituent of birdseed from which many records may be derived. Noted first by H.C. Hart between Baldoyle and Portmarnock (5) (**DBN**).
FID.

Agrostis

A. capillaris L. *(A. tenuis, A. vulgaris)*

Common Bent   Native

| 1 | 2 | 3 | 4 | 5 | 6 | 7 | 8 |

Very common in grassland and sand-dunes, and on roadsides and banks. Var. **aristata** (Parn.) Druce has been recorded from a roadside, Glasnevin (4) and by the 9th lock on the Grand Canal at Clondalkin (7), MAF/64-69.
FID.

A. gigantea Roth

Black Bent   Native

| 1 | 2 | 5 | 6 | 7 | 8 |

Occasional on the edges of arable fields and roadsides in 1 & 2. Not included in *Colgan* or *Suppl.* First recognized in a collection made by W.B. Bruce in 1905 from Skerries (2) (**DBN**).
5. Between Swords and Malahide, about 1.25 km east of Swords, ENL, DN/88.
7. Sides of the River Dodder at Firhouse, JP/85. Garden weed at Prospect House, DK/82. Weed in the flower-beds of T.C.D. Botanic Garden, DK/92.
8. Field margin, north-west of Sandyford Industrial Estate, SR/86. One patch at Ballyogan tiphead, SR, JR/94.

A. stolonifera L. *(A. alba)*

Creeping Bent   Native

| 1 | 2 | 3 | 4 | 5 | 6 | 7 | 8 |

Widespread and abundant in abandoned pastures, marshes and waste ground. Var. **palustris** (Huds.) Farw. has been recorded from the county, MAF/64-69.
FID.

A. canina L.

Velvet Bent   Native

Colgan: 1. Sparingly in Westown wood, near the Naul, 1894; 3. Near Rowlestown, 1893; and 5. Frequent on Howth Head, 1895: *N.C.* 6, 7, 8. Abundant on Slieve Thoul on Seecawn, on Mount Pelier, at Kilmashoge, &c., 1900-1903: *N.C.*

| (1) | (3) | 5 | 6 | 7 | 8 |

Common in upland grassland and heathland.

A. vinealis Schreber *(A. canina* subsp. *montana)*
Brown Bent   Native

6	8

Rare, in grassland. Probably under-recorded as it is easily mistaken for **A. canina** in which it
was formerly included.
6. Near Badgerhill, JP, ENL/87. Hedgerow at Knockandinny, JP/87. Fields, south and east of
    Esker, JP, ENL/87. Field margins, south of Ballymakaily Mill, JP/89.
8. North facing slope of Two Rock Mountain, SR/87. Roches Hill, SR/89.

- -

Ammophila

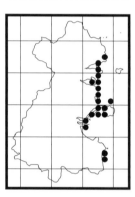

A. arenaria (L.) Link *(Psamma arenaria)*
Marram   Native

2	3	5	8

Abundant in sand-dunes. Common along the coasts in 2, 3 & 5;
rare in 8.
8. Sandy area, east of Pigeon House, SR, HOR/83. Shore below
    Killiney Railway station and to the south of Killiney SR,
    HOR/83 & SR/84.

- -

Alopecurus

A. pratensis L.
Meadow Foxtail   Native

I	2	3	4	5	6	7	8

Widespread and very common in pastures and on roadsides.
FID.

- -

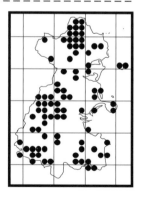

A. geniculatus L.
Marsh Foxtail   Native

I	2	3	4	5	6	7	8

Common in damp muddy areas, often forming large
stands near the sea.

A. myosuroides Hudson
Black-grass   Alien

| 2 | 4 | 5 |

Very rare.
2. Three large clumps in a cabbage field on the east side of the road near Corduff Hall, DD/85.
4. Base of a cut-away wooded slope at Luttrellstown, DD/91.
5. Alexandra Quay, Dublin Port, SR, JR/94.

Phleum

P. pratense L.
Timothy   Native

| I | 2 | 3 | 4 | 5 | 6 | 7 | 8 |

Widespread and very common in pastures and on roadsides.
FID.

P. bertolonii DC. (*P. pratense* subsp. *bertolonii*)
Smaller Cat's-tail   Native

| 6 | 8 |

Apparently rare but probably under-recorded because of its similarity to the previous species.
6. Fields, east of Athgoe Castle, JP/86, **NCR**.
8. Roadside at Barnacullia, SR/91. Grassy area between Oaktree Road and Brewery Road, Stillorgan, SR/92.

P. arenarium L.
Sand Cat's-tail   Native

| 2 | 3 | 5 | 8 |

Common in sand-dunes in 2, 3 & 5; rare in 8.
8. Sand-dunes at South Wall, east of Pigeon House, SR, HOR/83. Formerly recorded at Sandymount early last century but not refound there.

Bromus

B. racemosus L.
Smooth Brome   Native
Colgan: 4. About the Botanic Gardens, Glasnevin: *Wade Rar.* Along the banks of the Royal Canal near Lotts: *Ir. Flor.*
Brunker MS: 1. Bog of the Ring, '56.

| (1) | 4 |

Extremely rare.
4. Rediscovered in disturbed ground c. 1 km to south-west of St Margaret's, MN/90.

B. hordeaceus L. *(B. mollis)*
Soft-brome   Native

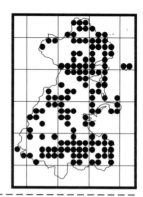

| 1 | 2 | 3 | 4 | 5 | 6 | 7 | 8 |

Common on waste and dry sandy ground especially near the sea.
Also in meadows where it often appears to have been sown.
FID.

B. hordeaceus x B. lepidus (B. x pseudothominei P.M. Smith; *B. thominei* auct. non Hardouin)

| (8) |

Not refound at Sandyford where it was recorded by M.J. Gorman in 1935; its first and only
site in the county.

B. lepidus O. Holmb.
Slender Soft-brome   Probably introduced

| (4) | 5 | 6 | 8 |

Rare. Not refound at its site at Cabra (4) where it had been found by W.B. Bruce in 1905 (**DBN**).
5. Sand-hills at the southern end of Malahide Island, west of Malahide, ENL/84.
6. Monastery Road, Clondalkin, MAF/64-69.
8. Gravel car park on the west side of Leopardstown Racecourse, SR/85.

Bromopsis

B. ramosa (Hudson) Holub *(Bromus asper, B. ramosus)*
Hairy-brome   Native

| 1 | 2 | 3 | 4 | 5 | 6 | 7 | 8 |

Common in shaded hedgerows and woodland.
FID.

B. erecta (Hudson) Fourr. *(Bromus erectus)*
Upright Brome   Native

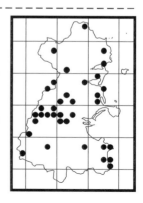

Colgan: 2. Roadside banks at Ballough, 1903; abundant along the railway cuttings from the
Delvin river to Rush, and 3. South of Donabate, 1904; on banks near Swords, 1902: *N.C.* 4.
"Found under hedges near Finglas: *Dr Scott*": *Mack. Rar.* Along the Royal Canal and river
Tolka (*J. White*) *Cyb.* Abundant at Finglas Quarries, 1894; on Knockmaroon Hills, 1902;
abundant along the Midland Railway from Broadstone to Clonsilla, and along rock cuttings
of the Royal Canal from Clonsilla to near Blanchardstown, 1903: *N.C.* 5. Sandy fields near
Kilbarrick church: *Ball 1839.* At Santry, 1895; in profusion on Baldoyle race-course, 1902;
abundant at Raheny quarries and along the railway from Raheny to Malahide and from

Howth Junction to Howth, 1904; &c. 6. Frequent along the Grand Canal and abundant along the railway from Hazelhatch to Clondalkin, and 7. From Clondalkin to Kingsbridge, 1903; banks near Tallaght, 1895; &c: N.C. 8. At Loughlinstown *(Scully) Cyb. II.* By the railway near Seapoint, below Killiney Hill, and between Shankill and Carrickmines, 1902: N.C. One of the characteristic grasses of Co. Dublin, abundant in many parts of the calcareous lowlands though apparently quite local elsewhere in Ireland. Its usual Dublin habitat is dry banks, but occasionally, as at Loughlinstown and Baldoyle, it grows in profusion in open pastures or meadows.

Suppl: 5. Feltrim Hill and St Doolagh's Quarries (1955). This is now a characteristic plant of railway cuttings and embankments and along the margins of both canals, besides having other stations. It has probably spread since Colgan's time.

| 1 | 2 | 3 | 4 | 5 | 6 | 7 | 8 |

Occasional on roadsides, railway banks, undisturbed grassland and in sand-hills. Sometimes locally abundant; rare in 7 & 8.
7. Tymon Lane, now overgrown, DK/83.
8. Short turf just east of the tower on Dalkey Hill, SR/91. Still in grassland, west of the Bray Road at Loughlinstown, SR, JR/84.

Anisantha

A. diandra (Roth) Tutin ex Tzvelev *(Bromus diandrus)*
Great Brome   Alien

| 2 | 3 |

Rare but locally common on sandy fallow and disturbed ground near the sea in 2 and 3.
2. Rogerstown sand-hills, DD/82, **NCR**.
3. Corballis, DD/84.

A. sterilis (L.) Nevski *(Bromus sterilis)*
Barren Brome   Native

| 1 | 2 | 3 | 4 | 5 | 6 | 7 | 8 |

Common on waste ground, and occasional on the edges of woodland and scrub and other open dry areas; usually near buildings. *FID.*

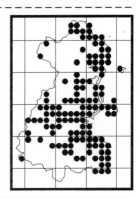

Ceratochloa

C. carinata (Hook. & Arn.) Tutin *(Bromus carinatus)*
California Brome   Alien

| 8 |

Very rare.
8. Grass verge on Pigeon House Road beside Ringsend Park, SR/87. This was its first Irish record (Reynolds 1988b). This site has since been re-seeded, but several plants survive by the road to the East Link Toll Bridge, SR/94.

417

Brachypodium

B. pinnatum (L.) P. Beauv.
Tor-grass   Possibly introduced in Co. Dublin

Suppl: 5. Tramline between Stella Maris and Summit, Howth (J.S. Thomson, *I.N.*, XXX, 1921). 8. By railway at Stillorgan Reservoir (J.P. Brunker, 1943).

| 5 | 8 |

Very rare, on abandoned railway and tram lines.
5. Still on Howth on a steep roadside bank at The Summit, ENL/84.
8. Still in Stillorgan on the disused railway line, on the south-west side of the reservoirs, SR/83, 84.

B. sylvaticum (Hudson) P. Beauv.
False Brome   Native

| I | 2 | 3 | 4 | 5 | 6 | 7 | 8 |

Widespread and common, shaded roadsides, hedgerows and woodlands.
FID.

Elymus

E. caninus (L.) L. *(Agropyron caninum)*
Bearded Couch   Native

Colgan: 4. Plentiful at Woodlands: *Mack. Cat.* and in 1904, in the wood and on wall-tops! At Saint Catherine's, 1895-1901: *N.C.* At Knockmaroon: *Ir. Flor.* 6. Abundant in Lucan demesne, 1895-1904; and 7. Sparingly by the Dodder below Rathgar bridge, 1903: *N.C.* 8. Glendruid, Carrickmines *(More) Cyb. II.*
Brunker MS: Still at Colgan's Dodder station (7) in 1957 and at Woodland's station (4) in 1953.

| 4 | 6 | 7 | 8 |

Occasional in woodlands and on shaded roadsides in 4, 6, 7 and 8, and the River Liffey Valley.

Elytrigia

E. repens (L.) Desv. ex Nevski *(Agropyron repens, Elymus repens)*
Common Couch, Scutch   Native

| I | 2 | 3 | 4 | 5 | 6 | 7 | 8 |

Widespread and abundant on roadsides, in neglected pastures and ruderal habitats.
FID.

----

var. **aristatus** Baumg.

| I | 2 | 4 | 5 | 8 |

Common, particularly near the coast.

E. repens x **E. juncea** (**E.** x **laxa** (Fries) Kerguelen; *Elymus* x *laxus; Agropyron* x *laxum*)
Native

☐(2) ☐ 5

Recorded from Co. Dublin in *CC1* and *CC2*, presumably on the basis of W.B. Bruce's 1905 record of **Agropyron acutum** from Skerries and/or D.K. Stewart's 1905 record from Sutton. **Agropyron acutum**, however, was the name often applied to the plant later known as **A. obtusiusculum**, the reputed hybrid between **Agropyron pungens** and **A. junceiforme** (*i.e.* **Elytrigia atherica** x **E. juncea**). Some doubt may attach to these records as **E. juncea** hybridises with both **E. repens** and **E. atherica** in Ireland and these species are not always easily distinguished. In both of the localities where **A. acutum** was recorded **E. juncea** also occurred as well as **E. repens**. A specimen collected by Bruce in 1905 (**DBN**) certainly has **E. juncea** in its parentage. The other parent could be either **E. repens** or **E. atherica**; however, the latter seems slightly more likely as some of the leaf margins are minutely ciliate.
5. By the Broad Meadow Estuary in a saltmarsh near Prospect Point, DD/94.

- -

E. atherica (Link) Kerguelen ex Carreras Mart. *(Elymus pycnanthus, Agropyron pungens)*
Sea Couch   Native

Colgan: 2. On the shore near Rush, a large form which has been cultivated in the Botanic Gardens, Glasnevin, under the name *Triticum Moorei: Rec. Add.* Shore near Skerries, 1900 *(Praeger) Top. Bot.* 5. Shore near Sutton, 1904: *N.C.*
Suppl: 2. Still at Skerries (1947) and at Rush (1956).

☐(2) ☐ 5

5. Still near Sutton, at the base of a wall above the salt-marsh, behind Sutton Railway Station, DD/78-92.

- -

E. juncea (L.) Nevski subsp. **boreoatlantica**
(Simonet & Guinochet) N. Hylander
(Agropyron junceum, Elymus farctus subsp. *boreali-atlanticus)*
Sand Couch   Native

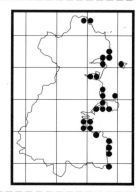

☐ 2 ☐ 3 ☐ 5 ☐ 8

Common on fore-dunes and sea-shores.
Extensive stands of a large sterile **Elytrigia** occur on the coast just inside the county boundary (with Co. Meath) in District 2. They may be **E. juncea** x **E. atherica** (*i.e.* **E.** x **obtusiuscula**).

- -

Leymus

L. arenarius (L.) Hochst. *(Elymus arenarius)*
Lyme-grass   Native

Colgan: 2. On the coast below Skerries in two places, profusely, 1882 *(Hart) Journ. of Bot.,* 1883, p. 246. In considerable quantity along the beach at Skerries, spreading for about 100 yards, 1902: *N.C.*
Suppl: 2. Still at Skerries (1946). At Rogerstown Harbour (1956). 5. On the North Bull

(J.P. Brunker and R.W. Scully in *I.N. XXVI*, 1922) - still there and spreading (1955).

8. Along the railway and the shore at Killiney (J.P. Brunker 1939-1957). Pigeon House (1950-1956).

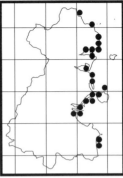

Common on sand-dunes in 2, 3 & 5; rare in 8. Very rare in Colgan's time. It was commonly planted as a sand-binding species and may have been introduced originally to many of its present stations in the county.

8. North end of Sandymount Strand, DNFC/83. Sandy area, east of Pigeon House, SR, HOR/83. Beach, 0.5 km south of Whiterock, Killiney, J.S. Jackson/66. Below Killiney railway station and on the coast south of the Martello Tower at Killiney, SR, HOR/83. One patch on the stony shore at the base of the cliffs south of the Shanganagh River, SR/91.

- -

Hordeum

H. murinum L.
Wall Barley   Alien

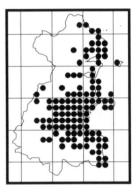

Common in dry sandy ground, waste places and at the base of walls in urban situations. This is a very characteristic Dublin species. It was first recorded in 1727 by Threlkeld "Upon the Sides of the Highway and on the Walls leading to Bagatrath" (*Colgan*).

FID.

- -

H. secalinum Schreber
Meadow Barley   Native

Colgan: 3. Abundant at Broad Meadows, north of Swords, 1891 *(Barrington) Cyb.II.* Sparingly by the Ward river at Brackenstown, 1903: *Colgan 1904.* 4. On the banks of the Royal Canal, also in low meadows at Scribblestown *(Mr Brinkley) Templeton MS.* About Finglas and Glasnevin: *Ir. Flor.* By the Canal towards Castleknock *(J. White):* fields at Glasnevin *(Moore) Cyb.* 5. At Raheny and moist meadows in the Lots: *Ir. Flor.* At Portmarnock *(Moore) Cyb.* Abundant in marshy ground by a brackish pond known as Smylie's pond, Dollymount, 1904: *N.C.*

Suppl: 3. Still at Scribblestown (J.P. Brunker, 1922). 4. Still by Broad Meadow Water (1948).

2   3   (4)   5

Very rare, though sometimes locally abundant in grassland near the sea. Legally protected under the Wildlife Act of 1976 as an endangered species.

2. Abundant in rough pasture above the salt-marsh at Balleally, DD/87, **NDR**.
3. Green road in agricultural land, east of Turvey Bridge, and abundant on a salt-marsh north of Turvey House, PR, DD/83, 91.
5. A few plants in a field and salt-marsh beside the Mayne River at Baldoyle, DN/89, 91 & DD/91.

Danthonia

D. decumbens (L.) DC. *(Triodia decumbens, Sieglingia decumbens)*
Heath-grass   Native

Colgan: 1. At Streamstown, Naul Hills, 1903; 2. Near the shore south of Skerries, 1893; 3. To the north of Portrane peninsula, 1895; 5. By the shore at Portmarnock, and abundant on the higher parts of Howth Head, 1903: *N.C.*

| (1) | 2 | (3) | 4 | 5 | 6 | 7 | 8 |

Common in damp grassland and moorland in the upland areas of 7 & 8; rare elsewhere.

2. Grassland on a rock outcrop at Cardy Point, DD/87. Still south of Skerries, DD/90.
4. Bank of a drainage ditch at Dunsoghly, MN/83, **NDR**. Calcareous grassland at the Magazine Fort in the Phoenix Park, MN/88.
5. Near The Summit, Howth Head and nearby at Kilrock, Howth, ENL/84 & PG/87, 88. Ben of Howth, DN/89.
6. North end of Brittas Ponds, DNFC/83. Valley between Brittas and Saggart Hill, south of Glenaraneen, DNFC/90.
7. Waste ground at the rear of the monastery at Clondalkin, PWJ, MSS/85.
8. Bank above the Vico Bathing Place, SR, JR/84. Dalkey Quarry, HOR, ENL, EMcA/84. Railway bank, east of Shanganagh Cemetery, SR/87.

Molinia

M. caerulea (L.) Moench
Purple Moor-grass   Native

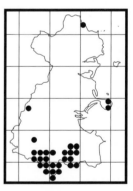

Colgan: 2. Near Balbriggan 1904; 3. At Balcarrig and near Raheen Point, Portrane, 1894; 4. By the Tolka above Blanchardstown, 1895; by the Royal Canal at Clonsilla, 1901; 5. Abundant on the upper parts of Howth Head, 1904; and 6. Sparingly by the Grand Canal near Hazelhatch, 1902: *N.C.*

Suppl: 3. Still at Portrane (1953). 4 & 6. Still along both canals (1956).

| 2 | (3) | 4 | 5 | 6 | 7 | 8 |

Common in moorland in the uplands of 7 & 8 and on high ground on Howth Head; rare elsewhere.

Subsp. **arundinacea** (Schrank) K. Richter has been recorded below the cromlech west of Kiltiernan, SR, JR/88.

2. Still on sea-cliffs at Hampton Hall, RF/90.
4. Still by the Royal Canal at Clonsilla, MS/73.

Phragmites

P. australis (Cav.) Trin. ex Steudel *(P. communis)*
Common Reed   Native

Colgan: 2. Abundant on wet drift banks by the shore from Hampton to Balbriggan, 1904; in drains by the shore near Rogerstown, 1901; 3. Sparingly near Newbridge House and near Turvey bridge, 1894; abundant in ditches at Balcarrig, Portrane, 1904, and 4. At Broughan bridge, south of the Ward, 1900: *N.C.* 5. Shore from Clontarf to Kilbarrick, and marsh behind Kilbarrick: *Ir. Flor.* Abundant in Baldoyle Pits and in ditches near Kilbarrick, in the central marsh, Howth Head, and by the shore west of the Baily, 1903; 8. By the Shanganagh river near its mouth, and in adjacent ditches, 1904: *N.C.*

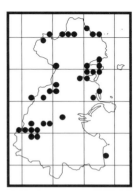

| 1 | 2 | 3 | 4 | 5 | 6 | 7 | 8 |

Common on banks of the Grand Canal; occasional in large stands along the coast in 3 & 5; rare elsewhere.

1. Bog of the Ring, GS/86, **NDR**.
2. Still abundant on cliffs between Hampton Hall and Balbriggan and as far south as Skerries, DD/90.
4. Still at Broghan Bridge and nearby, MN/84. Pond in the People's Garden in the Phoenix Park, MN/87.
7. Grand Canal from Rialto eastwards, DD/88-91, **NDR**.
8. Still present and forming extensive patches at the mouths of the Shanganagh River and Deansgrange stream to the north of it, DD/83, SR/96.

Spartina

S. maritima (Curtis) Fern. forma **dublinensis**
Small Cord-grass   Alien

| 3 | 5 |

3. In clumps of '**S. townsendii**' at Corballis and south of the sand-dune promontory (Boyle 1976).
5. North Bull Island, in lower saltmarsh, with **S. anglica** (Boyle 1977). With '**S. townsendii**' at Baldoyle (Boyle 1976). Not relocated recently.

S. maritima x **S. alterniflora** (**S.** x **townsendii** Groves & J. Groves)
Townsend's Cord-grass   Alien

| 5 |

Present on North Bull Island in 1970s (Boyle 1977), but apparently extinct there now.

S. anglica C.E. Hubb.
Common Cord-grass   Alien

| 2 | 3 | 5 |

2. Widespread in Rogerstown Estuary, TC/93.
3. Widespread in Malahide Estuary (Ní Lamhna 1982), TC/93.
5. Widespread in Baldoyle Estuary and on mud flats at North Bull Island (Boyle 1972, 1977), TC/93.

SPARGANIACEAE

Sparganium

S. erectum L. *(S. ramosum)*
Branched Bur-reed   Native

| 1 | 2 | 3 | 4 | 5 | 6 | 7 | 8 |

Common in rivers, canals, pools, marshes and drains; occasional in 8.

----

subsp. **microcarpum** (Neuman) Domin.

| (4) |

Not refound from the Royal Canal at Finglas (4) where it was found by N. McArdle in 1905.

----

subsp. **neglectum** (Beeby) Schinz & Thell. *(S. neglectum)*
Native

Colgan: 3. Abundant by a marshy overflow of the Broad Meadow Water near Fieldstown, and 4. Frequent by the Royal Canal above Lucan Station, 1903: *Colgan 1904.*

| (3) | 4 | 8 |

4. Scribblestown, MN/88. Luttrellstown, MS/76.
8. Small marsh near the Roadstone Works at Ballycorus, SR/89. Stream, east of Cabinteely, SR/89. River Dodder above Orwell Bridge, SR/89.

S. emersum Rehmann *(S. simplex)*
Unbranched Bur-reed   Native

Colgan: 1. In Garristown Bog, and in the Bog of the Ring, 1893; 2. In Balrothery Pond, 3. Abundant by the Ward river below Chapelmidway, and 4. Abundant by the Tolka river from Damastown to Blanchardstown, 1893; in the Royal Canal at Lucan 1895: *N.C.* 5. Marsh near the summit of Howth: *Flor. Howth.* 7. By the Dodder above Old Bawn, 1896: *N.C. Suppl:* 2. Foreshore at Skerries (1951). 6. Grand Canal above Gollierstown (1956). 7. In River Camac beside Canal aqueduct, Inchicore (1934). River Dodder above Orwell Falls (1922 and 1956). Former Dartry Dye Works pond (1956).

| (1) | (2) | 3 | 4 | 5 | 6 | 7 |

Common in canals, rivers and reservoirs, and still in the River Tolka Valley (4) where it appears to have spread.

3. Knocksedan Reservoir, MN, PR/85 & DN/90.
4. Ward River, west of Coolatrath Bridge, MN/88. Phoenix Park, MN/88. River Liffey at Conyngham Road, MN/88. Grand Canal at Lucan, DN/90.
5. River Tolka at Drumcondra, DN/90.
6. Banks of the Grand Canal, north of Clondalkin, JP/83. Pond on the south side of Grand Canal at Collinstown Bridge, MN/88 & DN/89. Grand Canal at Ballymakaily Mill, MN/89.
7. River Liffey millrace at Fonthill, MN/90. Grand Canal at 7th lock, DN/90. Palmerston Marsh, DD/82. Grand Canal at Drimnagh, DN/89.

FID.

TYPHACEAE

Typha

T. latifolia L.
Bulrush   Native

Colgan: 1. Sparingly at the Bog of the Ring, 1893, and at Garristown bog, 1902; 4 and 5. Frequent, as near Finglas, at Dunsoghly, the Ward, Clonsilla, Baldoyle Pits and Portmarnock Pits, 1894-1903; 7. Ponds near Whitehall, Crumlin, 1896, and sparingly in Glenasmole, 1901: *N.C.* 8. In quarry holes near the base of Carrigollogher, 1896-1901: *J. Meade.* Near Willbrook, Rathfarnham, 1903; by the railway near Dalkey, 1904: *N.C.*

Suppl: 7. Watery Lane, Clondalkin (1953). Near Whitehall, Crumlin (1956).

Common in the Royal Canal but rare in the Grand Canal; occasional elsewhere.
2. Drains near Balleally, DD/84, **NDR.**
3. Quarry near Donabate, PR/88, **NDR.**
5. Plentiful in wet fields beside Sluice River, Portmarnock, DN/89 and in several other sites nearby.
6. Grand Canal near Springfield, DD, CB/87, **NDR.**
7. Water tank in Pearse Station, Westland Row, DNFC/79, still there in 1997. South end of the southern reservoir in Glenasmole, DK/c.65 & SR/89.

FID.

T. angustifolia L.
Lesser Bulrush   Native

Colgan: Abundantly in ponds between Sandymount and Merrion: *Wade Dubl.* Found in old brick holes in meadows below Ringsend and at the side of Dublin Bay: *Templeton MS* - where a good pencil sketch of the plant is given. Lake at Sandymount: *Mack. Cat.* Marshes near Irishtown: *Ir. Flor.* Not seen recently. The marshy land referred to in the above records has been drained and is now for the most part built on, and the plant is no doubt quite extinct.

| 7 | (8) |

Very rare.
7. Small marsh between the two reservoirs in Glenasmole, DD/90.

LILIACEAE

Narthecium

N. ossifragum (L.) Hudson
Bog Asphodel   Native
Suppl: 6. Not confirmed from Slieve Thoul, which is now partly
covered by forestry plantations.

Common in flushes and pools in moorland and mountain blanket-bog.
Little suitable ground now survives on Slieve Thoul (6) where it was recorded in 1895
(*Colgan*), and which has now been densely planted with conifers.
5. Small boggy area on the edge of Howth Golf-course, Howth Head, DN/89. Central Marsh
    on Howth Head and to the south-east, DN/90.

Scilla

S. verna Hudson
Spring Squill   Native
Colgan: 3. Abundant on Lambay: *Flor. Lambay.* Occasional in the Portrane peninsula, as near Corballis, 1893; near Balcarrig and
near the Martello tower, 1903: *N.C.* 5. On the dry pasture ground to the west of the Lighthouse, Howth, and on Ireland's
Eye: *Wade Rar.* Abundant on Ireland's Eye, 1899, and on many parts of Howth Head, especially on the east and south-east
sides, 1903; on Carrick Hill, 1900, and sparingly on the western end of Feltrim Hill, 1902: *N.C.* 8. At the Ring's end neere
Dublin *(Mr Heaton)'': How's Phytologia.* On the shore between Dunleary and Dalkey: *Mack. Rar.* On Killiney Hill, *Mack. Cat.*
and in 1902 near the top! Banks by the sea near the tunnel at Vico, 1897: *J. Meade.* Frequent on Dalkey island and abundant
on the cliffs opposite to it, extending to Sorrento Point, 1901; banks north of the Lead Mine, below Killiney Hill, 1902: *N.C.*
Suppl: 5. Still on the remnant of Feltrim Hill (1955), but no longer at the site of Carrickhill. 8. Still at Vico (1954).

| 3 | 5 | 8 |

Rare, though sometimes locally abundant along the coast.
3. Opposite the entrance to the Island Golf-course, DD/82. Still on Lambay Island at the
    north-west corner and on the eastern side, DD/82, 91. Frequent along the cliff walk at
    Portrane, PR/84. East of Corballis, PR/84.
5. Shore behind Sutton Railway Station, ENL/83. Scattered on Howth Head at the Baily
    Lighthouse, Kilrock and Redrock, DD/82, 84 & PG/87, 88. Plentiful from Redrock towards
    Drumleck. South shore of Ireland's Eye, ENL/85.
8. Cliffs to the south of Coliemore Harbour, HOR/83. Still on Dalkey Island, SR, DN, CB/91.

Hyacinthoides

H. non-scripta (L.) Chouard ex Rothm.
(Scilla non-scripta, S. nutans)
Bluebell   Native

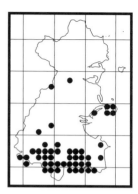

Colgan: 3. In woods at Brackenstown: *Wade Dubl.* Abundant on Lambay island: *Flor. Lambay.* Copses about Knocksedan, 1894; 4. In St Catherine's wood, 1904; 5. Abundant on Ireland's Eye, 1899, and on Howth Head, 1902: *N.C.* 6, 7, 8. Abundant in many stations in the uplands, and also in the demesne at Lucan: *N.C.* This species appears to be quite absent from the north of the county and is generally rare in the limestone areas. The white-flowered variety is recorded for Lambay *(Ir. Flor.)* and for Ireland's Eye *(Flor. Howth)*, and the flesh-coloured variety for the Little Dargle *(Ir. Flor.)*; but these colour varieties are distinctly rare in the county.

3	4	5	6	7	8

Common in deciduous woodlands and under bracken in open ground; occasional in lightly grazed hillside pastures; rare in the north.
FID.

H. hispanica (Miller) Rothm.
Spanish Bluebell   Alien

1	2	3	5	7	8

Occasional on waste ground, roadsides and in woodland. A discard or escape from gardens, sometimes naturalized. At least some of the material recorded from the county under this category may be of hybrid origin between this species and **H. non-scripta**.
FID.

Allium

A. triquetrum L.
Three-cornered Garlic   Alien

3	4	5	8

Occasional on shaded roadside verges where, in places, it forms almost pure stands. A garden escape or throw-out often found in the grounds of large estates. Particularly common on the southern side of Howth (5), and near the Bride's Glen River at Heronsford Lane and below Killiney Railway Station (8), SR, HOR/85, 87.

A. ursinum L.
Ramsons   Native

Colgan: 2. Gormanstown woods, 1894; 3. Very abundant in Brackenstown wood, 1903; and 4. In Woodlands and Saint Catherine's wood, 1904: *N.C.* 5. In Howth demesne: *Flor. Howth.* abundant here in 1903: *Miss L. Colgan.* 6. Very abundant in Lucan demesne, 1904: *N.C.* 7. Sparingly in hedgebanks near Drimnagh, 1900 *(N.C.). Top. Bot.* 8. In Bride's Glen, 1902: *N.C.* Abundant by roadsides near Old Connaught, and in profusion in Thornhill wood south of Old Connaught, 1895: *W.H. Bloomer.*

Suppl: 7. The station at Drimnagh is now gone, this being a built-up area (1956).

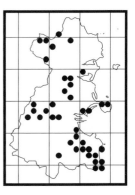

Occasional and locally abundant, sometimes completely covering the ground, in woods and hedgerows. Very common in the woodlands of the River Liffey Valley (4), Santry Woods (5) and in woodlands in 7 & 8.

3. Still abundant in Brackenstown Woods, DD/82.
4. Ditch at the U.S. Embassy in Phoenix Park, PR/88. Hedgebank in the grounds of St Helena's, Finglas, DD/74.
5. Still very plentiful in the grounds of Howth Demesne, PG, DN/91. By the Naniken Stream in St Anne's Park, Raheny, PG/88.

A. carinatum L.
Keeled Garlic   Alien

Brunker MS: 7. Bushy Park, Terenure, '40 and '55.

(4) 7 8

Very rare.

7. Many plants on banks of the River Dodder beside Bushy Park, SR, HOR/84.
8. East of Rathfarnham road bridge, SR/87. Roadside bank west of Shankill, SR/87, **NDR**.

A. vineale L.
Wild Onion   Native

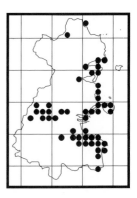

Colgan: 2. Sparingly in Rush sandhills, 1902; and 3. Abundant in sandy banks, Portrane peninsula, 1903: N.C. Broad Meadow near Swords, 1891 *(Barrington) Cyb. II.* 4. Abundantly in fields near the Observatory, Scribblestown: *Wade Dubl.* Near the pond in the Viceregal grounds, Phoenix Park, 1880: *More MS.* Very abundant in dry banks at the Strawberry Beds, 1901: N.C. 5. "In some Meadows near *Bally Griffin in Fingall,* copiously": *Threlkeld.* Plentiful at Portmarnock and Feltrim Hill *(Moore) Cyb.* and in 1904! Quarry at Malahide, 1897; abundant on Carrick Hill 1900; &c.: N.C. 7. "Upon the Bankside of the Mill-race above *Island bridge* upon the Back of the House where the Sign of the *Salmon* is": *Threlkeld.* Railway banks near Island Bridge, 1903; frequent amongst the eskers at Drimnagh, 1900; very abundant in pastures near Lansdown valley, 1895: N.C. 8. Abundant on banks by the railway between Merrion and Booterstown, 1903; *Scully.* Quarry near Dalkey church, 1901; on the top of Killiney Hill, 1902: N.C.

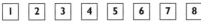

Common in consolidated sand-dunes and on calcareous sandy soils of the River Liffey, Tolka and Dodder Valleys.

1. Roadside banks north of Oldtown, GS/86, **NDR**.
6. Banks of the River Liffey at Lucan, JP, PR/83, **NDR**.
FID.

Asparagus

A. officinalis L. subsp. **officinalis**
Garden Asparagus   Alien

| 5 | 7 |

Very rare, in sand-dunes. All plants seen have been the erect cultivated form and not the procumbent subsp. **prostratus** (Dumort.) Corbiere, which occasionally occurs on sand-dunes in counties Wicklow, Wexford and Waterford.
5. Sand-dune grassland 0.5 km south of the Country Club at Portmarnock, DD/78. Several plants near the north end of St Anne's Golf-course on North Bull Island, DNFC/84, 86, ENL, CB/85, PG/92. Several plants near the beach at Portmarnock, on the north-east corner of the golf-course, DN/89.
7. Waste ground at Ringsend, SR/89.

IRIDACEAE

Iris

I. pseudacorus L.
Yellow Iris, Yellow Flag   Native

| 1 | 2 | 3 | 4 | 5 | 6 | 7 | 8 |

Common in wet pastures, riversides, canal banks and drains.
FID.

I. foetidissima L.
Stinking Iris   Probably introduced

Suppl: Included only in Colgan's Appendix, but it is now firmly established in his station on Ireland's Eye, where it is increasing (1956). 3. Surgalstown (1953). Still on Lambay (1954).

| 1 | 2 | 3 | 4 | 5 | 6 | (7) | 8 |

Rare, on roadsides near habitation. A relic of cultivation.
1. Walshestown, DD/84, **NDR**.
2. Roadside, west of Collinstown Bridge, DD/84, **NDR**.
3. Prospect Point, PR/87.
4. Roadside near Ashtown Railway Station, DD/91.
5. Still on Ireland's Eye in sand-hills, ENL, DD/82 & PG/91. Howth Demesne, PG, DN/91.
6. Churchyard at Newcastle Village, JP/84, **NDR**. Woodland near habitation on the Tallaght to Clondalkin road, 1.25 km south-south-east of Clondalkin, JP, D.Scott/85.
8. Grounds of U.C.D. Belfield, HOR/85. Just west of the Church at Foxrock, SR/84. Cabinteely Park, HOR/84. Between Vico Road and the railway, Killiney, SR, HOR/83. Just north of Booterstown Marsh, SR, JR/92.

Crocosmia

C. pottsii (MacNab ex Baker) N.E. Brown x **C. aurea** (Hook.) Planchon **(Crocosmia** x **crocosmiiflora** (Lemoine ex Burb. & Dean) Nicholson; *Tritonia x crocosmiiflora*)
Montbretia   Alien

| 4 | 5 | 6 | 7 | 8 |

Occasional on roadsides, ruins and river banks. Not included in *Colgan* or *Suppl.*
FID.

ORCHIDACEAE

Cephalanthera

C. longifolia (L.) Fritsch *(C. ensifolia)*
Narrow-leaved Helleborine   Native
Suppl: 7. Wet thicket near E. end of Lower Dam, Glenasmole (J. Hinchcliffe, c. 1930 and J.P. Brunker, 1933).

| 7 |

7. Still near the east end of the lower dam in Glenasmole, R.Piper/70.

Epipactis

E. palustris (L.) Crantz
Marsh Helleborine   Native
Colgan: 3. In the sandhills at Portane about 1872 *(Hart) Flor. Howth & MS.* 5. Plentiful among the sandhills at Baldoyle Strand (Portmarnock): *Templeton MS.* not later than 1820. Plentiful in a marshy hollow of Portmarnock sandhills, 1901: *Miss R. Mahaffy* some hundreds of plants here associated with *Orchis incarnata, Gymnadenia conopsea* and *Listera ovata,* 1904: *N.C.* Boggy meadows beyond the town of Howth: *Ir. Flor.* 7. At a mountain foot in a moist meadow S. of Templeogue, July, 1735: *Annot. in Threlkeld.* Glenasmole *(Rev. C.F. & Arcy) Colgan 1895a.* 8. Jamestown, half a mile beyond Kilgobbin *(Dr Stokes)* 1801; plentiful in a bog in the neighbourhood of Killiney Bay: *Templeton MS.* Foot of the Dublin mountains, particularly near Stagstown and Kingstown: *Wade Rar.* Kingston Lodge near the Scalp (Wade's Kingstown) in 1860: *Rev. S.A. Brenan.* At Old Connaught, 1904: *J. Meade.*
Suppl: 3. Corballis sandhills (1942).
DNFC Annual Report for 1968: ?7. Report of discovery "near Tallaght" of a new station. No further details, but known to be Whitestown, Tallaght (fide DD).

| 3 | 5 | 7 | (8) |

Rare, in dune-slacks and marshes.
3. Still at Portrane in a dune-slack, on the extreme southern part of Malahide Island, PR/83.
5. Still in the Alder Marsh on North Bull Island and east of The Farm, J.S. Jackson/64, MS/65, 75 & HJH/85. Still in shallow depressions on the southern end of Portmarnock Golf-course, DN, RF/88 & DN/89.
7. Whitestown, Tallaght, DNFC/68. Marsh, 200 m north-west of St Ann's Chapel, Glenasmole, DD, SR/88.

E. helleborine (L.) Crantz *(E. latifolia)*
Broad-leaved Helleborine   Native

Colgan: 4. By the Royal Canal near Blanchardstown, 1892: *C.B. Moffat.* Frequent in Abbotstown wood, 1895: *N.C.* 5. In Portmarnock sands: *Mack. Cat.* In considerable quantity in marshy hollows of Portmarnock sandhills, 1901: *Miss R. Mahaffy.* About Glasnevin *(Moore) Cyb.* Sparingly in Howth demesne: *Hart 1897.* In Malahide demesne, 1897: *Miss S. Colgan.* 6. In a copse near the Salmon Leap, 1904: *R.Ll. Praeger & Dr McWeeney.* 7. Sparingly in Bushy Park, and by the Dodder between the Park and Rathgar Bridge, 1902 *(Praeger) Ir. Nat. XI.,* p. 322. 8. In a wood near Ballybetagh, 1895: *Colgan 1895a* and in 1902! Sparingly on the roadside at Old Connaught, 1897; several plants in Old Connaught demesne and a few in Cork Abbey demesne, 1900: *J. Meade.*

Suppl: 8. Rockfield, Dundrum (R.W. Scully, 1918). Roadside at Novice's Hill, Kiltiernan (J.P. Brunker, 1931-1956). Although Colgan records this plant from ten widely separated stations it has not been re-found in any of them.

| 4 | 5 | (6) | 7 | 8 |

Rare, in woods and shaded hedgerows. Early records of this taxon from Portmarnock sand-hills may refer to **E. phyllanthes** (see Brunker 1954a).
4. Oonavarra Hill and by the River Liffey at Lucan, JS, DD, ENL/84. Edge of the lawn by the house at Beech Park, Clonsilla, JS/84. Single plant in Knockmaroon Woods, CB, MN/85. Hedge by the Royal Canal at the lock gate, c. 1 km west of Ashtown, MN/83. Still at and near Abbotstown Woods, DD/73, MN/91.
5. On a mound by a pond in St Anne's Park, Raheny, PG/87, 88.
7. Midway along the eastern side of the southern reservoir in Glenasmole, SR/89. Slopes east of the northern reservoir in Glenasmole, MN/90.
8. Druid's Glen, D. Burke/88.

- -

E. leptochila (Godfery) Godfery
Narrow-lipped Helleborine   Native

| 7 |

7. Near the waterworks in Glenasmole, R. Piper/70, **NIR**.

- -

E. phyllanthes G.E. Smith
Green-flowered Helleborine   Native

| 5 |

Extremely rare. See also the discussion under **E. helleborine**.
5. A few plants in a damp depression in sand-hills south of the Country Club in Portmarnock, HJH/83, **NCR**, & DD/85. Two plants amongst **Salix repens** at Portmarnock, DD/92.

- -

Neottia

N. nidus-avis (L.) Rich.
Bird's-nest Orchid   Native

Colgan: 4. "In the thickets among the rotten leaves, Luttrell's-town wood ... flowering so early as April": *Wade Rar.* In Luttrell's-town wood *(Mr Brinkley);* seen in abundance by Dr Taylor and myself, July, 1814: *Templeton MS.* First record in 1804: *Wade Rar.* The flowering season given in Wade's record points to *Lathraea* rather than to *Neottia,* but there can be no question as to the accuracy of Templeton's later record. As Luttrell's-town wood (Woodlands) is a most suitable locality, and this speceis is known to be uncertain in its appearances, it seems advisable to retain it in the county flora in spite of the absence of any recent record.

(4)

Not refound at its site in Luttrellstown (4) despite recent careful searches. However, like Colgan we are unwilling to exclude this species from the flora because of its sporadic appearances.

‒ ‒

Listera

L. ovata (L.) R. Br.
Common Twayblade   Native

Suppl: 1. Roadside between Commons Upper and Cockle's Bridge (1953).

| 1 | (2) | 3 | (4) | 5 | 6 | 7 | 8 |

Occasional in damp pastures in the uplands; rare in dune-slacks. This species has declined considerably since Colgan's time when it was frequent or locally abundant.
1. Still near Garristown on a roadside bank to the north-west towards the Ardcath road near Commons Upper, GS/87.
8. North slope of Ticknock at 150 m, V. Rowe/84. Dalkey Quarry, SR/85.

‒ ‒

L. cordata (L.) R. Br.
Lesser Twayblade   Native

Colgan: 7. In Kelly's Glen *(C. Ball) Rec. Add.* Near Ballinascorney, 1876: *Greenwood Pim.* On Kippure mountain *(Hart) Flor. Howth* and in 1904! On Feather Bed mountain, 1867 *(Hart) Colgan 1895a* abundant here in 1902! Frequent on Glendhu mountain, 1884-1901; abundant on Glassavullaun mountain, 1896, and on Seecawn, 1903: *N.C.* 8. Slopes between Kilmashogue and Three Rock mountain: *Colgan 1895a.* In Glencullen *(Greenwood Pim) Cyb II.* Frequent on Glencullen mountain and near the summit of the Two Rock mountain, 1903: *N.C.*
Suppl: Tibradden (J.P. Brunker, 1920). Still on Glendhu (1956) and Seecawn (1955).

| (7) | 8 |

Very rare but probably under-recorded as it is an inconspicuous plant. Usually occurs under heather in moorland.
8. West slope of Two Rock Mountain, SR, ENL, HOR/84. Just south of the cairn at Fairy Castle on Two Rock Mountain, SR/87. Ridge to the west and slopes to north and north-west of Prince William's Seat, DNFC/86.

‒ ‒

Spiranthes

S. spiralis (L.) Chevall. *(S. autumnalis)*
Autumn Lady's-tresses   Native

Colgan: 4. In Phoenix Park, between Chapelizod and the Magazine *(Leslie Ogilby) Ir. Flor.* 5. On the North Bull, *circa* 1885 *(More) Cyb. II & MS.* and in 1900 *(Praeger) Top. Bot.* 8. On Bray Commons, 1810 *(Mackay) Cat. & Flor. Hib.* Near the commons at Bullock: *Ir. Flor.* At Loughlinstown and near the shore between Dalkey and Bray *(Moore);* at Killiney *(Miss M. O'Kelly) Cyb.* Pastures near the mouth of the Shanganagh river, 1899; abundant on the north side of Loughlinstown Commons and several plants on banks by the sea a mile and a half north of the Bray river, 1903: *N.C.*
Suppl: 3. Balcarrick, Donabate (Miss H. Roe, 1955). 4. Still at the same station in Phoenix Park *(I.N.,* 1906) and (1957). 5. Still on North Bull E. of "The Farm" (1957). 8. Still on Loughlinstown Common (J.P. Brunker, 1918), but has not been seen recently in spite of frequent searches.

Very rare, in unimproved calcareous grassland and low sand-dunes.
4. Still between Chapelizod and the Magazine Fort in grazed calcareous grassland, Phoenix Park, JS, MN, ENL/83.
5. Edge of the Alder Marsh on North Bull Island, DD, BB/84 & DN/91.
8. Lawn north-west of Shankill, CM/84.

Hammarbya

H. paludosa (L.) Kuntze *(Malaxis paludosa)*
Bog Orchid   Native

Colgan: 7. In marshy places about Kelly's Glen, river Dodder, July 1814: *Templeton MS.* At the top of Kelly's Glen on the right above Grierson's (now Cobb's) Lodge, abundantly, both before and after the publication of *Flora Hibernica* in 1836 *(John Bain): Colgan 1893.* Abundant in one spot by the Slade Brook, Glenasmole (probably the same locality as the preceding), as many as 33 plants found growing in a space of 3 yards square, 1901: *N.C.* 8. Above the school at Holly Park (now St Columba's College) in swampy ground towards Ticknock, *circa 1837: John Bain.* In considerable quantity on Glendhu mountain, 1884: *Colgan 1893,* and again in the same spot in 1894! Mountain slope south-west of Glencullen Bridge, 1894 *(Dr Leitch) Colgan 1895a* and in 1899! On the Two Rock mountain above Glencullen Chapel, 1899: *N.C.*
Suppl: 7. Still in the same bog at the head of Glenasmole where it has been identified almost every year up to 1957. 8. Confirmed from Three Rock Mountain, near Ticknock (Herbarium National Museum, C. Waterfall, 1905). Not seen since. Never confirmed in Glendhu or Glencullen.

 7 (8)

Very rare, in flushes in boggy ground. An inconspicuous species that is difficult to find because of its small size, and sporadic occurrence. Legally protected in Ireland under the Wildlife Act of 1976. The mountain slope south-west of Glencullen Bridge is now forested.
7. Bohernabreena, MS/63. Runnels at the bottom of the slope west of the River Dodder to the south-west of the southern reservoir in Glenasmole, SR/86, M. McGuirk/94.
8. South-west of Glencullen Bridge, WAW/53, 63. Site destroyed in 1992.

Platanthera

P. chlorantha (Custer) Reichb. *(Habenaria chloroleuca)*
Greater Butterfly-orchid   Native

Colgan: 6. On the northern slope of Slieve Thoul, 1895: *Rev. C.F. d'Arcy.* In Crooksling glen, 1895: *N.C.* 7. Between Lugmore and Kiltyloones (Kiltalown) near the mountain called Tallaght: *Wade Dubl. (as H. bifolia).* Abundant in Glenasmole, as below St Anne's, 1895, on Glassavullaun mountain, 1896, and near Ballymorefinn, 1903; in the Brakes of Ballinascorney, 1903: *N.C.* 8. Not very plentifully in the higher pastures, Stagstown: *Wade Dubl.* Abundant in damp pastures above the Little Dargle, Stagstown, 1900: *N.C.*
Suppl: Still at Brittas (1952). Lugmore Glen (1956) and abundant about St Anne's, Glenasmole (1957). Not confirmed from District 8.

6 7 8

Rare, in damp grassland and slopes in upland areas.
6. Slopes of the river valley below Slieve Thoul, DD/82.

7. Scattered in the Glenasmole Valley west of Castlekelly, on the east side of the southern reservoir in Glenasmole and nearby in a marsh 300 m north-west of St Ann's Chapel, and between the two reservoirs in Glenasmole, DD, EMcA/83, DNFC/88 & SR/89. One plant in an ungrazed field on the northern slopes of Mountpelier, CB, SR/90.
8. Ticknock, DK/c.65. Dry field at the top and east of the Ticknock road, M. Friel/87. Meadow below Barnacullia by the right-of-way to Kilgobbin, PC/72-74, 88.

Anacamptis

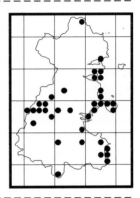

A. pyramidalis (L.) Rich. *(Orchis pyramidalis)*
Pyramidal Orchid   Native

(1)	2	3	4	5	(6)	7	8

Occasional in dune-grassland, sandy roadside cuttings, railway banks and unimproved pastures inland; rare in 8.
8. Many plants on a steep bank by the Bray Road below Loughlinstown Hospital, SR/85.
FID.

Pseudorchis

P. albida (L.) A. & D. Löve *(Habenaria albida, Leucorchis albida)*
Small-white Orchid   Native
Colgan: 7. In pastures on the side of Kelly's glen, Dodder river: Templeton MS – not later than 1820 – still there in 1894: Dr McWeeney. 8. Near the Three Rock mountain, Co. Wicklow: Wade Rar. (Wicklow is here probably a mistake for Dublin.) Suppl: 7. Still in pastures at St Anne's, Glenasmole (1957).

7	(8)

Legally protected under the Wildlife Act of 1976 as an endangered species in Ireland.
7. Still in Glenasmole near the northern reservoir, R. Piper/70.

Gymnadenia

G. conopsea (L.) R. Br. *(Habenaria conopsea)*
Fragrant Orchid   Native
Suppl: 1. Abundant on site of Garristown Bog (H.J. Hudson, 1934).

(1)	(2)	(3)	4	5	(6)	7	(8)

Rare, in damp grassland, marshes and roadside banks. Garristown Bog (1) is now drained. Like most other orchids in Dublin this species declined considerably in the 20th century.
4. Roadside bank just north of Mulhuddart on the Navan Road, DD/74. Railway embankment west of Cross Guns Bridge by the Royal Canal, DNFC/82. Wet flush by the River Tolka at Blanchardstown, DNFC/88.
5. Roadside at Balscadden, Howth, PG/87, 88. Kilrock, Howth, PG/90.
7. Marsh, 500 m north-west of St Ann's Chapel, Glenasmole, DNFC/88. By the River Dodder, 1 km south of Oldbawn Bridge, CB/94.
FID.

Gymnadenia conopsea × **Dactylorhiza maculata** (× **Dactylodenia legrandiana** (Camus) Peitz; *Dactylogymnadenia legrandiana*)
Native

| 5 |

A very rare hybrid.
5. Alder Marsh, North Bull Island, TC/78.

Coeloglossum

C. viride (L.) Hartman *(Habenaria viridis)*
Frog Orchid   Native

Colgan: 1. Naul Hills near Streamstown, 1903; 2. By the railway between Rush and Skerries, 1894, and in sandy pastures by the sea north and south of Skerries, 1895: *N.C.* 5. Plentiful in meadows east side of Howth: *Mack. Cat.* - frequent here below Cabeena Lodge, 1897! Lands of Santry, and between Feltrim Hill and the North Road: *Ir. Flor.* 6. Sparingly about Rathcoole, 1893; above Saggard Slade, 1894; to the east of Brittas, 1895; and North of Slieve Thoul, 1902: *N.C.* 7. On the basalt below Ballinascorney gap and in pastures south of Mount Pelier, 1893; on Mount Seskin, 1894; abundant above Friarstown and Piperstown, 1895; at Saint Anne's, Glenasmole, 1900: *N.C.* 8. Here and there near the Three Rock mountain: *Wade Rar.* Very abundant below Ticknock, 1895; and frequent at Ballybrack, Glencullen, 1903: *N.C.* At Delbrook, Dundrum; *Tatlow 1898*. *Suppl:* 7. Still at Mount Pelier (1919), Mountseskin (1919), Glenasmole (1948), and above Piperstown (1953). On col above Ballinascorney Gap (1954).

| (1) | (2) | 5 | (6) | 7 | 8 |

Extremely rare.
5. Twenty plants in herb-rich, lightly grazed grassland above Casana Rock, Howth, CB/91.
7. Still in St Anne's Fields in Glenasmole, R. Piper/70.
8. Ticknock, D. Minchin/c.67.

Dactylorhiza

Many of the earlier records are not attributable with certainty to the currently recognised taxa. In order to avoid further confusion, *Colgan* records are not included.

D. fuchsii (Druce) Soó *(Orchis fuchsii)*
Common Spotted-orchid   Native

| 1 | 2 | 3 | 4 | 5 | 6 | 7 | 8 |

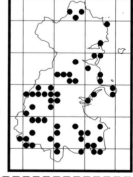

Occasional in dune-slacks, damp grassland, marshes and riversides. Rare in 1. Not recognised as a separate species in *Colgan* and included in **D. maculata**.
1. One plant in the western part of Bog of the Ring, GS/87.
FID.

D. fuchsii × **D. purpurella** (**D.** × **venusta** (Stephenson & T.A. Stephenson) Soó)
Native

| 5 |

5. North Bull Island, TC/75, but not noted during the present survey.

434

D. maculata (L.) Soó *(Orchis maculata, Orchis ericetorum)*
Heath Spotted-orchid   Native
In *Colgan*, **D. maculata** (as *O. maculata*) included **D. fuchsii**, but the species are listed separately in *Suppl.*

| (1) | (2) | (3) | (4) | **5** | (6) | **7** | **8** |

Occasional in dune-slacks, pastures, heathland and marshes in the upland parts of 7 and 8, and on the North Bull Island (5).

D. maculata x **D. incarnata** (**D.** x **carnea** (Camus) Soó; *D.* x *claudiopolitana*)
Native

| **5** |

5. North Bull Island, TC/75, but not noted during the present survey.

D. incarnata (L.) Soó *(Orchis incarnata, O. latifolia)*
Early Marsh-orchid   Native
Suppl: 7. By R. Dodder above Oldbawn (1952) and above St Anne's, Glenasmole (1952). 8. Ballybetagh Bog (1948).

| **3** | **5** | (7) | (8) |

----

subsp. **incarnata**

| **5** | (8) |

Rare, in marshes. Plants which were possibly this subspecies were found in a marshy meadow south of Ballybetagh Bog (8), SR, JR/87.
5. Damp ground at Kilrock, Howth, PG/87, 88, 90. North Bull Island, KF/63.

----

subsp. **coccinea** (Pugsley) Soó

| **3** | **5** |

Occasional in dune-slacks.
3. Malahide, RMcM/c.65. Sand-hills on Malahide Island, PR/85.
5. East of The Farm and south-east of the Royal Dublin Golf-course on North Bull Island, HJH/85. Alder Marsh, North Bull Island, DNFC/84. On the edges of ponds in Portmarnock Golf-course, DN/89.

D. purpurella (Stephenson & T.A. Stephenson) Soó *(Orchis purpurella, D. majalis* subsp. *purpurella)*
Northern Marsh-orchid   Native
Suppl: 5. Abundant in "Alder-marsh" on North Bull (1948). 8. Ballybetagh Bog (1948). Probably present in Colgan's time but not then segregated.

| **5** | **7** | **8** |

Rare, in dune-slacks, marshes and wet meadows.
5. Alder Marsh on North Bull Island, PWJ/77 & PG/89, 90. North Bull Island, MS/65.
7. St Anne's Fields, in Glenasmole, R. Piper/70, **NDR**.
8. Wet meadow, south of Ballybetagh Bog on the county boundary, SR/88.

D. traunsteineri (Sauter ex Reichenb.) Soó *(O. traunsteinerioides)*
Narrow-leaved Marsh-orchid   Native

Suppl: 8. Ballyman Glen (J.P. Brunker, 1940-1957), where it occurs sparingly on the Dublin side of the stream (here the county boundary), as well as in the original station on the Wicklow side of the glen.

(8)

Orchis

O. mascula (L.) L.
Early-purple Orchid   Native

| (1) | **2** | **3** | **4** | (5) | (6) | **7** | **8** |

Rare, in woodland and scrub. *Colgan* noted that it was frequent and locally abundant in copses, moist pastures and banks. In *Suppl* it was still regarded as common. It is a species which has declined dramatically in Dublin this century.

2. Lane, running north-west from Rathmooney (planted in a garden from a parent population of local origin which we have been unable to relocate), DD, RF/85.
3. Amongst **Ulex europaeus**, at Knocksedan Reservoir, MN/83. Sandy grassland at Burrow, Portrane, PR, DD/83.
4. 'Rabbit Warren' woods at Luttrellstown, JS/83.
7. Still in Glenasmole in St Anne's Fields, R. Piper/70. Cot and Slade brooks, south of Glenasmole Lodge, HOR/85. Woodland south-west of Friarstown House, and nearby in a wood to the south by the River Slade at Ballymaice, JP/86 & JP, MWJ/88. Western slope above the northern reservoir in Glenasmole, MN/90.
8. Ballyman Glen, south of Ballyman House, CM, D. Maxwell/c. 79.

O. morio L.
Green-winged Orchid   Native

Colgan: 2. Abundant in pastures east of Baldrummond, 1895; west of Haystown, Lusk, and between Haystown and Whitestown, 1900; 3. Abundant in sandy pastures near the shore at Portrane, 1894-99: *N.C.* 5. Between Kilbarrick and Warren Lodge and below Carrickbrack: *Flor. Howth.* Sparingly in the sandhills, North Bull, 1903: *Scully.* Abundant on Feltrim Hill, 1902; 6. In Saggard Slade and in pastures north of Milltown, 1895; 7. Frequent in pastures in Glenasmole and at Piperstown, 1895: *N.C.* 8. Lands about Loughlinstown: *Ir. Flor.* Below Ticknock, 1895: *N.C.* At Delbrook, Dundrum: Tatlow 1898. *Suppl:* Frequent. 2. Abundant in Rush sandhills (1945). Near Lowther Lodge, Gormanstown (1946). 3. Pastures near Knocksedan (1932). 5. Swamp near Howth Summit tram stop (J.P. Brunker, 1918). 8. Killiney (1932).

| **2** | **3** | **5** | (6) | **7** | (8) |

Rare, in stable dune-grassland and unimproved sandy pastures. Legally protected under the Wildlife Act of 1976 as an endangered species in Ireland. Like the last species, this has also suffered a great decline this century in Dublin.

2. Short grazed coastal grassland north of Loughshinny, RF/88, 91. In short dune-grassland at the south and south-west ends of Rush Golf-course, DD/83, 91.
3. Scattered, but quite frequent in some places, on the Portrane Peninsula, PR/84 & DD/91. Sandy hollows, north of Burrow, Portrane, PR/84. Baring (1915a) recorded it on Lambay but it may be an error for *O. mascula.*
5. Six plants in grassland at Windgate Road, Howth, CB/91.

7. Still in Glenasmole at St Anne's Fields, R. Piper/70. A few plants in grassland north of St Ann's Graveyard, Glenasmole, CB, PH/91. South-west of Piperstown, DN, PG, C. Breen/92.

Ophrys

O. apifera Hudson
Bee Orchid   Native

Colgan: 2. At Kenure Park and in Rush sandhills, 1891 *(Miss A.G. Kinahan) Cyb. II & MS.* At Skerries, 1892 *(Rev. T.B. Gibson) Colgan 1895a.* 3. Sandhills at Portrane, 1864 *(Moore) Herb. Glasnevin* and in 1869: *Hart MS.* 4. By the Royal Canal above Blanchardstown, 1902: *N.C.* 5. In the mid-way between Stockoole and St Doulough's: *Wade Rar.* Portmarnock sands, near the south end, abundantly: *Mack. Cat.* Sparingly at Beechfields and more plentifully at Sea Lawn, 1881-87 *(Miss Mahaffy) Flor. Howth.* In Santry demesne, 1890: *Rev. T.B. Gibson.* Banks by the shore near Robb's walls, Malahide, 1897: *Miss S. Colgan.* Railway bank near Malahide, 1900 *(N.C.) Top. Bot.* 7. Green Hills, near Drimnagh: *Colgan 1895a.* 8. Sparingly behind the Rev. Mr Dowling's school at Blackrock: *Wade Dubl.* Meadows by the sea between Ballybrack and Bray, in some abundance, 1886: *Praeger 1894a.* Sparingly at the foot of Killiney Hill, 1894: *Colgan 1895.* A couple of dozens of plants above the bathing place at Vico, 1898-1902: *N.C.* Sparingly at Delbrook, Dundrum: *Tatlow 1898.*

Suppl: 4. Finglas Quarries (Rev. H. Jennings, 1922). 5. Still near Robswalls (J.P. Brunker, 1919), North Bull (J.A.J. Palmer, 1933) and 1947), St Doolagh's Quarries (1930-1955). In 1933 very large plants were seen here, one having twelve blossoms on a single stem. 7. Small quarry opposite Mount St Joseph's, Clondalkin (A.W. Stelfox, 1953). 8. Loughlinstown Common (M.R. Eaton, 1920). Still at Vico in 1958.

Rare, in dune-grassland, limestone quarries and on sandy roadside cuttings.
3. Common in sand-hills on the east side of Malahide Island, PR/85.
4. Calcareous grassland at Corduff, Blanchardstown, MN, PR, RF/83. Bank of the Royal Canal above Blanchardstown Bridge, DD/68.
5. Calcareous grassland in St Doolagh's Quarry, DD/67, 68. Scattered in small quantities in sand-hills south-west of the roundabout at the end of the causeway on North Bull Island, and east of The Farm and in the Alder Marsh, CB, ENL/86, HJH/85, DN/88 & PG/88, 89. Rough of the eastern side of Portmarnock Golf-course, DN/89.
6. Bank of the Grand Canal between 12th lock and Gollierstown, G.W.D. Bailey/66. Grassed-over waste from the quarry at Gollierstown, MN/90.
7. Two plants in calcareous grassland at Gallanstown, DD/92.
8. Common on a steep bank by the Bray Road below Loughlinstown Hospital, SR/85. Vico bathing place, M. ffrench-Mullen, DD/69 & WAW/53, 70s. Bank at Shankill Railway Station, Dara Shaw-Smith/96.

SUPPLEMENTARY LIST
OF CASUAL PLANTS AND ALIEN PLANTS
WHICH ARE NOT FULLY NATURALIZED

The following is a list of casual and alien plants which have been recorded in Co. Dublin since the publication of Colgan's *Flora* (1904). Particular emphasis has been given to recent records, i.e. those noted during the present survey. Species listed in Colgan's Appendix of "Errors, casuals and aliens not fully naturalised" have not been repeated here if there is no more recent record for them. The list includes plants which have not been deliberately planted and those which have not become fully naturalized at the present time.

The Dublin Port region is a particularly rich area for casuals and aliens. The casuals found there as well as on roadsides, wasteground and rubbish dumps generally fail to persist for more than a year or so, and are not widely distributed. At Dublin Port, the main source of alien seed is imported cereals and animal feed. Elsewhere, alien plants often originate as garden escapes or discards. Some garden plants, as well as planted hedges, may persist long after a garden has been abandoned. Trees which are planted are included in the list only if there is evidence that they self-seed or spread vegetatively.

SELAGINELLACEAE

Selaginella kraussiana (Kunze) A. Braun   Krauss's Clubmoss
7. Established on west bank of the stream beside the walled garden in Massey Woods, DNFC/80s, SR/94.

ADIANTACEAE

Adiantum capillus-veneris L.   Maidenhair Fern
Although native in parts of Ireland, this fern is a garden escape in Co. Dublin.
7. Naturalized on walls in Ranelagh from Sallymount Avenue to Appian Way, MWJ/88.

PTERIDACEAE

Pteris cretica L.   Ribbon Fern
4. Under a grille in Parnell St. (*FID*).

PINACEAE

Picea sitchensis (Bong.) Carriere   Sitka Spruce
A commonly planted species used for forestry. It occasionally seeds itself in and around plantations.

Larix decidua Miller   European Larch
A frequently planted species used for forestry. It sometimes seeds itself in and around plantations. **L. kaempferi** (Lindley) Carriere, Japanese Larch, and the hybrid between European and Japanese Larch, **L.** x **marschlinsii** Coaz, are also planted.

Pinus sylvestris L.   Scots Pine
A commonly planted tree in parks and demesnes which frequently seeds itself.

P. contorta Douglas ex Loudon   Lodgepole Pine
Occasionally planted for forestry, and capable of regenerating.

TAXACEAE

Taxus baccata L.   Yew
Planted in Co. Dublin; occasionally self-seeds.

NYMPHAEACEAE

Nymphaea alba L.   White Water-lily
Ponds and lakes throughout the county, but always originally planted.

RANUNCULACEAE

Consolida ajacis (L.) Schur (*Delphinium ajacis*)   Larkspur
8. Ringsend Dump (Curtis & Wyse Jackson 1979). A casual on disturbed ground at Cabinteely, SR/84; near Ringsend Park, SR, HOR/85; Sandyford Industrial Estate, SR/93; by Pigeon House Road, SR/94.

BERBERIDACEAE

Berberis darwinii Hook. x **B. empetrifolia** Lam. (**B.** x **stenophylla** Lindley)
Hedge Barberry
5. Cliff top near The Needles, Howth, DN/90. Very rarely self-seeding.

PAPAVERACEAE

Eschscholzia californica Cham.   Californian Poppy
Garden escape, and never more than a casual (*FID*).

PLATANACEAE

Platanus occidentalis L. x **P. orientalis** L. (**P.** x **hispanica** Miller ex Muenchh.; *P. hybrida*)
London Plane
A commonly planted street tree, rarely self-sown (*FID*).

CANNABACEAE

Cannabis sativa L.   Hemp
8. On dumped soil at Dun Laoghaire, SR/85; on rubble and garden rubbish in Irishtown, Patrick Wyse Jackson/87.

MORACEAE

Ficus carica L.   Fig
4. Near Mountjoy Prison, on bank of Royal Canal, HJH/80 (*FID*).
7. By the Grand Canal, west of Huband's Bridge, MS, A. Austin/91.

- -

FAGACEAE

Castanea sativa Miller   Sweet Chestnut
Occasionally planted throughout the county, particularly in the larger estates and parks. Very
rarely self-sown.

Quercus cerris L.   Turkey Oak
Commonly planted.
4. Seedlings are occasionally found near mature trees, e.g. in Phoenix Park.
7. Seedling at Earlsfort Terrace (*FID*).

- -

BETULACEAE

Carpinus betulus L.   Hornbeam
Frequently planted as specimen trees (including the fastigiate form), and as hedges.
7. West of and below Mount Seskin, PWJ, MWJ/86.

- -

CHENOPODIACEAE

Chenopodium glaucum L.   Oak-leaved Goosefoot
5. Dublin Port, SR/89.

C. urbicum L.   Upright Goosefoot
(4). Custom House Docks, J.P. Brunker.

C. murale L.   Nettle-leaved Goosefoot
Already considered by *Colgan* to be a decreasing species in the county. There are records for
this casual in the 1950s in 6 and 7 (*Suppl*).
5. Dublin Port, SR/90,91.

C. ficifolium Smith   Fig-leaved Goosefoot
There are a few 19th century records in *Colgan*.
5. Wasteground east of Fairview Park and the railway, SR/86.

Bassia scoparia (L.) Voss (*Kochia scoparia*)   Summer-cypress
5. Dublin Port, SR/91.

Salsola kali L. subsp. **ruthenica** (Iljin) Soó   Spineless Saltwort
5. Dublin Port, SR/89.

AMARANTHACEAE

Amaranthus retroflexus L.   Common Amaranth
This species was found on Howth at the end of the 19th century.
4. North side of River Liffey in Dublin city, MSS/c.88.
5. Dublin Port, SR/88-91.

CARYOPHYLLACEAE

Arenaria balearica L.   Mossy Sandwort
5. Footpath on Howth Head, J. White/64 (**DBN**).

Silene muscipula L.
5. Dublin Port, SR/90.

S. gallica L. (*S. anglica*)   Small-flowered Catchfly
Formerly recorded as a colonist on sandy soils amongst vegetable crops at Portmarnock in the
19th century and at Baldoyle in 1900.
5. Dublin Port, SR/90.

Vaccaria hispanica (Miller) Rauschert (*Saponaria vaccaria*)   Cowherb
There are several old records for this species as a casual in the county.
5. Dublin Port, SR/89.

POLYGONACEAE

Persicaria campanulata (Hook.f.) Ronse Decraene (*Polygonum campanulatum*)
Lesser Knotweed
A rare introduction, found only in 5 and 8.

P. wallichii Greuter & Burdet *(Polygonum polystachyum)*   Himalayan Knotweed
6. Tallaght quarry, JP/83.
8. By a stream at Little Bray, HOR/86.

P. amplexicaulis (D. Don) Ronse Decraene *(Polygonum amplexicaule)*   Red Bistort
7. Fitzwilliam Square (*FID*).
8. Roadside between Carrickmines Station and Cabinteely, Barrington/31 (**DBN**); among
    shrubs and on wasteground near the ferry port, Dun Laoghaire, SR, HOR/84.

Fallopia baldschuanica (Regel) Holub *(F. aubertii, Polygonum baldschuanicum)*   Russian-vine
2. North of coastguard station, Rush, DD/87.
5. Hedgerow at Malahide, DN/88; wasteground at Dublin Port, DN/88. Portmarnock,
TC, MWJ/96.
8. Ringsend Dump, SR/93.

CLUSIACEAE (*GUTTIFERAE*)

Hypericum calycinum L.   Rose-of-Sharon
In Dublin city, naturalized on wasteground near gardens (*FID*).
3. Established in sand-dunes at Corballis, SR/97.
8. North slope of Three Rock Mountain above Barnacullia, HOR/83.

H. androsaemum L. x **H. hircinum** L. (**H.** x **inodorum** Miller; *H. elatum*)   Tall Tutsan
6. In grassland at Jobstown, JP/86.

MALVACEAE

Malva pusilla Smith (*M. borealis*)   Small Mallow
There is one 19th century record in *Colgan*.
5. On infill at Dublin Port, SR/90.

VIOLACEAE

Viola spp., including **V.** x **wittrockiana** Gams ex Kappert   Garden Pansies
Occasional on roadsides and waste ground.

TAMARICACEAE

Tamarix gallica L.   Tamarisk
8. Young plants on Ballyogan tiphead, SR/93.

SALICACEAE

Populus alba L.   White Poplar
Quite commonly planted; occasionally well established from suckers in hedgerows even after the parent trees have disappeared.

P. alba L. x **P. tremula** L. (**P.** x **canescens**) (Aiton) Smith   Grey Poplar
Occasional; planted, but can spread by suckering.
6. By the Grand Canal north of Newcastle, JP/84.
7. By road 1 km east of Firhouse, MWJ, DAW/87.
8. By wall of Stillorgan Reservoir near Sandyford Industrial Estate, SR, HOR/85.

P. nigra L.   Black-poplar
This species, particularly var. **italica** Muenchh. (Lombardy Poplar) and **P. nigra** x **P. deltoides** Marsh. (**P.** x **canadensis** Moench) are frequently planted in Dublin. Hobson (1991) provides no evidence that **P. nigra** is native in the county.

Salix alba L. x **S. fragilis** L. (**S.** x **rubens** Schrank)   Hybrid Crack-willow
5. North Bull Island, KF/63.
6. Field margin, near stream, Fortunestown, JP/80s.

S. triandra L. x **S. viminalis** L. (**S. x mollissima** Hoffm. ex Elwert)   Sharp-stipuled Willow
6. Canal bank, Clondalkin, JP/80s.

S. purpurea L. x **S. viminalis** L. (**S. x rubra** Hudson)   Green-leaved Willow
4. By the Tolka at Blanchardstown, MN/88.

S. viminalis L. x **S. caprea** L. x **S. cinerea** L. (**S. x calodendron** Wimmer)   Holme Willow
5. In field on Thormanby Road, Howth, DN/89; Portmarnock, DN/89.
7. Roadside at top of Glenasmole valley, MN/89.

S. viminalis L. x **S. caprea** L. x **S. aurita** L. (**S. x stipularis** Smith)   Eared Osier
8. South end of Leopardstown racecourse, near the pond, SR/88.

S. viminalis L. x **S. cinerea** L. (**S. x smithiana** Willd.)   Silky-leaved Osier
2. Drain by roadside, north-west of Lusk, DD/84.

- -

CAPPARACEAE

Cleome hassleriana Chodat   Spiderflower
8. Ringsend, PWJ/80s.

- -

BRASSICACEAE (*CRUCIFERAE*)

Matthiola incana (L.) R.Br.   Hoary Stock
Only rarely found away from gardens.
5. Near the coast, Malahide, PG/88.
8. On coastal clay cliff south of Killiney railway station, SR/88-94.

Cardamine bulbifera (L.) Crantz   Coralroot
5. Malahide Castle, in the demesne (Lamb 1983).
8. Marley Park (Jackson 1983).

Aubrieta deltoidea (L.) DC.   Aubretia
A common garden plant occasionally found on Ringsend Dump and elsewhere.

Lunaria annua L.   Honesty
An occasional garden escape.
4. Gravel pits in Phoenix Park (Reilly 1993).
5. St Doolagh's quarries, DNFC/83.
7. Wasteground near Clondalkin, PWJ, MSS/87.

Lobularia maritima (L.) Desv.   Sweet Alison
Occasional as a garden escape, and on rubbish dumps.

Draba muralis L.   Wall Whitlowgrass
This species was recorded as abundant on the walls of the Botanic Gardens, Glasnevin, last century (*Colgan*).

7.   As a weed in Trinity College Botanic Garden, PWJ/80s.
(8). Wall top, Merrion Ave. (Praeger 1946b).

Camelina sativa (L.) Crantz   Gold-of-pleasure
There are a number of records by J.P. Brunker and others for this casual in the county pre-1960.
5. North Bull Island, G.J. Sheehan/65 (**DBN**).
8. Ballyogan tiphead, SR/94.

Neslia paniculata (L.)Desv.   Ball Mustard
5. Alexandra Quay, Dublin Port, SR/93.

Lepidium sativum L.   Garden Cress
Record in *Colgan*, "on the shore of Dublin Bay near Howth, 1799, perhaps from the wreck of a vessel".
1. Waste ground, Bog of the Ring, DS/64 (**DBN**).
8. Ballyogan tiphead, SR/94.

L. ruderale L.   Narrow-leaved Pepperwort
Some old records for this species may be referable to **L. densiflorum**.
4. Dunsink tiphead, SR/93.
7. Leeson Street, DN/91.
8. Nutley Lane, DN/91.

Brassica oleracea L.   Cabbage
Occasional on wasteground and rubbish dumps as a garden discard.

B. fruticulosa Cirillo   Twiggy Turnip
5. Dublin Port, SR/90.

Raphanus sativus L.   Garden Radish
2. Grassy bank at Rogerstown Pier, DD/88.
4. Disturbed ground by road south of St Margaret's, DNFC/90.
8. South-east of Stepaside, HOR/85; roadside at Laughanstown, SR, HOR/85.

ERICACEAE

Gaultheria shallon Pursh   Shallon
5. In grass on either side of the cliff path near Drumleck Point, Howth, DN/89.

G. mucronata (L.f.) Hook. & Arn. (*Pernettya mucronata*)   Prickly Heath
5. Established in disused quarry, Ben of Howth, CB/91.
6. Tallaght quarry, JP/83; roadside south of Jobstown, JP/86.

PRIMULACEAE

Cyclamen hederifolium Aiton   Cyclamen
An occasional relic of garden cultivation.

GROSSULARIACEAE

Ribes rubrum L.　Red Currant
Commonly cultivated and occasionally self-sown.

R. nigrum L.　Black Currant
Commonly cultivated and occasionally self-sown; it also grows easily from discarded cuttings.

R. sanguineum Pursh　Flowering Currant
Commonly cultivated as a garden shrub or hedge. Occasional in hedgerows.

R. uva-crispa L.　Gooseberry
Commonly cultivated, and occasionally self-sown; mainly in suburban areas.

- -

CRASSULACEAE

Crassula helmsii (Kirk) Cockayne　New Zealand Pigmyweed
4. National Botanic Gardens, DS/90, DN/93.
7. Pond at top of Ballinascorney Gap, JP, DD/89, DN/90. Originally introduced with other aquatic plants.

Sedum telephium L.　Orpine
7. Walkinstown, PWJ, MWJ/87.

- -

SAXIFRAGACEAE

Tellima grandiflora (Pursh) Douglas ex Lindley　Fringe-cups
8. Naturalized by stream in Marley Park, P. Jackson/85, SR/94.

- -

ROSACEAE

Spiraea salicifolia L. x **S. douglasii** Hook. (**S.** x **pseudosalicifolia** Silverside)
Confused Bridewort
6. In hedges, Brittas, DNFC; Jobstown, JP/86; Glenaraneen, JP/87.

Duchesnea indica (Andrews) Focke　Yellow-flowered Strawberry
7. Garden in Dublin City, Des Murphy/70 (**DBN**).
8. Garden in Dun Laoghaire, not deliberately introduced, Margaret Ramming/93.

Acaena novae-zelandiae Kirk　Pirri-pirri-bur
5. Malahide Castle (McClintock 1979). **Acaena** sp. was found in St Anne's Park, Raheny, PG/88.

A. ovalifolia Ruiz Lopez & Pavon　Two-spined Acaena
(6). Naturalized in a demesne at Lucan in the 1920s (McClintock 1979).

Alchemilla mollis (Buser) Rothm.　Lady's-mantle
7. Wasteground off Earlsfort Terrace, PWJ, JRA/81 (*FID*).

Rosa rugosa Thunb. ex Murray Japanese Rose
Usually planted.
6. In hedgerows near Fettercairn House, JP/86.
7. In abandoned pastures and waste ground off Greenhills Road, PWJ, HOR, SR/84.

Prunus cerasifera Ehrh. Cherry Plum
In hedges; not effectively naturalized.
2. North of Gracedieu, DD/83.
8. Leopardstown racecourse, SR/83; old estate, south of Dundrum, SR/84; Brewery Road near Stillorgan reservoirs, SR, HOR/85.

P. cerasus L. Dwarf Cherry
2. Hedgerows at Newlawn House, DD/85, and Balbriggan, RF/86; roadside near an old ruin west of Corn Mill, Balbriggan, DD/87.

P. padus L. Bird Cherry
2. Hedgerow, Man O' War Inn, DD/84.
6. Hedgerow at Aderrig, JP/89.

P. lusitanica L. Portugal Laurel
Usually planted.
4. River Tolka at Abbotstown, MN, JS/84.
6. Field margin, north-east of Newcastle, JP/80s.

Pyrus pyraster (L.) Burgsd. Wild Pear
4. Near Corduff (Nelson and Walsh 1993).

Cotoneaster simonsii Baker, **C. lacteus** W. Smith, **C. horizontalis** Decne. and **C. integrifolius** (Roxb.) Klotz have been recorded occasionally in Co. Dublin as garden escapes. Many other species are cultivated and may become naturalized from bird-sown seeds.

Cotoneaster franchetii Bois Franchet's Cotoneaster
7. On wall of ruin, Mount Venus, DK, SR/88 (**TCD**).

Crataegus laevigata (Poiret) DC. (*C. oxyacanthoides*) Midland Hawthorn
8. Kilgobbin, under beech, probably planted, PC/72. Also formerly known from Upper Churchtown (1930) and bank of the River Dodder below Ballsbridge (1947) (*Suppl*).

FABACEAE (*LEGUMINOSAE*)

Securigera varia (L.) Lassen (*Coronilla varia*) Crown Vetch
4. In roadside hedge opposite entrance to Laurel Lodge, between Castleknock and Blanchardstown, DD/83, MN/86.

Vicia faba L. Broad Bean
Occasional, e.g. on rubbish dumps, at Dublin Port. Does not become established.
FID.

Lens culinaris Medikus   Lentil
4. On wasteground near health food shop, Gardiner Street, JRA/79 (*FID*).

Pisum sativum L.   Garden Pea
Occasional; does not become established.
5. Dublin Port, SR/90,94.
8. Ballyogan tiphead, SR/94; purple-flowered, the variety grown for fodder, on Ringsend Dump, SR/94.

Cicer arietinum L.   Chick Pea
5. On wasteground near health food shop, Gardiner Street, JRA/79 (*FID*).

Medicago polymorpha L. (*M. denticulata*)   Toothed Medick
There are several records for this species in Dublin around 1900.
5. Wasteground by River Tolka, east of Ballybough, DD/85.
8. Ringsend Dump, SR/90.

Lupinus arboreus Sims   Tree Lupin
2. Wasteground at Malahide, DN/88.
8. Ringsend Dump, DNFC/80s.

Laburnum anagyroides Medikus   Laburnum
Occasionally self-seeding, but usually near established plants (*FID*).
_ _

GUNNERACEAE

Gunnera tinctoria (Molina) Mirbel   Giant-rhubarb
5. Established in wet birch grove on Ben of Howth, CB/91.
_ _

THYMELAEACEAE

Daphne laureola L.   Spurge-laurel
4. Naturalized on railway bank near Cross Guns Bridge (*FID*); in beech wood beside old castle at Castleknock College, JS, MN/83; Luttrellstown, JS,MN/84.
_ _

ONAGRACEAE

Fuchsia magellanica Lam. (incl. *F. gracilis*)   Fuchsia
Occasionally planted and sometimes persisting in hedges (*FID*).

Circaea alpina L.   Alpine Enchanter's-nightshade
(8). A weed at Lonsdale, Grove Ave., Blackrock in 1939 (Praeger 1946b).
_ _

VISCACEAE

Viscum album L.   Mistletoe
Occasionally found in gardens throughout the county, mainly in old orchards on apple trees.

4. On an apple tree just outside the National Botanic Gardens, Glasnevin; on trees in the Gardens since the 19th century (Synnott 1992a).

(7). Formerly on trees at Lansdowne Road outside the old Trinity College Botanic Garden, DAW/pre-1960.

EUPHORBIACEAE

Euphorbia lathyris L.   Caper Spurge
An occasional garden escape.

VITACEAE

Parthenocissus quinquefolia (L.) Planchon and **P. inserta** (A. Kerner) Fritsch

Virginia-creeper

Not effectively naturalized, but persist on wasteground and old walls; also regenerate from cuttings (*FID*).

LINACEAE

Linum usitatissimum L.   Flax
A constituent of bird-seed, and cultivated as a crop for linseed-oil. On wasteground in Dublin City (*FID*), at Dublin Port, and occasionally on roadsides.

HIPPOCASTANACEAE

Aesculus hippocastanum L.   Horse-chestnut
Widely planted, especially in the centre and south of the county. Self-sown in hedgerows, parks and gardens (*FID*).

ACERACEAE

Acer platanoides L.   Norway Maple
Commonly planted; sometimes self-seeding.

A. macrophyllum Pursh   Oregon Maple
7. Seedlings, Trinity College, Dublin (*FID*).

A. campestre L.   Field Maple
Occasional in hedges far from habitation.
3. Hedgerow at Balheary House, DD, PR/84; hedgerow, Forrest Great, DD/86.

OXALIDACEAE

Oxalis articulata Savigny   Pink-sorrel
5. Amongst brambles, Hill of Howth (Young 1958).

O. incarnata L.   Pale Pink-sorrel
8. Ringsend Dump, SR/93.

GERANIACEAE

Geranium endressii Gay   French Crane's-bill
3. In wet ditch beside Portrane Road, Donabate, JP/82.

G. endressii Gay x **G. versicolor** L. (**G.** x **oxonianum** Yeo)   Druce's Crane's-bill
8. Barnaslingan Lane, south-east of Kiltiernan, SR, HOR/84.

G. versicolor L. (*G. striatum*)   Pencilled Crane's-bill
A garden escape which tends to persist.
3. Corballis Junction, PR, DD/83.
5. Still at St Anne's Park, Raheny (*Suppl*), PG/88.
8. In wood at U.C.D. Belfield, DN/85.

G. phaeum L.   Dusky Crane's-bill
5. Baskin Lane, Cloghran (DNFC Annual Report 1965).

TROPAEOLACEAE

Tropaeolum majus L.   Nasturtium
An occasional garden escape.

BALSAMINACEAE

Impatiens parviflora DC.   Small Balsam
4. Base of wall at bridge over River Tolka north of Ashtown, and nearby, MN, PR/85.
7. Damp lane by Biochemistry and Zoology buildings, Trinity College (*FID*); still there, JR/94.

APIACEAE (*UMBELLIFERAE*)

Bupleurum subovatum Link ex Sprengel   False Thorow-wax
Specimens in **DBN** labelled **B. protractum** and **B. rotundifolium** are referrable to
B. subovatum.
5.   North Bull Island causeway, BB/82 (**DBN**).
(7). Wasteground at Inchicore, C.B. Moffat/24 (**DBN**) [not **B. rotundifolium**, Moffat (1924)];
    Liffey Junction, Dr Bewley/27 (**DBN**).

Carum carvi L.   Caraway
Known as a casual in the county since the 19th century.
5. North Wall, J.P. Brunker/34; North Bull Island causeway, PG/88.
8. Wasteground at Sandyford Industrial Estate, SR/83.

SOLANACEAE

Physalis peruviana L.   Cape-gooseberry
8. Ballyogan tiphead, SR/93.

Lycopersicon esculentum Miller   Tomato
Temporarily established plants originating from washed-up seeds deposited with sewage were found on the coast: Skerries and Rush Harbour (2), Sandymount Strand, Merrion Strand, Seapoint, Sandycove and the shore south of Killiney near Sewage works (8). Inland, plants originate from discarded fruit and domestic rubbish.

Solanum tuberosum L.   Potato
Generally a casual derived from discarded domestic tubers, though some clumps appear to persist for a few years.

Datura stramonium L.   Thorn-apple
8. Ringsend dump, PWJ/late 1970s.

CONVOLVULACEAE

Calystegia pulchra Brummitt & Heyw.   Hairy Bindweed
(2). Balrothery, D. McClintock/57 (McClintock 1960).
8.   Vico, at top of railway cutting, C. Pearson/46 (**TCD**); seaward-facing bank just north of Killiney railway station, SR/92.

BORAGINACEAE

Echium pininana Webb & Berth.   Giant Viper's-bugloss
5. South slopes of Howth Head (Nelson 1994).

Pulmonaria officinalis L.   Lungwort
6. Roadside hedgerow south-east of Casement Aerodrome, JP/86.

Symphytum grandiflorum DC.   Creeping Comfrey
(5). Roadside near Baily P.O., Howth, S. Clark/60 (**TCD**).

Trachystemon orientalis (L.) Don   Abraham-Isaac-Jacob
5. St Anne's Park, Raheny, PG/88.

Myosotis sylvatica Hoffm.   Wood Forget-me-not
This is the common garden species, which seeds freely and occasionally escapes.

Lappula squarrosa (Retz.) Dumort. (*Echinospermum lappula*)   Bur Forget-me-not
Colgan gives old records for this casual.
5. Dublin Port, SR/88.

LAMIACEAE (*LABIATAE*)

Mentha spicata L. x **M. suaveolens** Huds. (**M.** x **villosa** Huds.)   Apple-mint
8. Persistent in an abandoned garden by Pigeon House Road, SR/94.

PLANTAGINACEAE

Plantago arenaria Waldst. & Kit.   Branched Plantain
There are several 19th century records for Co. Dublin.
(2). Sandy field, Rush, M.J. Gorman/35 (**DBN**).

OLEACEAE

Syringa vulgaris L.   Lilac
Occasionally persistent, mainly in hedgerows; usually spreads by suckering.

Ligustrum ovalifolium Hassk.   Garden Privet
Occasional in hedges throughout the county.

SCROPHULARIACEAE

Antirrhinum majus L.   Snapdragon
Widespread as a garden escape, especially in the city and suburbs.

Hebe salicifolia (G. Forster) Pennell   Koromiko
5. Self-sown, east of Black Linn, Ben of Howth, DK/93.

H. elliptica (G. Forster) Pennell x **H. speciosa** (R. Cunn. ex Cunn.) Cockayne & Allan
(**H. franciscana** (Eastw.) Souster)   Hedge Veronica
A common seaside hedging plant, occasionally naturalized.
5. Howth, near The Needles, DAW/67, DN/90, and at Lion's Head, DN/90.
8. North of Sorrento Point, Dalkey, DK/89. Colgan recorded 'Shrubby Veronica' in the same
   area, though he was not sure which species it was (*Colgan*).

OROBANCHACEAE

Lathraea clandestina L.   Purple Toothwort
4. Known at the National Botanic Gardens, Glasnevin, since the 1940s, and still there on willow
and poplar by the Tolka and millrace, DS/94; nearby on the bank of the River Tolka in the
grounds of Clonliffe College, Brennan/57 (**DBN**).

CAMPANULACEAE

Campanula persicifolia L.   Peach-leaved Bellflower
8. Ringsend Dump, SR/93.

C. trachelium L.   Nettle-leaved Bellflower
Although native in parts of Ireland, in Co. Dublin this is a garden escape.
8. Under trees, off Sandymount Ave., HOR/85; wasteground at the south end of Leopardstown
   racecourse, SR/85.

CAPRIFOLIACEAE

Lonicera nitida E. Wilson   Wilson's Honeysuckle
Widespread in hedges in the county, sometimes far from houses. Always originally planted or as a discard from cultivation.

DIPSACACEAE

Dipsacus sativus (L.) Honck.   Fuller's Teasel
8. Ringsend Dump, SR, JR/90-94.

D. fullonum L. x **D. sativus**
8. Ringsend Dump, with both its parents, SR,DN/95 (Reynolds 1997. *Watsonia* **21**:285-289).

ASTERACEAE (*COMPOSITAE*)

Echinops bannaticus Rochel ex Schrader   Blue Globe-thistle
7. Of garden origin, persisting in wasteground west of Cherry Orchard Hospital, Ballyfermot, MWJ/87.

Onopordum acanthium L.   Cotton Thistle
8. Ringsend Dump, R. Rohu/83, PWJ, Q. Cronk/86, SR/94.

Centaurea solstitialis L.   Yellow Star-thistle
(4). Custom House Docks, J.P. Brunker/23.

Tragopogon porrifolius L.   Salsify
(3). Lambay Island (Stelfox 1923c).
8. As a garden weed, Dun Laoghaire, M. ffrench-Mullen/75.

Pilosella aurantiaca (L.) F. Schultz & Schultz-Bip.   Fox-and-cubs
4. Top of Knockmaroon Hill, MN/88.

P. aurantiaca subsp. **carpathicola** (Naeg. & Peter) Sojak
6. In grassland at Casement Aerodrome, JP/80s.

Aster novi-belgii L. sensu lato   Michaelmas-daisy
'Michaelmas-daisy' can be any of several species and hybrids. It is an occasional garden escape, and until recently records were usually aggregated into this taxon.

A. laevis x **A. novi-belgii** (**A. x versicolor** Willd.)   Late Michaelmas-daisy
8. In grassland just north of Booterstown Marsh, SR/92.

A. novi-belgii L. sensu stricto   Confused Michaelmas-daisy
8. In grassland just north of Booterstown Marsh, SR/92.

A. novi-belgii. x **A. lanceolatus** (**A.** x **salignus** Willd.)   Common Michaelmas-daisy
5. Dublin Port, SR/88.
7. By the Grand Canal near Charlemont Place, A. Austin, SR/94.
8. In grassland just north of Booterstown Marsh, SR/92.

Conyza sumatrensis (Retz.) E. Walker   Guernsey Fleabane
5. Dublin Port, by Tolka Quay Road, SR/88-94.

Artemisia stelleriana Besser   Hoary Mugwort
(5). A garden escape naturalized on North Bull Island from 1891 to 1924, when the dune on
      which it was growing was swept away (Brunker 1952).

Chamaemelum mixtum (L.) All.
5. On infill at Dublin Port, SR/90.

Senecio fluviatilis Wallr. (*S. sarracenicus*)   Broad-leaved Ragwort
Colgan recorded this as a relic of cultivation at Bohernabreena and by the River Dodder (7).
4. A weed in Roe's Nurseries, Mulhuddart, in 1973 (**DBN**).

Doronicum pardalianches L.   Leopard's-Bane
4. On bank of River Liffey at Broomfield, MN/88.

Calendula officinalis L.   Pot Marigold
An occasional garden escape on wasteground and rubbish dumps.

Helianthus annuus L.   Sunflower
Occasionally found on rubbish dumps; also on infill at Dublin Port, SR/88-92.

HYDROCHARITACEAE

Lagarosiphon major (Ridley) Moss   Curly Waterweed
7. Pond at top of Ballinascorney Gap, JP, DD/89, DN/90. Originally introduced with other
aquatic plants.

POACEAE (*GRAMINEAE*)

Sasa palmata (Burb.) Camus   Broad-leaved Bamboo
4. Spreading by the river, possibly naturalized, in the grounds of Luttrellstown House, JP/83.

Briza maxima L.   Greater Quaking-Grass
5. Cliff path at Doldrum Bay, Howth, DD/70s, CB/92.
8. Among grass and brambles by Pigeon House Road, SR/94.

Poa chaixii Villars   Broad-leaved Meadow-grass
8. Naturalized under beech trees beside the pond at the south end of Leopardstown
racecourse, MAF/93.

Avena sativa L.　Oat
Roadsides, from spilled grain; Dublin Port; occasional on wasteground and rubbish dumps.

Gaudinia fragilis (L.) P. Beauv.　French Oat-grass
(8). Ringsend in 1906 (Scannell 1972).

Lagurus ovatus L.　Hare's-tail
Often grown as an ornamental grass.
5. Dublin Port, SR/93.
7. Kildare Street, MS/73 (**DBN**).
FID.

Apera spica-venti (L.) P. Beauv.　Loose Silky-bent
Colgan noted that this species was "a casual not seen recently".
5. Alexandra Quay, Dublin Port, SR/94.

Polypogon monspeliensis (L.) Desf.　Annual Beard-grass
(4). Roadside at Cabra, J.P. Brunker/22.
(7). Frequent from Indian grain screenings, St. James's Gate, J.P. Brunker.

Anisantha madritensis (L.) Nevski (*Bromus madritensis*)　Compact Brome
Not refound at Liffey Junction (4). *Colgan* considered this species to be synonymous with
A. diandra (*Bromus diandrus*), a species which is now widespread in parts of District 2.

Hordeum vulgare L.　Six-rowed Barley,　Four-rowed Barley
A casual arising from spilled seed, mainly on roadsides and wasteground; Dublin Port.

H. distichon L.　Two-rowed Barley
Frequent as a casual from spilled seed, mainly on roadsides and wasteground; Dublin Port.

H. jubatum L.　Foxtail Barley
5. Boundary of St Anne's Golf-course, and on introduced soil near Royal Dublin Clubhouse, Bull
　Island, PG/93; new golf-course at Portmarnock, CB, DD/94.
(7). Rubbish dump, Kimmage, J.P. Brunker/47 (**DBN**).

Triticum aestivum L.　Bread Wheat
Roadsides in Dublin Port, where grain is unloaded; many plants had long awns, SR/94.

T. spelta L.　Spelt Wheat
5. On infill at Dublin Port, SR/90.

Panicum miliaceum L.　Common Millet
5. On infill at Dublin Port, SR/90.

Echinochloa crusgalli (L.) P. Beauv.　Cockspur
5. Dublin Port, SR/88,89,91.

Setaria pumila (Poiret) Roemer & Schultes (*S. glauca*)   Yellow Bristle-grass
Previously recorded from the Dublin area (Grierson 1922).
5. Dublin Port, SR/90.

S. viridis (L.) P. Beauv.   Green Bristle-grass
Previously recorded from the Dublin area (Grierson 1922).
5. Dublin Port, SR/88-91; East Wall Road, SR/89.
8. Near the toll bridge, Ringsend, SR/90.

LILIACEAE

Kniphofia sp.   Red-hot-poker
5. Plentiful on cliff slope at Lion's Head, Howth, DN/90.

Ornithogalum angustifolium Boreau   Star-of-Bethlehem
A garden outcast.
2. Top of bank at Milverton, Skerries, H. Bird/90 (**DBN**).
5. Established by the cliff path over the Needles, Howth (Brunker 1922); at edge of a fairway, Portmarnock, DN/89.

Allium schoenoprasum L.   Chives
8. Ringsend Dump, DNFC/86.

Nothoscordum gracile (Aiton) Stearn   Honey-bells
4. A widespread and persistent weed at the National Botanic Gardens, DS/92.

Tristagma uniflorum (Lindley) Traub   Spring Starflower
8. A garden throwout persisting at the top of the shore, north of the Martello Tower, Killiney, SR, HOR/83, SR/94.

Leucojum aestivum L.   Summer Snowflake
5. Howth demesne, spreading from its original place of planting, DN, PG/91.

Narcissus tazetta L. x **N. poeticus** L. (**N.** x **medioluteus**, Miller; *N. biflorus*)
Primrose-peerless
Colgan described this species as frequent around the obelisk on Killiney Hill, where it had persisted for upwards of a century.
8. Still by the obelisk on Killiney Hill, DNFC/83.

Narcissus spp.   Daffodil
Plants occur occasionally on wasteground throughout the county, having arisen from bulbs discarded with garden rubbish. They may persist for a long time, but never become naturalized.
FID.

IRIDACEAE

Libertia formosa Graham   Chilean-iris
5. Well naturalized on slopes east of Lion's Head, Howth, SR, JR/95.

Crocus spp.   Crocus
Rare garden escapes or discards.

AGAVACEAE

Cordyline australis (G. Forster) Endl.   Cabbage-palm
A distinctive tree grown in many Dublin gardens and sea-front parks. Occasionally self-sown.

1. Rosa pimpinellifolia Burnet Rose herbarium sheet now in the Department of Botany,
Trinity College, Dublin. The specimen, from Blackrock, is believed to have formed part of an early
18th century *hortus siccus* belonging to Caleb Threlkeld. The annotation reads:
"No. XVIII Rosa pimpinellae folio. pimpinella sive pomifera Minor.
The pimpernell-Rose Rectius. This Growes very plentifully
upon the Sandy Brows below the black rock, Near the sea."

2. Fitzsimon's Wood, Sandyford: It is probably the best example in the county of spontaneous woodland on acid soil, and is dominated by Downy Birch *Betula pubescens*. Old maps show that woodland has long existed in the vicinity.

3. North Bull Island, saltmarsh: Saltmarshes on the east coast are extensive, with the only shrubby saltmarsh species in Ireland, Sea-purslane *Atriplex portulacoides,* giving them a distinctive appearance. Annual Glasswort *Salicornia* species occur on the mudflats and in salt pans.

4. The Needles, Howth: The rocky cliffs of Howth are mostly hard acid quartzites which support a   low species diversity. They abound in garden escapes and the South African Hottentot-fig *Carpobrotus edulis* has spread extensively on the cliffs.

5. Boranaraltry, Glencullen Valley: Acid grassland often develops in uplands on thin mineral-deficient soils which are subjected to high annual rainfall. This hillside at Boranaraltry is a typical example of sheep-grazed *Agrostis-Festuca* acid grassland with tufts of Mat-grass *Nardus stricta*.

6. Grand Canal, Mespil Road: This canal has the richest flora of any of
Dublin's waterways. It contains representatives of almost all of the
aquatic plants found elsewhere in the county.

7. Glenasmole Valley: Bracken *Pteridium aquilinum* is often the dominant plant on the sides
of the sheltered valleys in the uplands of Co. Dublin. It invades former pastures and
stops short of exposed ridges and wet moorland.

8. North Bull Island, the Alder Marsh: The Marsh is part of a dune-slack system of recognised international importance. It takes its name from its distinctive species Alder *Alnus glutinosa*, and supports a rich flora which includes several orchid species.

9. Ringsend Dump: Some 200 species were recorded in this area reclaimed from the sea. Many of the exotic plants originate from infill of garden origin and others, for example, Hoary Mustard *Hirschfeldia incana,* arrived via the port as grain contaminants.

10. Phoenix Park, east of Chapelizod Gate: The unimproved calcareous grassland
supports a characteristic calcicole flora including Salad Burnet
Sanguisorba minor and Pale Flax *Linum bienne.*

11. North Bull Island, fore-dunes: In Co. Dublin, sand-dunes are generally restricted to the coastal area
north of the River Liffey. Annual species, such as Sea Rocket *Cakile maritima,* are the first colonisers
of the fore-dunes followed by perennial grasses such as Marram *Ammophila arenaria.*

12. Loughshinny: This part of the coastline north of Dublin City is covered by glacial deposits.
The low, eroded clay banks support a community of tall herbs including
Wild Carrot *Daucus carota* and Lady's Bedstraw *Galium verum*.

13. The Ben of Howth looking north: Fire is a major influence which shapes and maintains the
dwarf-shrub heathland. Heather *Calluna vulgaris* and Western Gorse *Ulex gallii* regenerate
vegetatively and Bell Heather *Erica cinerea* is also characteristic of this habitat.

14. River Liffey, Strawberry Beds: Dublin's largest waterway has a rich aquatic and riparian flora. Aquatics include an interesting range of Pondweeds. Tall grasses grow along its margins, with native and planted tree species in the woodland.

15. Baldongan, north Co. Dublin: The distinct agricultural tradition of north Dublin has helped the survival of arable weed species including Field Pansy *Viola arvensis* and Tall Ramping-fumitory *Fumaria bastardii*.

16. Brickfields, Portmarnock: Marsh and damp grassland plants are present in these slightly saline wetlands. Bulrush *Typha latifolia,* Grey Club-rush *Schoenoplectus tabernaemontani* and Purple-loosestrife *Lythrum salicaria* are prominent.

17. Kippure Mountain: Kippure has the best developed moorland/blanket bog in Co. Dublin, with a calcifuge flora including Heathers, Cottongrass *Eriophorum* species and Deergrass *Trichophorum cespitosum.*

18. Ononis repens Common Restharrow herbarium sheet now in the Department of Botany, Trinity College, Dublin, believed to have formed part of an early 18th century *hortus siccus* belonging to Caleb Threlkeld. The annotation reads: " No. LXXXI Anonis non spinosa purpurea purple -Rest harrow. The Tingallian Irish Call it **Strong=bow.** olat Hircum hoc planta. Irish **Srang boh Agus Srang tarrain.** In the County of Wicklow **Tri an Tarrain.**"

19. Rosa stylosa Short-styled Field-rose, one of the rarest of the Irish roses
found in some north county hedgerows.

20. Mercurialis annua Annual Mercury, very common as a weed of waste ground and gardens.

21. Gentianella amarella Autumn Gentian, rare in sand-dunes and limestone grassland.

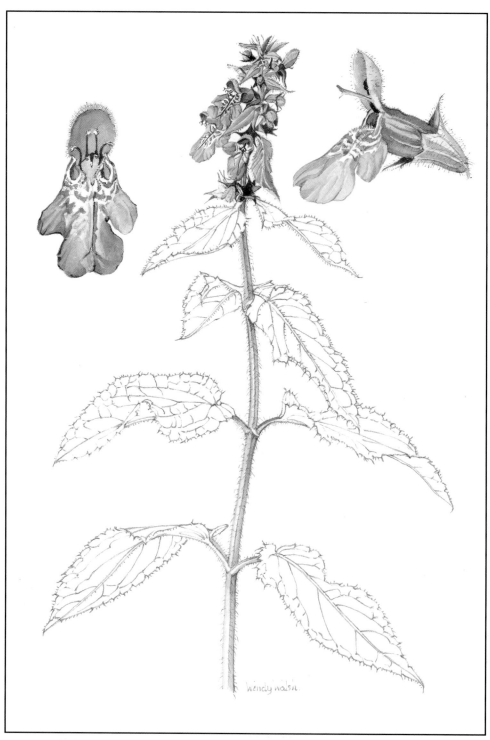

22. Stachys x ambigua Hybrid Woundwort, occasional on stream, river and canal banks.

23. Scrophularia umbrosa Green Figwort, a very rare plant in Ireland, in greatest abundance in the Liffey Valley.

24. Seriphidium maritimum Sea Wormwood, rare in saltmarshes and on sea-cliffs.

APPENDIX 1

AN ANNOTATED BIBLIOGRAPHY (1904–1996) AND REFERENCES FOR THE SYSTEMATIC AND SUPPLEMENTARY LISTS

M. Wyse Jackson

INTRODUCTION

Nathaniel Colgan included a bibliography in his *Flora of the County Dublin* (1904. Hodges, Figgis and Co., Dublin) which listed the "principal books, papers, printed notes, mss., & herbaria relating to the flora of County Dublin"; the present work follows on from that of Colgan and brings the floristic bibliography of the county up to date.

The following bibliography comprises works which have appeared since Colgan's *Flora* and which, for the most part, contain localised records of vascular plant and stonewort taxa from Co. Dublin. Although the majority of Dublin flora records are contained within published works such as books, scientific periodicals and conference proceedings, many are also to be found in unpublished material such as theses, reports, environmental impact statements, annotated Floras and maps, letters, memoranda and in databases. The frequently high quality of information to be gleaned from such unpublished sources demands their inclusion in this bibliography. A number of important works which do not contain actual records, but in which records have been represented by distribution maps or census lists have also been included, as have a number of bibliographies which refer the reader to sources for Dublin records.

Herbaria are an important source of records and a number of public and private herbaria contain significant collections of Dublin plants. These have not been included in this bibliography but are listed in Kent, D.H. and Allen, D.E. (1984. *British and Irish Herbaria*. Botanical Society of the British Isles, London). Theses are another important source of records. Only those submitted for higher degrees, and those to which there was access, have been included here; theses submitted for primary degrees which include floristic data for the county are to be found in the Botany and Geography Departments of the University of Dublin (Trinity College) and in the Botany Department of the National University of Ireland, University College, Dublin.

Comments in parentheses following entries are those of the compiler. Annotations have not been provided where these have been deemed to be unnecessary. Nomenclature of plant names in the annotations follows Stace, C.A. (1991. *New Flora of the British Isles*. Cambridge University Press, Cambridge) for vascular plants and Allen, G.O. (1950. *British Stoneworts (Charophyta)*. The Haslemere Natural History Society, Arbroath) and Moore, J.A. (1979. The current status of the Characeae (Stoneworts) in the British Isles. *Watsonia* 12: 297-309) for stoneworts. Journals that have been scanned for records and the abbreviations employed for them here are listed below.

It hardly needs stating that any attempt at the compilation of a complete floristic bibliography will inevitably fail. With this in mind it has nonetheless been attempted to compile as full a bibliography as possible, following the comments of Praeger, R.Ll. (1901. Irish topographical botany. *Proceedings of the Royal Irish Academy* 7: civ): "In bibliography it is well to err on the side of fulness, since a note or record, apparently trivial, may supply a missing link or fill a gap in some chain of argument or some plant's history. On this account I have not hesitated to include many references which might be thought trivial by those who have not experienced the difficulty of exploring to their ultimate limit the nooks and crannies of botanical records."

JOURNALS SCANNED AND ABBREVIATIONS USED

Biology and Environment: Proceedings of the Royal Irish Academy. Section B. Vols **93-96** (3) (1996), (*Biol. Env. Proc. RIA* (B)), a continuation of *Proceedings of the Royal Irish Academy.* Section B.

Botanical Journal of the Linnean Society. Vols **47-122** (4) (1925-1996). (*Bot. J. Linn. Soc.*).

Botanical Society of the British Isles Year Book. **1949-1953**.

BSBI Abstracts. Vols **1-26** (1971-1996).

BSBI News. Nos **1-74** (1972-1997 [No. **74** dated January 1997, published December 1996]).

Bulletin of the Irish Biogeographical Society. Nos **1-19** (1976-1996). (*Bull. IBS*).

Dublin Naturalists' Field Club Annual Reports. **1904-1971**.

Fieldfare (Bulletin of the Dublin Naturalists' Field Club). **1974-1975**.

Glasra. Vols **1-10** (1976-1987).

Glasra (new series). Vols **1-2** (2) (1990-1995).

Irish Botanical News. Nos **1-6** (1991-1996).

Journal of Botany (London). Vols **42-80** (1904-1942). (*J. Bot.*).

Journal of Life Sciences, Royal Dublin Society. Vols **1-5** (1979-1985). (*J. Life Sci. R. Dubl. Soc.*).

Newsletter of the Irish Biogeographical Society. Nos **4-5, 8-13** (old series) and **1-14** (new series) (1977-1996).

Proceedings of the Botanical Society of the British Isles. Vols **1-7** (1954-1969). (*Proc. BSBI*).

Proceedings of the Royal Irish Academy. Section B. Vols **25-92** (1904-1992). (*Proc. RIA* (B)). Continued as *Biology and Environment: Proceedings of the Royal Irish Academy.* Section B.

Pteridologist. Vols **1-3** (1) (1984-1996).

Report of the Botanical Society and Exchange Club of the British Isles. Vols **2** (pp. 489-610)-**5** (1911-1920). (*BEC*).

Report of the Watson Botanical Exchange Club. Vols **2-4** (1906-1934).

The Fern Gazette. Vols **9** (4)-**15** (3) (1964-1996).

The Irish Naturalist. Vols **13-33** (1904-1924). (*IN*).

The Irish Naturalists' Journal. Vols **1-25** (8) (1925-1996). (*INJ*).

The Scientific Proceedings of the Royal Dublin Society, New Series. Vols **10-27** (1904-1957).

The Scientific Proceedings of the Royal Dublin Society, Series A. Vols **1-6** (1959-1980).

The Scientific Proceedings of the Royal Dublin Society, Series B. Vols **1-3** (1960-1976).

The Scientific Transactions of the Royal Dublin Society, Series II. Vols **8-9** (1904-1909).

Watsonia. Vols **1-21** (2) (1949-1996).

BIBLIOGRAPHY AND REFERENCES

Adam, P. (1987). Some observations on Irish saltmarsh vegetation. *Bull. IBS* **10**: 42-55. (Includes records from North Bull Island and Malahide Island).

Adams, J. (1907). Altitude attained by nettle and dock. *IN* **16**: 222. (Seahan mountain, at 487 m).

Adams, J. (1908a). The new flora of burnt ground on the hill of Howth: A study of plant dispersal. *IN* **17**: 133-134. (See also Adams (1908b), Pethybridge (1908) and Praeger (1908c)).

Adams, J. (1908b). The burnt ground on Howth Head. *IN* **17**: 268. (See also Adams (1908a), Pethybridge (1908) and Praeger (1908c)).

Akeroyd, J.R. (1980). Two alien legumes from waste ground in Dublin. *Bull. IBS* **4**: 50-51. (*Cicer arietinum* L. and *Lens culinaris* Medikus in north Dublin City).

Akeroyd, J.R. (1982). *Senecio viscosus* L. in Ireland. *INJ* **20**: 361-364. (Notes its occurrence in Dublin prior to 1930).

Akeroyd, J.R. (1983). Further notes on *Trifolium occidentale* D.E. Coombe in Ireland. *INJ* **21**: 32-34. (Lists stations for this species at Sutton, Skerries, North Bull Island and Dalkey Island. *Trifolium scabrum* L. is also noted in the latter three localities).

Akeroyd, J.R. (1984a). *Parapholis incurva* (L.) C.E. Hubbard - a grass overlooked in Ireland. *INJ* **21**: 228-230. (Notes its occurrence at Sutton).

Akeroyd, J.R. (1984b). Weeds. Pp. 39-45 in: Wyse Jackson, P. and Sheehy Skeffington, M. *The Flora of Inner Dublin*. Royal Dublin Society in association with the Dublin Naturalists' Field Club, Dublin. (Records *Rumex crispus* var. *crispus* L. and var. *littoreus* (J. Hardy) Akeroyd from Dublin, as well as several non-native species).

Akeroyd, J.R. (1988). *Plantago major* subsp. *intermedia* in Ireland. *BSBI News* **49**: 39. (Notes its occurrence in several Dublin localities).

Akeroyd, J.R. and Doogue, D.A. (1988). *Plantago major* subsp. *intermedia* (DC.) Arcangeli (Plantaginaceae) in Ireland. *INJ* **22**: 441-443. (Noted in several Dublin localities).

Akeroyd, J.R., Jury, S.L. and Hora, C.J. (1987). Some noteworthy Irish plants. *BSBI News* **45**: 35. (*Plantago major* subsp. *intermedia* (DC.) Arcang. and *Fumaria officinalis* subsp. *wirtgenii* (Koch) Arcang. are noted from Dublin).

Akeroyd, J.R. and Preston, C.D. (1984). *Halimione portulacoides* (L.) Aellen on coastal rocks and cliffs. *Watsonia* **15**: 95-103. (Sites at Dun Laoghaire, Howth Head, Portrane, Skerries and Balbriggan).

Allen, C.W. (1936a). Dublin Naturalists' Field Club. *INJ* **6**: 104. (News and excursion reports. Includes records from Feltrim Hill).

Allen, C.W. (1936b). Dublin Naturalists' Field Club. *INJ* **6**: 152. (Excursion reports. Includes records from the valley of the River Ward).

Allen, C.W. (1938). Dublin Naturalists' Field Club. *INJ* **7**: 96. (Excursion reports. Includes records from Ireland's Eye).

Allen, D.E. (1988a). Some *Rubus* discoveries of 1987. *BSBI News* **49**: 39-40. (*R. purbeckensis* Barton & Riddelsd. and *R. ordovicum* Newton are noted from Dublin).

Allen, D.E. (1988b). A second Welsh bramble in Ireland. *BSBI Welsh Bulletin* **46**: 7-8. (*Rubus ordovicum* Newton in Dublin. Erroneously cited as *R. aequalidens* Newton in *BSBI Abstracts* **19**: 32).

Allen, D.E. (1990). Two further Irish bramble forays. *INJ* **23**: 257-262. (Many species are recorded from Dublin).

Allen, D.E. (1993). Further Irish bramble records. *INJ* **25**: 249-253. (Includes Dublin records for *Rubus ordovicum* Newton, *R. boudiccae* A.L. Bull & Edees (new to Ireland), *R. procerus* P.J. Mueller *ex* Boulay cv 'Himalayan Giant', *R. purbeckensis* W.C. Barton & Riddelsd. and *R. robii* (W.C.R. Watson) Newton).

Allen, D.E. (1994). Brambles of north-west Ireland. *INJ* **24**: 375-376. (Notes the occurrence in the Naul Hills of a single bush of a distinctive, as yet undescribed, species of *Rubus*).

Anonymous (1905). Dublin Naturalists' Field Club. *IN* **14**: 115. (News and excursion reports. Includes records from Lucan).

Anonymous (1906). Dublin Naturalists' Field Club. *IN* **15**: 273-274. (News and excursion reports. Includes records from Portmarnock).

Anonymous (1907). Dublin Naturalists' Field Club. *IN* **16**: 247-248. (Excursion reports. Includes records from Jobstown).

Anonymous (1908a). Dublin Naturalists' Field Club. *IN* **17**: 7-8. (News and excursion reports. Includes records from Santry).

Anonymous (1908b). Dublin Naturalists' Field Club. *IN* **17**: 164. (Report of excursion to Dalkey Island).

Anonymous (1913). Dublin Naturalists' Field Club. *IN* **22**: 227. (Report of excursion to Glenasmole).

Anonymous (1914). Dublin Naturalists' Field Club. *IN* **23**: 223-224. (Excursion reports. Includes records from Jobstown and Seefin).

Anonymous (1915a). Dublin Naturalists' Field Club. *IN* **24**: 43-44. (News and excursion reports. Includes records from Lucan and Howth).

Anonymous (1915b). Dublin Naturalists' Field Club. *IN* **24**: 134-135. (Report of excursion to Balrothery).

Anonymous (1916a). Dublin Naturalists' Field Club. *IN* **25**: 15-16. (Excursion reports. Includes records from Lucan and Jobstown).

Anonymous (1916b). Dublin Naturalists' Field Club. *IN* **25**: 168. (Report of excursion to Dingle Glen).

Anonymous (1917a). Dublin Naturalists' Field Club. *IN* **26**: 124. (Report of excursion to Feltrim Hill and Malahide).

Anonymous (1917b). Dublin Naturalists' Field Club. *IN* **26**: 138-139. (Report of excursion to Glenasmole).

Anonymous (1917c). Dublin Naturalists' Field Club. *IN* **26**: 168. (Report of excursion to North Bull Island).

Anonymous (1917d). Dublin Naturalists' Field Club. *IN* **26**: 187-188. (Excursion reports. Includes records from Portrane).

Anonymous (1919). Dublin Naturalists' Field Club. *IN* **28**: 43. (News and excursion reports. Includes records from Portmarnock).

Anonymous (1921a). Dublin Naturalists' Field Club. *IN* **30**: 100. (Excursion reports. Includes records from Lucan).

Anonymous (1921b). Dublin Naturalists' Field Club. *IN* **30**: 132-133. (Excursion reports. Includes records from Glenasmole).

Anonymous (1922). Dublin Naturalists' Field Club. *IN* **31**: 137-139. (Excursion reports. Includes records from Ireland's Eye and the Scalp).

Anonymous (1924a). Dublin Naturalists' Field Club. *IN* **33**: 98-100. (News and excursion reports. Includes records from Balrothery).

Anonymous (1924b). Dublin Naturalists' Field Club. *IN* **33**: 140-141. (Excursion reports. Includes records from Kilmashogue and Howth).

Anonymous (1926). Dublin Naturalists' Field Club. *INJ* **1**: 167. (Excursion reports. Includes records from Howth).

Anonymous (1929). A.S.U. (Dublin), 1928-29. *INJ* **2**: 249-250. (Excursion reports. Includes records from the upper River Dodder, Malahide and Mount Venus).

Anonymous (1932). Dublin Naturalists' Field Club. *INJ* **4**: 103. (Report of excursion to Glenasmole).

Anonymous (c. 1936). *Flora of Alexandra Road District, Dublin. 1933 to 1936*. Unpublished, Dublin. (Probably compiled by H.J. Hudson, this handwritten, four page manuscript is an annotated checklist of the flora of the Alexandra Road (Dublin Docks) area. A total of 118 species are listed, including many aliens. These, it is suggested, are largely derived from sweepings from granaries. Copy held by the Dublin Naturalists' Field Club).

Anonymous (1961a). *Reseda alba* in Co. Dublin. *INJ* **13**: 215. (At Portmarnock).

Anonymous (1961b). *A Supplement to Colgan's Flora of the County Dublin*. The Stationery Office, Dublin. (A concise, systematic account of the Dublin flora, based on the results of twenty-five years of field work by the Dublin Naturalists' Field Club).

Anonymous (1962). *Epilobium nerterioides*. P. 425 in: Wallace, E.C. (Ed.) (1962). Plant records. *Proc. BSBI* **4**: 419-433. (Record for *Epilobium brunnescens* (Cockayne) Raven & Engelhorn from Sutton).

Anonymous (1977). *A Study of Bull Island, Co. Dublin*. Unpublished report prepared for Dublin Corporation. An Foras Forbartha, Dublin. (Includes brief descriptions of the flora and vegetation of the island).

Anonymous (1981). *Areas of Scientific Interest in Ireland*. An Foras Forbartha, Dublin. (The scientific interest of thirty-five Dublin sites is briefly described. Details of species occurring at some sites are provided. The bulk of this work, including the site descriptions, was written by R.N. Goodwillie).

Anonymous (1986). *Liffey Valley Special Amenity Area Order Study. Lucan Bridge to Palmerston*. Unpublished report. Dublin County Planning Department, Dublin. (Includes on pp. 5-7 a section which provides details of the rarer species and their localities).

Anonymous (1988a). *Dublin Naturalists' Field Club Submission to Dublin Corporation City Development Plan. April 1988*. Unpublished report. (Includes plant records from twelve site complexes of conservation interest within Dublin City).

Anonymous (1988b). *Environmental Impact Study of Proposed Major Road through St. Helen's, Booterstown*. Unpublished report prepared for Dun Laoghaire Corporation. An Foras Forbartha and Environmental Research Unit, Dublin. (Records from Booterstown Marsh are on p. 70).

Anonymous (1994). *Grand Canal Corridor Study. Grand Canal Dock to Lucan Bridge Road. Strategy and Proposals*. Report prepared by Brady Shipman Martin for Department of Arts, Culture and The Gaeltacht. The Stationery Office, Dublin. (Notes the presence in this section of the canal of *Butomus umbellatus* L., *Ceratophyllum demersum* L. and *Groenlandia densa* (L.) Fourr.).

Anonymous (undated, c.1994). *Portmarnock Saltmarsh: A Threatened Habitat*. Unpublished report, Dublin. (This manuscript, lodged in the ENFO library, St Andrew's Street, includes a basic description of the saltmarsh and its flora).

Anonymous (1995). *Royal Canal Corridor Study. Spencer Dock to Allen Bridge. Strategy and Proposals*. Report prepared by RPS Cairns Ltd for Department of Arts, Culture and The Gaeltacht. The Stationery Office, Dublin. (Notes the presence in the Dublin City section of the canal of *Groenlandia densa* (L.) Fourr. and *Tolypella intricata* (Trent. ex Roth) Leonh.).

Anonymous (undated). Annotation in a copy of Anonymous (1961b). *A Supplement to Colgan's Flora of the County Dublin*. The Stationery Office, Dublin. (Notes the occurrence up to 1957 of *Hammarbya paludosa* (L.) Kuntze at Ticknock. Now in the library of the National Botanic Gardens, Glasnevin).

Atkinson, M.D. (1996). The distribution and naturalisation of *Lathraea clandestina* L. (Orobanchaceae) in the British Isles. *Watsonia* **21**: 119-128. (Includes records from Clonliffe and Glasnevin).

Bagwell, M. (1944). September wild flowers in County Dublin. *Wild Flower Magazine* January-April 1944: 5-6. (Includes records from Chapelizod, Malahide, Portmarnock, Rush and both canals).

Bailey, J.P., Child, L.E. and Conolly, A.P. (1996). A survey of the distribution of *Fallopia* x *bohemica* (Chrtek & Chrtková) J. Bailey (Polygonaceae) in the British Isles. *Watsonia* **21**: 187-198. (A pre-1920 record for *Fallopia japonica* (Houtt.) Ronse Decraene from 10 km square O 02, most of which lies within Co. Dublin, is mapped).

Baker, H.G. (1954). The *Limonium binervosum* complex in western and northern Ireland. *Proc. BSBI* **1**: 131-141. (Includes a reference to a specimen collected from Howth in 1829).

Bangerter, E.B. and Kent, D.H. (1957). *Veronica filiformis* Sm. in the British Isles. *Proc. BSBI* **2**: 197-217. (Includes records from Howth and Monkstown).

Bangerter, E.B. and Kent, D.H. (1962). Further notes on *Veronica filiformis*. *Proc. BSBI* **4**: 384-397. (Includes records from Stepaside and Booterstown).

Bangerter, E.B. and Kent, D.H. (1965). Additional notes on *Veronica filiformis*. *Proc. BSBI* **6**: 113-118. (Includes a record from Clontarf).

Baring, C. (1915a). Notes on the fauna and flora of Lambay. *IN* **24**: 68-71. (Notes the occurrence of *Orchis morio* L., *Anacamptis pyramidalis* (L.) Rich., *Circaea lutetiana* L. and *Blechnum spicant* (L.) Roth. Both orchid records also noted in *BEC* **4**:503).

Baring, C. (1915b). *Orchis pyramidalis* on Lambay. *IN* **24**: 215. (*Anacamptis pyramidalis* (L.) Rich.).

Biological Flora of the British Isles. (A long-running series of papers published in *The Journal of Ecology*. Papers frequently include mapped records of vascular plants from Dublin. Papers in the series published between 1962 and 1989 with distribution maps covering the British Isles are listed in Preston (1990)).

Boatman, D.J. (1956). *Mercurialis perennis* L. in Ireland. *Journal of Ecology* **44**: 587-596. (Includes records from Finglas and Santry).

Bobear, J.B. (1964). *A Taxonomic Study of Irish* Euphrasia *L*. Unpublished Ph.D. thesis. University of Dublin, Trinity College. (Includes morphometric analyses of populations from Malahide, Portmarnock and Stepaside).

Bobear, J.B. (1969). An analysis of populations of Irish *Euphrasia* L *Watsonia* **7**: 68-91. (Includes biometric analyses of populations from Malahide and Portmarnock).

Böcher, T.W., Larsen, K. and Rahn, K. (1955). Experimental and cytological studies on plant species, 2. *Plantago coronopus* and allied species. *Hereditas* **41**: 423-453. (Includes a chromosome count for a plant of *Plantago coronopus* L. from Dublin).

Boyle, H. (1969). Letter to *Irish Times*, 18th December. (Notes the occurrence of *Butomus umbellatus* L. by the Grand Canal, Dublin City.

Boyle, K. and Bourke, O. (1990). *The Wicklow Way, A Natural History Field Guide*. Cospoir, Dublin. (Mentions some of the commoner plants to be encountered at the Dublin end of the walk).

Boyle, P.J. (1972). Spartina *in Ireland*. Unpublished Ph.D. thesis. National University of Ireland, University College Dublin. (Notes *Spartina* taxa from Baldoyle, Corballis and North Bull Island).

Boyle, P.J. (1973). Corrected chromosome number for *Spartina* in Ireland. *Nature* **244**: 311. (Notes *Spartina anglica* C.E. Hubb. from Baldoyle).

Boyle, P.J. (1976a). A first record of the fungus *Claviceps purpurea* on *Spartina* in Ireland. *INJ* **18**: 325-326. (Notes *Spartina anglica* C.E. Hubb. and *S.* x *townsendii* Groves & J. Groves from Baldoyle, Corballis and North Bull Island).

Boyle, P.J. (1976b). *Spartina* M9. A variant *Spartina* in three regions north of Dublin. *The Scientific Proceedings of the Royal Dublin Society*, Series A **5**: 415-427. (Notes the occurrence of a variant of *Spartina* occurring at Baldoyle, Corballis and North Bull Island).

Boyle, P.J. (1977). *Spartina* on Bull Island. Pp. 88-92 in: Jeffrey, D.W. (Ed.). *North Bull Island Dublin Bay, a Modern Coastal Natural History*. Royal Dublin Society, Dublin. (The ecology, distribution and morphology of *Spartina* taxa on the island is discussed).

Boyle, P.J. and Kavanagh, J.A. (1961). A Spartinetum at Baldoyle in Ireland. *Nature* **192**: 81-82. (Notes *Spartina anglica* C.E. Hubb. from Baldoyle).

Bradley, W. and Austin, A. (1991). *Survey and Report on Waterstown Park, Palmerston, Dublin*. Unpublished report to Dublin County Council prepared on behalf of the Dublin Naturalists' Field Club. (A total of 227 species are listed from several sites within the park).

Bradley, W. and Austin, A. (1992). Update on Waterstown park (formerly Palmerston tiphead). *Dublin Naturalists' Field Club Newsletter* **January to March 1993**: 2. (Notes the occurrence of *Butomus umbellatus* L., *Galeopsis tetrahit* L., *Pulicaria dysenterica* (L.) Bernh. and *Sinapis arvensis* L.).

Bradshaw, D.B. (1917). *Filago minima* at Howth. *IN* **26**: 17.

Brady, A. (1974). *Oenothera erythrosepala* Borbás at Donabate, Co. Dublin. *INJ* **18**: 95.

Braun-Blanquet, J. and Tüxen, R. (1952). Irische Pflanzengesellschaften. *Veröffentlichungen des Geobotanischen Institutes Rübel in Zürich* **25**: 224-415. (Includes relevés recorded in Dublin, and references to such, on pp. 243-244, 280-281, 288-289, 354-358 and 379).

Briggs, J. and Perring, F.H. (1994). BSBI winter mistletoe survey 1994-96. *BSBI News* **67**: 11-13. (A post-1950 record for *Viscum album* L. is mapped).

Britten, J. (1905). Aylmer Bourke Lambert in Ireland. *J. Bot.* **43**: 219. (Includes old records for *Lathraea squamaria* L. from between Dun Laoghaire and Newtown and *Geranium columbinum* L. from Blackrock).

Bruce, W.B. (1907a). *Allium scorodoprasum* in Co. Dublin. *IN* **16**: 348-349. (Lucan demesne).

Bruce, W.B. (1907b). *Lycopodium alpinum* in Co. Dublin. *IN* **16**: 368. (Summit of Cruagh mountain).

Bruce, W.B. (1910). *Cnicus pratensis* in Co. Dublin. *IN* **19**: 155. (*Cirsium dissectum* (L.) Hill, *Pseudorchis albida* (L.) Á. & D. Löve, *Platanthera chlorantha* (Custer) Reichenb., *Orchis morio* L., *Dactylorhiza maculata* (L.) Soó and *Antennaria dioica* (L.) Gaertner at St Anne's, Glenasmole).

Brun-Hool, J. and Wilmanns, O. (1982). Plant communities of human settlements in Ireland. 2. Gardens, parks and roads. *J. Life Sci. R. Dubl. Soc.* **3**: 91-103. (Includes twenty-five relevés from Dublin sites. Reprinted in White (1982)).

Brunker, J.P. (1918). A new station for *Lathraea squamaria* in Co. Dublin. *IN* **27**: 110. (At Glenasmole).

Brunker, J.P. (1921). *Cnicus pratensis* in Co. Dublin. *IN* **30**: 79. (*Cirsium dissectum* (L.) Hill at St Anne's, Glenasmole).

Brunker, J.P. (1922). Plants of County Dublin. *IN* **31**: 94-95. (Includes Dublin records for seventeen species).

Brunker, J.P. (1924). Increase of *Saxifraga stellaris* in Glenasmole. *IN* **33**: 68.

Brunker, J.P. (1937). *Juncus acutus* Linn. in Co. Dublin. *INJ* **6**: 195-196. (North Bull Island).

Brunker, J.P. (1944a). New botanical county records. *INJ* **8**: 184. (*Brachypodium pinnatum* (L.) P. Beauv. noted from Stillorgan).

Brunker, J.P. (1944b). *Flora of St. James's Gate.* Unpublished report, Dublin. (This typescript report, a copy of which is held by the Dublin Naturalists' Field Club, forms part of a report by Brunker on grain contaminants brought to the Guinness Brewery. It contains records for some two hundred species occurring in the grounds of the brewery, the Grand Canal Basin and Victoria Quay by the R. Liffey. Many of the records are for ephemerals and grain-contaminant exotics, but some aquatic and other native species are also included).

Brunker, J.P. (1948). *Poa compressa* L. and *Hordeum nodosum* in Co. Dublin. *INJ* **9**: 214. (*Poa compressa* and *Hordeum secalinum* Schreber at Rathmines and near Swords, respectively).

Brunker, J.P. (1949). *Rumex maritimus* L. in Co. Dublin. *INJ* **9**: 340. (Near Donabate).

Brunker, J.P. (1950a). *Nasturtium amphibium* R.Br. in Co. Dublin. *INJ* **10**: 81. (*Rorippa amphibia* (L.) Besser in the Broad Meadow Water).

Brunker, J.P. (1950b). *Flora of the County Wicklow.* Dundalgan Press, Dundalk. (A few records from Dublin are noted, including the introduced *Asparagus officinalis* L. subsp. *officinalis* from North Bull Island).

Brunker, J.P. (1952). *Sisymbrium irio* L. in the Dublin district. *INJ* **10**: 319-320. (At Swords and Ballsbridge).

Brunker, J.P. (1953). *Sisymbrium irio* in a new station. *INJ* **11**: 108. (At Loughshinny).

Brunker, J.P. (1954a). *Epipactis phyllanthes* G.E. Sm. in County Wicklow. *INJ* **11**: 135. (Includes a record from Portmarnock).

Brunker, J.P. (1954b). *Melandrium noctiflorum* L. in County Dublin. *INJ* **11**: 206. (*Silene noctiflora* L. noted at Portrane and *Rumex maritimus* L. still at its Beaverstown station. The record for the former species was also reported in Wallace, E.C. (Ed.) (1955). Plant records. *Proc. BSBI* **1**: 325-338).

Brunker, J.P. (undated a). *Flora of Ireland's Eye.* Annotations in copy of O'Connor, P. (1934). *Liosta de Phlanndaí na hÉireann. Hand-list of Irish Plants.* (3rd edn). The Stationery Office, Dublin. (A checklist of the island's flora, recorded on visits in 1924, 1931, 1936, 1940, 1941, 1942, 1943, 1944, 1947, 1950, 1952, 1962 and 1963. Many of the records were published in Anonymous (1961b). Copy held by the Dublin Naturalists' Field Club).

Brunker, J.P. (undated b). Annotations in his copy of Colgan, N. (1904). *Flora of the County Dublin.* Hodges, Figgis & Co., Dublin. (Contains many Dublin records, the great majority of which were published in Anonymous (1961b). Now in the possession of D.W. Nash).

Brunker J.P. (undated c, pre-1961). *Manuscript List of the Flora of the North Bull.* Unpublished, Dublin. (Copies are in the library of the National Botanic Gardens, Glasnevin and in the files of the former An Foras Forbartha, now held by the Department of the Environment, Dublin. It is the basis for Carvill's (1975) updated manuscript flora of the island. See also Hudson and Brunker (undated)).

Cabot, D. (1987). Booterstown marsh. Pp. 13-14 in: O'Sullivan, J. and Cannon, S. (Eds). *The Book of Dun Laoghaire.* Blackrock Teachers' Centre, Blackrock. (Describes vegetation types and lists both dominant and rare species occurring in the marsh).

Caffrey, J. (1991). Aquatic plants and plant management in the Inchicore area of the Grand Canal. Pp. 66-68 in: Conaghan, M., Gleeson, O. and Maddock, A. (Eds). *The Grand Canal. Inchicore and Kilmainham.* The Stationery Office, Dublin. (Includes specific locality details for several species).

Carrothers, E.N. (1960). *Spartina townsendii* H. & J. Groves in counties Louth and Down, *INJ* **13**: 188. (Includes records from several sites in Dublin).

Carvill, P.H. (1974a). *Glyceria declinata* Breb. and *G. x pedicellata* in Co. Dublin. *INJ* **18**: 23 (Records for both from Kilgobbin and for the former from Ballyedmonduff and the Scalp. This note was duplicated in *INJ* **18**: 203 (1975)).

Carvill, P.H. (1974b). A note on the status and ecology of elder, *Sambucus nigra* L. *Fieldfare* **1974**: 1. (At Kilgobbin, Stepaside and Sandyford).

Carvill, P.H. (1975). *An Annotated Checklist of the Vascular Plants of the North Bull Island*. Unpublished, Dublin. (Handwritten manuscript lodged in the library of the School of Botany, Trinity College, Dublin. Update of Brunker (undated c, pre-1961). This work has been kept up to date by P. Grant).

Carvill, P.H. (Compiler) (1977). Vascular plants. Pp. 130-133 in: Jeffrey, D.W. (Ed.). *North Bull Island Dublin Bay, a Modern Coastal Natural History*. Royal Dublin Society, Dublin. (Lists many species from the island).

Carvill, P.H. (1980). Floristic notes from Co. Dublin (H21). *Bull. IBS* **4**: 23-27. (Records for thirty-one taxa).

Carvill, P.H. and Wyse Jackson, P.S. (1983). *Galinsoga ciliata* (Raf.) Blake in Ireland. *INJ* **21**: 31. (*G. quadriradiata* Ruiz Lopez & Pavon is reported from two sites in Dublin city and south Co. Dublin).

Clabby, G. and Osborne, B.A. (1994). History, distribution and ecology of *Mycelis muralis* (L.) Dumort. (Asteraceae) in Ireland. *Biol. Env. Proc. RIA* (B) **94**: 57-73. (Some twenty records from Dublin are listed).

Clark, S.C. (1968). The structure of some *Ulex galii* [sic] heaths in eastern Ireland. *Proc. RIA* (B) **66**: 43-51. (Includes nine species lists from Howth and south Co. Dublin).

Clement, E.J. and Foster, M.C. (1994). *Alien Plants of the British Isles*. Botanical Society of the British Isles, London. (Dublin records for *Acer macrophyllum* Pursch, *Brassica fruticulosa* Cirillo, *Conyza sumatrensis* (Retz.) E. Walker, *Hieracium gougetianum* Gren. & Godron and *Senecio cineraria* DC. are cited).

Clifford, H.T. (1958). Studies in British Primulas VI. On introgression between primrose (*Primula vulgaris* Huds.) and cowslip (*P. veris* L.). *The New Phytologist* **57**: 1-10. (Records of hybrids from Rush).

Colgan, N. (1905). *Artemisia maritima* - a new station for Co. Dublin. *IN* **14**: 247. (Near Balbriggan).

Colgan, N. (1906). *Orobanche minor* in Co. Dublin. *IN* **15**: 219. (Notes its rapid spread in north-east Dublin).

Colgan, N. (1907a). Leaf-pitting in *Arum maculatum*. *IN* **16**: 177. (Near Ballybrack and Saggart).

Colgan, N. (1907b). Fertility of *Senecio albescens* (*S. cineraria* x *jacobaea*). *J. Bot.* **45**: 306. (Killiney).

Colgan, N. (1908). Phanerogams and vascular cryptogams. Pp. 75-86 in: Cole, G.A.J. and Praeger, R.Ll. (Eds). *Handbook to the City of Dublin and the Surrounding District* (British Association Guide). University Press, Dublin. (Summary account of vascular plant flora of Co. Dublin).

C[olgan], N. (1910). Plant form and migration. *IN* **19**: 56-59. (Review of Die nordischen *Alchemilla vulgaris*-Formen und ihre Verbreitung. *Acta Societatis Scientiarum Fennicae* **37** (10):1-170 (1909). Includes several records for Dublin).

Colgan, N. (1912). The burnt ground flora of Killiney Hill. *IN* **21**: 72-76.

Colgan, N. (1913). Further notes on the burnt ground flora of Killiney Hill. *IN* **22**: 85-93.

Colgan, N. (1917a). *Elymus arenarius* and *Asparagus officinalis* on the North Bull, Dublin. *IN* **26**: 34-35. (*Leymus arenarius* (L.) Hochst. and *Asparagus officinalis* L. subsp. *officinalis*. Records also reported in Druce, G.C. (Ed.). Report for 1917. *BEC* **5**: 1-204).

Colgan, N. (1917b). Notes on apparent mnemic action in *Chlora perfoliata*. *IN* **26**: 189-193. (Observations on the time of day at which flowers of *Blackstonia perfoliata* (L.) Hudson open. Includes records for this species from Killiney and North Bull Island).

Colgan, N. (1918). Notes on some alien plants of County Dublin. *IN* **27**: 86-90. (Details of nine alien species and one hybrid are provided).

Colgan, N. (undated). Annotations in his copy of Hart, H.C. (1887). *The Flora of Howth*. Hodges, Figgis & Co., Dublin. (Now in the possession of D.A. Doogue).

Collen, E.A. (1982). *North Bull Island, Dublin Bay. Development and Management for Educational Purposes*. Unpublished M.Sc. thesis. Environmental Sciences Unit, University of Dublin, Trinity College. (Includes on pp. 100-102 lists of species commonly occurring on the sand dunes, salt marsh and alder marsh of North Bull Island).

Conolly, A.P. (1977). The distribution and history in the British Isles of some alien species of *Polygonum* and *Reynoutria*. *Watsonia* **11**: 291-311. (Includes records for *Fallopia sachalinensis* (F. Schmidt *ex* Maxim.) Ronse Decraene from Howth and the Phoenix Park).

Cope, T.A. and Stace, C.A. (1978). The *Juncus bufonius* L. aggregate in western Europe. *Watsonia* **12**: 113-128. (The occurrence in Dublin of *J. foliosus* Desf. and *J. ambiguus* Guss. is noted).

CORINE Biotopes Database for Ireland. (This database, which is held by the National Parks and Wildlife Service, Dublin, holds information on vegetation communities and significant species of flora for several Dublin sites).

Craig, A.J. (1968). *Ornithopus perpusillus* L. in Co. Wicklow, H20. *INJ* **16**: 26. (Its occurrence on Howth Head is also re-confirmed).

Crosbie, M. (1937). Blue-flowered pimpernel near Malahide. *INJ* **6**: 299. (*Anagallis arvensis* L. subsp. *caerulea* Hartman).

Cross, J.R. (1982). The invasion and impact of *Rhododendron ponticum* in native Irish vegetation. *J. Life Sci. R. Dubl. Soc.* **3**: 209-220. (Its occurrence in heath vegetation on Howth Head is noted. Relevé data from this habitat are tabulated. Reprinted in White (1982)).

Curran, P.L. (1965). *Avena fatua* L. in north County Dublin. *INJ* **15**: 55-56. (Well established in Colgan's District 3, Nethercross).

Curran, P.L. (1968). Chromosome numbers of some Irish plants. *INJ* **16**: 7-9. (Includes chromosome counts for eight species from Dublin sites).

Curran, P.L. (1983). *Avena fatua* L. - 20 years of progress by a weed. *INJ* **21**: 49. (Notes its frequent occurrence by the Finglas to Slane road).

Curry, J.P. (1976). The arthropod fauna of some common grass and weed species of pasture. *Proc. RIA* (B) **76**: 1-35. (Includes records from Glasnevin for several common species).

Curtis, T.G.F. (1982). *The Taxonomy and Biosystematics of the Genus* Dactylorhiza *Necker ex Nevski in Ireland*. Unpublished Ph.D. thesis. University of Dublin, Trinity College. (Includes records from North Bull Island).

Curtis, T.G.F. (1991a). A site inventory of the sandy coasts of Ireland - their types and distribution. Pp. 6-17 in: Quigley, M.B. (Ed.). *A Guide to the Sand Dunes of Ireland*. European Union for Dune Conservation and Coastal Management, c/o Department of Geography, Trinity College, Dublin. (Two sandhill and six dune sites are listed for Dublin).

Curtis, T.G.F. (1991b). The flora and vegetation of sand dunes in Ireland. Pp. 42-66 in: Quigley, M.B. (Ed.). *A Guide to the Sand Dunes of Ireland*. European Union for Dune Conservation and Coastal Management, c/o Department of Geography, Trinity College, Dublin. (Notes the presence of vegetation referable to the Festuco-Galietum maritimi (Onno) Br.-Bl. & De Leeuw association on old, decalcified dunes at Malahide).

Curtis, T.G.F. and FitzGerald, R.A. (1994). The re-discovery of *Carex divisa* Hudson, Divided sedge, in Ireland. *INJ* **24**: 496-498. (Notes several old records from Dublin).

Curtis, T.G.F. and McGough, H.N. (1988). *The Irish Red Data Book. 1 Vascular Plants*. The Stationery Office, Dublin. (Dublin records are mapped).

Curtis, T.G.F. and Wyse Jackson, P.S. (1979). Ringsend Dump, Dublin. *Irish Biogeographical Society Newsletter* **9**: 4. (The aliens, *Phalaris canariensis* L. and *Consolida ajacis* (L.) Schur are noted).

Dannenberg, I. Markgraf- (1952). Studien an irischen *Festuca*-rassen. *Veröffentlichungen des Geobotanischen Institutes Rübel in Zürich* **25**: 114-142. (Includes a record for *Festuca ovina* var. *firmula* (Hack.) Hegi from Glendoo Mountain).

Devitt, T. (1980). *Genetic Variation in Peripheral and Central Populations of* Cochlearia officinalis. Unpublished M.Sc. thesis. National University of Ireland, University College Dublin. (Includes records from North Bull Island and Malahide).

Doogue, D.A. (1968). Plant records from Co. Dublin. *INJ* **16**: 79. (*Ulex gallii* Planchon, *Lathraea squamaria* L. and *Trifolium micranthum* Viv. Records also reported in Wallace, E.C. (Ed.) (1968). Plant records. *Proc. BSBI* **7**:563-566).

Doogue, D.A. (1975a). Some changes in the Dublin flora. *Fieldfare* **1975**: 3-4. (Includes records for *Epipactis helleborine* (L.) Crantz, *Crambe maritima* L. and a ray-floreted form of *Senecio vulgaris* L.).

Doogue, D.A. (1975b). Two forms of lesser celandine in Dublin. *Fieldfare* **1975**: 5. (*Ranunculus ficaria* L. subsp. *ficaria* and subsp. *bulbilifer* Lambinon).

Doogue, D.A. (1984). History of the flora. Pp. 5-24 in: Wyse Jackson, P. and Sheehy Skeffington, M. *The Flora of Inner Dublin*. Royal Dublin Society in association with the Dublin Naturalists' Field Club, Dublin. (An account of the history of the recording of the flora of the inner city. Includes many early records).

Doogue, D.[A.] (1986). Getting started. Pp. 54-74 in: Dublin Naturalists' Field Club. *Reflections and Recollections (Occasional Publications of the Dublin Naturalists' Field Club* 1). Dublin Naturalists' Field Club, Dublin. (Illustrations of *Ophrys apifera* Hudson and *Spiranthes spiralis* (L.) Chevall. from North Bull Island are on p. 62).

Doogue, D.A. (1988). The Dublin Naturalists' Field Club in its second century. Pp. 55-64 in: Wyse Jackson, P.S., Moriarty, C. and Akeroyd, J.R. (Eds). *In the Field of the Naturalists*, (*Occasional Publications of the Dublin Naturalists' Field Club* 2). Dublin Naturalists' Field Club, Dublin. (Dublin sites for several species are noted, including *Anisantha diandra* (Roth) Tutin ex Tzvelev from Rush and *Groenlandia densa* (L.) Fourr. from the Grand Canal).

Doogue, D.A. (1993). *Rare Plant Survey of Co. Dublin, 1991-1993*. Commissioned report to the National Parks and Wildlife Service, Dublin. (Includes many recent Dublin records for rare and threatened vascular plants).

Doogue, D.A. (1994). *The Composition of the Hedges of Leinster, Ireland, with particular reference to the Taxonomy and Ecology of the Genus Rosa Linnaeus*. Unpublished Ph.D. thesis. University of Dublin, Trinity College. (Includes Dublin records for several *Rosa* taxa).

Doogue, D.A., Kelly, D.L. and Wyse Jackson, P.S. (1985). The progress of *Epilobium ciliatum* Rafin. (*E. adenocaulon* Hausskn.) in Ireland, with some notes on its hybrids. *INJ* **21**: 444-446. (Includes Dublin records for *E. ciliatum* Raf., *E. ciliatum* x *E. montanum* L. and *E. ciliatum* x *E. hirsutum* L.).

Doogue, D.[A]. and Parnell, J.[A.N.] (1992). Fragments of an eighteenth century herbarium, possibly that of Caleb Threlkeld in Trinity College, Dublin (TCD). *Glasra (new series)* **1**: 99-109. (Several early Dublin records are listed).

Doogue, D.A. and Walsh, W. (1989). Some Liffey valley plants. Pp. 76-77 in: Healy, E., Moriarty, C. and O'Flaherty, G. *The Book of the Liffey from Source to the Sea*. Wolfhound Press, Dublin.

[Downey, M.] (1991). *Groenlandia densa* (L.) Fourr in the Royal Canal, Dublin. *INJ* **23**: 383-384. (See Dromey (1991)).

Doyle, G.J. (1982). Narrative of the excursion of the international society for vegetation science to Ireland, 21-31 July 1980. *J. Life Sci. R. Dubl. Soc.* **3**: 43-64. (Includes records from North Bull Island and Malahide Island).

Doyle, J. (1934). *Spartina townsendi* H. & J. Groves at the North Bull, Co. Dublin. *INJ* **5**: 158.

Doyle, J. (1935). Co. Dublin Plants. *INJ* **5**: 307. (*Butomus umbellatus* L. and *Lemna gibba* L. are noted from the River Dodder).

Drabble, E. (1909). The British pansies. *J. Bot.* **47** (Suppl.): 1-32. (Includes a record for *Viola tricolor* subsp. *curtisii* (E. Forster) Syme from North Bull Island).

Drabble, E. (1930). Notes on Irish pansies. *J. Bot.* **68**: 141-143. (Includes a record for *Viola tricolor* subsp. *curtisii* (E. Forster) Syme from Portmarnock).

Drabble, H. (1937). Pansy records. *BEC* **11**: 319-324. (Notes the occurrence of *Viola curtisii* var. *sabulosa* Bor. at Portmarnock, its only site in Britain or Ireland).

Dromey, M. (1991). *Groenlandia densa* (L.) Fourr in the Royal Canal, Dublin. *INJ* **23**: 383-384. (Authorship of this note was erroneously attributed to M. Downey).

Dromey, M., Johnston, B. and Keane, S. (1992). *Ecological Survey of the Grand Canal.* Unpublished report to the Wildlife Service and Waterways Section, Office of Public Works, Dublin. (Includes many records from the Grand Canal).

Dromey, M., Johnston, B. and Nairn, R. (1991). *Ecological Survey of the Royal Canal. Final Report 1990.* Unpublished report to the Wildlife Service and Waterways Section, Office of Public Works, Dublin. (Includes many records from the Royal Canal).

Druce, G.C. (1909a). Notes on Irish plants. *IN* **18**: 209-213. (*Populus nigra* L. is noted from Dublin).

Druce, G.C. (1909b). Some additions to my paper on the Irish flora. *IN* **18**: 250. (A variant of *Hieracium sommerfeltii* Lindeb. is recorded from Glasnevin).

Druce, G.C. (1911). The international phytogeographical excursion in the British Isles, III - The floristic results. *The New Phytologist* **10**: 306-328. (Includes records from North Bull Island. Reprinted, with original pagination, as a supplement to *BEC* **3** (6) (1914)).

Druce, G.C. (1912a). *Sagina nodosa* var. *moniliformis.* P. 14 in: Druce, G.C. (Ed.). Report for 1911. *BEC* **3**: 1-57. (Record for *S. nodosa* var. *moniliformis* Lange from North Bull Island).

Druce, G.C. (1912b). *Juncus ranarius.* P. 35 in: Druce, G.C. (Ed.). Report for 1911. *BEC* **3**: 1-57. (*J. ambiguus* Guss. is recorded from North Bull Island).

Druce, G.C. (1912c). Notes on Irish plants. *IN* **21**: 235-240. (Includes records from North Bull Island).

Druce, G.C. (1914a). *Apium moorei.* Pp. 324-325 in: Druce, G.C. (Ed.). Report for 1913. *BEC* **3**: 303-440. (*A. x moorei* (Syme) Druce is recorded from Co. Dublin).

Druce, G.C. (1914b). *Salicornia dolichostachya.* Pp. 334-335 in: Druce, G.C. (Ed.). Report for 1913. *BEC* **3**: 303-440. (Record for *S. dolichostachya* Moss from North Bull Island).

Druce, G.C. (1915). *Linaria arenaria.* P. 70-71 in: Druce, G.C. (Ed.). Report for 1914. *BEC* **4**: 1-108. (Includes a record for *Artemisia stelleriana* Besser from North Bull Island, supposedly derived from Lord Ardilaun's garden).

Druce, G.C. (1918). *Viola canina* var. *sabulosa.* P. 98 in: Druce, G.C. (Ed.). Report for 1917. *BEC* **5**: 1-204. (Record for *V. canina* var. *sabulosa* Reichb. from North Bull Island).

Druce, G.C. (1920a). *Eschscholzia douglasii.* P. 637 in: Druce, G.C. (Ed.). Report for 1919. *BEC* **5**: 536-799. (Record for *E. californica* Cham. from Dublin).

Druce, G.C. (1920b). *Medicago hispida* var. *apiculata.* P. 647 in: Druce, G.C. (Ed.). Report for 1919. *BEC* **5**: 536-799. (Record for *M. polymorpha* L. from Dublin).

Druce, G.C. (1920c). *Carthamnus tinctorius.* P. 663 in: Druce, G.C. (Ed.). Report for 1919. *BEC* **5**: 536-799. (Record for *C. tinctorius* L. from Dublin).

Druce, G.C. (1920d). *Rumex salicifolius*. P. 678 in: Druce, G.C. (Ed.). Report for 1919. *BEC* **5**: 536-799. (Record for *R. salicifolius* Weinm. from Dublin).

Druce, G.C. (1920e). *Cannabis sativa*. P. 679 in: Druce, G.C. (Ed.). Report for 1919. *BEC* **5**: 536-799. (Record for *C. sativa* L. from Dublin).

Druce, G.C. (1920f). The extinct and dubious plants of Britain. Pp. 730-799 in: Druce, G.C. (Ed.). Report for 1919. *BEC* **5**: 536-799. (An old record for *Trifolium retusum* L. from near Kilbarrack Church is noted. See Parnell and Webb (1991)).

Druce, G.C. (1932). *The Comital Flora of the British Isles*. T. Buncle and Co., Arbroath. (The occurrence in Dublin of many species is indicated. However, as pointed out by Praeger (1934e) and Webb (1952a), this work is unreliable, on account of the many discrepancies and misprints it contains).

Dublin Naturalists' Field Club (1905-1972). Annual reports for 1904-1971. In: *Report[s] and Statement[s] of Accounts for the Year[s] 1904-1971, Officers and Committee[s] for 1905-1972, and Lists of Members*. Dublin Naturalists' Field Club, Dublin. (Each report contains details of club excursions and interesting botanical finds are frequently noted. Later issues contain separate Flowering Plant Group reports. An almost complete set is held in the archives of the Dublin Naturalists' Field Club).

Dublin Naturalists' Field Club (1975-1996, ongoing). *Newsletter*. Unpublished and issued quarterly to Club members. (Includes some records from Dublin sites. Copies are held in the Club archives).

Dudman, A.A. and Richards, A.J. (1994). Seven new species of *Taraxacum* Wigg. (Asteraceae), native to the British Isles. *Watsonia* **20**: 119-132. (Notes the occurrence of *T. haworthianum* A.A. Dudman & A. Richards in Dublin).

Dudman, A.A. and Richards, A.J. (1995). *Dandelions of the British Isles*. BSBI Handbook. (Unpublished draft. Co. Dublin records are mapped).

Edees, E.S. and Newton, A. (1988). *Brambles of the British Isles*. The Ray Society, London. (Twenty-nine species of *Rubus* are reported from Dublin).

Environmental Consultancy Services (1990). *Proposed Business and Industrial Park Vancroft Ltd., Environmental Impact Statement*. Appendix B: Environmental Impact Assessment of the Proposed Development on the Flora and Fauna. Unpublished, Dublin. (Includes a list of 128 species from this Fairview site).

Fahy, E. (1974). *The Sluice River Marsh - An Area of Scientific Interest in County Dublin*. Unpublished report prepared for Dublin County Council. An Foras Forbartha, Dublin. (Includes species lists from different parts of the marsh).

Fahy, E., Goodwillie, R.N., Rochford, J. and Kelly, D. (1975). Eutrophication of a partially enclosed estuarine mudflat. *Marine Pollution Bulletin* **6** (2): 29-31. (Includes records for *Ruppia maritima* L. and *Spartina* x *townsendii* Groves & J. Groves from Rogerstown Estuary).

Farragher, M.A. (1961). *The Biology of Native Sand Lucerne (Medicago sylvestris) with a Consideration of its Agronomic Value*. Part two of an unpublished M.Agr.Sc. thesis. National University of Ireland, University College Dublin. (Includes sites for *Medicago sativa* L. subsp. *varia* (Martyn) Arcang. at Portmarnock, Malahide and Rush (p. 347)).

Farragher, M.A. (1969). *Zerna erecta* (Huds.) S.F. Gray in Ireland. *INJ* **16**: 164-166. (Notes the occurence of *Bromopsis erecta* (Hudson) Fourr. var. *erecta* and var. *villosa* Leight in Dublin).

Farragher, M.A. (1973). Some recently recorded grass varieties. *INJ* **17**: 345-347. (Varieties of *Agrostis, Bromus, Bromopsis, Festuca* and *Poa* spp. are recorded from Dublin sites).

Farragher, M.A. (1975). *Poa pratensis*, a pubescent form. *INJ* **18**: 256. (Noted at Clondalkin).

Farragher, M.A. and Curran, P.L. (1962). Observations on native sand-lucerne (*Medicago* x *varia* Martyn). *The Scientific Proceedings of the Royal Dublin Society*. Series B **1**: 59-66. (Notes the occurrence of *Medicago sativa* L. subsp. *varia* (Martyn.) Arcang. on sand dunes at Rush and Portmarnock).

Farrell, L. and Randall, R.E. (1992). The distribution of *Mertensia maritima* (L.) Gray, Oyster plant, in Ireland. *INJ* **24**: 135-140. (Notes old records for the species from Portmarnock, Loughshinny and Skerries-Balbriggan. Last Dublin record was in 1858).

Fay, P.J. and Jeffrey, D.W. (1995). The nitrogen cycle in sand-dunes. Pp. 151-166 in: Jeffrey, D.W., Jones, M.B. and McAdam, J.H. (Eds). *Irish Grasslands - Their Biology and Management*. Royal Irish Academy, Dublin. (Includes a vegetation map of North Bull Island).

Feehan, J. (1990). Plant life. Pp. 17-18 in: O'Sullivan, J. (Ed.). *Environmental Impact Study of Proposed Quarry and Ancillary Works at Glenasmole Quarry, Glassamucky, Bohernabreena, Co. Dublin*. Unpublished, Dublin. (The flora and vegetation of the quarry are described).

Ferguson, I.K. (1962). *Salicornia* in Ireland. *Proc. BSBI* **4**: 470. (Notes the occurrence in Dublin of a species of *Salicornia* L. apparently identical with *S. nitens* P. Ball & Tutin).

Ferguson, I.K. (1964). *A Study of the Taxonomy of* Salicornia *L. in Ireland*. Unpublished Ph.D. thesis. University of Dublin, Trinity College. (Includes records from Baldoyle and North Bull Island).

ffrench-Mullen, M. (1975). A close look at garden weeds. *Fieldfare* **1975**: 7-8. (Includes records for *Solanum nigrum* L. and *Tragopogon porrifolius* L. from Dun Laoghaire).

Goodwillie, R.N. (1967). *Crambe maritima* in Co. Wicklow. *INJ* **15**: 307. (The record is actually from Killiney, Co. Dublin; see Goodwillie (1968). Record also reported in Wallace, E.C. (Ed.) (1968). Plant records. *Proc. BSBI* **7**: 195-199).

Goodwillie, R.N. (1968). *Spergularia rubra* in Co. Wicklow. *INJ* **16**: 26. (Clarifies a Dublin record for *Crambe maritima* L.).

Goodwillie, R.N. (1980). *Observations on the Ecological Implications of Alternative Layouts for St. Anne's Golf Course, Bull Island*. Unpublished report prepared for Dublin Corporation. An Foras Forbartha, Dublin.

Goodwillie, R.N. (1984). *Ecological Monitoring of Sediment at Bull Island*. Unpublished report prepared for Dublin Corporation. An Foras Forbartha, Dublin. (Reports the expansion in range of *Spartina anglica* C.E. Hubb. at North Bull Island).

Goodwillie, R.N. (1986). *Survey of Booterstown Marsh with Suggestions for Management*. Unpublished report prepared for Dun Laoghaire Corporation. An Foras Forbartha, Dublin. (The vegetation of the marsh in 1970 and 1986 is mapped and briefly discussed on pp. 7-8).

Goodwillie, R.N., Craig, M. and Haworth, R. (1973). *Dodder Valley Survey*. Unpublished report prepared for Dublin County Council. An Foras Forbartha, Dublin. (Includes records for several species from Bohernabreena, including *Parnassia palustris* L.).

Goodwillie, R.N. and Fahy, E. (1973). *A Preliminary Report on Areas of Scientific Interest in County Dublin*. Unpublished report prepared for Dublin County Council. An Foras Forbartha, Dublin. (Noteworthy species are listed from many sites).

Goodwillie, R.N., Goodwillie, O. and Brandt, E. (1971). *Ecological Survey of Bull Island Mudflats and Booterstown Marsh*. Unpublished report to the Department of Lands, Dublin.

Goodwillie, R.N. and Ní Lamhna, É. (1988). *Management Plan for Portmarnock Sand Dunes*. Unpublished report prepared for Dublin County Council. An Foras Forbartha, Dublin. (A list of the rarer species with their approximate localities is provided).

Goodwillie, R.N., Ní Lamhna, É. and Webb, R. (1988). *A Second Report on Areas of Scientific Interest in County Dublin*. Unpublished report prepared for Dublin County Council. (Noteworthy species are listed from many sites. A list of the Dublin records for legally protected species is appended).

Goodwillie, R.N., O'Donovan, G. and Fay, P. (1987). *Ecological Impact of Mowing Natural Grassland on Bull Island.* Unpublished report prepared for Dublin County Council. An Foras Forbartha, Dublin. (Includes data on species occurrence, biomass and phenology in grassland subject to mowing for a golf practice course).

Gornall, R.J. (1988). The coastal ecodeme of *Parnassia palustris* L. *Watsonia* **17**: 139-143. (Notes the occurrence in Dublin of var. *condensata* Travis & Wheldon).

Graham, G.G. and Primavesi, A.L. (1993). *Roses of Great Britain and Ireland.* Botanical Society of the British Isles, London. (Includes mapped records from Dublin).

Grierson, R. (1920). Adventive plants of the Glasgow area. *BEC* **5**: 719-721. (Includes a record for *Eschscholzia californica* Cham. from Dublin).

Grierson, R. (1922). Adventive plants of the Dublin area, 1921. *BEC* **6**: 406. (Eleven species are listed).

Groves, E.W. (1958). *Hippophae rhamnoides* in the British Isles. *Proc. BSBI* **3**: 1-21. (Includes records for this species from near Rush and from Rogerstown coastguard station).

Groves, H. and Groves, J. (1912). *Nitella gracilis* in West Cornwall. *J. Bot.* **50**: 348-349. (Includes an erroneous record for this species from Glencullen).

Groves, J. and Bullock-Webster, G.R. (1920). *The British Charophyta. Vol. 1, Nitelleae.* The Ray Society, London. (The occurrence in Dublin of several taxa is noted).

Groves, J. and Bullock-Webster, G.R. (1924). *The British Charophyta. Vol. 2, Chareae.* The Ray Society, London. (The occurrence in Dublin of several taxa is noted).

Gunn, W.F. (1912). *Saponaria vaccaria* in Dublin. *IN* **21**: 223. (*Vaccaria hispanica* (Miller) Rauschert at the North Wall).

Hackett, M.E. (1934). Dublin Naturalists' Field Club. *INJ* **5**: 93. (Excursion reports. Includes records from Portrane).

Hackett, M.E. (1935). Dublin Naturalists' Field Club. *INJ* **5**: 183. (News and excursion reports. Includes records from Balrothery and the Bog of the Ring).

Hackney, P. (1980). A first record of *Spartina* x *townsendii* H. and J. Groves in NE Ireland. *INJ* **20**: 46. (Mentions its occurrence on North Bull Island).

Hackney, P., James, K.W. and Ross, H.C.G. (1983). *A List of Photographs in the R.J. Welch Collection in the Ulster Museum. Volume 2, Botany, Geology.* Ulster Museum, Belfast. (Includes several references to photographs of Dublin plants).

Hall, P.M. (Ed.) (1938). Plant records. *BEC* **11**: 463-524. (Includes records for *Myosotis collina* var. *mittenii* Baker [= *M. ramosissima* Rochel or *M. discolor* Pers.] from Howth and *Dactylorhiza incarnata* subsp. *coccinea* (Pugsley) Soó from North Bull Island).

Hall, P.M. (1939). The British species of *Utricularia*. *BEC* **12**: 100-117. (Dublin records for *U. vulgaris* L. and possibly *U. intermedia* Hayne).

Harrington, M. (1974). *Catalogue of the Collection of Potamogeton in the Herbarium, National Botanic Gardens, Glasnevin, of Plants Collected in Ireland.* Unpublished manuscript lodged in the library of the National Botanic Gardens, Glasnevin. (Includes details of Dublin localities for nine taxa).

Haughton, J.P. (1944). Dublin Naturalists' Field Club. *INJ* **8**: 228. (Excursion reports. Includes records from Howth).

Haughton, J.P. (1945). Dublin Naturalists' Field Club. *INJ* **8**: 318. (News and excursion reports. Includes records from Howth).

Healy, B. (1975). Fauna of the salt-marsh, North Bull Island, Dublin. *Proc. RIA* (B) **75**: 225-244. (Includes records for several vascular plant species).

Healy, B. (1994). *Lagoons and Other Enclosed Brackish Waters in The Republic of Ireland*. Unpublished report. University College, Dublin. (Notes *Ruppia maritima* L. and *Spartina* sp. from the Broad Meadow Water estuary, Malahide. Copy held by the National Parks and Wildlife Service).

Hickie, D.A. (1985). *A Hedge Study of North Co. Dublin*. Unpublished M.Sc. thesis. Environmental Sciences Unit, University of Dublin, Trinity College. (General survey of hedge type and removal, largely lacking floristic details).

Hobson, D.D. (undated, c.1989). *Records of* Populus nigra *var.* betulifolia *in Ireland*. Unpublished. (Eight trees from Blackrock Park and one from Ranelagh are listed. This manuscript is lodged in the School of Botany, Trinity College, Dublin).

Hobson, D.D. (1991). The status of *Populus nigra* L. in the Republic of Ireland. *Watsonia* **18**: 303-305. (The occurrence of this species as an introduction at two sites in Dublin is indicated).

Hobson, D.D. (1993). *Populus nigra* L. in Ireland - an indigenous species? *INJ* **24**: 244-247. (Notes the occurrence of 15 specimens of this species in Dublin).

Höck, F. (1904). Ankömmlinge in der Pflanzenwelt Mitteleuropas während des letzten halben Jahrhunderts. *Beihefte zum botanischen Centralblatt* **17**: 210. (*Azolla filiculoides* Lam. near Dublin, but possibly not in the county).

Howard, H.W. and Lyon, A.G. (1951). Distribution of the British watercress species. *Watsonia* **2**: 91-92. (Includes records for *Rorippa nasturtium-aquaticum* (L.) Hayek and *R. microphylla* (Boenn.) N. Hylander x *R. nasturtium-aquaticum* from Miltonsfields and Finglas, respectively).

Hudson, H.J. (1957). Changes in Dublin's flora. *INJ* **12**: 190-192. (Discusses the changes which have taken place in the Dublin flora since the publication of Colgan's *Flora of the County Dublin* in 1904).

Hudson, H.J. and Brunker, J.P. (undated). Annotations in copy of Hanbury, F.J. (1886). *The London Catalogue of British Plants* (8th edn). George Bell & Sons, London. (Contains records from North Bull Island additional to those on Brunker's (undated, pre-1961) manuscript list. Copy held by the Dublin Naturalists' Field Club).

Hutchinson, C.D. (1975). Birds of the estuaries and tidal marshes. Pp. 37-45 in: Hutchinson, C.D. (Ed.). *The Birds of Dublin and Wicklow*. Irish Wildbird Conservancy, Dublin. (Notes the presence of *Salicornia europaea* L., *Spartina* x *townsendii* Groves & J. Groves and *Zostera angustifolia* (Hornem.) Reichb. in several Dublin estuaries).

Hylander, N. (1960). Irländska färger och vyer. Några reseintryck av en botanist. *Föreningens för Dendrologi och Parkvård Årsbok Lustgården* **1960**: 23-30. (Includes records from Howth).

Ingrouille, M.J. and Stace, C.A. (1986). The *Limonium binervosum* aggregate (Plumbaginaceae) in the British Isles. *Bot. J. Linn. Soc.* **92**: 177-217. (A new variety, *L. procerum* var. *hibernicum* Ingrouille is described, based on material from Donabate. It also occurs at Portrane, North Bull Island and Killiney).

Jackson, P.J. (1983). *Cardamine bulbifera* (L.) Crantz - A first record for Ireland? *INJ* **21**: 49. (Its occurrence in Marley Park, Rathfarnham is noted).

Jeffrey, D.W. (Ed.) (1977). *North Bull Island Dublin Bay, a Modern Coastal Natural History*. Royal Dublin Society, Dublin. (Includes sections on the vascular plant flora and vegetation communities; see Boyle (1977), Carvill (1977), McNamee and Jeffrey (1977), Moore (1977) and Moore and O'Reilly (1977)).

Jeffrey, D.W. (1981). Howth natural history. Pp. 129-136 in: McBrierty, V.J. (Ed.). *The Howth Peninsula: its History, Lore and Legend*. North Dublin Round Table, Dublin. (Includes details of several vegetation types on the peninsula).

Jeffrey, D.W. (1984). Case history: North Bull Island - an assessment of a nature conservation resource. Pp. 67-80 in: Jeffrey, D.W. (Ed.). *Nature Conservation in Ireland - Progress and Problems*. Royal Irish Academy, Dublin. (Notes the occurrence on the island of *Spartina anglica* C.E. Hubb., *Hippophae rhamnoides* L. and *Salvia verbenaca* L.).

Jeffrey, D.W., Madden, B., Rafferty, B., Dwyer, R., Wilson, J. and Allott, N. (1992). *Algal Growths and Foreshore Quality. Technical Report No. 7. Dublin Bay Water Quality Management Plan.* Environmental Research Unit, Dublin. (Makes mention of *Zostera, Ruppia, Spartina* and *Salicornia* spp. from Merrion Gates and North Bull Island).

Jeffrey, D.W. and Walsh, E. (1983). *A Students Guide to North Bull Island.* Royal Dublin Society, Dublin. (Describes the different vegetation types on the island and lists the common species).

Jermy, A.C., Arnold, H.C., Farrell, L. and Perring, F.H. (1978). *Atlas of Ferns of the British Isles.* Botanical Society of the British Isles and British Pteridological Society, London. (Dublin records are mapped).

Jermy, A.C., Chater, A.O. and David, R.W. (1982). *Sedges of the British Isles.* (2nd edn). Botanical Society of the British Isles, London. (Dublin records are mapped).

Johnson, T. (1910). Die flora von Ireland, *Vegetationsbilder* Heft 5-6: Plates 25-36. (Includes plates of *Crithmum maritimum* L. from Howth and Lambay Island, and *Armeria maritima* (Miller) Willd. from Lambay Island).

Jonsell, B. (1968). Studies in the north-west European species of *Rorippa* s.str. *Symbolae Botanicae Upsalienses* **19**: 1-221. (Records for *R. palustris* (L.) Besser from Dublin are on p. 187).

Kay, Q.O.N. and Ab-Shukor, N.A. (1988). *Trifolium occidentale* D.E. Coombe, new to Wales. *Watsonia* **17**: 168-170. (Points out the occurrence of this species at Skerries).

Kelly, D.L. (1965). *Flora of St. Columba's College.* Unpublished manuscript. (A detailed flora of this Rathfarnham school which includes records for 262 vascular plant species. Copies retained by the author and at the college by R.M. McMullen).

Kelly, D.L. (1985). Plant records from about Ireland, 1965-1983. *INJ* **21**: 416-419. (Includes records for *Euphrasia anglica* Pugsley from Kilmashogue mountain and *Agrostis gigantea* Roth from Templeogue).

Kelly, D.L. (1990). *Cornus sericea* L. in Ireland: an incipient weed of wetlands. *Watsonia* **18**: 33-36. (Includes records from Lucan, Santry and Ashtown).

Kelly, D.L. and Synnott, D.M. (1993). Bryophytes of the Phoenix Park. Dublin, *Glasra (new series)* **2**: 73-81. (Ninety-seven moss and liverwort taxa are recorded from the park. Includes records for several tree species. Reprinted in Reilly *et al.* (1993)).

Kent, D.H. (1964). *Senecio squalidus* L. in the British Isles - 9, Ireland. *INJ* **14**: 203-205. (Includes three Dublin records).

King, A.L.K. (undated a). Annotations in her copy of Colgan, N. (1904). *Flora of the County Dublin.* Hodges, Figgis & Co., Dublin. (Now in the possession of M.J.P. Scannell).

King, A.L.K. (undated b). Annotations in her copy of Anonymous (1961b). *A Supplement to Colgan's Flora of the County Dublin.* The Stationery Office, Dublin. (This inter-leaved copy includes three records - *Thlaspi arvense* L. (Lambay Island), *Papaver somniferum* L. (Mount Merrion) and *Butomus umbellatus* L. (Grand Canal), the latter with a comment in another hand suggesting that it is an error. Now in the library of the National Botanic Gardens, Glasnevin).

King, J.J. and Nash, D.W. (1994). The charophyta of County Dublin (H21). *Biol. Env. Proc. RIA* (B) **94**: 255-264. (Details Dublin localities for eleven species).

Kirk, F. (1993). *Nature in the Phoenix Park.* The Stationery Office, Dublin. (*Viola hirta* L. and *Spiranthes spiralis* (L.) Chevall. are noted as occurring in the park).

Knowles, M.C. (1917). *Elymus arenarius* on the North Bull. *IN* **26**: 56. (*Leymus arenarius* (L.) Hochst.)

Lamb, J.G.D. (1983). *Cardamine bulbifera* in Co. Dublin. *INJ* **21**: 136. (Notes the occurrence of this species in the demesne at Malahide Castle).

Lambe, E. (1971). *A Phytosociological and Ecological Analysis of Irish Weed Communities*. Unpublished Ph.D. thesis. National University of Ireland, Dublin. (Analyses the composition of north Co. Dublin weed communities).

Lousley, J.E. (1944). Notes on British Rumices: II. *BEC* **12**: 547-585. (Includes a Dublin record for *Rumex salicifolius* Weinm.).

[Lousley, J.E. (1964). *Calceolaria chelidonioides*. *Proc. BSBI* **5**: 338-341. Record incorrectly cited as "H21, Dublin. Belvoir Park". Belvoir Park is in vice-county H38, Down].

Maconchy, G.E.C. (1920). A note on some Howth clovers. *IN* **29**: 119-120. (Notes the occurrence on Howth Head of *Trifolium micranthum* Viv., *T. striatum* L., *T. ornithopodioides* L., *Ornithopus perpusillus* L., *Erodium moschatum* (L.) L' Hér. and a white-flowered form of *Geranium molle* L.).

Maconchy, G.E.C. (undated). Annotations in his copy of Colgan, N. (1904). *Flora of the County Dublin*. Hodges, Figgis & Co., Dublin. (An inter-leaved copy containing many records. Now in the library of the National Botanic Gardens, Glasnevin).

Madden, B., Jennings, E. and Jeffrey, D.W. (1993). Distribution and ecology of *Zostera* in Co Dublin. *INJ* **24**: 303-310. (*Zostera angustifolia* (Hornem.) Reichenb. and *Z. noltii* Hornem. are recorded from Dublin Bay, Baldoyle estuary and Malahide estuary. The authors suggest that *Z. marina* L. probably no longer occurs in Dublin).

M[alone], E. (1931). Dublin Naturalists' Field Club. *INJ* **3**: 221. (Excursion reports. Includes records from Ireland's Eye and Malahide Island).

Manton, I. (1950). *Problems of Cytology and Evolution in the Pteridophyta*. Cambridge University Press, Cambridge. (Includes a Dublin record for the "large form" of *Equisetum variegatum* Schleicher).

Marsden-Jones, E.M. and Turrill, W.B. (1954). *British Knapweeds. A Study in Synthetic Taxonomy*. Ray Society, London. (Includes records from Dublin for forms of *Centaurea nigra* L.).

Marshall, J.B. (1964). Notes on British *Crepis* - 2. Variants of *Crepis capillaris* (L.) Wallr. *Proc. BSBI* **5**: 325-333. (Includes a record from Clontarf).

Massy, A.L. (1923). Red cowslips. *IN* **32**: 63. (Near Feltrim Hill).

Mawhinney, K., Goodwillie, R.N. and Webb, R. (1984a). *A Report on the Portmarnock Sand Dunes with Special Reference to a Possible Special Amenity Area Order*. Unpublished report to Dublin County Council, An Foras Forbartha, Dublin.

Mawhinney, K., Goodwillie, R.N. and Webb, R. (1984b). *Liffey Valley Study - Sites of Ecological and Geological Interest*. Unpublished report to Dublin County Council, An Foras Forbartha, Dublin.

McCarron, E.G. (1993). *The North Bull Island Special Amenity Order*. Unpublished report to Dublin County Council, Dublin. (Includes a brief description of the vegetation and mentions notable plant species found on the island).

McClintock, D. (1960). *Calystegia pulchra*. P. 407 in: Wallace, E.C. (Ed.) (1960). Plant records. *Proc. BSBI* **3**: 394-419. (Record from Balrothery).

McClintock, D. (1972a). New Zealand Epilobiums in Britain. *Watsonia* **9**: 140-142. (Notes the occurrence of specimens of *E. pedunculare* Cunn. collected from a Dublin garden in 1938).

McClintock, D. (1972b). *Gaudinia fragilis* (L.) Beauv. *Watsonia* **9**: 143-146. (Includes a 1906 record from Ringsend).

McClintock, D. (1975). Exotics 1974. *Wild Flower Magazine* **374**: 8-10. (*Hieracium gougetianum* Gren. & Godron established on walls in Dublin).

McClintock, D. (1979). *Acaena* in Ireland. *INJ* **19**: 365-367. (Lists records from Dublin for *A. novae-zelandiae* Kirk and *A. ovalifolia* Ruiz Lopez & Pavon).

McCullen, J. (1993). A landscape history of the Phoenix Park, Dublin. *Glasra (new series)* **2**: 3-129. (Includes details of the locations and dates of planting of trees in the park. Reprinted in Reilly *et al.* (1993)).

McEvoy, A. and Goodwillie, R.N. (1980). *Ecological Monitoring of Sediment at Bull Island.* Unpublished report prepared for Dublin Corporation. An Foras Forbartha, Dublin. (Notes the occurrence of *Spartina anglica* C.E. Hubb. and *Salicornia* spp. on the North Bull Island mudflats).

McMullen, R.M. (1967). *Monotropa* in Dublin area. *INJ* **15**:307. (*M. hypopitys* subsp. *hypophegea* (Wallr.) Holmboe at Glenasmole. Record also reported in Wallace, E.C. (Ed.) (1968). Plant records. *Proc. BSBI* **7**: 195-199).

McMullen, R.M. (1985). Glenasmole, Co. Dublin. 28th August. *Watsonia* **15**: 305. (Report of re-discovery of *Potamogeton perfoliatus* L., *Ranunculus aquatilis* L. and *R. trichophyllus* Chaix at the upper lake. Authorship of report erroneously attributed to R. McMullan).

McNamee, K.A. (1976). *An Experimental Study of an Irish Salt-marsh.* Unpublished Ph.D. thesis. University of Dublin, Trinity College. (Includes records from North Bull Island).

McNamee, K.A. and Jeffrey, D.W. (1977). Ecophysiology of saltmarsh plants. Pp. 100-103 in: Jeffrey, D.W. (Ed.). *North Bull Island Dublin Bay, a Modern Coastal Natural History.* Royal Dublin Society, Dublin. (Aspects of the ecophysiology of *Plantago maritima* L., *Triglochin maritimum* L., *Armeria maritima* (Miller) Willd., *Atriplex portulacoides* L., *Juncus maritimus* Lam. and *J. gerardii* Loisel. are considered).

Mills, J.N. and Stace, C.A. (1974). Chromosome numbers of British plants, 2. *Watsonia* **10**: 167-168. (Includes a count for *Hieracium gougetianum* Gren. & Godron from Dublin).

Minchin, D. and Minchin, C. (1996). The Sea-pea *Lathyrus japonicus* Willd. in Ireland, and an addition to the flora of West Cork (H3) and Wexford (H12). *INJ* **25**: 165-169. (Notes an 1833 record for the species from Howth. This record must, however, be withdrawn as, according to N. McMillan *in litt.*, it is based on a specimen of an Everlasting-pea of garden origin).

Moffat, C.B. (1906). *Spiranthes autumnalis* in the Phoenix Park. *IN* **15**: 279.

Moffat, C.B. (1912). *Spiranthes autumnalis* in the Phoenix Park. *IN* **21**: 206.

Moffat, C.B. (1921a). The mountain pansy and its time of flowering. *IN* **30**: 80. (Includes a record for *Viola lutea* Hudson from near Brittas).

Moffat, C.B. (1921b). *Acaena sanguisorbae* an alien colonist. *IN* **30**: 98-99. (Includes a record from Lucan, re-determined by McClintock (1979) as *A. ovalifolia* Ruiz Lopez & Pavon).

Moffat, C.B. (1923). The study of common wild flowers: a plea for closer study. *IN* **32**: 21-27. (Notes morphological and phenological peculiarities of some Dublin plants).

Moffat, C.B. (1924). *Silene noctiflora* in Co. Dublin. *IN* **33**: 110. (Noted on waste ground at Inchicore, in company with *Thlaspi arvense*, L., *Sisymbrium irio* L., *Melilotus officinalis* (L.) Lam., *Senecio squalidus* L., *Matricaria discoidea* DC., *Ballota nigra* L. and *Bupleurum 'rotundifolium'* L.).

Mooney, E.P., Goodwillie, R.N. and Douglas, C. (1991). *Survey of Mountain Blanket Bogs of Scientific Interest* [Interim title]. Unpublished draft report to National Parks and Wildlife Service, Dublin. (Includes records from Castlekelly for several common bogland species)

Moore, J.A. (1986). *Charophytes of Great Britain and Ireland.* Botanical Society of the British Isles, London. (Includes mapped records from Dublin).

Moore, J.A. and Greene, D.M. (1983). *Provisional Atlas and Catalogue of British Museum (Natural History) Specimens of the Characeae.* Institute of Terrestrial Ecology, Abbots Ripton. (Includes records from Dublin for several taxa).

Moore, J.J. (1954). Some observations on the microflora of two peat profiles in the Dublin mountains, *The Scientific Proceedings of the Royal Dublin Society*, New Series **26**: 379-395. (Blanket bog vegetation and several vascular plant species are reported from Tibradden and Glendoo Mountains).

Moore, J.J. (1960). A re-survey of the vegetation of the district lying south of Dublin (1905-1956). *Proc. RIA (B)* **61**: 1-36. (Examines vegetation composition of this area and the changes thereto since the original survey by Pethybridge and Praeger (1905)).

Moore, J.J. (1977). Vegetation of the dune complex. Pp. 104-106 in: Jeffrey, D.W. (Ed.). *North Bull Island Dublin Bay, a Modern Coastal Natural History*. Royal Dublin Society, Dublin. (The vegetation communities of the dunes are described and the principal species listed).

Moore, J.J. and O'Reilly, H. (1977). Saltmarsh: vegetation pattern and trends. Pp. 83-87 in: Jeffrey, D.W. (Ed.). *North Bull Island Dublin Bay, a Modern Coastal Natural History*. Royal Dublin Society, Dublin. (The distribution on the island of the various salt marsh vegetation communities is described and mapped).

Moriarty, C. (1989). *On Foot in Dublin and Wicklow: Exploring the Wilderness*. Wolfhound Press, Dublin. (Localities for noteworthy species are cited).

Moriarty, C. (1991). *Down the Dodder. Wildlife, History, Legend, Walks*. Wolfhound Press, Dublin. (Includes records from many sites along the river).

Moss, C.E. (1912). The international phytogeographical excursion in the British Isles, XII - Remarks on the characters and nomenclature of some critical plants noticed on the excursion. *The New Phytologist* **11**: 398-414. (*Salicornia dolichostachya* Moss is described as new and its occurrence in Dublin (North Bull Island) is noted).

Moss, C.E. (1914). *The Cambridge British Flora, Volume II: Salicaceae to Chenopodiaceae*. Cambridge University Press, Cambridge. (The occurrence in Dublin of several species is indicated).

Moss, C.E. (1920). *The Cambridge British Flora, Volume III: Portulacaceae to Fumariaceae*. Cambridge University Press, Cambridge. (The occurrence in Dublin of several species is indicated).

Murphy, D.P. (1972). *Orobanche* hosts at Glasnevin. *INJ* **17**: 279. (At the National Botanic Gardens *O. hederae* Duby is parasitic on three taxa belonging to the Araliaceae and *O. minor* Smith on two belonging to the Geraniaceae and Campanulaceae).

Murphy, J.P. (1981). *Senecio* x *albescens* Burbidge & Colgan at Killiney, Co. Dublin: a seventy-eight years old population. *Watsonia* **13**: 303-311. (Hybridization study with some distributional information).

Nairn, R.G.W. (1986). *Spartina anglica* in Ireland and its potential impact on wildfowl and waders - a review. *Irish Birds* **3**: 215-228. (Notes the occurrence of this species at North Bull Island and Baldoyle, Malahide and Rogerstown Estuaries).

Nash, D.W. (1995). Stations for *Senecio viscosus* L. in Ireland. *INJ* **25**: 59-66. (Lists thirty-three Dublin sites for the species since 1981).

Nash, D.W. (1996). The North Bull Island, Co. Dublin (v.c. H21). 8th October. *BSBI News* **71**: 75-76. (Field meeting report which lists notable species seen on the day).

Nash, D.W. and King, J.J. (1993). The genus *Tolypella* in Co Dublin (H21). *INJ* **24**: 329-332. (Includes recent records for the stoneworts *T. glomerata* (Desv.) Leonh., *T. intricata* (Trent. *ex* Roth) Leonh., *T. prolifera* (Ziz *ex* A. Braun) Leonh. and several macrophyte species, including *Groenlandia densa* (L.) Fourr.).

Nash, M. (1987). Flora and fauna. Pp. 7-12 in: O'Sullivan, J. and Cannon, S. (Eds), *The Book of Dun Laoghaire*. Blackrock Teachers' Centre, Blackrock. (Lists the common species to be found in the area and includes localities for the most noteworthy).

National Parks and Wildlife Service Files, Dublin. (Paper files containing detailed floristic information on many Dublin sites are maintained).

National Parks and Wildlife Service Sites Database, Dublin. (This database holds detailed floristic information relating to many Dublin sites, in particular those surveyed as part of a national survey of Areas of Scientific Interest carried out between 1992 and 1994).

National Parks and Wildlife Service Protected and Threatened Plants Databases, Dublin. (These databases contain details of Dublin records for species protected under the Flora (Protection) Order, 1987 and for species which, though not protected under this Order, are regarded as threatened in Ireland).

Nelson, E.C. (1979). Records of the Irish flora published before 1726. *Bull. IBS* **3**: 51-74. (Includes a record for *Scilla verna* Hudson from Ringsend, published in 1650).

Nelson, E.C. (1988). Introduction, pp. xiii-lii, [to] *The First Irish Flora. Synopsis Stirpium Hibernicarum. Caleb Threlkeld*. Boethius Press, Kilkenny. (This facsimile edition of Threlkeld's Flora includes several 18th century records, and some contemporary records from Dublin are found on pp. xxv, xxxi and xxxviii).

Nelson, E.C. (1994). Ergasiophygophytes in the British Isles - plants that jumped the garden fence. Pp. 17-30 in: Perry, A.R. and Ellis, R.G. (Eds), *The Common Ground of Wild and Cultivated Plants*. National Museum of Wales, Cardiff. (Reports *Echium pininana* Webb & Berth. on Howth Head).

Nelson, E.C. (1996). A.B. Lambert's annotated *Flora Anglica*, its Irish-Linnaean connections, and an account of his Irish expedition, 1790. *Watsonia* **21**: 79-88. (Includes Dublin records for twenty species, almost all of them noted by Lambert).

Nelson, E.C. and Walsh, W.F. (1993). *Trees of Ireland: Native and Naturalized*. Lilliput Press, Dublin. (Reports several Dublin records, including one for *Pyrus pyraster* (L.) Burgsd. from Corduff).

Newton, A. (1986). An Irish bramble foray. *INJ* **22**: 62-67. (Several species are reported from Dublin).

Nic Lughadha, E.M. and Parnell, J.A.N. (1989). Heterostyly and gene-flow in *Menyanthes trifoliata* L. (Menyanthaceae). *Bot. J. Linn. Soc.* **100**: 337-354. (Study carried out on a Glencullen population).

Ní Lamhna, É. (1972). *Species List for Malahide Sand-dune: Salt-marsh System*. Unpublished list issued at the Botanical Society of the British Isles, Irish Regional Branch Meeting, 24.9.1972. (Over 180 vascular plant, bryophyte and algal taxa are listed. Lodged in the library of the National Botanic Gardens, Glasnevin).

Ní Lamhna, É. (1973). An account of the B.S.B.I. field excursion to Malahide sand dunes. Pp. 43-44 in: *Botanical Society of the British Isles. Report of Recorders' Conference, Dublin, September 1972*. The Irish Regional Committee of the B.S.B.I., Dublin.

Ní Lamhna, É. (1982a). *Preliminary Report on Fitzsimon's Wood, Sandyford, Co. Dublin*. Unpublished report prepared for Dublin County Council. An Foras Forbartha, Dublin. (Includes a short description of the vegetation of the wood).

Ní Lamhna, É. (1982b). The vegetation of saltmarshes and sand-dunes at Malahide Island, County Dublin. *J. Life Sci. R. Dubl. Soc.* **3**: 111-129. (Phytosociological study of much of the island. Includes many records in the form of relevés and descriptions of the various plant communities occurring. Two new vegetation associations, the Limonietum binervosi Ní Lamhna and the Sagino nodosae-Tortelletum flavovirentis Ní Lamhna, are described. Reprinted in White (1982)).

Ní Lamhna, É. (1989). *A Wildlife Park for the Dodder Banks from Oldbawn Bridge to Firhouse Bridge*. Unpublished report prepared for the Irish Wildbird Conservancy, Dublin. (Includes a short list of plants).

Ó Briain, M. (1977). *Vegetation Survey of Rogerstown Estuary, Autumn 1976*. Unpublished report for Aer Lingus Young Scientists Exhibition, Dublin.

Ó Briain, M. (1991). Use of a *Zostera* bed in Dublin Bay by light-bellied Brent Geese, 1981/82 to 1990/91. *Irish Birds* **4**: 299-316. (*Zostera noltii* Hornem. at Merrion Gates).

O'Brien, W. (1907). *Polystichum aculeatum* in Co. Dublin. *IN* **16**: 178. (Near Balrothery).

O'Callaghan, J. (1911). County Dublin plants. *IN* **20**: 164. (*Vaccinium oxycoccos* L. on the north side of Kippure mountain).

Ó Críodáin, C. (1988). *Parvocaricetea in Ireland*. Unpublished Ph.D. thesis. National University of Ireland, University College Dublin. (Includes relevés from the Featherbed, Glencullen Mountain, Killakee Mountain and Piperstown, assigned to the Sphagneto-Juncetum effusi McVean and Ratcliffe association).

O'Mahony, E. (1927). Red Campion in a new Dublin locality. *INJ* **1**: 180. (Clontarf).

O'Neill, A. (1971). *The Hill of Howth. A Conservation Study for An Taisce*. An Taisce, Dublin.

O'Reilly, H. (1976). A new station for *Diaphasium* (*Lycopodium*) *alpinum* (L.) Rothm. in Co. Dublin. *INJ* **18**: 334. (Seahan mountain).

O'Reilly, H. (1984). Preface. Pp. ix-x in: Wyse Jackson, P. and Sheehy Skeffington, M. *The Flora of Inner Dublin*. Royal Dublin Society in association with the Dublin Naturalists' Field Club, Dublin. (Notes several plant species of woodlands and calcareous grasslands from inner city sites).

O'Reilly, H. and Pantin. G. (1957). Some observations on the salt marsh formation in Co. Dublin. *Proc. RIA* (B) **58**: 89-128. (The vegetation and species composition of salt marshes at North Bull Island, Baldoyle, Malahide and Rogerstown is described).

O'Sullivan, A.M. (1973). *A Bibliography of the Irish Flora 1960 - 1972*. An Foras Talúntais, Dublin. (Lists 456 titles, some of which contain records from Dublin).

Otte, M.L. (1994). *A Re-evaluation of the Management Policy Concerning* Spartina - *Grasses at the North Bull Island Saltmarshes*. Unpublished report prepared for Dublin Corporation. (*Spartina anglica* C.E. Hubb. at North Bull Island).

Page, C.N. (1982). *The Ferns of Britain and Ireland*. Cambridge University Press, Cambridge. (Dublin records are mapped).

Palmer, J.A. (1915). *Lathraea squamaria* in south Dublin. *IN* **24**: 135. (Glenasmole).

Palmer, J.A. (undated). Annotations in his copy of Colgan, N. (1904). *Flora of the County Dublin*. Hodges, Figgis & Co., Dublin. (Now in the possession of C. Brady).

Palmer, M.A. and Bratton, J.H. (Eds) (1995). *A Sample Survey of the Flora of Britain and Ireland*. Joint Nature Conservation Committee, Peterborough. (An edited, single volume version of Rich and Woodruff (1990), the results of the Botanical Society of the British Isles Monitoring Scheme 1987-1988. Dublin records are mapped).

Parnell, J.A.N. (1985). Biological Flora of the British Isles - *Jasione montana* L. *Journal of Ecology* **73**: 341-358. (This species is noted from two sites on Howth Head).

Parnell, J.A.N. (1986). Chromosome numbers of Irish plants, 1. *Watsonia* **16**: 82-83. (Includes a count for *Spergularia rupicola* Lebel ex Le Jolis from Dun Laoghaire).

Parnell, J.A.N. and Webb, D.A. (1991). The *Flora Hibernica* herbarium of J.T. Mackay. *INJ* **23**: 359-364. (Several Dublin records are discussed).

Perring, F.H. (1956). *Spiranthes spiralis* (L.) Chevall. in Britain, 1955. *Proc. BSBI* **2**: 6-9. (Notes the occurrence of this species in Dublin).

Perring, F.H. (1996). A bridge too far - the non-Irish element in the British flora. *Watsonia* **21**: 15-51. (The presence in Dublin of several species is indicated).

Perring, F.H. and Sell, P.D. (Eds) (1968). *Critical Supplement to the Atlas of the British Flora*. Thomas Nelson and Sons, London. (Many records from Dublin are mapped, including one for *Festuca filiformis* Pourret).

Perring, F.H. and Walters, S.M. (Eds) (1962). *Atlas of the British Flora.* Thomas Nelson and Sons, London. (The original field cards on which many of the records mapped in this work were based are currently held by the National Parks and Wildlife Service, Dublin. The records are also held by the Biological Records Centre, Abbots Ripton as hard copy and on a database).

Perring, F.H. and Walters, S.M. (Eds) (1976). *Atlas of the British Flora.* (2nd edn). EP Publishing, Wakefield. (Errors in the 1st edition are corrected and the distributions of certain species are updated).

Perring, F.H. and Walters, S.M. (Eds) (1990). *Atlas of the British Flora.* (3rd edn). Botanical Society of the British Isles, London. (Includes an index and bibliography to distribution maps published between 1962 and 1989. See Preston (1990)).

Pethybridge, G.H. (pre-1905). Vegetation Maps of the North Dublin Coast. Unpublished. (The various types of coastal vegetation occurring between North Bull Island and the county boundary north of Balbriggan are marked on these six inches to one mile (1:10,560) maps. These maps are lodged in the Herbarium of the National Botanic Gardens, Glasnevin).

Pethybridge, G.H. (1908). The new flora of the burnt ground on the hill of Howth. *IN* **17**:160. (See also Adams (1908a, b) and Praeger (1908c)).

Pethybridge, G.H. and Praeger, R. Ll. (1905). The vegetation of the district lying south of Dublin. *Proc. RIA* (B) **25**: 124-180. (Definitive, early work on those plant associations found in the county south of the city. A multi-coloured, vegetation map of the area at a scale of one inch to one mile is included. See also Moore (1960)).

Philipson, W.R. (1937). A revision of the British species of the genus *Agrostis* Linn. *Bot. J. Linn. Soc.* **51**: 73-151. (Includes a Dublin record for *A. stolonifera* L. var. *stolonifera* on p. 96).

Phillips, R.A. (1907). *Allium scorodoprasum* in Co. Dublin. *IN* **16**: 348-349. (Lucan demesne).

Phillips, R.A. (1920). The distribution of *Brachypodium pinnatum* Beauv. in Ireland. *IN* **29**: 75. (Includes a record from near Inchicore).

Phillips, R.A. (1924). New localities for some rare plants in Ireland. *IN* **33**: 129-131. (Includes a record for *Rumex pulcher* L. from between Portrane and Donabate).

Piper, R. (1970). *Glenasmole Orchids.* Unpublished. (This manuscript is lodged in the files of the former An Foras Forbartha, now held by the Department of the Environment, Dublin. It details recent findings of many of the noteworthy orchid taxa occurring at Glenasmole. Accompanying this single typed sheet are several foolscap sheets with further details and sketch maps of localities for orchid taxa noted by the author).

Portmarnock Youth Project Team (1985). *Portmarnock. A Closer Look.* Wolfhound Press, Dublin. (The most common plants found in the saltmarshes and sand dunes of the peninsula are listed on pp. 67-78).

Praeger, R.Ll. (1904a). Additions to "Irish Topographical Botany" in 1903. *IN* **13**: 1-15. (This, and the other "Additions to Irish Topographical Botany" listed below, all include several records from Dublin).

Praeger, R.Ll. (1904b). Botanizing en route (Dublin and Wicklow). *IN* **13**: 156. (Mentions the occurrence of *Crepis biennis* L. at Killiney).

Praeger, R.Ll. (1904c). *Trifolium striatum* inland in Louth. *IN* **13**: 172. (Also notes its occurrence at Feltrim Hill).

Praeger, R.Ll. (1904d). The flora of Dublin. *IN* **13**: 296-299. (Review of N. Colgan's *Flora of the County Dublin.* Includes several records overlooked by Colgan).

Praeger, R.Ll. (1905a). Additions to "Irish Topographical Botany" in 1904. *IN* **14**: 21-29.

Praeger, R.Ll. (1905b). The distribution of fumitories in Ireland. *IN* **14**: 156-163. (Seven taxa are recorded from Dublin).

Praeger, R.Ll. (1906a). Irish Topographical Botany: supplement, 1901-1905. *Proc. RIA* (B) **26**: 13-45. (Includes several Dublin records).

Praeger, R.Ll. (1906b). Additions to "Irish Topographical Botany" in 1905. *IN* **15**: 47-61.

Praeger, R.Ll. (1907). Phanerogams and vascular cryptogams. In: Contributions to the natural history of Lambay, Co. Dublin. *IN* **16**: 90-99 (Lambay Island flora).

Praeger, R.Ll. (1908a). Additions to "Irish Topographical Botany" in 1906-1907. *IN* **17**: 28-37.

Praeger, R.Ll. (1908b). Vegetation-study in the Dublin district. Pp. 72-75 in: Cole, G.A.J. and Praeger, R.Ll. (Eds). *Handbook to the City of Dublin and the Surrounding District* (British Association Guide). University Press, Dublin. (A general account of the vegetation of the county).

Praeger, R.Ll. (1908c). Flora of burnt ground at Howth. *IN* **17**: 186. (See also Adams (1908 a, b) and Pethybridge (1908)).

Praeger, R.Ll. (1913). Additions to "Irish Topographical Botany" in 1908-1912. *IN* **22**: 103-110.

Praeger, R.Ll. (1920). Ferns in Dublin city. *IN* **29**: 108. (Five species are recorded).

Praeger, R.Ll. (1921). Notes on Down and Dublin plants. *IN* **30**: 101-103. (*Cirsium dissectum* (L.) Hill, *Eriophorum latifolium* Hoppe, *Carex pallescens* L. and *Dactylorhiza fuchsii* (Druce) Soó var. *okellyi* (Druce) R. Bateman & Denholm are recorded from Glenasmole).

Praeger, R.Ll. (1922). Botany. Pp. 65-75 in: Fletcher, G. (Ed.). *Leinster: East and West*. Cambridge University Press, Cambridge. (Includes several interesting records from Dublin, including *Juncus subnodulosus* Schrank from Lambay Island).

Praeger, R.Ll. (1928). The distribution of some Irish ferns. *INJ* **2**: 77-78. (*Athyrium filix-femina* (L.) Roth is recorded from Fitzwilliam Square).

[Praeger, R.Ll. (1929a). *Equisetum litorale. INJ* **2**: 191. (From Kilgobbin Castle, but record withdrawn in *INJ* **5**: 36 (1934))].

Praeger, R.Ll. (1929b). Report on recent additions to the Irish fauna and flora (terrestrial and freshwater). *Proc. RIA* (B) **39**: 1-94. (Includes several records from Dublin).

Praeger, R.Ll. (1932). Some noteworthy plants found in or reported from Ireland. *Proc. RIA* (B) **41**: 95-124. (The distribution of *Scrophularia umbrosa* Dumort. in Dublin is detailed).

Praeger, R.Ll. (1934a). *Caltha radicans* in Ireland. *INJ* **5**: 98-102. (*Caltha palustris* L. var. *radicans* (T.F. Forster) Hook. is recorded from Oldbawn).

Praeger, R.Ll. (1934b). A contribution to the flora of Ireland. *Proc. RIA* (B) **42**: 55-86. (Many records and sources for records from Dublin are listed).

Praeger, R.Ll. (1934c). The standing of certain plants in Ireland. *J. Bot.* **72**: 68-75. (*Iris foetidissima* L. is noted from Howth, Ireland's Eye and Lambay Island).

Praeger, R.Ll. (1934d). *Lathraea squamaria. J. Bot.* **72**: 210. (Includes a record from Glasnevin).

Praeger, R.L. (1934e). *The Botanist in Ireland.* Hodges, Figgis and Co., Dublin. (The floristic character of the county is described in detail and localities for many noteworthy species are cited. A census list of the Irish flora is included. Reprinted without the census list in 1974).

Praeger, R.Ll. (1935). Recent advances in Irish field botany. *J. Bot.* **73**: 42-46. (Notes the occurrence in Dublin of *Equisetum* x *trachyodon* A. Braun).

Praeger, R.Ll. (1937a). *Brachypodium pinnatum* in Ireland. *INJ* **6**: 159-161. (A review of the Irish records, including two from Dublin).

Praeger, R.Ll. (1937b). *The Way That I Went*. (1st edn). Hodges, Figgis and Co., Dublin, Methuen and Co., London. (Includes several records from Dublin, as on pp. 252 and 263. 2nd edn in 1939, 3rd edn in 1947, reprints in 1969, 1971 and 1980).

Praeger, R.Ll. (1939). A further contribution to the flora of Ireland. *Proc. RIA* (B) **45**: 231-254. (Includes several records from Dublin).

Praeger, R.Ll. (1943). Dodder at Howth. *INJ* **8**: 86. (*Cuscuta epithymum* (L.) L.).

Praeger, R.Ll. (1946a). Things left undone. *INJ* **8**: 322-327. (Draws attention to a previously unpublished record for *Brachypodium pinnatum* (L.) P. Beauv. from near Balbriggan).

Praeger, R.Ll. (1946b). Additions to the knowledge of the Irish flora, 1939-1945. *Proc. RIA* (B) **51**: 27-51. (Includes several records from Dublin).

Praeger, R.Ll. (1950). *Natural History of Ireland*. Collins, London. (Several species, characteristic of the neighbourhood of Dublin, are noted on p. 118. Reprinted in 1972).

Praeger, R.Ll. (1951). Hybrids in the Irish flora: a tentative list. *Proc. RIA* (B) **54**: 1-14. (Localities for some taxa of hybrid origin occurring in Dublin are detailed).

Praeger, R.Ll., Patterson, R. and Welch, R.J. (1907). Lambay island: its geology, botany, history and antiquities. *Proceedings of the Belfast Naturalists' Field Club* (2)**5**: 512-517. (A summary of the Lambay Survey. See Praeger (1907)).

Prendiville, B. (1985). *Flora and Fauna of Portmarnock*. Privately printed, Dublin. (Describes several habitats on the spit and lists some of the characteristic plant species of each).

Preston, C.D. (1980). *Trifolium occidentale* D.E. Coombe, new to Ireland. *INJ* **20**: 37-40. (Details its occurrence on Howth Head).

Preston, C.D. (1990). An index and bibliography to distribution maps published between 1962 and 1989. Pp. 426-434 in: Perring, F.H. and Walters, S.M. (Eds), *Atlas of the British Flora*. (3rd edn). Botanical Society of the British Isles, London. (Lists distribution maps of vascular plants published between the publication of the first edition of the *Atlas of the British Flora* in 1962 and the end of 1989).

Preston, C.D. (1995). *Pondweeds of Great Britain and Ireland*. Botanical Society of the British Isles, London. (Includes mapped records from Dublin).

Preston, C.D., Croft, J.M., Dring, J.C.M. and Forrest, W.A. (1993). *Database and Atlas of Aquatic Vascular Plants in the British Isles. Part I: Distribution Maps*. *JNCC Report No. 147*. Institute of Terrestrial Ecology, Monks Wood. (Includes mapped records from Dublin for many taxa, including *Acorus calamus* L., *Crassula helmsii* (Kirk) Cockayne, *Hottonia palustris* L., *Potamogeton friesii* Rupr. and *P.* x *lintonii* Fryer).

Preston, C.D. and Sell. P.D. (1989). The Aizoaceae naturalized in the British Isles. *Watsonia* **17**: 217-245. (Notes the occurrence of *Carpobrotus edulis* (L.) N.E. Br. on Howth Head).

Preston, C.D. and Wolfe-Murphy, S. (1992). Irish pondweeds II. *Potamogeton* x *lintonii* Fryer. *INJ* **24**: 117-121. (*P.* x *lintonii* in the Grand Canal at Baggot Street, originally recorded as *P. obtusifolius* Mert. & Koch. *P. crispus* L. and *P. friesii* Rupr. are also reported from sites in Dublin).

Pritchard, N.M. (1959). *Gentianella* in Britain. I. *G. amarella*, *G. anglica* and *G. uliginosa*. *Watsonia* **4**: 169-192. (Notes the occurrence in Dublin of *G. amarella* (L.) Boerner subsp. *hibernica* N. Pritch.).

Pugsley, H.W. (1912). The genus *Fumaria* L. in Britain. *J. Bot.* **50** (Suppl.): 1-76. (Record on p. 14 of *F. purpurea* Pugsley var. *brevisepala* Pugsley from Killiney).

Pugsley, H.W. (1948). A prodromus of the British Hieracia. *Bot. J. Linn. Soc.* **54**: 1-356. (Dublin records on pp. 294, 301 and 318).

Reilly, P.A. (1993). The flowering plants and ferns of the Phoenix Park, Dublin. *Glasra (new series)* **2**: 5-72. (A comprehensive flora of the park comprising a synthesis of original field work and previously published records. Reprinted in Reilly *et al.* (1993)).

Reilly, P.A. (1995). Nicholas John Halpin (1790-1850): a little-known Irish botanist. *Glasra (new series)* **2**: 165-177. (Lists twenty species recorded by Halpin and correspondents from Dublin sites).

Reilly, P.A., Kelly, D.L., Synnott, D.M. and McCullen, J. (1993). *Wild Plants of the Phoenix Park.* The Stationery Office, Dublin. (See Kelly and Synnott (1993), McCullen (1993) and Reilly (1993)).

Reynolds, J.D. (1988). *Check-list of Biota at Booterstown Marsh, Co. Dublin.* Unpublished report to the Properties Committee of An Taisce, Dublin. (Species lists for both plants and animals).

Reynolds, J.D. and Reynolds, S.C.P. (1990). Development and present vegetational state of Booterstown Marsh, Co. Dublin, Ireland. *Bull. IBS* **13**: 173-188. (Includes species lists for the different vegetation types occurring in the marsh).

Reynolds, S.C.P. (1988a). The flora of County Dublin project. Pp. 31-38 in: Wyse Jackson, P.S., Moriarty, C. and Akeroyd, J.R. (Eds). *In the Field of the Naturalists. (Occasional Publications of the Dublin Naturalists' Field Club* **2**). Dublin Naturalists' Field Club, Dublin. (Details progress in recording for the Dublin flora and lists some of the more interesting finds including *Hirschfeldia incana* (L.) Lagrèze-Fossat).

Reynolds, S.C.P. (1988b). *Bromus carinatus* Hooker & Arnott, a grass new to Ireland. *INJ* **22**: 535-536. (*Ceratochloa carinata* (Hook. & Arn.) Tutin at Ringsend. Record also reported in Anonymous (Ed.) (1989). Plant records, *Watsonia* **17**: 463-486).

Reynolds, S.C.P. (1989a). *Spergularia marina* (L.) Griseb. x *S. rupicola* Lebel ex Le Jolis, a hybrid new to Ireland. *INJ* **23**: 114. (Recorded from the South Wall, Dublin Bay).

Reynolds, S.C.P. (1989b). Alien plants on Irish roadsides. *BSBI News* **53**: 38-39. (*Amaranthus retroflexus* L. at Dublin port).

Reynolds, S.C.P. (1990). Alien plants at Foynes and Dublin ports in 1988. *INJ* **23**: 262-268. (Twenty-six taxa are reported from Dublin port).

Reynolds, S.C.P. (1992). Distribution of alien and adventive plants at ports and on roadsides in Ireland in 1989. *INJ* **24**: 59-65. (Includes many records from Dublin. Localities for all taxa are detailed in an unpublished document lodged in the library of the National Botanic Gardens, Glasnevin).

Reynolds, S.C.P. (1993). Records of alien and adventive plants in Ireland 1990-1992. *INJ* **24**: 339-342. (Includes recent Dublin records for seventeen species).

Reynolds, S.C.P. (1994a). From a dump to a check-list of aliens. *Irish Botanical News* **4**: 28-29. (Records for aliens from Ballyogan rubbish dump).

Reynolds, S.C.P. (1994b). Records of alien and casual plants in Ireland 1993. *INJ* **24**: 515-517. (Includes recent Dublin records for eleven species).

Reynolds, S.C.P. (1994c). Letter to the Editor. *The Badger, Newsletter of the Irish Wildlife Federation* **53**: 7. (Notes several self-sown and deliberately introduced taxa at Irishtown Nature Park).

Reynolds, S.C.P. (1996a). Alien plants at ports and in coastal habitats on the east coast of Ireland. *Watsonia* **21**: 53-61. (Includes a list of sixty-six alien taxa found at Dublin Port between 1988 and 1994).

Reynolds, S.C.P. (1996b). Records of casual and alien plants in Ireland. *INJ* **25**: 186-189. (Includes many Dublin records).

Reynolds, S.C.P. (1997). *Conyza bilbaoana* also in Ireland, *BSBI News* **74**: 44-46. (*C. bilbaoana* J. Rémy is reported from several Dublin sites. *C. canadensis* (L.) Cronq. and *C. sumatrensis* (Retz.) E. Walker are reported from Dublin Port and *Senecio viscosus* L. from Heuston Station. Although dated January 1997, this number of *BSBI News* was, in fact, issued in December 1996).

Reynolds, S.C.P. and O'Reilly, H. (1986). *Elodea nuttallii* (Planchon) H. St John in County Dublin. *INJ* **22**: 119-120. (Several patches in the Deansgrange stream).

Reynolds, S.C.P. and Wyse Jackson, M.B. (1987). *An Annotated Check-list of Vascular Plants for the River Dodder Catchment Area.* Unpublished manuscript. (Frequency, locality and habitat details are provided for 414 taxa from the north-facing slopes of Kippure, Seefingan and Seahan, the Glenasmole valley and the River Dodder valley north to Firhouse. Copies retained by the authors).

Rich, T.C.G. (1988). *Hirschfeldia incana* (L.) Lagrèze-Fossat present in Ireland. *INJ* **22**: 531-532. (Dublin City).

Rich, T.C.G. (1991). *Crucifers of Great Britain and Ireland.* Botanical Society of the British Isles, London. (Includes mapped records from Dublin).

Rich, T.C.G. (1995). Records of the genus *Camelina* Crantz (Cruciferae) in Ireland. *Irish Botanical News* **5**: 22-27. (Dublin records for *C. microcarpa* Andrz. ex DC. and *C. sativa* (L.) Crantz).

Rich, T.C.G. and Reynolds, S.C.P. (1991). Cabbage patch VII - A single cabbage-way: *Brassica fruticulosa* Cyr. *BSBI News* **57**: 36-37. (Includes a record for this species from Dublin port).

Rich, T.C.G. and Scannell, M.J.P. (1990). *Potentilla erecta* (L.) Räusch. subsp. *strictissima* in Ireland. *INJ* **23**: 224-225. (Includes a record from Howth Head).

Rich, T.C.G. and Woodruff, E.R. (1990). *BSBI Monitoring Scheme 1987-1988.* 2 Volumes. Unpublished report to the Nature Conservancy Council. (Dublin records are mapped. See also Palmer and Bratton (1995)).

Richards, A.J. (1972). The *Taraxacum* flora of the British Isles. *Watsonia* **9** (Suppl.): 1-141. (The occurrence in Dublin of *T. expallidiforme* Dahlst. is indicated).

Riddelsdell, H.J. (1914). *Helosciadium moorei. IN* **23**: 1-11. (*Apium x moorei* (Syme) Druce in the Royal Canal at Lucan).

Rumsey, F.J. and Jury, S.L. (1991). An account of *Orobanche* L. in Britain and Ireland. *Watsonia* **18**: 257-295. (The occurrence in Dublin of *O. ramosa* L., *O. rapum-genistae* Thuill., *O. minor* Sm. var. *minor* and *O. hederae* Duby is indicated).

Rushton, B.S. (1982). Male sterility in natural populations of *Plantago coronopus* L. in Ireland. *J. Life Sci. R. Dubl. Soc.* **4**: 231-237. (Populations from two sites at Skerries are included).

Rushton, B.S. (1990). Variation in reproductive allocation of *Plantago coronopus* L. related to habitat type and geographical location. *Proc. RIA* (B) **90**: 175-192. (Populations from two sites at Skerries are included).

Rutherford, A. (1979). The BSBI Irish Ivy survey. *BSBI News* **22**: 8-9. (The occurrence of *Hedera helix* subsp. *hibernica* (Kirchner) D. McClint. at several sites in Dublin is indicated).

Ryves, T.B., Clement, E.J. and Foster, M.C. (1996). *Alien Grasses of the British Isles.* Botanical Society of the British Isles, London. (Dublin records for *Anisantha diandra* (Roth) Tutin *ex* Tzvelev, *Ceratochloa carinata* (Hook. & Arn.) Tutin, *Sasa palmata* (Lat.-Marl. *ex* Burb.) Camus, *Triticum spelta* L. and an unconfirmed one for *Alopecurus bulbosus* Gouan are cited).

Salmon, C.E. (1921). *Carex pairaei* in Ireland. *J. Bot.* **59**: 76. (*Carex muricata* L. subsp. *lamprocarpa* Celak. near Sandyford).

Scannell, M.J.P. (1961). *Valerianella locusta* var. *dunensis* Allen in Ireland. *INJ* **13**: 275. (Includes a record from Portmarnock).

Scannell, M.J.P. (1965). Plants from Ireland. *Proc. BSBI* **6**: 176. (Refers to the occurrence of *Juncus foliosus* Desf. in Dublin).

Scannell, M.J.P. (1971). *Ceratophyllum demersum* L. in County Dublin. *INJ* **17**: 61. (Grand Canal at Ballsbridge and Rathmines).

Scannell, M.J.P. (1972). *Gaudinia fragilis* - a further note. *BSBI News* **1**: 52. (Details a record from Ringsend, collected by G.H. Pethybridge on 3rd July 1906).

Scannell, M.J.P. (1973). An early record for *Gaudinia fragilis* (L.) Beauv. *INJ* **17**: 425. (Ringsend, 1906).

Scannell, M.J.P. (1975). *Ruppia cirrhosa* (Petagne) Grande, an addition to the flora of West Galway. *INJ* **18**: 220-221. (Dublin records for this species are detailed).

Scannell, M.J.P. (1976). *Ceratophyllum demersum* L. and fruit performance. *INJ* **18**: 348-349. (Fruiting plants noted in the Grand Canal near Ballsbridge).

Scannell, M.J.P. (1977). *Elodea nuttallii* (Planch.) St. John in the pond at Glasnevin. *INJ* **19**: 130. (National Botanic Gardens).

Scannell, M.J.P. (1979). *Epilobium angustifolium* L. in the flora of Dublin. *INJ* **19**: 327. (*Chamerion angustifolium* (L.) Holub is noted in Dublin city centre).

Scannell, M.J.P. (1984). Plant lists from *The Scientific Tourist Through Ireland* (1818). *Bull. IBS* **8**: 42-62. (Lists many pre-1818 records from Dublin).

Scannell, M.J.P. (1992). Untitled. *Irish Botanical News* **2**: 46. (Reprint of a letter noting F.W. Burbidge's practice of scattering exotic seeds about Dublin, and the subsequent establishment of *Leymus arenarius* (L.) Hochst. on North Bull Island).

Scannell, M.J.P. and McClintock, D. (1974). *Erica mackaiana* Bab. in Irish localities and other plants of interest. *INJ* **18**: 81-85. (Notes a plant of *Hieracium* sp. from the wall of Anna Liffey House, Lucan and *Epilobium komarovianum* A.Leveille planted in a garden at Clonsilla).

Scannell, M.J.P. and Synnott, D.M. (1972). *Census Catalogue of the Flora of Ireland*. The Stationery Office, Dublin. (Census listing of vascular plants showing occurrence in Dublin of many taxa).

Scannell, M.J.P. and Synnott, D.M. (1987). *Census Catalogue of the Flora of Ireland. Clár de Phlandaí na hÉireann*. (2nd edn). The Stationery Office, Dublin.

Scannell, M.J.P. and Synnott, D.M. (1989). Sources for the Census Catalogue of the Flora of Ireland. *National Botanic Gardens, Glasnevin. Occasional Papers* **3**. (The occurrence in Dublin of many vascular plant taxa is indicated).

Scannell, M.J.P. and Synnott, D.M. (1990). Records for the Census Catalogue of the Flora of Ireland in the herbarium, National Botanic Gardens, Glasnevin. *National Botanic Gardens, Glasnevin. Occasional Papers* **5**. (Details many records from Dublin based on specimens in the herbarium of the National Botanic Gardens).

Schönrogge, K., Walker, P. and Crawley, M.J. (1994). The distribution and abundance of alien host-alternating *Andricus* spp. (Hymenoptera: Cynipidae) on *Quercus* spp. (Oak) in Ireland. *Biol. Env. Proc. RIA* (B) **94**: 265-274. (The occurrence in Dublin of *Quercus cerris* L., *Q. petraea* (Mattuschka) Liebl., *Q. robur* L. and *Q. x rosacea* Bechst. is indicated).

Scott, D.W. (1975). *B.S.B.I. Mapping Scheme, Distribution Maps of 50 Common Plants*. Biological Records Centre, Monks Wood. (Dublin records are mapped).

Scully, R.W. (1919). *Eriophorum latifolium* in County Dublin, with some notes on the rarer county species. *IN* **28**: 89-90. (At Glenasmole).

Scully, R.W. (undated). Annotations in his copy of Colgan, N. (1904). *Flora of the County Dublin*. Hodges, Figgis & Co., Dublin. (Now in the library of the National Botanic Gardens, Glasnevin).

Sell, P.D. (1986). The genus *Cicerbita* Wallr. in the British Isles. *Watsonia* **16**: 121-129. (Notes the occurrence of *C. macrophylla* (Willd.) Wallr. subsp. *uralensis* (Rouy) Sell in Dublin).

Sheehy Skeffington, M.[J.] (1983). *An Ecophysiological Study of Nitrogen Budgets in an Eastern Irish Salt Marsh.* Unpublished Ph.D. thesis. University of Dublin, Trinity College. (Includes records from North Bull Island).

Sheehy Skeffington, M.J. (1984). Cultivated plants. Pp. 34-38 in: Wyse Jackson, P. and Sheehy Skeffington, M. *The Flora of Inner Dublin*. Royal Dublin Society and Dublin Naturalists' Field Club, Dublin. (Records the presence in the city of several naturalized and semi-naturalized species).

Sheehy Skeffington, M.J. (1995). Review of: Reilly, P.A., Kelly, D.L., Synnott, D.M. and McCullen, J. (1993). *Wild Plants of the Phoenix Park*. The Stationery Office, Dublin. *Watsonia* **20**: 442-444. (Several species are mentioned).

Sheehy Skeffington, M.J. and Jeffrey, D.W. (1985). Growth performances of an inland population of *Plantago maritima* in response to nitrogen and salinity. *Vegetatio* **61**: 265-272. (Notes the occurrence of *Plantago maritima* L. on North Bull Island).

Sheehy Skeffington, M.J. and Wymer, E.D. (1991). Irish salt marshes - an outline review. Pp. 77-91 in: Quigley, M.B. (Ed.). *A Guide to the Sand Dunes of Ireland*. European Union for Dune Conservation and Coastal Management, c/o Department of Geography, Trinity College, Dublin. (Includes details of salt marsh vegetation from several Dublin sites).

Sheehy Skeffington, M.[J.] and Wyse Jackson, P.[S.] (1984). Some sites of botanical interest. Pp. 25-32 in: Wyse Jackson, P. and Sheehy Skeffington, M. *The Flora of Inner Dublin*. Royal Dublin Society in association with the Dublin Naturalists' Field Club, Dublin. (Describes the flora and vegetation of several inner city sites).

Showler, A.J. and Rich, T.C.G. (1993). *Cardamine bulbifera* (L.) Crantz (Cruciferae) in the British Isles. *Watsonia* **19**: 231-245. (Includes records from Malahide Castle demesne and Marley Park).

Simpson, D.A. (1984). A short history of the introduction and spread of *Elodea* Michx in the British Isles. *Watsonia* **15**: 1-9. (Notes the occurrence of *E. nuttallii* (Planch.) H. St John) in Dublin).

Simpson, D.A. (1985). *Elodea nuttallii* (Planch.) St. John in Ireland. *INJ* **21**: 497-498. (In a pond at the National Botanic Gardens, Glasnevin).

Simpson, D.A. (1986). Taxonomy of *Elodea* Michx in the British Isles. *Watsonia* **16**: 1-14. (The alien *E. nuttallii* (Planch.) H. St John noted as occurring in a pond at the National Botanic Gardens, Glasnevin).

Simpson, N.D. (1960). *A Bibliographical Index of the British Flora*. Privately printed, Bournemouth. (A definitive work which lists many sources of records for the county, from the earliest times up to 1960).

Slater, F. (1955). *Viola tricolor* subsp. *curtisii*. P. 326 in: Wallace, E.C. (Ed.) (1955). Plant records. *Proc. BSBI* **1**: 325-338. (Record from North Bull Island).

Stace, C.A. (Ed.) (1975). *Hybridization and the Flora of the British Isles*. Academic Press and B.S.B.I., London, New York and San Francisco. (Notes the occurrence of several hybrid taxa in Dublin).

Stace, C.A. (1991). *New Flora of the British Isles*. Cambridge University Press, Cambridge. (Notes the occurrence in Dublin of several taxa, e.g. *Senecio cineraria* DC., *Spergularia marina* (L.) Griseb. x *S. rupicola* Lebel ex Le Jolis).

Stelfox, A.W. (1920). *Poa compressa* in Dublin: a tragedy. *IN* **29**: 108. (Details the apparent disappearance of a small colony of this species from a wall in Rathmines).

Stelfox, A.W. (1921a). Note on *Carex muricata* L. and its segregates *C. contigua* Hoppe and *C. pairaei* Schultz. *IN* **30**: 31-32. (*C. muricata* L. subsp. *lamprocarpa* Celak. near Sandyford).

Stelfox, A.W. (1921b). *Carex axillaris* in Co. Dublin. *IN* **30**: 145-146. (*C. otrubae* Podp. x *C. remota* L. at Malahide and Castle Bagot).

Stelfox, A.W. (1922a). *Poa compressa* survives! *IN* **31**: 95. (Re-discovered on a wall in Rathmines).

Stelfox, A.W. (1922b). *Littorella lacustris* in Co. Dublin. *IN* **31**: 130. (Edge of Upper Reservoir, Glenasmole).

Stelfox, A.W. (1923a). A hybrid sedge new to Co. Dublin. *IN* **32**: 39. (*Carex hostiana* DC. x *C. viridula* Michaux at Brittas).

Stelfox, A.W. (1923b). The cranberry in Glenasmole. *IN* **32**: 63. (*Vaccinium oxycoccos* L.).

Stelfox, A.W. (1923c). *Rubia peregrina* L. and *Tragopogon porrifolius* L. on Lambay. *IN* **32**: 88.

Stelfox, A.W. (1923d). The golden samphire near Rush, Co. Dublin. *IN* **32**: 88. (*Inula crithmoides* L.).

Stelfox, A.W. (1929). *Cephalanthera ensifolia* in Co. Dublin. *INJ* **2**: 247. (*C. longifolia* (L.) Fritsch at Glenasmole).

Stelfox, A.W. (1935). *Alnus incana* Willd. in South Kerry. *INJ* **5**: 308. (Also planted and self-sown at Glenasmole).

Stelfox, A.W. (1936). *Lemna gibba* in the Dodder, Co. Dublin. *INJ* **6**: 21.

Stelfox, A.W. (1952). The present standing of the clubmoss, *Lycopodium clavatum* L., in Co. Dublin. *INJ* **10**: 249. (Two localities in the south of the county are detailed).

Stelfox, A.W. (1958). Galls on willows. *INJ* **12**: 304-305. (Notes galls on *Salix fragilis* L. at Donnybrook and Ballsbridge).

Stelfox, A.W. (undated). Annotations in his copy of Colgan, N. (1904). *Flora of the County Dublin.* Hodges, Figgis & Co., Dublin. (Formerly in the possession of H.M. Parkes).

Stewart, N.F. (1991-1993). Irish Wetland Survey: Species Lists. Copies lodged with the National Parks and Wildlife Service, Dublin. (Includes many records for aquatic macrophytes and stoneworts from Balrothery, Feltrim, Glasnevin, Huntstown quarry, Phoenix Park, Talbotstown and both canals).

Stewart, N.F. and Church, J.M. (1992). *Red Data Books of Britain and Ireland: Stoneworts.* The Joint Nature Conservation Committee, Peterborough. (Includes Dublin records for *Nitella mucronata* (A. Braun) Miquel, *Tolypella intricata* (Trent. ex Roth) Leonh. and *T. prolifera* (Ziz ex A. Braun) Leonh. Erroneous records for *Nitella gracilis* (Smith) Agardh are noted. King and Nash (1994) refer the Glasnevin record for *Nitella mucronata* included in this work to *N. gracilis*).

Synnott, D.M. (1968). Unpublished fern records of J.R. Kinahan, c. 1854. *INJ* **16**: 39-42. (Includes Dublin records for *Ceterach officinarum* Willd., *Dryopteris filix-mas* (L.) Schott and *Polystichum aculeatum* (L.) Roth).

Synnott, D.M. (1978). The status of *Crataegus laevigata* (Poiret) DC. in Ireland. *Glasra* **2**: 49-55. (Includes a record from Kilgobbin).

Synnott, D.M. (1981). *Epilobium adenocaulon* Hausskn. in Ireland. *INJ* **20**: 234. (*E. ciliatum* Raf. at Glasnevin).

Synnott, D.M. (1990). The bryophytes of Lambay island. *Glasra (new series)* **1**: 65-81. (Includes a brief account of the vegetation as well as records for several vascular plant species).

Synnott, D.M. (1992a). Irish mistletoe, a 'herbarium' record! *BSBI News* **60**: 12. (Notes a recent increase in the number and size of plants of *Viscum album* L. in the National Botanic Gardens, Glasnevin).

Synnott, D.M. (1992b). Rare and protected plants at the Botanic Gardens, Glasnevin. *Irish Botanical News* **2**: 5-8. (Includes records for *Chaenorhinum minus* (L.) Lange, *Kickxia elatine* (L.) Dumort. and *Senecio viscosus* L. as weeds in the Gardens).

Thomson, J.S. (1921). *Brachypodium pinnatum* in Co. Dublin. *IN* **30**: 99. (Recorded from Howth).

Wade, A.E. (1958). The history of *Symphytum asperum* Lepech. and *S. x uplandicum* Nyman in Britain. *Watsonia* **4**: 117-118. (Notes *S. x uplandicum* from Dublin).

Walsh, M.L. (1958). Galls on willows. *INJ* **12**: 304. (*Lathraea clandestina* L. and *Salix fragilis* L. are recorded from by the River Tolka, Clonliffe).

Walsh, W.F. (undated). *Four Reproductions in Full Colour Made From Watercolour Paintings by Wendy Walsh of Wildflowers Found Growing in Ireland.* Publisher not cited. (Four plates, including one depicting *Rosa canina* L. from Lusk).

Walsh, W.F. and Nelson, E.C. (1987). *An Irish Florilegium II.* Thames and Hudson, London. (Plate 7 depicts *Campanula rotundifolia* L. from Lambay Island).

Walsh, W.F., Ross, R.I. and Nelson, E.C. (1983). *An Irish Florilegium.* Thames and Hudson, London. (Plate 18 depicts *Ulex europaeus* L. from near Lusk).

Warburg, E.F. (1951). *Veronica filiformis*. P. 48 in: Wallace, E.C. (Ed.) (1951). Plant records. *Watsonia* **2**: 36-62. (Howth golf links).

Waterfall, C. (1912). *Euphorbia paralias*, Linn. P. 120 in: Wheldon, J.A. (Ed.). Report for 1911. *BEC* **3**: 58-146. (Record from North Bull Island).

Watson, W.C.R. (1958). *Handbook of the Rubi of Great Britain and Ireland*. Cambridge University Press, Cambridge. (Includes several records from Dublin).

Webb, D.A. (1950). Narrative of the excursion [The ninth International Phytogeographical Excursion. Ireland, 8th to 25th July, 1949]. *INJ* **10**: 3-8. (Notes *Ulex europaeus* L. and *U. gallii* Planchon from near Glendoo Mt.).

Webb, D.A. (1952a). Irish plant records. *Watsonia* **2**: 217-236. (The occurrence in Dublin of many species is noted).

Webb, D.A. (1952b). *Alchemilla vulgaris* agg. in Ireland: a preliminary report. *INJ* **10**: 298-300. (*Alchemilla filicaulis* subsp. *vestita* (Buser) Bradshaw is noted from Kiltiernan and Bohernabreena and *A. glabra* Neyg. from Bohernabreena and Glenasmole).

Webb, D.A. (1957). Botany. I: vegetation and flora. Pp. 40-58 in: Meenan, J. and Webb, D.A. (Eds). *A View of Ireland*. Local executive of the British Association for the Advancement of Science, Dublin. (Dublin records for *Scilla verna* Hudson and *Umbilicus rupestris* (Salisb.) Dandy are mapped).

Webb, D.A. (1972). Two recent arrivals in central Dublin. *INJ* **17**: 245. (*Chamerion angustifolium* (L.) Holub and *Senecio squalidus* L.).

Webb, D.A. (1977). *An Irish Flora*. (6th edn). Dundalgan Press (W. Tempest) Ltd, Dundalk. (The occurrence in Dublin sites of several species is indicated in this work and in the five previous editions of 1943, 1953, 1959, 1963 and 1967. See also Webb, Parnell and Doogue (1996)).

Webb, D.A. (1979). Three trees naturalized in Ireland. *INJ* **19**: 369. (*Sorbus intermedia* (Ehrh.) Pers. in a quarry on the north face of Killiney Hill).

Webb, D.A. (1984). Unpublished county records for *Taraxacum* spp. from the herbarium of Trinity College, Dublin. *INJ* **21**: 326-327. (Includes records for *T. lacistophyllum* (Dahlst.) Raunk., *T. atactum* Sahlin & Soest and *T. quadrans* Oellgaard from Dublin).

Webb, D.A., Parnell, J.A.N. and Doogue, D.A. (1996). *An Irish Flora*. (7th edn). Dundalgan Press (W. Tempest) Ltd, Dundalk. (The occurrence in Dublin sites of several species is indicated in this work and in the six previous editions of 1943, 1953, 1959, 1963, 1967 and 1977 - see Webb (1977)).

Webster, S.D. (1988). *Ranunculus penicillatus* (Dumort.) Bab. in Great Britain and Ireland. *Watsonia* **17**: 1-22. (The occurrence in Dublin of var. *penicillatus* is noted).

Webster, S.D. (1991). *Ranunculus penicillatus* (Dumort.) Bab. in Ireland. *INJ* **23**: 346-354. (Subsp. *penicillatus* is recorded from four Dublin sites).

Wells, H.H.W. (1933). *Centaurea solstitialis* L. in Co. Dublin. *INJ* **4**: 245. (A single plant at Terenure).

White, J. (Ed.) (1982). *Studies on Irish Vegetation*. Royal Dublin Society, Dublin. (Several of the contributions to this work contain floristic records from Dublin. See Brun-Hool and Wilmanns (1982), Cross (1982), Ní Lamhna (1982b), White and Doyle (1982) and Willmanns and Brun-Hool (1982). Contributions previously issued in *J. Life Sci. R. Dubl. Soc.* **3** (1 & 2) (1982)).

White, J. and Doyle, G.J. (1982). The vegetation of Ireland: a catalogue raisonné. *J. Life Sci. R. Dubl. Soc.* **3**: 289-368. (Dublin localities are given for several vegetation associations. Reprinted in White (1982)).

Whitty, S. St J. (1924). *The Flaming Wheel*. Talbot Press, Dublin. (A series of nature studies which include several records from Dublin).

Wilde, J. (1993). *Conyza canadensis* (L.) Cronq. in Co Antrim (H39). *INJ* **24**: 298-299. (Notes 1984 and 1988 records for this species from Dublin).

Wilmanns, O. and Brun-Hool, J. (1982). Plant communities of human settlements in Ireland. I. Vegetation of walls. *J. Life Sci. R. Dubl. Soc.* **3**: 79-90. (Includes species lists from five Dublin sites. Reprinted in White (1982)).

Wolfe, A., Whelan, J. and Hayden, T.J. (1996). Dietary overlap between the Irish Mountain Hare *Lepus timidus hibernicus* and the Rabbit *Oryctolagus cuniculus* on coastal grassland. *Biol. Env. Proc. RIA* (B) **96**: 89-95. (Includes a list of plants on which Hares and Rabbits feed on North Bull Island).

W[olfe], V. (1974). Glenasmole, Sunday July 14th, *Fieldfare* **1974**: 8. (Includes records for *Crepis paludosa* (L.) Moench, *Dactylorhiza maculata* (L.) Soó, *Epipactis palustris* (L.) Crantz, *Gymnadenia conopsea* (L.) R. Br. and *Valeriana officinalis* L.).

Woodell, S.R.J. and Kootin-Sanwu, M. (1971). Intraspecific variation in *Caltha palustris*. *The New Phytologist* **70**: 173-186. (Includes a record from Glenasmole).

Wymer, E.D. (1984). *The Phytosociology of Irish Saltmarsh Vegetation*. Unpublished M.Sc. thesis. National University of Ireland, University College Dublin. (Includes floristic data for several Dublin saltmarsh sites).

Wyse Jackson, M.B. (1989). Observations on the Irish distribution of a plant with serious public health implications: Giant Hogweed (*Heracleum mantegazzianum* Sommier and Levier). *Bull. IBS* **12**: 94-112. (Details all known Dublin records for this species and its hybrid with *H. sphondylium* L.).

Wyse Jackson, M.B. (1991). *The Taxonomy and Biosystematics of* Cerastium fontanum *Baumgarten and Allied Species in Europe*. Unpublished Ph.D. thesis. University of Dublin, Trinity College. (Includes relevés from Ballinascorney, North Bull Island, Firhouse, Kippure and Portmarnock).

Wyse Jackson, M.B. (1995). Annotated records for rare, critical or under-recorded vascular plant taxa from Ireland. *INJ* **25**: 44-57. (Notes the occurrence in Dublin of twelve taxa and includes records for *Senecio viscosus* L.).

Wyse Jackson, P.S. (1981). *Rapistrum rugosum* (L.) All. in Ireland. *Bull. IBS* **5**: 15-18. (Sixteen records from Dublin are detailed. Records for *Brassica nigra* (L.) Koch are referable to *Hirschfeldia incana* (L.) Lagr.-Fossat, a species not recognised in Dublin at the time of publication of this paper).

Wyse Jackson, P.S. (1982a). Studying the flora of Dublin city. *Environmental Education Newsletter* **19**: 8-11. (Includes both localized and unlocalized records from the city).

Wyse Jackson, P.S. (1982b). Two records for *Senecio viscosus* L. in Dublin (H21). *INJ* **20**: 507. (Dublin city centre).

Wyse Jackson, P.S. (1982c). Ireland's other island. *The Sunday Tribune Magazine* 23rd May 1982: 8-12. (Includes records for *Asparagus officinalis* L., *Epipactis palustris* (L.) Crantz and *Salvia verbenaca* L. from North Bull Island).

Wyse Jackson, P.S. (1983). *The Taxonomy and Biosystematics of the Genus* Cochlearia *Linnaeus in Ireland*. Unpublished Ph.D. thesis. University of Dublin, Trinity College. (Includes records of hybrid taxa from North Bull Island).

Wyse Jackson, P.[S.] (1984). Introduction. Pp. 1-3 in: Wyse Jackson, P. and Sheehy Skeffington, M. *The Flora of Inner Dublin*. Royal Dublin Society in association with the Dublin Naturalists' Field Club, Dublin. (Notes *Quercus cerris* L. and *Parthenocissus* spp. as occurring in the inner city).

Wyse Jackson, P.S. (1988a). What role can field clubs play in conservation? Pp. 22-30 in: Wyse Jackson, P.S., Moriarty, C. and Akeroyd, J.R. (Eds). *In the Field of the Naturalists*. (*Occasional Publications of the Dublin Naturalists' Field Club* **2**). Dublin Naturalists' Field Club, Dublin. (Records the occurrence in north County Dublin of *Orchis morio* L.).

Wyse Jackson, P.S. (1988b). *Groenlandia densa* (L.) Fourr. in Dublin. *INJ* **22**: 457. (In the Cammock River near Walkinstown. Record also reported in Anonymous (Ed.) (1989). Plant records. *Watsonia* **17**: 463-486).

Wyse Jackson, P.S., Doogue, D.A., Parnell, J.A.N. and Reilly, P.A. (1987). *The Purchase and Establishment of a Nature Reserve at Donabate, Co. Dublin, for the Rare and Endangered Green-veined Orchid,* Orchis morio. Unpublished proposal to the Irish National Committee of the European Year of the Environment.

Wyse Jackson, P.[S.] and Sheehy Skeffington, M.[J.] (1984). *The Flora of Inner Dublin.* Royal Dublin Society in association with the Dublin Naturalists' Field Club, Dublin. (A detailed flora describing the distribution, abundance and preferred habitat of all native and introduced species and hybrids to be found growing in a wild state in Dublin city centre. The original field cards, the basis for most of the records in this work, are held in the archives of the Dublin Naturalists' Field Club).

Young, D.P. (1958). *Oxalis* in the British Isles. *Watsonia* **4**: 51-69. (Includes a record for *O. articulata* Savigny from the Hill of Howth).

APPENDIX 2

Bibliography from Nathaniel Colgan's
Flora of the County Dublin (1904), pp. xiii–xviii

ALPHABETICAL LIST
OF THE
PRINCIPAL BOOKS, PAPERS, PRINTED NOTES, MSS., & HERBARIA
RELATING TO THE FLORA OF COUNTY DUBLIN

References to the various Books, Papers, &c., are distinguished in the body of this work by the contractions printed in italics in the right hand margin of this List.

Anonymous:
Manuscript Annotations in a copy of Threlkeld's Synopsis in the R. I. Academy's Library giving records of Plants observed in Co. Dublin, chiefly between the years 1730-40, the handwriting being probably contemporary with the observations recorded. .... *Annot. in Threlkeld.*

Areschoug, Prof. Fredrik Wilhelm Christian :
Artemisia Stelleriana in Europe. - Journ. of Botany, 1894, p. 70.

Ball, John :
Botanical Notes of a Tour in Ireland. Annals of Nat. Hist., Vol. II., p. 28, 1839 .... *Ball 1839.*

Baily, Miss Katherine Sophia :
The Irish Flora. Dublin, 1833. Published anonymously, but known to be the work of Miss Baily, afterwards Lady Kane, the localities being supplied chiefly by Mr. John White. .... *Ir. Flor.*

Barrington, Richard :
Herbarium now in the possession of R.M. Barrington, M.A. of Fassaroe, Co. Wicklow, and including many interesting Co. Dublin species, collected chiefly in 1858 and 1859. .... *Herb. Barrington.*

Barrington, Richard Manliffe, M.A., F.L.S. :
Herbarium of Irish Plants, containing some of the rarer Co. Dublin species .... *Herb. R. M. Barrington.*

Burbidge, W.F., M.A., F.L.S., and **Colgan**, Nathaniel, M.R.I.A. :
A New Senecio Hybrid. - Ir. Nat., 1902, p. 311, and Journ. of Bot., 1902, p. 401.

Carroll, Rev. H. G. :
Herbarium of Plants chiefly collected in Co. Dublin and now preserved in the Science and Art Museum, Dublin .. *Herb. Carroll.*

Colgan, Nathaniel, M.R.I.A. :
Specularia hybrida in Dublin. - Ir. Nat., 1892, p. 144.
Notes on the Flora of Co. Dublin. - Ir. Nat., 1893, p. 283. .... *Colgan 1893.*
Artemisia Stelleriana in Ireland. - Journ. of Bot., 1894, pp. 22 and 104.
Carex axillaris and Filago minima in Co. Dublin. Ir. Nat., 1894, p. 292.
Matricaria discoidea DC. in Ireland. Ir. Nat., 1894, p. 215.
Further Notes on the Flora of County Dublin. - Ir. Nat., 1895, p. 54. .... *Colgan 1895.*
The Orchids of County Dublin. - Ir. Nat., 1895, p. 193. .... *Colgan 1895a.*
Scrophularia umbrosa (Dum.) in Ireland. - Ir. Nat., 1896, p. 182.
Elymus arenarius in Co. Dublin. - Ir , Nat., 1900, p. 269, and 1901, p. 49.
Carex aquatilis in Co. Dublin. - Ir. Nat., 1901, p. 49.
Some Recent Records for the Flora of Co. Dublin. - Ir. Nat., 1903, pp. 186-191. .... *Colgan 1903.*
Further Additions to the Flora of Co. Dublin, with Notes on some doubtful Records. Ir. Nat., 1904, p. 56. .... *Colgan 1904.*
See also under **Burbidge**.

Colgan, Nathaniel, and **Scully,** R.W. :
See under **Moore** and **More.**

Corry, Thomas Hughes, M.A. :
On some rare Irish Plants. - Journ. of Bot., 1882, p. 222.
Ranunculus confusus in Ireland. - Journ. of Bot., 1882, p. 347.

D'Alton, John :
History of the County of Dublin. Dublin, 1838. - Contains numerous records for the rarer County Dublin plants extracted from the *Irish Flora* and *Flora Hibernica,* and grouped according to localities.

Dowd, Michael:
Malva borealis near Dublin. - Journ. of Bot., 1870, p. 323.

Druce, George Claridge, M.A. F.L.S. :
Notes on the Flora of Cork, Kerry, and Dublin. - Journ. of Bot., 1894, p. 304. .... Druce 1891 [sic].

Focke, Dr. W.O. :
List of British and Irish Rubi in Herb. of late Mr. John Ball. - Journ. of Bot., 1891, p. 163. .... Focke 1891.

Groves, Henry, and **Groves,** James, F.L.S. :
Review of the British Characeae. - Journ. of Bot., 1880, pp. 97, 129, and 161. .... Groves 1880.
The Distribution of the Characeae in Ireland. - Ir. Nat., 1895, pp. 7 and 37. .... Groves 1895.
Notes on British Characeae, 1895-98. - Journ. of Bot., 1898, p. 40. .... Groves 1898.

Hart, Henry Chichester, B.A., F.L.S. :
Notes on the Flora of Lambay Island, County of Dublin. Read before R. I. Academy, Nov., 1882. Published in Proceedings, 2nd Series, Vol. III., p. 670, 1883 .... Flor. Lambay.
Elymus arenarius in Co. Dublin. - Journ. of Bot., 1883, p. 246.
The Flora of Howth, with Map and Introduction on the Geology and other Features of the Promontory. Dublin, 1887.   Flor. Howth.
Flora of Howth. - Journ. of Bot., 1891, p. 377 .... Hart 1891.
Notes on Co. Dublin Plants. - Journ. of Bot., 1897, p. 346. .... Hart 1897.
Manuscript Notes on Co. Dublin Flora. .... Hart MS.

Herbarium :
Of Glasnevin Botanic Garden, Dublin. - A General Irish collection, containing many interesting County Dublin plants gathered by Dr. David Moore and others. .... Herb. Glasnevin.
Of Science and Art Museum, Dublin. - Rich in Irish Plants, containing, amongst others collections of less importance, those of the late Dr. David Moore, of the late A. G. More, and of the late H. C. Levinge, also those made by Mr. H. C. Hart in various parts of Ireland. .... Herb. S. & A. Mus.
See also under **Barrington, Carroll, Scully,** and **Vowell.**

How, William :
Phytologia Britannica, Natales exhibens, Indigenarum Stirpium Sponte Emergentium. London, 1650. - A duodecimo volume giving some of the earliest published notices of Irish plants communicated by Rev. Richard Heaton, amongst them the earliest botanical record for County Dublin.

Kinahan, Professor John Robert, M.D., M.R.I.A., F.L.S. :
A List of the Ferns and their Allies found in the County Dublin, with special reference to the Dodder Valley. - Phytologist, 1854, p. 196. .... Kinahan 1854.
On the Abnormal Forms of Ferns. - Nat. Hist. Review, Vol. I., pp. 142 and 150, 1854.
On the Distribution of Ferns in Ireland. - Nat. Hist. Review, V., p. 175, 1858. .... Kinahan 1858.

Kinahan, Miss Amelia G. :
Manuscript List of Plants observed in County Dublin.

Knowles, Miss M. C. :
A List of the Irish Fumitories in the Herbarium of the National Museum, Dublin. - Ir. Nat., 1904, p. 33.

Mackay, James Townsend, Ll.D., A.L.S., M.R.I.A. :
A Systematic Catalogue of Rare Plants found in Ireland. - Trans. Dublin Socy., 1806, Vol. V., p. 121. ....*Mack. Rar.*
A Catalogue of the Indigenous Plants found in Ireland. - Trans. R. I. Academy, XIV., p. 103, 1825 - a paper read before
the Academy, June 28, 1824, and published in the following year. ....*Mack. Cat.*
Flora Hibernica. Dublin, 1836. ....*Flor. Hib.*
Additions to the Plants of Ireland since the Publication of Flora Hibernica. - Nat. Hist. Review, O.S., Vol. VI., p. 537, 1859.
....*Mackay 1859.*
Additional Plants for Flora Hibernica. - Nat. Hist. Review, O.S. Vol .VII., p. 443, 1860. ....*Mackay 1860.*

Mahaffy, Miss Rachel M. :
Additions to the Flora of Howth. - Ir. Nat., 1898, p. 270.

McArdle, David :
Clematis Vitalba (L) on the North Bull. - Ir. Nat., 1892, p. 125.
The Plants of Dalkey Island. - Ir. Nat., 1892, p. 133.
Selaginella selaginoides (Gray) in Co. Dublin. - Ir. Nat., 1893, p. 174.

McWeeney, Edmund Joseph, M.A. M.D. :
Manuscript List of Plants observed in Co. Dublin, chiefly along the Dodder Valley.

Meade, Joseph :
Elymus arenarius in Co. Dublin. - Ir. Nat., 1901, p. 20.
Manuscript List of Plants observed in Co. Dublin, chiefly in the neighbourhood of Old Connaught.

Moffat, Charles Bethune, B.A. :
Second Flowering of Artemisia Stelleriana. - Ir. Nat., 1895, p. 77.
Life and Letters of Alexander Goodman More. Dublin, 1898.

Molyneux, Thomas, M.D. :
Appendix to Threlkeld's Synopsis, containing the Names and Observations on such Plants as grow spontaneously in Ireland.

Moore, David, Ph.D., F.L.S., M.R.I.A. :
Notes on a Supposed new Variety of Orchis latifolia (Linn.) and on Orchis incarnata Var. extensa (Reichenbach). - Proc. Dublin Nat.
Hist. Socy., IV., p. 180, 1865.

Moore, David, and **More**, Alex. Goodman :
Contributions towards a Cybele Hibernica, being Outlines of the Geographical Distribution of Plants in Ireland. Dublin 1866. ...*Cyb.*
The Same - Second Edition, founded on the papers of the late Alex. Goodman More, F.R.S.E., F.L.S., M.R.I.A.,
by Nathaniel Colgan, M.R.I.A., and Reginald W. Scully, F.L.S. Dublin, 1898. ....*Cyb. II.*
Flora of the Counties of Dublin and Wicklow. - Sub-Kingdoms Phanerogamia and Pteridophyta in British Association
Guide. Dublin, 1878. ....*Guide.*

More, Alexander, Goodman, F.R.S.E., F.L.S., M.R.I.A.:
On Recent Additions to the Flora of Ireland. - Proc. R. I. Academy, 2nd. Series, Vol. I., p. 256, 1872. ....*Rec. Add.*
See also under **Moore** and **More**.

Newman, Edward, F.L.S. :
A History of British Ferns. - London, 1840. ....*Newman 1840.*

Phillips, Robert Albert :
Senecio squalidus in Dublin. - Ir. Nat., 1900, p. 245.

Pim, Greenwood, M.A., F.L.S., M.R.I.A. :
Manuscript List of Plants observed in Co. Dublin.

Praeger, Robert Lloyd, B.A., B.E., M.R.I.A. :
Irish Rubi. - Journ. of Bot., 1894, pp. 75 and 359.. *Praeger 1894.*
Notes on the Dublin Flora. - Ir. Nat., 1894, p. 8. .... *Praeger 1894a.*
Notes on the Flora of Howth. - Ir. Nat., 1895, p. 174 . ... *Praeger 1895.*
Medicago sylvestris in Ireland. - Ir. Nat., 1896, p. 249.
Matricaria discoidea DC. at Howth. - Ir. Nat., 1896, p. 298.
Irish Topographical Botany. - Proc. R. I. Academy, 3rd Series, Vol. VII., 1901. .... *Top. Bot.*
Gleanings in Irish Topographical Botany. - Proc. R. I. Academy, Vol. XXIV., Sec. B. 1902. .... *Praeger 1902.*
Dublin Plants. - Ir. Nat., 1904, p. 42. .... *Praeger 1904.*

Rutty, John, M.D. :
An Essay towards a Natural History of the County of Dublin. - 2 Vols. Dublin, 1772. .... *Rutty's Dublin.*

Scully, Reginald W., F.L.S. :
Erythraea pulchella (Fr.) and Polypogon monspeliensis (Desf.) on the North Bull. - Ir. Nat., 1894, p. 20.
Herbarium, chiefly of Co. Kerry Plants, but including some of the rarer Co. Dublin species.

Smith, Walter George, M.D. :
On the Discovery of Cuscuta Trifolii in Ireland. - Proc. Dublin Nat. Hist. Socy. (1868-69), V., 198, 1871.

Tatlow, Mrs. Emily Mary :
Wild Flowers in a County Dublin Garden. - Ir. Nat., 1898, p. 129.

Templeton, John, A.L.S. :
Catalogue of the Native Plants of Ireland observed by John Templeton, A.L.S. - A small MS. volume giving numerous localities for Irish plants, several of them in the County of Dublin, the records ranging in date from 1793 to 1820, now in the Library of the Royal Irish Academy, Dublin. .... *Templeton MS.*

Threlkeld, Caleb, M.D. :
Synopsis Stirpium Hibernicarum Alphabetice Dispositarum, sive Commentatio de Plantis Indigenis praesertim Dublinensibus instituta, being a Short Treatise of Native Plants, especially such as grow spontaneously in the vicinity of Dublin ; with their Latin, English and Irish Names : And an Abridgement of their Vertues. With several new Discoverys. Dublin, MDCCXXVII. .... *Threlkeld.*
Manuscript Annotations in above (see under **Anonymous**). .... *Annot. in Threlkeld.*

Vowell, Richard Prendergast :
Herbarium of Irish Plants, including many interesting Co. Dublin species. .... *Herb. Vowell.*

Wade, Walter, M.D. :
Catalogus systematicus Plantarum indigenarum in Comitatu Dublinensi inventarum. Dublin 1794. .... *Wade Dubl.*
Plantae Rariores in Hibernia Inventae. - Trans. Dubl. Socy., Vol. IV., 1804. .... *Wade Rar.*

Warburton, John, Rev. James **Whitelaw**, and Rev. Robert **Walsh** :
History of the City of Dublin. - 2 Vols, 4to. London, 1818 - Appendix XIII., *Botany of Dublin Bay and its Neighbourhood.*
.... *Warburton.*

White, John : *An Essay on the indigenous Grasses of Ireland.* - Dublin, 1808.

APPENDIX 3

OBITUARY OF NATHANIEL COLGAN

Reprinted from *The Irish Naturalist* (1919).Vol. **28**: 121-126.

Irish science is poorer for the death of Nathaniel Colgan, who passed away on October 2 at the age of 68. Developing an interest in natural history comparatively late in life, unequipped with a scientific training, and diffident, moreover, about seeking information from fellow-workers, Colgan nevertheless found himself - almost against his will, as one might say - drawn into the scientific life of Dublin. Courteous, humorous, and a real lover of nature, he earned the friendship and respect of a large body of Irish naturalists, and his death will be deplored widely.

If he acquired knowledge of many places and things outside of the daily round, this was due to his enquiring spirit and restless initiative, for fate had decreed for him an uneventful life. Born in Dublin, 28th May, 1851, he was educated at the Incorporated School, Aungier Street, and at the age of 20 obtained by examination a clerkship in the Dublin Metropolitan Police Court. In that service he spent his life, retiring under the age limit in 1916. It was characteristic of him that though offered several posts in London, he selected the only Irish post which was vacant. Throughout his life "his first, best country ever was at home," and the continental excursions which he undertook in later years had for their object not only the seeing of foreign lands, but the elucidating of problems of Irish interest by study of cognate questions in adjoining regions.

Long before science claimed him, he displayed an active interest in local literary matters. In 1873 he joined a little band who produced and circulated a manuscript magazine called "Varieties," his first contribution being a paper on Sir Thomas Browne and the "Religio Medici," which was followed a year later by one on Francois Rabelais. Later he saved the paper from extinction by assuming the editorship, in which he continued for several years. He had a facile pen, and succeeding years saw many contributions to the "Irish Monthly," "Tinsley's Magazine," and "Hibernia." These were largely sketches of European travel, for in 1875 he had undertaken the first of a series of summer tours which added greatly to the interest of life, and, when later on he took up systematic and distributional problems in botany and zoology, gave him a wide and intelligent outlook, and helped him to avoid that insular standpoint which is often difficult to banish when one's field of vision is restricted by a barrier of sea. On many of these trips he had pleasant and useful companions, whose comradeship ripened into life-long friendships. The names which appear most frequently in his notes of travel of this period and in correspondence of succeeding years are those of his brother William (now rector of Ballinlough, Co. Roscommon), K.D. Doyle (now an engineer in Argentina), and C.F. D'Arcy, the present Archbishop of Dublin.

France, Italy, Switzerland, Spain and Morocco were visited in turn, as well as places nearer home, such as the west of Ireland. As early as 1880 botanical notes begin to creep into his sketches. His first "botanical" paper, "Plant-hunting in the Dublin Mountains," published in "Irish Monthly," 1880, was a skit, of which the idea was possibly derived from Carlyle's "Sartor Resartus." In the following year "Plant-hunting in the Central Pyrenees," a series of five papers, was published in "Tinsley's Magazine." I have not been able to see this in Dublin, but, in spite of a suspicious similarity of title, I assume it was a serious contribution. His interest in Irish botany had evidently been growing during these years, for it was "in the course of a week's botanizing in the County Wicklow" in July, 1884, in the company of his brother and the future Archbishop, that he came upon *Saussurea alpina* on Tonlagee over Lough Ouler, its first station in eastern Ireland. This find had two important results for him, for through it he made the acquaintance of A.G. More, and, no doubt on the suggestion of the latter, sent a note on the plant to the "Journal of Botany" - his first communication to a scientific journal. The same plant brought about the acquaintance of the present writer with Colgan, occasioned by its discovery on the Mourne Mountains four years later. It was from this time onwards, and due largely to the influence of More - an adept at encouraging a taste for natural science and in directing it into practical channels - that he began to pay attention to local botany in more than a desultory way. Possibly a trip to Kerry in 1892 with R.W. Scully, who was getting to work at his exploration of that interesting region, was instrumental in deciding him on commencing systematic investigation into the flora of his own county. But it was characteristic of him that he went to work with no flourish of trumpets. Indeed, when in 1893 the Committee of the Dublin Naturalists' Field Club (of which Colgan was an original member) proposed to organize a botanical survey of the Dublin area, it was with some surprise that they learned that he was already at work on the same investigation.

Once taken up, the projected Flora of Dublin was pushed forward with energy. Never was a county more thoroughly examined, and from the floristic point of view his book, published in 1904, was a model in its painstaking accuracy and careful detail. But he was no more than embarked on this work before another larger task devolved upon him. A.G. More died in 1895, and under the terms of his will Colgan and his friend Scully were appointed to complete and see through the press the new edition of "Cybele Hibernica" for which More had been collecting materials for many years. Although More's annotated copy of "Cybele" provided much of the additional matter which had accumulated since 1866 in the way of fresh stations for the rarer plants, much more was required before the work could assume the shape in which in 1898 it was produced. The whole vexed question of nomenclature had to be faced; wide investigations into the correct allocation of old records, the soil relations of the flora, the Irish names of plants, were undertaken; so that the new "Cybele" bore abundantly the impress of both the energy and the care of its foster-parents. The test of time confirms the value of the work of Colgan and Scully, and deepens the debt of gratitude which Irish botanists owe to them. On the publication of "Cybele" Colgan returned with energy to the "Flora of County Dublin," which was duly published six years later.

I am not acquainted with the circumstances which first attracted him to the Mollusca. No doubt so many years of steady work at the Flowering Plants led to a desire for a change of study; and since 1900 he had been living close to the sea at Sandycove, where marine life offered itself to his attention. But shortly after the publication of the Dublin Flora we find him working hard at the Marine Mollusca, encouraged and aided by the knowledge which A.R. Nichols freely placed at his disposal. A small aquarium was started, and dredging expeditions, especially in Dalkey Sound and the Malahide estuary, were undertaken, mostly in conjunction with the little band of marine zoologists who formed the "Dublin Marine Biological Association." Special attention was paid to the Nudibranchs, and many valuable observations on this fascinating group were made and recorded. When the Clare Island Biological Survey was commenced in 1909, Colgan undertook the Mollusca, and also an enquiry into the local Irish names of animals and plants.

He had joined the Dublin Naturalists' Field Club on its foundation in 1886, and in 1894 had been elected a member of the Royal Irish Academy, but for many years these societies seldom saw him, a certain diffidence restraining him from mingling freely with his fellow-members, or taking an active part in their proceedings. Indeed, so far as I am aware, his first appearance as the reader of a paper at a scientific meeting was when he presented his Clare Island reports to the Academy in 1911. The jolly parties in whose company he carried out shore-collecting and dredging around that western isle melted the slight shyness which was constitutional with him, and his fellow-workers on those occasions will remember him as the best of good company. About the same time he accepted the Vice-Presidency of the Dublin Field Club - which he had previously declined more than once - and two years later he became President. When the Cosmos Club, founded for the discussion of scientific problems, was established in 1917, Colgan at once became one of its most active members, and contributed materially to the lively debates which characterized its meetings.

The list of his writings (other than his many contributions to this Journal) which appears below well expresses the successive phases of his interests. His mind had a strong leaning to the archaeological and historical side of any subject which caught his attention, and his acquaintance with several European languages enabled him to pursue these studies beyond the limits set for most Irish naturalists. One may instance his papers "The Shamrock in Literature" (*infra*), "An Irish Naturalist in Spain in the Eighteenth Century" (*I. N.*, xx., 1), and "On the Occurrence of Tropical Drift Seeds on the Irish Atlantic Coasts" (*infra*), which was published only four days before his death. In science he called himself a sceptic, by which he meant the adoption of a critical attitude towards many statements which others were willing to accept as proven. "But *is it?*" was his frequent question, and many an entertaining discussion followed. His kindly "scepticism" was one of his most attractive traits, and often led to a critical examination of premises which shed valuable light on the subjects which he studied.

One who knew him better than any of his friends writes:- "It could be said of him, truly, *humani nil a me alienum puto*. He loved his kind (hence his enjoyment of humour in literature or society); he loved his country and helped to know it and make it known in his own quiet way; he loved true knowledge, and followed its beck along many paths. His contribution therefore to humanity, knowledge and culture is a real one, and worthy of imitation."

R. Lloyd Praeger.

LIST OF THE PRINCIPAL PAPERS PUBLISHED BY N. COLGAN OTHER THAN THOSE IN THE IRISH NATURALIST

In preparing the following rough list, as also the foregoing memoir, I have received much assistance from Mr. C.B. Moffat, which I would like to acknowledge. A tolerably complete bibliography of Colgan's writings can be obtained by adding to this list the entries under his name in the Author Index to the *Irish Naturalist*, vols. i-xxv., published in that Journal in December, 1916, and in the subsequent annual indexes.

1877.   A day at the Odilienkloster in Alsace. *Irish Monthly.*
1878.   Notes on North Italy (six papers). *Ibid.*
1879.   Netherland genre pictures. *Ibid.*
         A translation from Richter. *Ibid.*
1880.   Up and round Mont Blanc. (four papers). *Ibid.*
         Dexterity, a colloquy. *Ibid.*
1881.   A Bull-fight at Granada in 1880. *Ibid.*
         Translation in sonnet form of Petrarch's sonnet cxxix. *Ibid.*
         A peep at the Moghrebins (three parts). *Temple Bar.*
         From Liverpool to Gibraltar. *Tinsley's Magazine.*
1882.   A day on Mount Vesuvius. *Ibid.*
         From the North Wall to Naples (four parts). *Hibernia.*
         A peep at eastern Sicily (three parts). *Ibid.*
         A tramp at home (two parts). *Ibid.*
         Half-hours in the National Gallery (two parts). *Ibid.*
         Fernan Caballero (two parts). *Ibid.*

1883. Plant hunting in the Dublin Mountains. *Irish Monthly*.
1884. Plant-hunting in the Central Pyrenees (five parts). *Tinsley's Magazine*.
1885. *Saussurea alpina* in County Wicklow. *Journal of Botany*.
1886. Scrambles in the Kerry Highlands (four parts). *Dublin University Review*.
1888. A day on the Rympfischorn. *Irish Monthly*.
1892. *Ajuga pyramidalis* in the Aran Islands. *Journal of Botany*.
1894. *Artemisia Stelleriana* in Ireland. *Ibid*.
1897. The Shamrock in literature - a critical chronology. *Journ. Roy. Soc. Antiquaries Ireland*.
1898. Cybele Hibernica, 2nd edition (with R.W. Scully).
1904. Flora of the County Dublin.
1908. Articles "Phanerograms and Vascular Cryprogams" and "Marine Mollusca" in British Association Handbook to the Dublin District. Contributions towards a revision of the genus Lomanotus. *Ann. Mag. Nat. Hist.*
1909. Notes on locomotion and the use of slime-threads in the Marine Mollusca. *Ibid.*
1911. "Gaelic plant and animal names" and "Marine Mollusca" of Clare Island Survey. *Proc. R. I. Academy*.
1912. Self-evisceration in the Asteroidea. *Ann. Mag. Nat. Hist.*
1919. On the occurrence of tropical drift seeds on the Irish Atlantic coasts. *Proc. R. I. Academy*.

TOPOGRAPHICAL INDEX

The Topographical Index lists both the localities in Co. Dublin where plants were recorded during the Dublin Naturalists' Field Club's survey and the place names used in Part I of this *Flora* (but not those in *Colgan* or *Suppl*). Also included are a small number of place names outside Co. Dublin, usually near the county boundary, which have been referred to elsewhere in the Topographical Index or in the text.

The maps (published by the Director at the Ordnance Survey, Phoenix Park, Dublin) most used during the survey were:
District Map of Dublin, 1: 63,360 (1 inch to 1 mile)
Sheet 13, Meath, 1: 126,720 (1/2 inch to 1 mile)
Sheet 16, Kildare, Wicklow, 1: 126,720 (1/2 inch to 1 mile)
Map of Greater Dublin, 1: 20,000 (3.17 inches to 1 mile)
Map of the Phoenix Park, Dublin, 1: 10,560 (6 inches to 1 mile)
Since the completion of the Field Club's survey, the District Map of Dublin and 1/2 inch maps have been replaced by Discovery Series, 1: 50,000, for example, No. 50, Dublin City and District, which covers most of the southern part of the county.

In the Topographical Index, the entries are listed alphabetically. A locality or place name is followed by the District number(s) in brackets, further information where considered necessary and the four digit National Grid reference for the 1 km x 1 km square in which it occurs. The grid reference is made up of the Sub-Zone or Grid letter (N or O for Co. Dublin) followed by the two digit Easting co-ordinate which is separated by a space from the two digit Northing co-ordinate, for example, Rockbrook (7) O 13 24 and Hazelhatch (6) 3 km NW Newcastle N 98 31.

Where a locality (e.g. a golf-course or park) or a town extends into more than one 1 km x 1 km square, only one grid reference is given, for example, St Anne's Park (5) Raheny O 20 37 and Malahide (5) O 22 45.

Where the spelling of a place name varies on different maps, in the literature and on road signs, an alternative spelling may be given in brackets. The spelling of place names generally follows Ordnance Survey maps unless the commonly used form is different. Alternative names are cross-referenced.

For more obscure localities, directions and distances (to the nearest 0.25 km) are given from larger places. A large scale street map of Greater Dublin should be consulted for specific roads.

For mountains, the grid references refer to the highest points above sea level.

The courses of rivers and their tributaries within Co. Dublin are briefly described and the grid references given for them usually refer to their point of entry to the sea or to another river.

Large topographical features, for example, the Glenasmole Reservoirs and Howth Head, are not given a grid reference, but their locations are described.

Abbotstown House (4) 1.5 km NE Blanchardstown; Veterinary Research Laboratory O 09 39

Abbotstown Lake (4) Just WSW Abbotstown House O 09 39

Aderrig (6) 3 km SW Lucan O 00 33

Aghfarrell (7) 3 km ESE Brittas O 05 20

Albert College (5) Now part of public park and Dublin City University, 2 km SSW Santry O 15 38

Alder Marsh, North Bull Island (5) Just NE St Anne's Club-house O 24 37

Alexandra Basin, Quay (5) Dublin Port O 18 34

Allenton House, Housing Estate (7) 0.75 km ESE Oldbawn O 09 25

Allagour (7) W of Northern Glenasmole Reservoir O 08 22

Ardgillan Castle, Park (2) 1.5 km E Balrothery O 21 61

Ardla (2) Townland 1.5 km WSW Skerries O 23 60

Ardmore Housing Estate (5) 1 km NW Artane O 18 38

Artane (5) O 19 38

Ashtown (4) O 11 37

Ashtown Railway Station (4) O 11 37

Astagob (4) Abandoned sand and gravel pits, 1.25 km SW Castleknock O 07 36

Athgoe Castle (6) 2 km SSW Newcastle N 98 26

Badgerhill (6) 2 km NNE Kilteel N 99 23

Baggot Street Bridge (7) Grand Canal, Dublin City O 16 32

Baily Lighthouse (5) SE Howth Head O 29 36

Balbriggan (2) O 20 63

Balbriggan Golf-course (2) O 20 61

Balcarrick (3) 2 km SE Donabate O 24 49

Balcarrick Golf-course (3) 1.5 km SE Donabate O 24 49

Baldongan Castle, Cross Roads (2) 3 km SW Skerries O 23 57

Baldonnel Aerodrome (6) 4 km WSW Clondalkin (= Casement Aerodrome) O 03 29

Baldoyle (5) O 24 40

Baldoyle Estuary (5) N of Baldoyle

Baldoyle Industrial Estate (5) 1 km WSW Baldoyle O 23 39

Baldoyle Race Course (5) NW Baldoyle O 24 40

Baldwinstown (1) 2 km E Garristown O 09 58

Balgriffin (5) 4 km WNW Baldoyle O 21 41

Balheary (3) 3 km NNW Swords O 16 49

Balheary House (3) 1.5 km N Swords O 18 48

Balleally Dump (2) 2 km S Lusk O 21 52

Ballinascorney Gap (7) 4 km ENE Brittas between Knockannavea and Slievenabawnoge

Ballinascorney Gap, Stone Cross (7) 4 km ENE Brittas O 07 22

Ballinascorney House (7) 3.5 km ENE Brittas O 06 21

Ballinteer (8) O 16 26

Ballinteer Community School (8) O 16 27

Ballisk (3) Just NE Donabate O 23 50

Ballsbridge (7 & 8) O 17 32

Ballybetagh Bog (8) 1.5 km SSW Kiltiernan O 20 20

Ballybetagh Wood (8) 1.25 km S Kiltiernan O 20 20

Ballyboden (7 & 8) 2 km SSW Rathfarnham O 13 27

Ballyboghil (1, 2 & 3) O 14 53

Ballybough (5) Dublin City O 16 35

Ballybrack (8) Glencullen Valley O 17 20

Ballybrack (8) 2.5 km N Shankill O 25 24

Ballycorus Lead Mines (8) 2 km SE Kiltiernan O 22 20

Ballycorus Roadstone Works (8) 2 km ESE Kiltiernan O 22 21

Ballycullen (7) 0.75 km SSE Firhouse O 11 26

Ballyedmonduff (8) E side Two Rock Mtn O 18 22

Ballyfermot (7) O 10 33

Ballykea (2) 1.75 km W Loughshinny O 25 56

Ballymadun (1) 3 km SSW Garristown O 06 54

Ballymaice (7) 3.5 km SSW Tallaght O 08 23

Ballymakaily Mill (6) By Grand Canal 2.5 km S Lucan O 02 32

Ballyman Glen, River (8) Along county boundary 1.25 km NE Enniskerry, Co. Wicklow O 23 18

Ballyman Glen Bridge (8) Ballyman R. on county boundary O 22 18

Ballymorefinn Hill (7) W of Southern Glenasmole Reservoir O 08 20

Ballymun (4 & 5) O 15 39

Ballyogan Tiphead (8) 1.5 km E Stepaside O 20 23

Balrickard (1) 4.5 km SE Naul O 17 59

Balrothery (2) O 20 61

Balrothery Lough/Reservoir (2) 0.5 km SW Balrothery O 19 60

Balscaddan (2) 3 km WNW Balbriggan O 17 64

Balscadden (5) Just E Howth Harbour O 29 39

Barberstown House (4) 4 km SW Swords. O 14 44

Barnacullia (8) 1.25 km W Stepaside O 18 23

Barnageeragh (2) 2.5 km WNW Skerries O 23 61

Barnaslingan Lane (8) 0.5 km SE Kiltiernan O 21 21

Barnhill Bridge (4) 2 km WNW Clonsilla O 03 38

Basin Street Upper (7) O 13 33

Beech Park (4) 0.5 km WSW Clonsilla O 04 37

Belcamp Park (5) 2 km W Balgriffin O 19 41

Belgard (6) 2 km NW Tallaght O 06 29

Belgree House (4) 4 km N Mulhuddart O 06 44

Ben of Howth (5) 1.5 km S Howth village O 28 37

Beshellstown (1) 3 km NE Garristown O 09 60

Bettyville House (2) 2.25 km NE Ballyboghil O 15 55

Bishop's Lane (8) 0.75 km W Kiltiernan O 20 21

Black Banks, Raheny (5) Junction of Howth Road and James Larkin Road O 23 38

Blackrock (8) O 21 29

Blackrock College (8) O 20 29

Blackrock Park (8) O 21 29

Blake's Cross (2) On District 3 boundary 3.5 km SW Lusk O 19 51

Blanchardstown (4) O 08 38

Bluebell Industrial Estate (7) O 09 32

Bog of the Ring (1) 2.5 km SW Balrothery O 17 60

Bohernabreena (7) 2.5 km S Tallaght O 09 25

Bohernabreena Reservoirs (7) (= Glenasmole Reservoirs)

Booterstown (8) O 20 30

Booterstown Graveyard (8) Bellevue Avenue, off Rock Road O 19 30

Booterstown Marsh (8) O 20 30

Boranaraltry Bridge (8) Glencullen R. 2 km W Glencullen O 16 20

Borranstown House (1) 3.25 km SW Garristown O 15 56

Brackenstown (3) 1.25 km W Swords O 16 46

Bray, Co. Wicklow (-) On District 8 boundary O 26 18

Bray Harbour, Co. Wicklow (-) O 26 19

Bride's Glen (8) 1 km SW Loughlinstown O 24 22

Brittas (6) O 03 21

Brittas Ponds (6) Just N Brittas O 03 22

Broad Strand, Howth (5) Shore at Doldrum Bay just E of The Needles O 28 36

Broad Meadow Estuary (3 & 5) (= Broad Meadows)

Broad Meadow River, Water (3) Flows E along District 1 boundary, then SE to enter the estuary at O 19 47

Broad Meadows (3 & 5) Between mouth of Broad Meadow River and Malahide Island (= Broad Meadow Estuary, Malahide Estuary)

Broadstone (4) Phibsborough O 14 35

Broadstone Railway (4) SSW Cabra O 13 35

Broghan Bridge (4) 5.5 km NNW Finglas O 10 44

Broghan House (4) 4.5 km NNW Finglas O 11 43

Broomfield Estate (4) 2 km NE Lucan O 04 36

Bull Island (5) (= North Bull Island)

Bull Wall (5) Sea wall at S end North Bull Island O 21 35

Burrow, The (3) 1.25 km NW Portrane O 24 51

Burrow Road (5) Just N Sutton O 25 39

Burrow Road (8) 0.25 km W Stepaside O 18 23

Burton Hall (8) Just SE Sandyford Industrial Estate O 19 26

Bushy Park (7) O 13 29

Cabinteely (8) O 23 24

Cabinteely Park (8) O 23 25

Cabra (4) O 13 36

Cammock River (6 & 7) Flows ENE through Clondalkin, Inchicore and Kilmainham to R. Liffey at O 13 34

Cappagh Hospital (4) 1.75 km WNW Finglas O 11 39

Cardiff's Bridge (4) Tolka R. 3 km W Glasnevin O 12 37

Cardy Point, Rocks (2) 2.5 km N Balbriggan O 19 65

Car Ferry Terminal, Dublin Port (5) O 20 34

Carrickgollagan (8) 3 km SE Kiltiernan O 23 20

Carrickmines (8) O 22 24

Carysfort College (8) Blackrock O 21 28

Casana Rock (5) E side Howth Head O 30 38

Casement Aerodrome (6) 4 km WSW Clondalkin (= Baldonnel Aerodrome) O 03 29

Castlekelly (7) 0.75 km ESE head of Southern Glenasmole Reservoir O 10 20

Castleknock (4) O 09 37

Castleknock College (4) Just SW Castleknock O 08 36

Castlewarden House, Co. Kildare (-) 4.75 km SW Newcastle, near District 6 boundary N 97 24

Causeway, North Bull Island (5) Causeway from shore to Island O 22 37

Central Marsh, Howth (5) 0.25 km S Howth Reservoir O 28 37

Chapelmidway (3) 5.75 km W Swords O 12 46

Chapelmidway Bridge (3 & 4) Just S Chapelmidway O 12 46

Chapelizod (4) O 10 34

Cherryhound (4) 6 km NNW Finglas O 09 44

Christ Church Cathedral (7) Dublin City O 15 33

Churchtown (8) O 16 28

City Basin (4) Disused reservoir, Dublin City O 15 35

Citadel Pond (4) Phoenix Park, W People's Garden O 12 34

Clanaboy House (4) 1 km NE Lucan O 03 35

Claremont Strand (5) (= Hole-in-the-Wall Beach) 1 km NE Sutton O 26 39

Cloghran (5) 3 km S Swords O 17 44

Cloghran House (4) 3.5 km ENE Mulhuddart O 09 41

Clonard Cross (2) 2 km WSW Balbriggan O 18 63

Clondalkin (6 & 7) O 07 31

Clondalkin Common (6) W side Clondalkin O 06 31

Clonee, Co. Meath (-) Near District 4 boundary O 03 41

Clonsilla (4) O 05 38

Clonsilla Railway Station (4) O 04 38

Clonskeagh Bridge (7 & 8) R. Dodder O 17 30

Clontarf (5) O 20 35

Clontarf Castle (5) O 19 36

Clontarf Golf-course (5) O 18 37

Cockles Bridge (1) Delvin R., 1 km N Baldwinstown O 09 59

Coldblow (4) 1 km NW Lucan O 02 35

Colganstown House (6) 1.5 km NW Newcastle N 98 29

Coliemore Harbour (8) 1 km ESE Dalkey O 27 26

Collins Bridge (4) Royal Canal, 1.25 km NNW Lucan O 02 36

Collinstown Bridge (2) 2.25 km NNE Lusk O 21 56

Colt Island (2) 1.25 km ENE Skerries O 26 61

Commons Upper (1) 1.5 km N Garristown O 07 60

Conyngham Road (4) Dublin City O 12 34

Cookstown Industrial Estate (6) 1 km NW Tallaght O 07 28

Coolatrath Bridge (4) Ward R. 3.5 km NW St Margaret's O 10 45

Cooldrinagh House (6) 2.25 km W Lucan O 01 35

Coolmine House (4) 2 km ENE Clonsilla O 06 38

Coolock (5) O 19 39

Coolquoy (3) 8 km W Swords O 09 46

Corballis (3) O 24 48

Corballis Golf-course (3) O 24 48

Corballis House (3) 1.25 km SE Donabate O 23 48

Corcagh House, Demesne (6) 1.75 km SW Clondalkin O 05 30

Corduff (4) 1 km NW Blanchardstown O 07 39

Corduff Bridge (2) 3 km SW Lusk O 19 52

Corduff Hall (2) 2.75 km SW Lusk O 19 52

Corduff House (2) 2.25 km SSW Lusk O 20 52

Cork Abbey (8) 1 km NW Bray O 26 19

Corn Mill, Balbriggan (2) 1 km S Balbriggan O 19 62

Cornelscourt (8) O 22 25

Corr Castle (5) 0.5 km E Sutton O 26 39

Corrig Mountain (7) O 09 19

Cosh, The (5) Peninsula and golf-course 0.5 km N Sutton (= The Cush) O 25 39

Cot Brook (7) Flows N from Kippure to enter R. Dodder at O 10 20

Coultry Dump (5) Ballymun, 1 km W Santry O 15 40

Courtlough House (2) 5.25 km WSW Skerries O 20 58

Crinken (8) 1 km S Shankill O 25 20

Croke Park (5) Dublin City O 16 35

Crooksling Glen (6) 2 km S Saggart O 03 24

Cross Guns Bridge (4) Royal Canal, Phibsborough O 15 36

Cross of the Cage (2) 3.75 km S Balbriggan O 21 60

Cruagh Mountain (7) O 13 21

Cruagh Wood (7) 2 km S Rockbrook O 12 22

Crumlin (7) O 12 31

Cunard (7) E side of Southern Glenasmole Reservoir O 10 20

Curragha Bog (1) 4 km SW Garristown, along county boundary (former bog) O 04 56

Cush, The (5) Golf-course on peninsula 0.5 km N Sutton (= The Cosh) O 25 39

Custom House (4) Dublin City O 16 34

Dalkey (8) O 26 26

Dalkey Hill (8) O 26 26

Dalkey Island (8) O 27 26

Dalkey Quarry (8) O 26 26

Dallyhaysy (1 & 2) 3 km SW Balbriggan O 17 62

Damastown (4) 1 km ENE Clonee O 04 41

Darndale (5) O 20 40

Davitt Road (7) By Grand Canal O 11 32

Daws Bridge (2 & 3) 0.5 km S Blake's Cross O 19 51

Deansgrange (8) O 22 26

Deansgrange Stream (8) Flows SE from Deansgrange to just S Killiney at O 26 23

Deer Park Golf-course, Hotel (5) Just W Howth village O 28 38

Delaford (7) 0.5 km NE Firhouse O 11 27

Delvin River (1 & 2) Flows NE from Garristown to 3 km NW Balbriggan at O 18 66

Dermotstown (1) 2.5 km W Balrothery O 17 61

Dingle, The (8) Glen 1 km ENE Kiltiernan O 21 22

Diswellstown House (4) 1.75 km SW Castleknock O 07 36

Dodsboro Housing Estate (6) 0.5 km SW Lucan O 02 34

Dodder, River (7 & 8) Flows N from Kippure, then NE to Ringsend at O 17 34

Dodder Valley Park (7) Along R. Dodder from Oldbawn to Templeogue

Doldrum Bay (5) S side Howth Head O 28 36

Dolphin's Barn (7) O 13 32

Donabate (3) O 22 49

Donabate Railway Station (3) O 22 49

Donaghmede (5) O 22 39

Dornaville (1) 1.75 km NE Naul, on District 2 boundary O 16 62

Drimnagh (7) O 11 32

Druid's Glen (8) 0.75 km E Carrickmines O 22 24

Drumcondra (5) O 16 36

Drumleck Point (5) Southernmost point of Howth Head O 28 36

Dubber Cross (4) 2 km N Finglas O 13 41

Dublin Airport (4 & 5) Mainly in District 5 O 16 43

Dublin Port (5, 7 & 8) Mainly in (5) N side R. Liffey E of East Wall Road O 18 34

Dun Laoghaire (8) O 24 28

Dun Laoghaire Swimming Baths (8) Just SE East Pier O 24 28

Dundrum (8) O 17 27

Dunsink Observatory (4) 2.5 km WSW Finglas O 10 38

Dunsink Tiphead (4) 2.5 km W Finglas O 10 38

Dunsoghly (4) 4.5 km NNW Finglas O 12 43

Dunsoghly Castle (4) Just W Dunsoghly O 11 43

Earlscliffe House (5) Overlooking Doldrum Bay, Howth Head O 28 36

Earlsfort Terrace (7) Dublin City O 16 32

East Link Toll Bridge (5 & 8) R. Liffey at Ringsend O 18 34

East Mountain (5) Howth Head O 29 38

Edmondstown (7 & 8) O 13 25

Eighth Lock (8th Lock) (7) Grand Canal, 1.75 km NE Clondalkin O 08 32

Elm Park Golf-course (8) 1 km NW Booterstown O 19 30

Embankment (6) 1.25 km SE Saggart O 04 25

Enniskerry, Co. Wicklow (-) Near District 8 boundary O 22 17

Esker (6) 1 km SE Lucan O 04 34

Fairview (5) O 17 36

Fairview Park (5) O 17 36

Fairy Castle (8) Cairn on Two Rock Mtn O 17 22

Fancourt (2) 1.25 km E Balbriggan O 21 63

Farm, The (5) North Bull Island, NE Royal Dublin Club-house O 22 36

Farmleigh (4) 1 km SSE Castleknock O 09 36

Featherbed (7) Just SW Killakee Mtn O 12 20

Feltrim (5) 1.5 km S Malahide O 21 44

Feltrim Hill, Quarry (5) 1.5 km SW Malahide O 20 44

Fern Hill (8) 1.25 km NW Stepaside O 18 24

Fettercairn House (6) 1.75 km WNW Tallaght O 07 28

Fieldstown House (1) 5 km SW Ballyboghil O 11 50

Finglas (4) O 13 39

Finglas Bridge (4) Tolka R. 1.75 km SE Finglas O 14 37

Finglas Industrial Estate (4) 2 km SSE Finglas O 13 37

Firhouse (7) O 11 27

Fitzsimon's Wood (8) 0.5 km SW Sandyford O 17 25

Five Roads, The (2) 4 km NW Lusk, on District 1 boundary O 18 57

Fonthill House (7) 2 km WNW Palmerston O 06 35

Forrest Great (3) 3.25 km SW Swords O 15 44

Forrest Little (3) 2.75 km SSW Swords O 16 44

Fort Bridge (7) R. Dodder 2 km SSW Oldbawn O 09 24

Fortunestown (6) 1.25 km ENE Saggart O 05 27

Fox and Geese (7) O 09 31

Fox Hole (5) 0.5 km E The Summit, Howth O 29 37

Foxrock (8) O 21 25

Foxrock Church (8) 1 km NE Foxrock O 21 26

Foxrock Railway Station (8) Now disused O 21 25

Friarstown (7) 3.5 km SSE Tallaght O 09 24

Furry Glen (4) W side Phoenix Park O 09 35

Gallanstown (4) 3.75 km NNE Mulhuddart O 07 43

Gallanstown (7) 1.5 km SW Ballyfermot O 08 32

Garristown (1) O 07 58

Gay Brook (5) Just W Malahide O 20 45

Glasnevin (4) O 15 37

Glasnevin Cemetery (4) O 14 37

Glassamucky Mountain (7) O 12 20

Glassavullaun (7) ENE side of Corrig Mtn O 09 19

Glenageary (8) O 24 27

Glenaraneen (6) 1 km NNW Brittas O 02 22

Glenasmole Lodge (7) 1 km SE head of Southern Glenasmole Reservoir O 10 19

Glenasmole Reservoirs (7) Northern (= Lower) and Southern (= Upper) Reservoirs in Glenasmole Valley

Glenasmole Valley (7) 5 km S Tallaght (= Kelly's Glen)

Glencullen (8) 2 km SW Kiltiernan O 19 20

Glencullen Bridge (8) Glencullen R. 1 km S Glencullen O 19 19

Glencullen Chapel (8) E side Glencullen O 19 20

Glencullen Mountain (8) O 17 18

Glencullen River (8) Flows SE through Glencullen Valley, leaving the county at Glencullen Bridge O 19 19

Glencullen Valley (8) Between Two Rock and Glencullen Mtns

Glendoo House (8) 1 km ENE summit of Glendoo Mtn O 15 20

Glendoo Mountain (7) (= Glendhu in *Suppl*) O 14 20

Goatstown (8) O 18 28

Golden Ball (8) 0.5 km NNW Kiltiernan O 20 22

Gollierstown (6) By Grand Canal 3 km NE Newcastle O 01 31

Gormanstown (2) On Co. Meath boundary O 16 66

Gormanstown Woods (2) On Co. Meath boundary O 16 66

Gracedieu (3) 3 km ESE Ballyboghil, on District 2 boundary O 18 52

Granard Bridge (4) Royal Canal 0.75 km SE Blanchardstown O 08 38

Grand Canal (6 & 7) Runs from W to E through Hazelhatch to Ringsend

Grand Canal Bank (7) O 13 33

Grand Canal Harbour (7) E terminus of Grand Canal O 17 33

Grange Castle (6) 3 km WNW Clondalkin O 03 31

Greenhills (7) 2.25 km NNE Tallaght O 10 29

Greenhollows Quarry (5) 1.5 km S Howth village O 28 37

Greygates (8) Mount Merrion O 19 29

Guinness Metal Bridge (7) R. Liffey 1 km N Palmerston O 08 35

Half Moon Bathing Place (8) South Wall, 0.5 km W Poolbeg Lighthouse O 22 33

Hampton Hall (2) 2.25 km SE Balbriggan O 21 62

Hand Park (2) 1 km E Rush O 27 54

Harold's Cross Bridge (7) Grand Canal O 14 32

Harristown House (4) 3.75 km NNE Finglas O 13 42

Haystown (2) 1.5 km NW Rush O 24 54

Hazelhatch (6) 3 km NW Newcastle N 98 31

Hazelhatch Bridge (6) Grand Canal N 98 30

Hell Fire Club (7) O 11 23

Hermitage Golf-course (6) S bank R. Liffey 2.5 km E Lucan O 05 35

Heuston Railway Station (7) Dublin City O 13 34

Hole-in-the-Wall (4) Turnstile gate in NE boundary wall of Phoenix Park O 11 36

Hole-in-the-Wall Beach (5) (= Claremont Strand) 1 km NE Sutton O 26 39

Holmpatrick Bridge (2) In Skerries village O 25 60

Howth (5) O 28 38

Howth Castle and Demesne (5) 1 km W Howth village O 27 39

Howth Golf-course (5) Just W Ben of Howth O 27 37

Howth Harbour (5) O 28 39

Howth Head (5) Peninsula NE Dublin City

Howth Railway Station (5) O 28 39

Howth Reservoir (5) O 28 38

Huband's Bridge (7) Grand Canal at Mount Street Upper O 17 33

Huntstown House (4) 3.5 km NW Finglas O 10 41

Huntstown Quarry (4) 2.5 km NW Finglas O 11 41

Hynestown Reservoir (1) 1 km SE Naul O 14 60

IMG Golf-course (5) Just E Portmarnock O 24 42

Inchicore (7) O 11 33

Infirmary Road (4) O 13 34

Ireland's Eye (5) Island 2 km N Howth O 28 41

Irishtown (8) O 18 33

Irishtown House (4) 4.5 km NE Mulhuddart O 08 44

Irishtown Park (8) Developed on part of Ringsend Dump O 20 33

Island Golf-course (3) On Malahide Island

Island Lake/Pond (4) (= Quarry Lake) Phoenix Park O 10 36

Islandbridge (7) O 12 34

J.F. Kennedy Industrial Estate (7) Just NE Fox and Geese O 09 31

Jobstown (6 & 7) O 06 26

Kelly's Glen (7) (= Glenasmole Valley)

Kelly's Glen (8) Between Kilmashogue and Tibradden Mtns. O15 22

Kennan Bridge (4) Royal Canal 1.25 km ESE Clonsilla O 06 37

Kilbarrack (5) O 23 39

Kilbogget Park (8) 0.5 km ESE Cabinteely O 24 24

Kilcrea House (3) 1.5 km SW Donabate O 21 48

Kilgobbin (8) 0.5 km N Stepaside O 19 24

Killakee (7) 2 km SW Rockbrook O 12 22

Killakee Mountain (7) O 12 20

Killeek (3) 1 km SW Knocksedan Bridge O 14 45

Killester (5) O 19 37

Killigeen, The (6) 3 km SW Rathcoole O 00 24

Killiney (8) O 25 25

Killiney Bay (8) O 26 24

Killiney Hill (8) O 26 25

Killiney Railway Station (8) O 25 24

Kill of the Grange (8) O 22 27

Killossery (3) 6.25 km NW Swords O 12 49

Kilmainham (7) O 12 33

Kilmashogue Lane (8) W side Kilmashogue Mtn O 14 24

Kilmashogue Mountain (8) O 15 23

Kilrock (5) Just W Nose of Howth O 29 38

Kilrock Quarries (5) Abandoned quarries 1 km W Nose of Howth O 29 38

Kilronan House (5) 2 km S Swords O 17 44

Kilshane Bridge (4) 4 km NW Finglas O 11 42

Kilteel, Co. Kildare (-) Near District 6 boundary N 98 21

Kiltiernan (8) (= Kilternan) O 20 22

Kiltiernan Cromlech (8) 0.75 km W Kiltiernan O 19 22

Kimmage Cross Roads (7) Dublin City O 13 30

Kingsbridge (7) (= Heuston Station) O 13 34

King's Hospital School (7) 1 km WNW Palmerston O 07 35

Kingswood Housing Estate (7) 2 km NNW Tallaght O 08 29

Kinsealy (5) (= Kinsaley) O 21 43

Kippure (7) O 11 15

Kirkpatrick Bridge (4) Royal Canal 1.25 km SW Blanchardstown O 07 37

Kitchenstown (1) 3 km ESE Naul O 15 60

Knockandinny Golf-course (6) 2.5 km NNW Brittas O 02 24

Knockannavea Wood (7) On Knockannavea Mtn 3.5 km NE Brittas O 06 23

Knockmaroon Gate, Hill, Woods (4) W side Phoenix Park O 09 35

Knocksedan Bridge (3) Ward R. 3 km W Swords O 15 46

Knocksedan Reservoir (3) On Ward R. 1.5 km W
    Knocksedan Bridge O 13 46

Lambay Island (3) 5 km E Portrane O 31 50

Lansdowne Station (8) 0.5 km NNE Ballsbridge
    O 18 32

Larch Hill (8) 1.25 km SE Rockbrook O 14 23

Laughanstown (8) O 23 23

Laurel Lodge Road (4) Castleknock O 08 37

Laurel Mount (1) Near Borranstown House, 3 km SW
    Garristown O 05 56

Leeson Street Bridge (7) Grand Canal O 16 32

Leixlip, Co. Kildare (-) Near Districts 4 and 6
    boundaries O 00 35

Leopardstown Park Hospital (8) 2.25 km S Stillorgan
    O 20 25

Leopardstown Race Course (8) 2.25 km SSE Stillorgan
    O20 25

Liffey Junction (4) Railway junction with bridge over
    Royal Canal 0.5 km N Cabra O 13 37

Liffey Millrace (7) S bank R. Liffey N and NW
    Palmerston O 07 35

Liffey, River (4, 5, 6, 7 & 8) Flows E through Leixlip to
    Ringsend at O 18 34

Liffey Valley (4, 6 & 7) Along R. Liffey W of Islandbridge

Lion's Bay (5) Howth Head, just E Lion's Head O 29 36

Lion's Head (5) S side Howth Head O 29 36

Lispopple (1) 3.2 km SSW Ballyboghil O 13 50

Lispopple Bridge (1 & 3) Broad Meadow R. just S
    Lispopple O 13 50

Lissen Hall Bridge (3) 2 km NNE Swords O 18 48

Little Bray (8) O 25 18

Little Dargle River (8) Flows NW from Ticknock
    through Marley Park at O15 26

Lock, 7th (7) Grand Canal 1.25 km SW Ballyfermot
    O 09 32

Lock, 8th (7) Grand Canal 1.75 km NE Clondalkin
    O 08 32

Lock, 12th (6) Grand Canal near Ballymakaily Mill
    O 02 32

Longford Bridge (4) Royal Canal at Ashtown Railway
    Station O 10 37

Loughlinstown (8) O 24 23

Loughlinstown Hospital (8) O 24 22

Loughshinny (2) 4 km SSE Skerries O 27 56

Lowtherstone (2) 3 km NW Balbriggan O 18 66

Lubber's Wood (3) 4.75 km NW Swords O 14 49

Lucan (6) O 03 35

Lucan Bridge (4) R. Liffey O 03 35

Lucan Demesne (6) 1 km WNW Lucan O 01 35

Lucan Quarry (4) Partly disused quarry 1 km NE Lucan,
    just NE Clanaboy House O 03 36

Lugmore Glen (7) Just E Tallaght Hill O 06 25

Lusk (2) O 21 54

Luttrellstown Estate, Demesne (4) (= Woodlands)
    1.5 km S Clonsilla O 05 36

Luttrellstown Lake (4) O 04 37

Lyons Tea Factory (7) S side Grand Canal at Davitt
    Road, Drimnagh O 11 32

Machinery Pond (4) Phoenix Park, at Mountjoy Cross
    O 10 36

Magazine Fort (4) Phoenix Park near Islandbridge Gate
    O 12 34

Malahide (5) O 22 45

Malahide Castle (5) O 22 45

Malahide Estuary (3 & 5) Between mouth of Broad
    Meadow River and Malahide Island (= Broad
    Meadows, Broad Meadow Estuary)

Malahide Island (3) Peninsula extending 2 km NE from
    Malahide Point

Malahide Point (3) 0.5 km N Malahide O 23 46

Man O' War (2) 2.75 km S Balrothery O 20 58

Marino (5) O 17 36

Marley Park (8) (= Marlay Park) O 15 26

Mareens Brook (7) Headwater stream of R. Dodder
    O 12 17

Massey Woods (7) 2 km SW Rockbrook O 12 23

Matt Bridge (1 & 2) 1.5 km NW Balrothery O 18 61

Mayne Bridge (5) Mayne R. between Baldoyle and
    Portmarnock O 23 41

Mayne River (5) Flows E from just S Dublin Airport to
    NW Baldoyle at Mayne Bridge O 23 41

Memorial Park (7) Just S and SW Islandbridge O 12 34

Merrion Gates (8) Junction of Strand Road and Merrion
    Road O 19 31

Merrion Square (7) O 16 33

Merrion Strand (8) O 19 31

Military Road (8) E Ballybrack O 25 24

Milltown Bridge (7 & 8) R. Dodder, old bridge just
    S Dundrum Road O 16 30

Milltown House (6) 4.5 km W Clondalkin O 02 30

Milverton Estate (2) 2 km SW Skerries O 23 59

Monaspick, Co. Wicklow (-) 1.25 km SW Brittas on
    District 6 boundary O 02 20

Montpelier Hill (4) Just E Phoenix Park O 13 34

Moorepark (1) 2.5 km NNW Garristown (mostly in
    Co. Meath) O 06 61

Mount Argus Church (7) Just SW Harold's Cross
    O 14 31

Mount Jerome Cemetery (7) Harold's Cross O 14 31

Mountjoy Cross (4) Crossroads 0.5 km NE Ordnance
    Survey Office, Phoenix Park O 10 36

Mount Merrion Woods (8) O 19 28

Mountpelier (7) Abandoned house on hill of same name
    3.5 km S Firhouse O 10 23

Mount Seskin (6 & 7) 2 km NE Brittas O 04 23
Mount Venus (7) 1 km W Rockbrook O 12 24
Mountain View Graveyard (4) 1.25 km NE Mulhuddart
 O 07 41
Mulhuddart (4) O 06 40
Mullan (3) 1 km S Donabate O 22 48
Murphy's Quarry (1) Near Nag's Head O 14 57

Nags Head (2) 4 km N Ballyboghil on District 1
 boundary O 14 57
National Botanic Gardens (4) Glasnevin O 14 37
Naul (1 & 2) O 13 60
Naul Hills (1) Just S of Naul
Needles, The (5) S side Howth Head, W Doldrum Bay
 O 28 36
Nevitt (2) 5 km SE Naul on District 1 boundary
 O 16 57
Newbridge House (3) 1.5 km W Donabate O 21 50
Newcastle (6) O 00 28
Newlawn House (2) 1.5 km ESE Ballyboghil O 16 53
Newpark House (4) 2.5 km NW St Margaret's O 11 45
Newport House (3) 2.5 km ENE Swords O 20 47
Newtown (6) 2.75 km SW Rathcoole O 00 24
North Bull Island (5) Dublin Bay E of Raheny, connected
 to mainland by Causeway and Bull Wall Bridge
North Bull Wall (5) (= Bull Wall) O 21 35
North Strand Road (5) Just SW Fairview O 17 35
North Wall Quay (5) Dublin City by R. Liffey O 17 34
Nose of Howth (5) NE Howth Head O 30 38

Oldbawn (7) O 09 26
Old Conna Hill (8) 3 km NW Bray O 24 20
Old Connaught (8) 2 km WNW Bray O 24 19
Oldcourt (7) 1.25 km SE Oldbawn O 10 25
Oldtown (1) 3 km W Ballyboghil O 11 53
Old Tallaght (7) O 09 27
Oonavarra Hill (4) Just NE Lucan, 0.75 km SW
 Clanaboy House O 03 35
Ordnance Survey Office (4) W side Phoenix Park
 O 10 36
Orwell Bridge (7 & 8) R. Dodder 0.75 km SSE Rathgar
 O 15 29
Owendoher River (7 & 8) Flows N through Rockbrook
 to enter R. Dodder just W of Rathfarnham at
 O 14 29

Pakenham Bridge (4) Royal Canal 1.25 km W Clonsilla
 O 03 38
Palmerston (7) O 08 35
Palmerston Hospital (7) (= Stewart's Hospital) O 08 35
Palmerston Marsh (7) Just E Palmerston by R. Liffey
 O 09 35

Palmerston Park (7) O 16 30
Palmerstown (1) 2.5 km SW Oldtown O 09 52
Palmerstown House (2) 3.5 km N Lusk O 21 57
Papal Nunciature (4) Phoenix Park; now Ashtown
 Castle Visitor Centre O 11 36
Peafield (5) 3 km SW Malahide O 19 45
Peamount Hospital (6) 2 km NE Newcastle O 01 30
People's Garden (4) SE corner Phoenix Park O 13 34
People's Pond (4) People's Garden, Phoenix Park
 O 13 34
Phibblestown House (4) 2.5 km WSW Mulhuddart
 O 04 39
Phibsborough (4) O 14 35
Phoenix Park (4) Park on W side Dublin City
Pigeon House (8) Complex of electricity generating
 stations O 20 33
Pine Forest (7) 2 km S Rockbrook O 13 22
Piperstown Hill (7) 5.25 km SSE Tallaght O 10 22
Poddle River (7) Flows NE through Kimmage and
 Harold's Cross O 14 31
Poolbeg Lighthouse (8) End of South Wall O 23 34
Portmarnock (5) O 24 42
Portmarnock Brickfields (5) 0.5 km W Portmarnock
 O 23 42
Portmarnock Bridge (5) Sluice R. just SW Portmarnock
 O 23 42
Portmarnock Golf-course (5) On Portmarnock
 Peninsula O 24 41
Portmarnock Peninsula (5) Extending 2.5 km SE
 Portmarnock
Portmarnock Point (5) O 25 40
Portmarnock Raceway (5) 1 km W Portmarnock
 O 22 42
Portmarnock Railway Station (5) 1 km SW
 Portmarnock O 22 42
Portmarnock Sand-hills (5) E side Portmarnock
 Peninsula
Portobello Bridge (7) Grand Canal O 15 32
Portrane (3) (= Portraine) O 25 50
Portrane Green (3) N side of Portrane O 25 50
Portrane Hospital (3) 0.5 km S Portrane (= St Ita's
 Hospital) O 25 50
Portrane Marsh (3) 1 km W Portrane O 24 50
Portrane Martello Tower (3) 1 km ESE Portrane
 O 26 50
Portrane Peninsula (3) Between Rogerstown and
 Malahide Estuaries
Powerstown House (4) 2.5 km NW Mulhuddart
 O 05 42
Prince William's Seat (8) Highest point of Glencullen
 Mtn O 17 18
Prospect House (7) Formerly on Knocklyon Road,
 Firhouse O 11 27

Prospect Point (3) 2.25 km NE Swords O 20 47

Quarry Lake, Pond (4) Phoenix Park, 0.25 km ENE Ordnance Survey Office O 10 36

'Rabbit Warren' (4) in Luttrellstown Estate O 05 36

Raheen Point (3) 2.5 km WNW Portrane O 23 51

Raheny (2) 1 km E Lusk O 22 54

Raheny (5) O 21 38

Raheny Quarries (5) Just NNW Raheny, now filled in O 21 38

Ranelagh Bridge (4) Royal Canal 1 km ESE Blanchardstown O 09 38

Rathcoole (6) O 02 26

Rathfarnham (8) O 14 29

Rathfarnham Bridge (7 & 8) R. Dodder O 14 29

Rathmichael House (8) 1.5 km W Shankill O 23 21

Rathmines (7) O 15 31

Rathmooney (2) 1.5 km NW Lusk O 20 55

Red Island (2) Promontory 0.5 km NE Skerries O 25 61

Redgap (6) 2 km SSW Rathcoole O 01 24

Redrock (5) SE Redrock Martello Tower, Howth Head O 27 36

Redrock Martello Tower (5) W side Howth Head O 26 37

Reynoldstown (2) 1.75 km NE Naul O 14 61

Rialto (7) O 13 33

Richardstown (2) 2 km ESE Ballyboghil on District 3 boundary O 17 53

Ringsend (8) O 18 33

Ringsend Bridge (7 & 8) R. Dodder O 18 33

Ringsend Dump (8) Reclaimed land 0.75 km ESE Irishtown O 19 33

Ringsend Park (8) O 18 33

River Valley Park (3) Along Ward R. just W Swords O 17 46

Robin Hood Industrial Estate (7) Walkinstown O 10 31

Robswalls (5) 2 km SE Malahide O 24 45

Roches Hill (8) 0.5 km WSW Killiney Hill O 25 25

Rockabill (2) 7 km ENE Skerries O 32 62

Rockbrook (7) O 13 24

Rocklands House (8) Just WNW Leopardstown Park Hospital O 19 25

Roganstown Bridge (1 & 3) Broad Meadow River 3.5 km S Ballyboghil O 14 50

Roganstown House (3) 5 km NW Swords O 14 49

Rogerstown (2) 2 km SW Rush O 24 53

Rogerstown Boat Club (2) 2 km SW Rush O 24 53

Rogerstown Creek (2 & 3) Just east of Daws Bridge at head of Rogerstown Estuary O 20 51

Rogerstown Dump (2) 1.5 km SW Rush, now a park O 23 52

Rogerstown Estuary (2 & 3) N of Portrane Peninsula

Rogerstown Harbour (2) 2 km SW Rush O 24 52

Roper's-rest (7) Now Greenville Avenue off South Circular Road O 14 32

Rowlestown (1) 4 km SW Ballyboghil O 13 50

Royal Canal (4 & 5) Runs from W to E through Clonsilla to North Wall Quay

Royal Dublin Golf-course (5) S half of North Bull Island O 22 36

Royal Irish Academy (7) Dawson Street, Dublin City O 16 33

Rush (2) 26 54

Rush Caravan Park (2) Just N Rush O 26 54

Rush Golf-course (2) 1.5 km SW Rush O 25 53

Rush Railway Station (2) 3 km W Rush O 23 53

St Ann(e)'s Chapel, Graveyard (7) E side Southern Glenasmole Reservoir O 10 21

St Anne's Fields (7) Fields above St Ann(e)'s Chapel O 10 21

St Anne's Golf-course (5) N part of North Bull Island O 23 37

St Anne's Park (5) Raheny O 20 37

St Brigid's Home (6) 2.25 km NNE Brittas (= Crooksling Sanatorium) O 03 23

St Catherine's Estate, Woods (4) Along N side of R. Liffey NW of Lucan O 02 35

St Columba's College (8) 0.5 km S Marley Park O 15 25

St Doolagh's Church (5) 1 km S Kinsealy O 21 42

St Doolagh's Quarries (5) 1.25 km SSW Kinsealy O 20 42

St Edmundsbury (6) 1.5 km NE Lucan (= St Edmondsbury) O 05 35

St Enda's Park (8) 1.75 km S Rathfarnham O 14 27

St Fintan's Cemetery (5) 1.5 km SE Sutton O 26 38

St Fintan's Church (5) 0.5 km ESE Sutton O 26 39

St Helena's (4) 0.5 km S Finglas O 13 38

St Helen's (6) 2 km SSW Lucan O 02 33

St Ita's Hospital (3) 0.5 km S Portrane (= Portrane Hospital) O 25 50

St Loman's Hospital (6) 2.5 km W Palmerston O 06 35

St Margaret's (4) 5 km N Finglas O 13 43

St Mary's College (5) Griffith Avenue 0.5 km N Marino O 17 37

St Maur's G.A.A Club (2) 0.5 km W Rush O 25 54

St Patrick's Island (2) 2.5 km ENE Skerries O 27 61

St Philomena's Home (8) 0.5 km SW Stillorgan O 19 27

Saggart (6) O 03 26

Saggart Hill (6) 2 km NW Brittas O 01 22

Saggart Paper Mills (6) Just SW Saggart O 03 26

Sallynoggin (8) O 24 26

Salmon Leap (6) River Liffey just S Leixlip O 00 35

Saltpan Bay (3) Lambay Island O 31 51

Sandycove Railway Station (8) O 24 28

Sandyford (8) O 18 25

Sandyford Cross Roads (8) Just SE Sandyford O 18 25

Sandyford Industrial Estate (8) Adjoins Stillorgan
    Industrial Estate/Park O 19 26

Sandymount (8) O 18 32

Sandymount Strand (8) O 19 32

Santry (5) O 16 40

Santry Court (5) Santry Woods; house now
    demolished O 16 40

Santry Demesne, Woods (5) O 16 40

Scalp, The (8) 2.25 km SSE Kiltiernan O 21 20

Scholarstown Road (7) 1.5 km S Templeogue O 12 26

Scoil Mhuire (5) Griffith Avenue 0.25 km N Marino
    O 17 37

Scribblestown House (4) 2.25 km SW Finglas O 11 38

Seahan Mountain (7) (= Seecawn in *Colgan*) O 08 19

Seapoint Martello Tower (8) 1 km SE Blackrock O 22 29

Seecawn Brook (7) Flows NE from between Seahan and
    Corrig Mtns to Southern Glenasmole Reservoir at
    O 10 21

Seefingan (7) Mountain on county boundary O 08 17

Seventh Lock (7th Lock) (7) Grand Canal 1.25 km SW
    Ballyfermot O 09 32

Shackleton's Mills (4) By R. Liffey O 04 36

Shanganagh Cemetery (8) 1.5 km SSE Shankill O 25 20

Shanganagh River (8) (= Loughlinstown R.) Flows
    through Loughlinstown to coast S of Killiney at
    O 26 23

Shankill (8) O 25 21

Shenick's Island (2) 1.75 km SE Skerries O 26 59

Shielmartin Road (5) Howth Head 2 km SE Sutton
    O 26 37

Sillogue (4) 2.5 km NE Finglas O 14 41

Sir John Rogerson's Quay (7) Dublin City by R. Liffey
    O 17 34

Skerries (2) O 25 60

Skerries Railway Station (2) 1 km SW Skerries O 24 59

Slade (6) 1.25 km SSE Saggart O 03 25

Slade Brook (7) Flows NE from Seefingan to enter
    Dodder at O 10 20

Slade Valley (6) S Saggart O 03 24

Slievenabawnoge (7) O 08 22

Slieve Thoul (6) 2 km NW Brittas O 01 22

Slips (3) 0.75 km SSW Swords O 17 46

Sluice River (5) Flows from just E Dublin Airport
    through Kinsealy to Portmarnock Bridge at O 23 42

Smithfield (4) Dublin City O 14 34

Somerton House (4) Liffey Valley 2 km SW Castleknock
    O 07 35

Sorrento Park, Point (8) O 27 26

South Wall (8) E of Pigeon House to Poolbeg Lighthouse

Springfield (6) 2.75 km SE Lucan O 04 32

Square, The (6) Shopping Centre, Tallaght O 08 27

Stackstown (8) 0.5 km NE Kilmashogue Mtn O 16 24

Stamullin (2) On Co. Meath boundary O 14 65

Steeven's Lane (7) O 13 34

Stepaside (8) O 19 23

Stewart's Hospital (7) (= Palmerston Hospital) O 08 35

Stillorgan (8) O 20 27

Stillorgan Reservoirs (8) O 19 26

Stockhole (5) 1.75 km SSE Cloghran O 18 42

Stone Cross (7) Ballinascorney Gap O 07 22

Stoneybatter (4) 1 km E Phoenix Park O 14 34

Strawberry Beds (4) N side R. Liffey 2.5 km SW
    Castleknock O 06 35

Streamstown (1) Naul Hills, 4 km WSW Balrothery
    O 16 59

Summerhill (4) Dublin City O 16 35

Summit, The (5) Howth Head O 29 37

Sutton (5) O 25 39

Sutton Cemetery (5) Old cemetery 2 km SE Sutton
    O 27 37

Sutton House (5) W side Howth Head
    (= Sutton Castle Hotel) O 26 37

Sutton Railway Station (5) O 25 39

Sutton Strand (5) Just S Sutton O 25 39

Swords (3) O 18 46

Swords Castle (3) N side of Swords O 18 46

Sydney Parade (8) O 19 31

Tallaght (6 & 7) O 09 27

Tallaght Hill (6 & 7) O 06 25

Tallaght Quarry (6) W side Tallaght Hill O 05 25

T.C.D. (7) Trinity College Dublin O 16 33

Techrete (5) Just W Howth Railway Station
    (= Parson's Engineering Works) O 27 39

Templeogue (7) O 13 28

Terenure (7) O 14 30

Thormanby Road (5) E side Howth Head O 29 37

Thornton Lodge (3) 5.5 km NW St Margaret's O 09 48

Three Rock Mountain (8) O 17 23

Tibradden Mountain (7) O 14 22

Ticknock (8) (= Tiknock) 4 km S Dundrum O 16 23

Tobersool House (2) 4.5 km NW Balbriggan O 16 65

Tobertown (2) 4.5 km WNW Balbriggan O 15 64

Tolka Lodge (4) Just W Finglas Bridge O 13 37

Tolka River (4 & 5) Flows through Mulhuddart SE to
    Dublin Bay at Fairview O 17 35

Tonelagee Reservoir (3) (= Tonlegee) 4 km NW Swords
    O 14 48

Torca Wood (8) N side Dalkey Hill O 26 26

Trinity College Dublin (7) (= T.C.D.) O 16 33

Trinity College Dublin, Boat Club (7) S bank R. Liffey,
    Islandbridge O 12 34

Trinity College Dublin, Botanic Garden (7) Palmerston
    Park O 16 30

Tromanallison (7) Headwater stream of R. Dodder
    O 12 17

Turkinstown (2) 2.5 km SSW Balbriggan O 18 61

Turnapin Bridge (5) Mayne R. 1.5 km N Santry O 17 41

Turvey Bridge (3) 3 km WNW Donabate O 19 50

Turvey House (3) 1.75 km WNW Donabate O 21 50

Twelfth Lock (12th Lock) (6) Grand Canal near
    Ballymakaily Mill O 02 32

Two Rock Mountain (8) O 17 22

Tymon (7) O 10 28

Tymon Lane (7) O 10 28

Tymon Park (7) O 10 29

Tyrrellstown (2) 2 km ENE Lusk O 23 55

University College Dublin, Belfield (8) (= U.C.D.)
    O 18 30

University College Dublin, Boat Club (4) N side R. Liffey,
    Islandbridge O 12 34

Verschoyles Hill (6) O 04 24

Vico Bathing Place (8) Just NE Whiterock, Killiney
    O 26 25

Walkinstown (7) O 10 31

Walshestown (1) 3.75 km SW Balrothery O 17 58

Walsh's Lane (8) 1.25 km W Glencullen O 17 20

Ward River (3 & 4) Flows E through Knocksedan to
    Swords, then NE to join Broad Meadow River at
    O 18 48

Waterstown Dump (7) S side R. Liffey just NW
    Palmerston O 08 35

Westmanstown (4) 2.5 km N Lucan O 02 37

Weston Aerodrome (6) 2.5 km WSW Lucan O 00 34

Whitechurch Road (8) 1 km E Edmondstown O 14 25

White's Gate (4) Phoenix Park just NW Ordnance
    Survey Office O 09 36

Whiterock (8) Coast E Killiney Hill O 26 25

Whitestown (2) 2 km SE Lusk O 22 52

Whitestown (7) Townland SW of Tallaght O 07 26

Whitewater Brook (5) SE side Howth Head O 29 36

Williamstown (8) Just SE Booterstown Marsh O 20 30

Wills Brook House (6) 1.5 km SE Lucan O 04 34

Wimbleton (2) 2.25 km NE Ballyboghil O 17 55

Winter Lodge (1) 4 km ENE Naul O 16 61

Woodbrook Golf-course, House (8) 1.5 km NNW Bray
    O 26 20

Woodlands (4) (= Luttrellstown) 1.5 km S Clonsilla
    O 05 36

Woodtown Park (7) 1 km NW Rockbrook O 12 25

Wren's Nest Weir (4) R. Liffey 3 km SW Clonsilla
    O 06 35

Yellow Walls (3 & 5) Just W Malahide O 21 46

Zoological Gardens (4) In Phoenix Park O 12 35

INDEX OF SCIENTIFIC
AND COMMON NAMES

Family names are in bold **CAPITALS**; genus, species and hybrid names are in **bold** print; synonyms (only those in recent usage are listed) are in *italics*; and common names are in ordinary print. Page numbers in **bold** refer to the Systematic and Supplementary Lists; those in ordinary print refer to Part I. The Bibliography in Appendix I contains a comprehensive list of literature sources for the Dublin flora and it should be consulted for complementary information.

A

Abraham-Isaac-Jacob **450**
Acaena 445
  novae-zelandiae 445
  ovalifolia 445
Acaena, Two-spined **445**
Acer 259, 448
  campestre 448
  macrophyllum 448
  platanoides 448
  pseudoplatanus 54, 61, 80, 86, 91, 98, **259**
ACERACEAE 259, 448
Achillea 359
  millefolium 69, 71, 72, 97, **359**
  ptarmica 357
Acinos **295**
  arvensis **295**
Adder's-tongue 30, 48, 53, 68, **127**
ADIANTACEAE 438
Adiantum 438
  capillus-veneris 59, **438**
Adoxa 326
  moschatellina 62, **326**
ADOXACEAE 326
Aegopodium 267
  podagraria 267
Aesculus 448
  hippocastanum 86, **448**
Aethusa 270
  cynapium 270
AGAVACEAE 456
Agrimonia 226
  eupatoria 226
  procera 226
Agrimony **226**
  Fragrant **226**
Agrostemma 168
  githago 93, **168**
Agrostis 76, 413
  canina 73, **413**
  capillaris 73, **413**
  gigantea 413

  stolonifera 66, 67, 69, 72, 85, 94, **413**
  vinealis 414
Aira 412
  caryophyllea 412
  praecox 412
AIZOACEAE 154
Ajuga 294
  reptans 294
Alchemilla 227, 445
  filicaulis 56, **227**
  glabra 56, **228**
  mollis 445
  xanthochlora 227
Alder 53, 68, 80, 84, 86, **154**
Alexanders 42, 69, **267**
Alisma 368
  lanceolatum 369
  plantago-aquatica 78, 79, **368**
ALISMATACEAE 368
Alison, Sweet **443**
Alkanet, Green **285**
Alliaria 190
  petiolata 190
Allium 426, 455
  carinatum 427
  schoenoprasum 455
  triquetrum 49, 69, **426**
  ursinum 27, 42, 86, **426**
  vineale 427
Alnus 154
  glutinosa 53, 68, 80, 84, 86, **154**
Alopecurus 414
  geniculatus 414
  myosuroides 96, **415**
  pratensis 414
Amaranth, Common **441**
AMARANTHACEAE 441
Amaranthus 441
  retroflexus 441
Ammophila 414
  arenaria 53, 61, 66, 67, 75, **414**